MATERIALS SCIENCES IN SPACE WITH APPLICATION TO SPACE PROCESSING

Edited by
Leo Steg
General Electric Company
Philadelphia, Pennsylvania

Volume 52
PROGRESS IN
ASTRONAUTICS AND AERONAUTICS

Martin Summerfield, Series Editor-in-Chief
Princeton University, Princeton, New Jersey

Technical papers selected from AIAA 12th Aerospace Sciences Meeting, January 1974; AIAA/ASME Thermophysics and Heat Transfer Conference, July 1974; AIAA/AGU Conference on Scientific Experiments of Skylab, Oct.-Nov. 1974; AIAA 10th Thermophysics Conference, May 1975; COSPAR Symposium on Materials Sciences in Space, June 1976; and papers invited by the Editor, subsequently revised for this volume.

Published by the American Institute of Aeronautics and Astronautics.

American Institute of Aeronautics and Astronautics
New York, New York

Library of Congress Cataloging in Publication Data
Main entry under title:

Materials sciences in space with application to space processing.

(Progress in astronautics and aeronautics; v. 52)
Includes bibliographies and indexes.
1. Chemical processes, Effect of reduced gravity on—Addresses, essays, lectures. 2. Matter, Effect of reduced gravity on—Addresses, essays, lectures. 3. Space environment—Addresses, essays, lectures. 4. Materials—Addresses, essays, lectures. I. Steg, Leo. II. AIAA Aerospace Sciences Meeting, 12th, Washington, D. C., 1974. III. Title: Space Processing. IV. Series.

TL507.P75 vol. 52 [TP155.7] 629.1′08s [620.1′1]
ISBN 0-915928-16-7 77-530

Table of Contents

Preface xiii

Chapter I Phenomenology 1

Convection Phenomena of Importance for Materials Processing in Space 3
SIMON OSTRACH

Crystal Growth in a Reduced Gravity Environment 33
J. R. CARRUTHERS

Electrophoresis 41
M. BIER

Capillary Pheomena in Microgravity 57
J. M. HAYNES

Possible Application of Controlled Processes in Space Technology 67
R. F. GANIEV, V. F. LAPTCHINSKY, AND A. S. OKHOTIN

Interface Phenomena and Transport Processes under Reduced Gravity 77
G. S. R. SARMA

Gravitational Effects on Combustion 89
A. L. BERLAD

Instabilities of Interfaces and Interfacial Convection 111
R. BRUCKNER

Gravitational Dynamics of Biosystems: Some Speculations 125
J. O. KESSLER AND M. BIER

Drop Dynamics in Space 151
T. G. WANG, M. M. SAFFREN, AND D.D. ELLEMAN

Natural Convection in Low-*g* Environments 173
PHILOMENA G. GRODZKA AND TOMMY C. BANNISTER

Fluid Dynamics and Kinematics of Molten Metals in the Low-Gravity Environment of Skylab 189
S. V. BOURGEOIS AND M. R. BRASHEARS

Studies of Rotating Liquid Floating Zones on Skylab IV 207
J. R. CARRUTHERS, E. G. GIBSON, M. G. KLETT, AND
B. R. FACEMIRE

Solution Calorimetry in Zero Gravity 223
W. HEMMINGER, F. HAESSNER, AND H. L. LUKAS

Jetting Action Due to Differential Evaporation in Space
Processing 235
C. H. LI

Chapter II Experimental Apparatus 253

Space Processing Experimental Apparatus: A Survey 255
MATHIAS P. SIEBEL

Thermal Design and Analyses of Skylab Multipurpose
Furnace and Experiments 285
J. W. H. CHI, R. G. SEIDENSTICKER, AND
C. S. DUNCAN

Free Suspension Processing: Selected User Interests
and Requirements 303
G. WOUCH AND H. L. BLOOM

Chapter III Applications 331

NASA Activities in Materials Sciences in Space 333
JAMES H. BREDT

Survey of the Microgravity Program in the Federal
Republic of Germany 347
A. BEWERSDORFF

Some Results of Studies in Space Technology
in the USSR 355
A.S. OKHOTIN, V. F. LAPTCHINSKY, AND
G. S. SHONIN

Low-Gravity Synthesis of Polymers with Controlled
Molecular Configuration 363
A. H. HEIMBUCH, J. A. PARKER, A. SCHINDLER, AND
H. G. OLF

Chapter IV Flight Results and Studies 381

Results from Metallurgical Flight Experiments 383
EUGENE McKANNAN

Static Free - Fluid Electrophoresis in Space 399
R. S. SNYDER AND R. E. ALLEN

Free-Flow Electrophoresis in Space 411
K. HANNIG AND H. WIRTH

Space Processing Program of the National Bureau of Standards 423
R. L. PARKER

Czochralski Growth of Crystals in 0 *g* and 1 *g* 437
H. WENZL

Interest and Difficulties of 0-*g* Studies of the Mechanisms of Eutectic Growth 447
CLEMENT LEMAIGNAN AND YVES MALMEJAC

Influence of the Force Field on Eutectic Structure of Alloys 455
A. S. OKHOTIN, L. K. LIVANOV, M. Ya. TZVILING, AND Yu V. CHESHLYA

Influence of Gravity on Chemical Vapor Deposition Processes 461
G. WAHL

Observations of the Liquid/Solid Interface in Low Gravity Melting 483
GUENTHER H. OTTO AND LEWIS L. LACY

The Stability of Liquid Dispersions in Low Gravity 495
LEWIS L. LACY AND GUENTHER H. OTTO

Solidification of NaCl-NaF Eutectic in Space 509
A. S. YUE AND J. G. YU

Low-Gravity Homogenization and Solidification of Aluminum Antimonide 523
CHOH-YI ANG AND LEWIS L. LACY

G-Jitter Convection of Confined Fluids in Low Gravity 535
L. W. SPRADLEY, S. V. BOURGEOIS, AND F. N. LIN

Superconducting Properties of Pb-Sn-In Alloys Directionally Solidified Aboard Skylab 567
W. T. ANDERSON JR. AND J. L. REGER

Index to Contributors to Volume 52 579

Progress in Astronautics and Aeronautics

Martin Summerfield, Series Editor
PRINCETON UNIVERSITY

VOLUMES	EDITORS
1. Solid Propellant Rocket Research. 1960	Martin Summerfield PRINCETON UNIVERSITY
2. Liquid Rockets and Propellants. 1960	Loren E. Bollinger THE OHIO STATE UNIVERSITY Martin Goldsmith THE RAND CORPORATION Alexis W. Lemmon Jr. BATTELLE MEMORIAL INSTITUTE
3. Energy Conversion for Space Power. 1961	Nathan W. Snyder INSTITUTE FOR DEFENSE ANALYSES
4. Space Power Systems. 1961	Nathan W. Snyder INSTITUTE FOR DEFENSE ANALYSES
5. Electrostatic Propulsion. 1961	David B. Langmuir SPACE TECHNOLOGY LABORATORIES, INC. Ernst Stuhlinger NASA GEORGE C. MARSHALL SPACE FLIGHT CENTER J.M. Sellen Jr. SPACE TECHNOLOGY LABORATORIES
6. Detonation and Two-Phase Flow. 1962	S.S. Penner CALIFORNIA INSTITUTE OF TECHNOLOGY F.A. Williams HARVARD UNIVERSITY
7. Hypersonic Flow Research. 1962	Frederick R. Riddell AVCO CORPORATION
8. Guidance and Control. 1962	Robert E. Roberson CONSULTANT James S. Farrior LOCKHEED MISSILES AND SPACE COMPANY
9. Electric Propulsion Development. 1963	Ernst Stuhlinger NASA GEORGE C. MARSHALL SPACE FLIGHT CENTER

10. Technology of Lunar Exploration. 1963	Clifford I. Cummings and Harold R. Lawrence JET PROPULSION LABORATORY
11. Power Systems for Space Flight. 1963	Morris A. Zipkin and Russell N. Edwards GENERAL ELECTRIC COMPANY
12. Ionization in High-Temperature Gases. 1963	Kurt E. Shuler, Editor NATIONAL BUREAU OF STANDARDS John B. Fenn, Associate Editor PRINCETON UNIVERSITY
13. Guidance anu Control - II. 1964	Robert C. Langford GENERAL PRECISION INC. Charles J. Mundo INSTITUTE OF NAVAL STUDIES
14. Celestial Mechanics and Astrodynamics. 1964	Victor G. Szebehely YALE UNIVERSITY OBSERVATORY
15. Heterogeneous Combustion. 1964	Hans G. Wolfhard INSTITUTE FOR DEFENSE ANALYSES Irvin Glassman PRINCETON UNIVERSITY Leon Green Jr. AIR FORCE SYSTEMS COMMAND
16. Space Power Systems Engineering. 1966	George C. Szego INSTITUTE FOR DEFENSE ANALYSES J. Edward Taylor TRW INC.
17. Methods in Astrodynamics and Celestial Mechanics. 1966	Raynor L. Duncombe U.S. NAVAL OBSERVATORY Victor G. Szebehely YALE UNIVERSITY OBSERVATORY
18. Thermophysics and Temperature Control of Spacecraft and Entry Vehicles. 1966	Gerhard B. Heller NASA GEORGE C. MARSHALL SPACE FLIGHT CENTER
19. Communication Satellite Systems Technology. 1966	Richard B. Marsten RADIO CORPORATION OF AMERICA
20. Thermophysics of Spacecraft and Planetary Bodies Radiation Properties of Solids and the Electromagnetic Radiation Environment in Space. 1967	Gerhard B. Heller NASA GEORGE C. MARSHALL SPACE FLIGHT CENTER

21. Thermal Design Principles of Spacecraft and Entry Bodies. 1969	Jerry T. Bevans TRW SYSTEMS
22. Stratospheric Circulation. 1969	Willis L. Webb ATMOSPHERIC SCIENCES LABORATORY, WHITE SANDS, AND UNIVERSITY OF TEXAS AT EL PASO
23. Thermophysics: Applications to Thermal Design of Spacecraft. 1970	Jerry T. Bevans TRW SYSTEMS
24. Heat Transfer and Spacecraft Thermal Control. 1971	John W. Lucas JET PROPULSION LABORATORY
25. Communication Satellites for the 70's: Technology. 1971	Nathaniel E. Feldman THE RAND CORPORATION Charles M. Kelly THE AEROSPACE CORPORATION
26. Communications Satellites for the 70's: Systems. 1971	Nathaniel E. Feldman THE RAND CORPORATION Charles M. Kelly THE AEROSPACE CORPORATION
27. Thermospheric Circulation. 1972	Willis L. Webb ATMOSPHERIC SCIENCES LABORATORY, WHITE SANDS, AND UNIVERSITY OF TEXAS AT EL PASO
28. Thermal Characteristics of the Moon. 1972	John W. Lucas JET PROPULSION LABORATORY
29. Fundamentals of Spacecraft Thermal Design. 1972	John W. Lucas JET PROPULSION LABORATORY
30. Solar Activity Observations and Predictions. 1972	Patrick S. McIntosh and Murray Dryer ENVIRONMENTAL RESEARCH LABORATORIES, NATIONAL OCEANIC AND ATMOSPHERIC ADMINISTRATION
31. Thermal Control and Radiation. 1973	Chang-Lin Tien UNIVERSITY OF CALIFORNIA, BERKLEY
32. Communications Satellite Systems. 1974	P.L. Bargellini COMSTAT LABORATORIES

33. Communications Satellite Technology. 1974	P.L. Bargellini COMSTAT LABORATORIES
34. Instrumentation for Airbreathing Propulsion. 1974	Allen E. Fuhs NAVAL POSTGRADUATE SCHOOL Marshall Kingery ARNOLD ENGINEERING DEVELOPMENT CENTER
35. Thermophysics and Spacecraft Thermal Control. 1974	Robert G. Hering UNIVERSITY OF IOWA
36. Thermal Pollution Analysis. 1975	Joseph A. Schetz VIRGINIA POLYTECHNIC INSTITUTE
37. Aeroacoustics: Jet and Combustion Noise; Duct Acoustics. 1975	Henry T. Nagamatsu, Editor GENERAL ELECTRIC RESEARCH AND DEVELOPMENT CENTER Jack V. O'Keefe, Associate Editor THE BOEING COMPANY Ira R. Schwartz, Associate Editor NASA AMES RESEARCH CENTER
38. Aeroacoustics: Fan, STOL, and Boundary Layer Noise; Sonic Boom; Aeroacoustic Instrumentation. 1975	Henry T. Nagamatsu, Editor GENERAL ELECTRIC RESEARCH AND DEVELOPMENT CENTER Jack V. O'Keefe, Associate Editor THE BOEING COMPANY Ira R. Schwartz, Associate Editor NASA AMES RESEARCH CENTER
39. Heat Transfer with Thermal Control Applications. 1975	M. Michael Yovanovich UNIVERSITY OF WATERLOO
40. Aerodynamics of Base Combustion. 1976	S.N.B. Murthy PURDUE UNIVERSITY
41. Communications Satellite Developments: Technology. 1976	Gilbert E. LaVean DEFENSE COMMUNICATIONS ENGINEERING CENTER William G. Schmidt CML SATELLITE CORPORATION
42. Communications Satellite Developments: Technology. 1976	William G. Schmidt CML SATELLITE CORPORATION Gilbert E. LaVean DEFENSE COMMUNICATIONS ENGINEERING CENTER

43. Aeroacoustics: Jet Noise, Combustion and Core Engine Noise. 1976	Ira R. Schwartz NASA AMES RESEARCH CENTER Henry T. Nagamatsu GENERAL ELECTRIC RESEARCH AND DEVELOPMENT CENTER Warren C. Strahle GEORGIA INSTITUTE OF TECHNOLOGY
44. Aeroacoustics: Fan Noise and Control; Duct Acoustics: Rotor Noise. 1976	Ira R. Schwartz NASA AMES RESEARCH CENTER Henry T. Nagamatsu GENERAL ELECTRIC RESEARCH AND DEVELOPMENT CENTER Warren C. Strahle GEORGIA INSTITUTE OF TECHNOLOGY
45. Aeroacoustics: STOL Noise; Airframe and Airfoil Noise. 1976	Ira R. Schwartz NASA AMES RESEARCH CENTER Henry T. Nagamatsu GENERAL ELECTRIC RESEARCH AND DEVELOPMENT CENTER Warren C. Strahle GEORGIA INSTITUTE OF TECHNOLOGY
46. Aeroacoustics: Acoustic Wave Propagation; Aircraft Noise Prediction; Aeroacoustic Instrumentation. 1976	Ira R. Schwartz NASA AMES RESEARCH CENTER Henry T. Nagamatsu GENERAL ELECTRIC RESEARCH AND DEVELOPMENT CENTER Warren C. Strahle GEORGIA INSTITUTE OF TECHNOLOGY
47. Spacecraft Charging by Magnetospheric Plasmas. 1976	Alan Rosen TRW INC.
48. Scientific Investigations on the Skylab Satellite. 1976	Marion I. Kent and Ernst Stuhlinger NASA GEORGE C. MARSHALL SPACE FLIGHT CENTER Shi-Tsan Wu THE UNIVERSITY OF ALABAMA
49. Radiative Transfer and Thermal Control. 1976	Allie M. Smith ARO INC.

50. Exploration of the Outer Solar System. 1977	Eugene W. Greenstadt TRW INC. Murray Dryer NATIONAL OCEANIC AND ATMOSPHERIC ADMINISTRATION Devrie S. Intriligator UNIVERSITY OF SOUTHERN CALIFORNIA
51. Rarefied Gas Dynamics Parts I and II. (two volumes) 1977	J. Leith Potter ARO INC.
52. Materials Sciences in Space with Application to Space Processing. 1977	Leo Steg GENERAL ELECTRIC COMPANY

(Other volumes are planned.)

PREFACE

This book appears in the 18th year of the space age and covers activities which span some 9 years. It has been a remarkable and turbulent period. In space, we have been to the moon and the planets. We set out to do this in order to explore nothing less than the origin of the solar system, the origin of the Universe, and the origin of life itself. Suffice it to say that there is much left for us to explore along these lines; but perhaps we have a deeper perception of the beauty, fragility, and finiteness of our planet and the rarity and complexity of life.

During this period, ecology, a formerly sedate "branch of science concerned with the interrelationship of organisms and their environment" (Webster), has become a household word. The energy, population, and environmental crises are with us—among others—and Neo-Malthusians would condemn us to existence in a closed system, a bleak and austere existence indeed (at least to some of us) in the face of a remarkably productive period in science and technology by which we escaped the Malthusians of the 19th century.

Now over the past decade there has been general understanding and acceptance of the contribution of space to science—to an understanding of the solar system and the physical universe, the impact that the discovery of another biology would have. There has been general and casual acceptance of space applications using the readily understood synoptic capability of satellites to provide worldwide services—in weather pictures, picture transmission and communication, Earth resource diagnostics, etc. This book deals with one of the emerging areas of space science and technology—namely, the exploration analysis, and application of phenomena in the environment of space. Now this environment is a bit unusual for us who have been sheltered by a protective (or is it blinding?) atmosphere, immersed in a benevolent (or is it restrictive) ocean of gravity, and limited to sizes of human (or is it ant heap?) dimensions in comparison to the scale of the universe.

The change in environment is radical:

a) Radiation, both solar and cosmic, unattenuated by the atmosphere.

b) An effectively arbitrarily high vacuum (as we go further away from Earth) with very high pumping rates.

c) A controllable gravity/force environment which includes microgravity as the initial condition.

And whereas, since we are comfortable at extrapolation, we have had relatively few problems with understanding and utilizing the synoptic position of satellites or using diagnostic science in the exploration of the universe from an Earth-based point of view, we are finding the exploration and application of phenomena away from our Earth-bound environment a much more difficult area to explore.

This book is in many ways a log of a journey of exploration in this new country. We have taken our instruments and machines and tried a few things, on drop towers, airplanes, and rockets for short periods of time and on Apollo, Skylab, and Apollo-Soyuz for extended periods. Like sensible explorers, we have taken the most comfortable roads into this strange country—the roads of convection, fluid physics, immiscibility, crystal growth—and we have indeed been rewarded with perfection in size in crystals, with deepened understanding of biological and chemical processes, and with some things we do not fully understand as yet; and, in an almost unconscious answer to the Neo-Malthusian, we have begun to think how we can utilize this newly found territory to our practical advantage, what institutional relationships are desirable in its exploration, and what prudent and economical options are available.

The editor and people interested in this field are indebted to altogether too many people to mention individually, to NASA and its counterpart agencies abroad for sponsoring this field of science and application, to the United States Congress for recognizing its potential importance in the future health of the nation, and to the international scientific community for affording it recognition and tolerance in this early "disreputable" phase. We should recognize early believers like Hans Wunscher, Wolfgang Steurer, Louis McCreight, and James Bredt. We are also indebted to Dr. Martin Summerfield, Series Editor of the AIAA Progress in Astronautics and Aeronautics series, of which this volume is a part, whose ability to identify emerging fields that are deserving of recognition is remarkable.

The papers in this volume come from a number of sources: the AIAA 12th Aerospace Sciences Meeting, January 1974; AIAA/ASME Thermophysics and Heat Transfer Conference,* July 1974; AIAA/AGU Conference on Scientific Experiments of Skylab, Oct.-Nov. 1974; AIAA 10th Thermophysics Conference, May 1975; and the COSPAR Symposium on Materials Sciences in Space, June 1976; and papers invited by the Editor. The book is a record of exploration rather than a text, and, if our findings continue to be as remarkable as they have been up to date, a definitive text will not be written for a long time.

Leo Steg
General Electric Company
Space Sciences Laboratory

November 1976

---

*The thermophysics portion of the Conference was the 9th Annual Thermophysics Conference

Chapter 1-Phenomenology

CONVECTION PHENOMENA OF IMPORTANCE FOR MATERIALS PROCESSING IN SPACE

Simon Ostrach*

Case Western Reserve University, Cleveland, Ohio

Abstract

The basic aspects of convection processes are delineated. It is shown that even in weak gravitational fields buoyancy can induce fluid motion. Furthermore, at reduced gravity, other nongravity forces such as surface or interfacial tensions, g jitter, thermal volume expansions, density differences due to phase changes, and magnetic and electric fields can induce fluid motions. The types of flows possible with these various driving forces are described, and criteria for determining the extent and nature of the resulting flows and heat transfer are presented. The different physical mechanisms that can occur separately and in combination are indicated, and the present state of knowledge of each of the phenomena is outlined. Specific research problems are described for many of the types of convection that are necessary to obtain greater understanding of their implications for space processing.

Introduction

It is a common impression that natural convection cannot occur in a low-gravity (say 10^{-6} g) environment, and, therefore, no fluid motions or enhanced heat transfer can be expected under that condition. Thus, much enthusiasm has been expressed for manufacturing processes in a reduced-gravitational environment. It should be said at the outset, however, that convection effects are not always deleterious. As will be indicated subsequently, in some situations, it may be desirable to have fluid flows in space processes, e.g., to

---

Presented as Paper D.3.1 at the COSPAR Symposium on Materials Sciences in Space, Philadelphia, Pa., June 9-10, 1976.

*Wilbert J. Austin Distinguished Professor of Engineering.

stir the fluid phase for mixing or cooling purposes or to help maintain concentration gradients. In any event, it is important to know the extent and nature of convection in space and the factors on which it depends in order either to minimize its effects or to utilize it to advantage.

Unfortunately, natural convection even in a normal environment is one of the more complex fluid phenomena, so that it is difficult to make specific predictions. The space environment further complicates the situation because there are a variety of nongravity forces that can induce fluid motion. Such nongravity driving forces, which usually are suppressed by gravity, include surface or interfacial tensions, thermal volume expansions, g jitter, and magnetic and electric fields. Furthermore, gravity-induced convection still can be appreciable even at 10^{-6} g and lower under certain conditions. Some evidence of fluid flows in space flight is reported in Refs. 1-3. A rather comprehensive presentation of the various types of natural convection possible in space manufacturing processes is given in Ref. 4. Related existing publications also are indicated therein. In Ref. 5, some of the convection types are related to spaceflight experiments.

In order to assess properly the effects of natural convection in a reduced-gravity environment, it is essential to comprehend fully all that is known about the phenomenon at present. Thus, an outline of the key aspects follows. A number of research studies will be suggested which would provide quantitative data that not only will define more clearly the nature and significance of such flows but also will help to indicate the design options available to deal effectively with convective phenomena in space.

The nature of convection will be discussed now. Most configurations related to materials processing are ones in which the fluid is confined by rigid boundaries. Internal convection problems are considerably more complex than external ones because the fluid boundary layer and core are closely coupled[6]. This constitutes the main source of difficulty in predicting the resulting flow and heat transfer. More than one core configuration (flow) sometimes is possible, and which actually will occur for a given set of conditions cannot be determined a priori. Furthermore, the entire flow is sensitive to the configuration geometry and to the imposed thermal boundary conditions.

To add to the complexity, there are essentially two basic modes of flow generated by a body force.[7] The first, which will be referred to as conventional convection, occurs whenever a density gradient (due to thermal, concentration, or other effects) is normal to the body force (gravitational) vector. In such a case, flow results immediately. The second mode, which will be called unstable convection, results whenever the density gradient is parallel but opposed to the body force. In this situation, the fluid remains in a state of unstable equilibrium (due to heavier fluid being above lighter fluid) until a critical density gradient is exceeded. A spontaneous flow then ensues which rather quickly becomes steady. This motion is usually in the form of cells or vortex rolls and, hence, causes more mixing than laminar conventional convection. It must be emphasized that this instability is different from the one that results in laminar flow becoming turbulent. The steady flow obtained after the critical condition is exceeded is laminar; this flow (as all others due to buoyancy) also can become turbulent under the proper conditions. The onset of the unstable motion is highly dependent on the confining boundaries; i.e., the motion can be delayed markedly by proper design of the configuration.[8,9]

As if all the foregoing were not sufficiently difficult to deal with, it should be pointed out that both modes of convection, conventional and unstable, also can occur in a given configuration (e.g., Refs. 10 and 11).

As was indicated previously, the space environment further complicates the picture because of the additional driving forces. Further complexities arise in materials processing because the fluid is not homogeneous, so that concentration gradients can cause density gradients in addition to temperature gradients. The density gradients due to those two causes can enhance or oppose each other in coupled ways. Relatively little work exists for normal natural convection with multiple coupled driving gradients and, particularly, for the types of geometric configurations which correspond to materials processing methods. It is, thus, perhaps not surprising that the effects and nature of natural convection under reduced-gravity conditions often are neglected, misinterpreted, or confused.

From the preceding discussion, it should be clear that, because different modes of convection are possible and are extremely sensitive to the configuration and boundary conditions, in order to assess convection effects at reduced gravity, the following information must be known specifically and explicitly: 1) both the magnitude and direction of any accelerations, the latter to help determine the mode of convection; 2) the geometric configuration; 3) the imposed boundary conditions; and 4) the material properties. Unfortunately, most existing literature on this subject is deficient in one or more of these.

General Considerations

For the reasons just given, it is necessary to study each problem by itself to obtain detailed information on the transport processes. However, considerable insight into the qualitative nature of the problem can be obtained from dimensional analysis. The first step in the understanding of such a complex phenomenon, therefore, is to obtain the relevant dimensionless parameters. These are best determined from the basic equations and boundary conditions that describe the phenomena.[12]

Parameters

For convection generated by an acceleration acting on a density difference (or gradient), the parameters are as follows:

1) The Grashof number Gr, which represents the ratio of buoyancy to viscous forces

$$Gr = g\Delta\rho d^3/\rho\nu^2 \tag{1a}$$

where $\Delta\rho$ denotes the density difference, g the acceleration, d a characteristic dimension, ρ a reference density, and ν the kinematic viscosity. If the density difference is due to a temperature difference (or gradients), Eq. (1) becomes

$$Gr = \frac{\beta g \Delta T d^3}{\nu^2} = \frac{\beta g (\partial T/\partial x) d^4}{\nu^2} \tag{1b}$$

where β is the fluid volumetric coefficient, ΔT is the temperature difference, and $(\partial T/\partial x)$ denotes a spatial temperature gradient. Note that for gases $\beta = 1/T$, where T is the absolute reference temperature.

2) The Rayleigh number

$$Ra = c_p\mu/k\ Gr = PrGr \tag{2a}$$

where c_p is the specific heat at constant pressure, μ the absolute viscosity, k the thermal conductivity coefficient, and Pr the Prandtl number, which is a measure of the rates of diffusion of vorticity to heat.

The Grashof number basically appears in the equations of motion, and, therefore, the fluid velocities are related directly to it. For large Grashof numbers (Gr>1), the fluid velocities U can be estimated from

$$U = \sqrt{Gr}\ (\nu/d) = \sqrt{\beta g \Delta T d} \tag{3a}$$

whereas for small Grashof numbers (Gr<1)

$$U = Gr\ (\nu/d) = \beta g \Delta T d^2/\nu \tag{3b}$$

The Rayleigh number, on the other hand, appears in the energy equation so that the heat transfer is related to it.

If the density difference in Eq. (1) is due to a difference in concentration, then it becomes

$$Gr_s = \frac{\alpha g \Delta c d^3}{\nu^2} = \frac{\alpha g (\partial c/\partial x) d^4}{\nu^2} \tag{1c}$$

where α is the concentration densification coefficient, Δc is the concentration difference, and $\partial c/\partial x$ represents a spatial concentration gradient. The corresponding solutal Rayleigh number is

$$Ra_s = [\alpha g (\partial c/\partial x) d^4]/\nu D \tag{2b}$$

where D is the diffusion coefficient.

Since fluid motions are of primary concern in most materials processing problems, the procedure to obtain an estimate of the velocities is as follows. From the direction of the acceleration and the configuration, determine which mode of convection is to be expected. For conventional convection, compute the Grashof number from the appropriate Eq. (1), and then use the corresponding velocity expression Eq. (3). If unstable convection is anticipated, the proper critical Rayleigh number for the configuration must be determined to see if such a flow actually will occur. In addition to Refs. 8 and 9, there are an increasing number of papers in which critical Rayleigh numbers are determined for various configurations subject to different conditions. Space limitations preclude a detailed discussion of them.[13] However, the essential physical aspects of the problems can be illustrated by Figs. 1 and 2. The effect of aspect ratio on the critical Rayleigh number is shown in Fig. 1 for vertical cylinders of square cross section with both conducting and insulated vertical boundaries. The solid lines represent theoretical results of Refs. 14-17, and the experimental data came from Refs. 18-20. There is good agreement between theory and experiment regardless of whether the cross section is rectangular or circular, although the form of the resulting flows may be

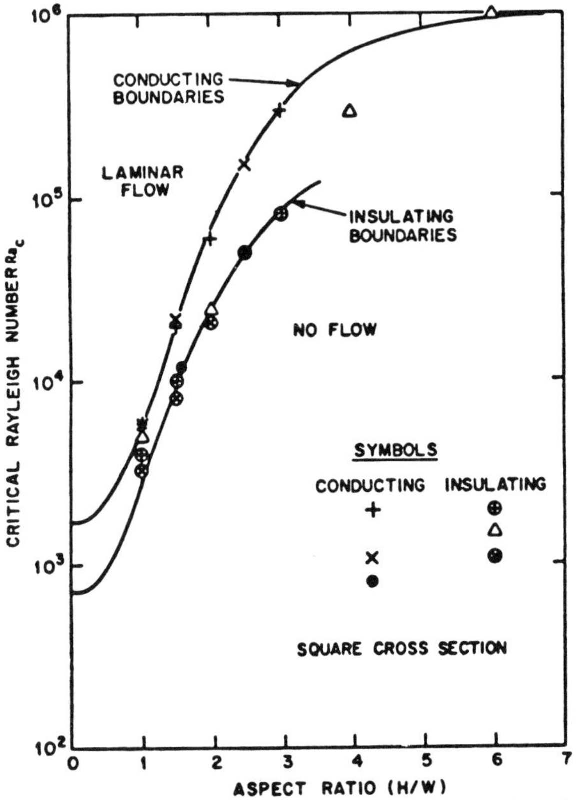

Fig. 1 Effect of aspect ratio on critical Rayleigh number for vertical cylinders.

different. Increasing the aspect ratio (containment) can be seen to be very stabilizing. The critical Rayleigh number is, however, insensitive to the aspect ratio for values of it greater than 5.

The stability of fluids in rectangular parallelepipeds heated from below was determined theoretically in Ref. 21 for a wide range of thermal boundary conditions on the lateral walls. Some of the results are presented in Fig. 2, where the critical Rayleigh number is plotted against aspect ratios for various rectangular cross sections. It is evident that, with increasing cross-sectional confinement (large H/W_y), the configuration is even more stable than for square or circular cross sections for which H/W_x and H/W_y are equal. This indicates another design option for delaying the onset of unstable convection.

When a rectangular cavity with one wall hotter than the other is rotated with respect to the gravity vector (or vice

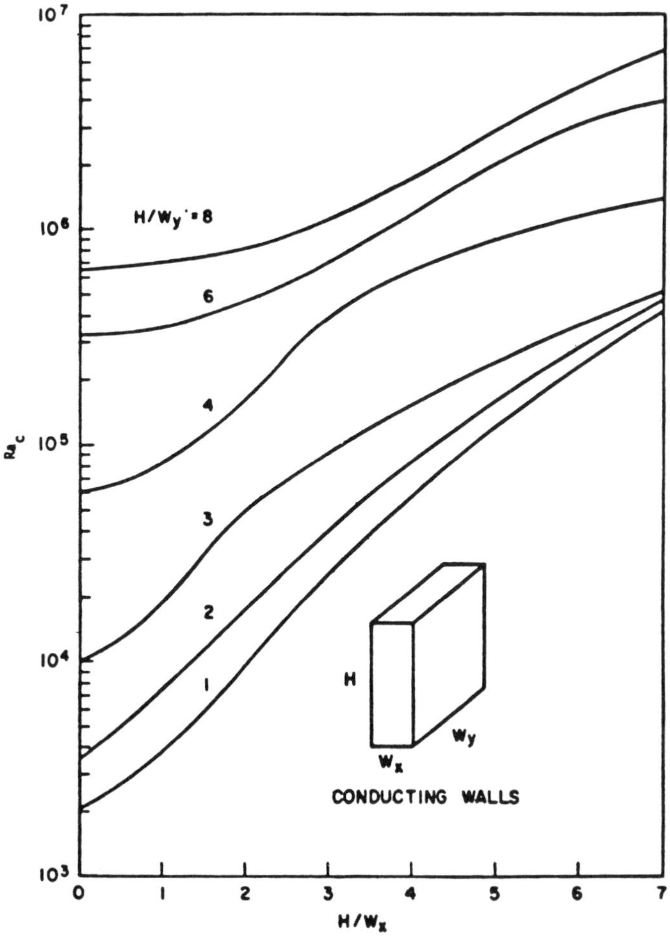

Fig. 2 Critical Rayleigh number as a function of aspect ratios.

versa), each of the natural convection modes (conventional and unstable) is obtained as limits, and for angles in between both modes interact. The types of flow are delineated in Refs. 10 and 11, and a summary of the results is shown in Fig. 3. The Rayleigh number is based on the distance and temperature difference between the hot and cold walls of the container. When the hot surface is below $\delta = 90°$, there is no convection until the classical Benard cells appear at $Ra_c = 1708$. At $\delta = -90°$, the hot surface is on top and the fluid layer is stratified stably, and again there will be no convection. However, when the slot is nearly vertical or rotated so that the hot wall is above a steady circulating two-dimensional unicellular flow, convection occurs with fluid rising along

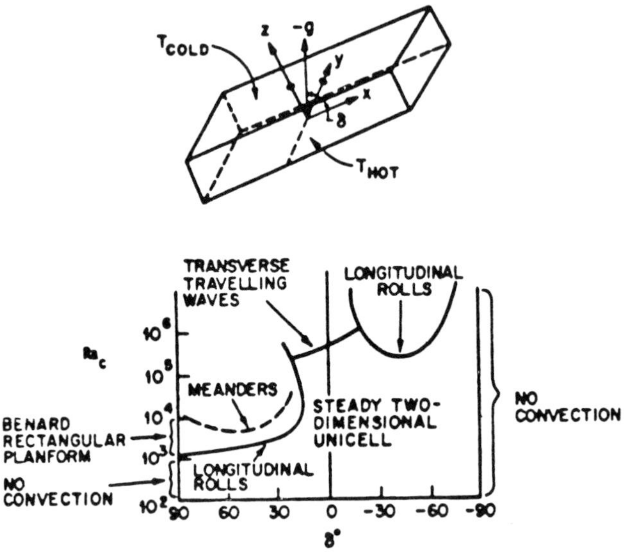

Fig. 3 Flow types with combined modes of convection.

the hot surface and descending near the cold surface. Longitudinal vortex rolls develop when the two basic modes interact or when the Rayleigh number is sufficiently large, and wavy flow patterns result.

Other aspects of the combined modes are treated in Refs. 22-24 for very shallow boxes. The combined effects of aspect ratio and inclination angle on the circulation and heat-transfer rate in a finite rectangular region were investigated primarily theoretically in Refs. 25 and 26 and experimentally in Ref. 27. It was found that, when the angle of inclination from horizontal was zero (unstable configuration), the flow pattern was a series of roll cells with axes parallel to each other and perpendicular to the long axes of the channel. When the inclination angle was increased slightly in steps, a series of roll cells persisted with their axes in the upslope, but the average Nusselt number (heat transfer) decreased. As the angle was increased further, a minimum Nusselt number was attained. Beyond that angle, the flow pattern changed to a single roll cell with its axes in the long dimension of the channel, and the associated Nusselt number increased. This flow pattern persisted as the angle was increased until the heated surface was horizontal but above the cold one. The Nusselt number passed through a maximum and then decreased to unity. This behavior was qualitatively the same for channels with aspect ratios from unity to 15, but the inclination angles corresponding to the Nusselt number extrema depend strongly on the aspect ratio. Comparison of the theoretical and experimental results indicated that the results of Ref. 26 can be utilized up to Ra = 10^5 and aspect ratios up to at least 8.4.

Scaling

The dimensionless parameters are extremely useful for reasons in addition to that of obtaining flow estimates. They indicate how to scale a problem, for example, to reduce convection or to study the phenomena in a model. They also indicate possible simplifications for analysis, the minimum number of experiments necessary, and how best to correlate data.[12]

Buoyancy-Induced Convection

The acceleration of gravity on Earth is essentially constant at a value of 980 cm/sec^3 (1 g). A steady and reduced value of acceleration is inherent in most spacecraft because of atmospheric drag, centripetal force due to vehicle rotation, gravity gradients, solar wind, and solar pressure. Superposed on this background of a uniform but weak acceleration field are temporally varying accelerations that are due to engine burns, attitude-control maneuvers, and onboard vibrations from machinery or astronaut movements.

Steady Microgravity Fields

Some of the steady accelerations associated with several missions are summarized in Tables 1 and 2 (taken from Refs. 28 and 29 and presented in Ref. 5). From the values of the accelerations presented in the tables, it would appear that the g levels are "small" and, therefore, that the environment is one of "zero gravity", and no convection is possible. This is the misconception that is so prevalent in much of the space processing work. However, the basis for estimating both

Table 1 Summary of steady reduced-gravity accelerations

Source	Type of Mission		
	Low-altitude Earth orbit	Low-altitude lunar orbit	Interplanetary trajectory
Atmospheric drag	5×10^{-5} g and lower	None	None
Centripetal force	1×10^{-6} g	3×10^{-7} g	3×10^{-14} g
Gravity gradient	3×10^{-9} g/cm	2×10^{-9} g/cm	4×10^{-17} g/cm
Venting thrust	All 10^{-4} to 10^{-6} g, neglecting drag		
Vehicle thrust	All 0.1 to 6 g		

Table 2 Steady g levels in Apollo missions

Apollo flight mode	Typical g level
Passive thermal control (PTC)	$3x10^{-6}$
Attitude hold in translunar or trans-Earth orbit	$7x10^{-8}$
Attitude hold in lunar orbit	$5x10^{-7}$

thermal and solutal convection effects was given previously. Under the most mundane conditions, e.g., temperature differences of 10°K at levels of about 20°C, and a characteristic length of 10 cm, the Grashof number (for thermal convection) at 1 g for a gas (like air) is of the order of 10^6, for a liquid (water) is like 10^7, and for a liquid metal (mercury) is about 10^9. Thus, it is clear that even in reduced-gravity levels as indicated in the tables the Grashof number is not negligible. For example, at 10^{-5} g velocities of the order of tenths of a millimeter per second would be induced in the liquid and liquid metal under the given conditions and about four times that in the gas. Further increases in the temperature (or density) difference and length would lead to even higher fluid velocities. Similar considerations apply for solutal convection. However, since concentration gradients in materials processing can be considerably greater than temperature gradients, for a given g level solutal convection effects could be significantly larger than those due to thermal convection. It is, thus, clear that the weak, steady acceleration fields can lead to fluid motions. These motions occur immediately with no delay in the case of conventional convection. There may, however, be no corresponding immediate change in heat transfer associated with the flows under certain conditions. For example, for conventional convection in a rectangular enclosure, it was found in Ref. 30 that the heat transfer will differ from that for pure conduction only if $Ra>500\ (\ell/d)$, where ℓ is the height and d the width of the enclosure.

The nature of conventional convection at reduced gravity will be similar to that at normal gravity, as summarized in Ref. 6. The essential difference is that in space, because the Grashof numbers are reduced significantly, the flow will be laminar, whereas on Earth it may be turbulent. Unstable convection will be less likely in space because the associated lower Rayleigh numbers may be lower than the critical.

Although there is, unfortunately, little experimental data on reduced-gravity convection, corroborative evidence is available from studies made for the cryogenic gas storage tanks for the Apollo 14 and subsequent flights. Although these ground-based and spaceflight studies of reduced-gravity convection are limited specifically to an unusual fluid (supercritical oxygen) and rather complex configurations (the Apollo tanks), the results are, nevertheless, of significance. For example, it was found that the natural convection in the Apollo tanks was sufficient to obviate the need for forced convection by mixing fans.[31] Data from Apollo 14[32] indicate increased convection with increases in the vehicle rotation rate (to to 3 rpm), as would be expected.

g Jitter

As contrasted to the nonuniformities of the gravity field, some of which must be accepted as part of the natural environment of an orbital vehicle, there are transient or time-varying perturbations to the gravity field at a point. The unsteady variations, which are referred to as g jitter, can arise from spacecraft maneuvers and mechanical vibrations.

Spacecraft maneuvers can produce g jitter magnitudes of 10^{-4} g and higher. This effect can be overcome if the space processing is performed during the drift mode. On the other hand, g jitter caused by mechanical vibrations cannot be controlled necessarily at their source. Mechanical vibrations that are transmitted to the experiment have the same effect as a time-varying gravity. They can be caused, for example, by astronaut movement, rotating and reciprocating machinery, and extravehicular activities. Arm and leg movements and console operations such as flipping switches are all significant in this respect.[33] During Skylab experiments, the g jitter has been estimated to be as large as 10^{-3} g, with the frequency spectrum of this random vibration from about one to several thousand Hertz. Evidence of g jitter in Apollo flights is presented in Refs. 1 and 3 and discussed in some detail in Ref. 5.

Some indications of the effects of g jitter on convection can be obtained by related research, such as that of Refs. 34-36. It was found that vibrations can either enhance substantially or retard local heat transfer, significantly increase total heat transfer, and drastically affect convection by altering the transitions from quiescent to laminar flow (critical Rayleigh number) and from laminar to turbulent flow. More detailed discussion of related work is presented in Ref. 37. In the last reference, specific consideration was given to models for evaluating g jitter effects, and they will be summarized herein. These are shown in Fig. 4 and are a rectangle heated from the side, one heated from below, and a

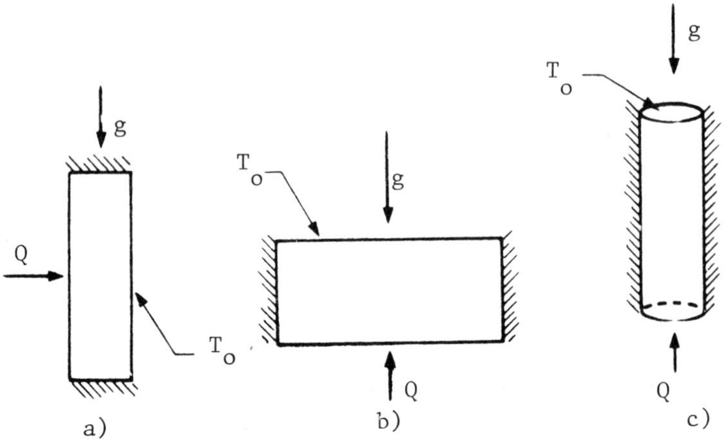

Fig. 4 Configurations for g jitter study.

cylinder heated from below. Mercury, helium, and water were chosen as the fluids to span the Prandtl number range from 10^{-2} to 10. Three representative types of g jitter (see Fig. 5) were investigated. Numerical solutions of the boundary-value problems were obtained, and the results are shown in Figs. 6 and 7. Isotherms are presented in Fig. 6 for three cases: 1) rectangular box of water heated from the side, 2) rectangular box of water heated from below, and 3) cylindrical container of mercury heated from below. The constant g solutions are for 10^{-3} g, and the sawtooth g jitter model

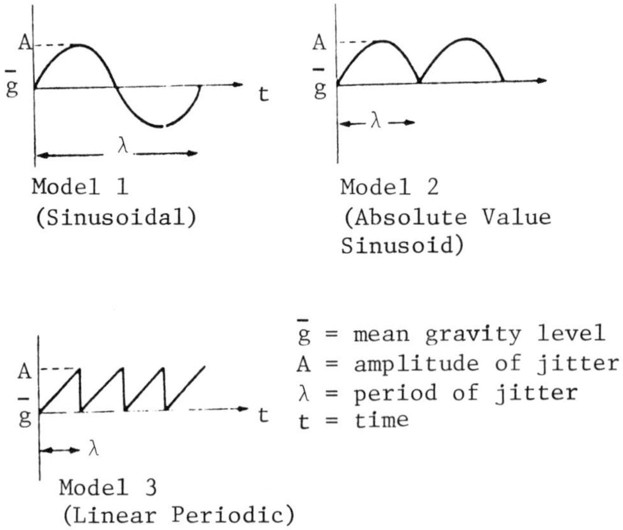

Fig. 5 Types of g jitter.

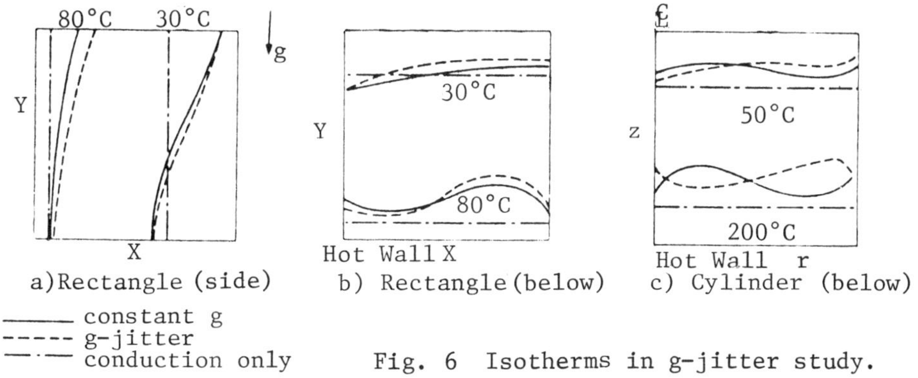

Fig. 6 Isotherms in g-jitter study.

is used, with the minimum g level being 10^{-3}, the amplitude of g variations 10^{-3}, and the period 1 sec. The wall temperature for the rectangular configurations were 95° and 25°C, with the other walls adiabatic. The 80°C isotherm in Fig. 6a is seen to be located farther into the water for the g jitter case than for constant g, and the basic shape is the same. The 80°C isotherm in Fig. 6b has penetrated somewhat farther for the g jitter case. Thus, the g jitter is shown to influence the temperature distributions significantly.

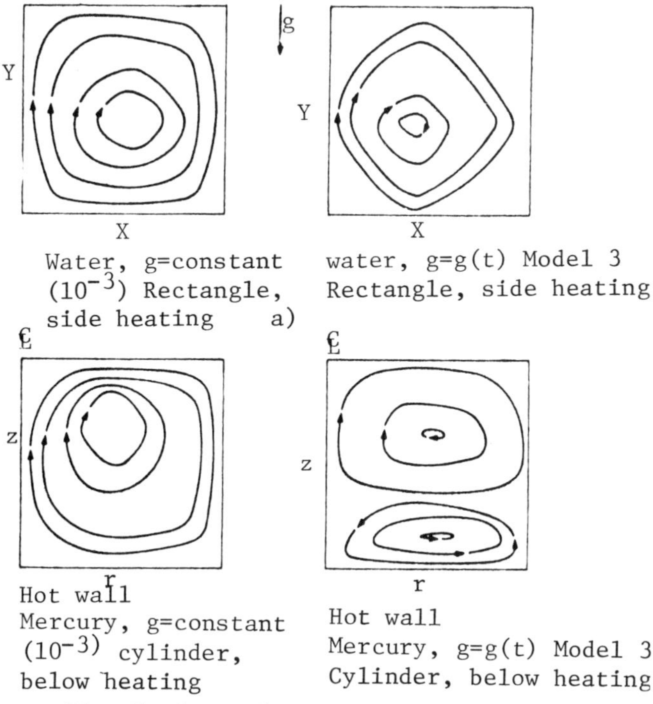

Fig. 7 Streamlines in g-jitter study.

For the mercury-filled cylinder heated from below, the wall temperatures are 200° and 25°C, with the sidewall adiabatic. The effect shown in Fig. 6c is more drastic. The 200°C isotherm for g jitter has a different shape. This behavior is due to the change in the flow from a single cell to a double cell (see Fig. 7). The streamline patterns (Fig. 7) give another indication of g jitter effects. The pattern with g jitter and the rectangle heated from the side is skewed toward the hot side, and the shape is altered. For heating the cylinder with mercury below, the effect is even more pronounced, as was mentioned previously. Thus, the flow patterns are also influenced significantly by g jitter. The examples just presented are representative of all of the cases investigated.

This phenomenon merits special consideration, not only because it represents a convection mode that is suppressed under normal gravitational conditions and that is significant at reduced gravity, but also because it is inherent in all spacecraft environments and cannot, therefore, be controlled easily. Much more fundamental work, therefore, is required. First of all, the relevant dimensionless parameters must be determined so that meaningful models for analysis and experiment can be defined. Data of the spacecraft environment must be obtained. Then extensive quantitative information should be obtained by studying configurations of various shapes subject to controlled disturbances of varying frequencies and amplitudes.

Surface-Tension-Induced Convection

Surface tension on the free surface of a liquid may, under some conditions, considerably affect liquid motion. The presence of an interface between two fluid phases can influence the motion of the fluids either when the interface has finite curvature or when the interfacial tension varies from point to point. In both cases, forces appear in the interfacial region which can affect or generate the fluid motion.

When the motion takes place in a gravitational field, the relative importance of surface tension can be estimated from the Bond number, $Bo = \rho dg^2/\sigma$, which indicates the ratio of gravitational to surface-tension forces, where σ is the surface tension. From the Bond number, it is clear that on Earth surface tension is important ($Bo<1$) only in small-scale configurations, i.e., where d is very small. Therefore, most existing work on the effect of surface tension deals with flow in capillaries and thin films or the motion of droplets or bubbles or short-wavelength water waves. In space, on the other hand, surface tension becomes a significant force whose influence on fluid motion must be assessed and understood.

Surface-tension gradients can arise from gradients in temperature or concentration. These surface-tension gradients can generate conventional convection flows or unstable cellular flows (see, e.g., Refs. 38-40), just as gravity induces such convective flows. When the surface-tension gradients and density differences are due to temperature gradients, the dimensionless parameter related to gravitational convection is the Rayleigh number, $Ra = \beta g \theta d^3/\nu\kappa$ and the corresponding one for surface tension induced flows is the Marangoni number, $Ma = (\partial\sigma/\partial T)\theta L/\rho\nu\kappa$, where β is the fluid volumetric coefficient, θ is a characteristic temperature difference, T is the fluid temperature ν is the kinematic viscosity, and κ is the thermal diffusivity. Note that the Marangoni number is independent of gravity. The relative magnitude of surface tension and buoyancy forces is given by the ratio $Ma/Ra = (\partial\sigma/\partial T)/(\rho\beta g d^2)$. Note that this is just the reciprocal of a modified Bond number. Again, it can be seen from this ratio that surface tension becomes orders of magnitude greater (under identical conditions) than the buoyancy in a reduced-gravity environment.

Conventional Convection

There are many possible modes of flow and configurations of interest in which surface tension can be significant. Consideration now will be given to a situation in which conventional convection will occur. The flow and heat transfer of a fluid in an open container can be expected to change markedly as gravity is reduced. For example, in a normal gravitational environment, the natural convection (due to buoyancy) may be turbulent (see Fig. 8a). In a somewhat reduced gravitational field (say 10^{-3} g), the gravity force still might predominate over the surface tension, but the natural convection would be quite different (Fig. 8b); i.e., it would be laminar with a single cell or double cell. In these situations, the free

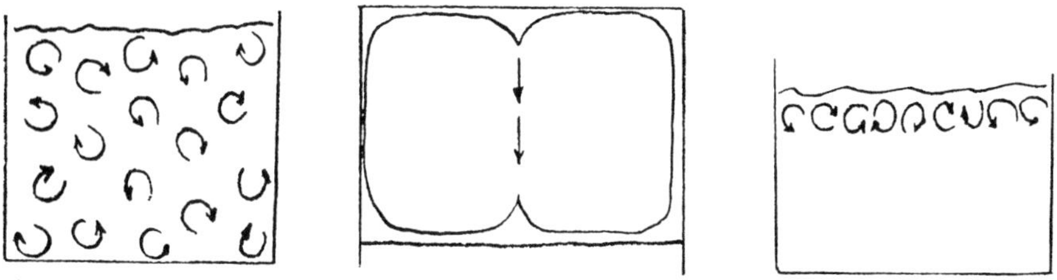

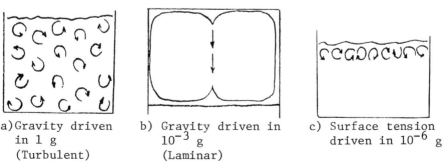

a) Gravity driven in 1 g (Turbulent)　　b) Gravity driven in 10^{-3} g (Laminar)　　c) Surface tension driven in 10^{-6} g

Fig. 8 Modes of convection as a function of g level.

surface can be said to be passive with respect to the convection in the sense that the fluid motion is induced solely by buoyancy. However, as gravity is reduced further (say 10^{-6} g), the surface tension becomes dominant and will generate the primary fluid motions. In such a case, the free surface becomes an active factor in the convection process.

Theoretical studies of related problems are reported in Refs. 41 and 42. An unbounded horizontal layer of fluid with a rigid lower surface and free upper surface is analyzed in Ref. 41. A linear temperature gradient is imposed along both of these surfaces. The velocity profiles due to buoyancy alone and surface tension alone are shown in Fig. 9. It can be seen therein that near the free surface there is a flow due to surface tension from the warm region toward the cooler, and a reverse flow occurs near the lower rigid surface. The profile due to buoyancy alone is of somewhat similar shape but less blunt. The flow due to surface tension in a square container with end walls at different temperatures is analyzed in Ref. 42, and the computer streamlines and isotherms are shown in Fig. 10. Once again, the strong flow near the free surface can be seen, with a reverse cell below. Several aspects of this analysis are questionable.

Since there did not appear to be any experimental study of conventional convection due to surface tension alone, the present author designed such an experiment to be carried out in NASA Lewis Research Center's 500-ft drop tower, in which approximately 5-1/2 sec. of reduced gravity (10^{-5} g) can be

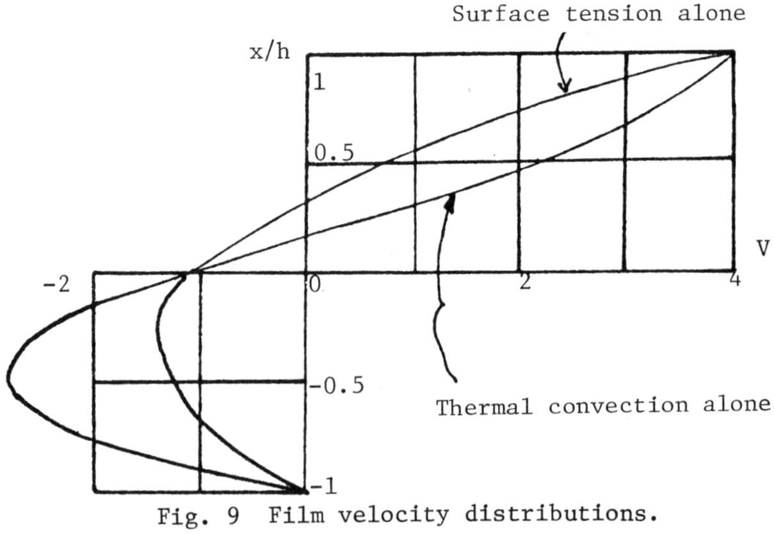

Fig. 9 Film velocity distributions.

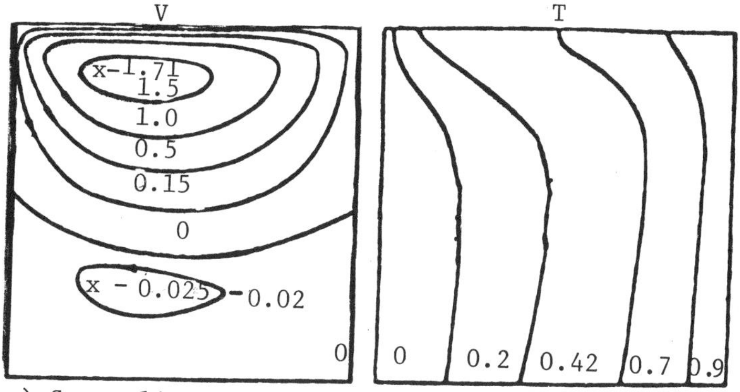

a) Streamlines b) Isotherms

Fig. 10 Surface-tension flow in a square.

obtained. The apparatus was a cylindrical plexiglass dish with a 10-cm diam. and a height of 3.10 cm. The inner wall of the dish is covered with a transparent teflon tape in order to yield a 90° contact angle with distilled water at room temperature (the test fluid). A temperature gradient is imposed by a radiant heat source above the free surface (see Fig. 11). With such a heating-from-above configuration, convection due to buoyancy even at normal gravity would be minimized. The 80 W heater is 3.17 cm long with a 0.63-cm diam.

Methylene blue dye is used to make the flow patterns visible. A few particles of the dye are dropped on the free

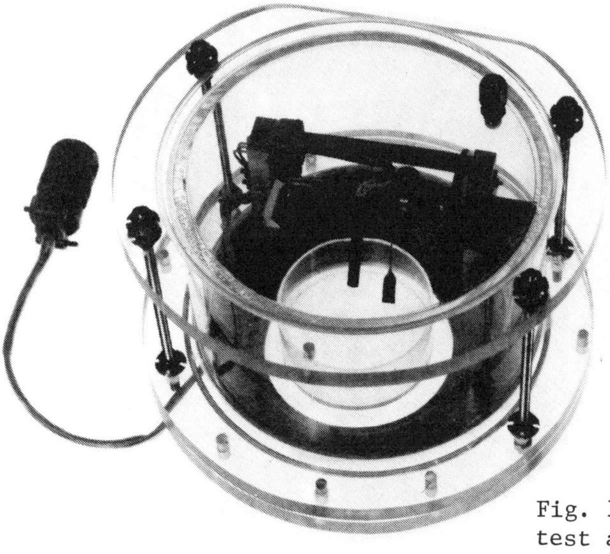

Fig. 11 Surface-tension test apparatus.

surface before the test starts and dissolves. Some of the dye spreads over the free surface, and the larger dye particles form vertical strands as they drop down to the bottom. A "tensiometer" was used to show that small quantities of the dye do not affect the surface tension of the distilled water. When the liquid moves, the dye strands also move and, thereby, indicate the fluid motion. Top and side views of the disk are recorded by means of two 16-mm high-speed Milikon movie movie cameras, which are mounted in the drop capsule as shown in Fig. 12. Five thermistor probes are placed so that their beads just touch the free surface in order to measure the surface temperature gradient. Some velocity data were taken without the thermistors. Two electronic clocks, which were visible in the films, recorded time. The test apparatus and instrumentation are mounted in a plexiglass leak-proof tank, which was maintained at 1 atm pressure. This entire package then is mounted in the drop capsule (Fig. 13).

Fig. 12 Test apparatus in drop capsule.

Fig. 13 Drop capsule.

For the test conditions of initial temperature 22°C, surface-tension gradient $d\sigma/dT$ = 0.16 dynes/cm/°C, characteristic temperature difference 5°C, and a characteristic length of 5 cm, the relevant dimensionless parameters for a normal gravitational environment are Ma = $2.76\text{x}10^5$, Gr = $1.8\text{x}10^6$, Ra = $1.12\text{x}10^7$, Bo = 278. It is clear from these that at 1 g the convection due to buoyancy is greater than that due to surface tension. However, at levels of 10^{-5} g_o, which are obtained in the drop tower, the values are Ma $\cong$ $2.76\text{x}10^5$, Gr = 18, Ra = 112, so that Ma/Ra = $15\text{x}10^3$. Thus the surface tension dominates buoyancy in the drop tower. Identical tests were performed in the laboratory and in the drop tower, so that comparisons could be made.

In the reduced-gravity tests, it was found that the surface-tension motion starts within microseconds after the heater starts to heat the surface (Fig. 14). It appears that

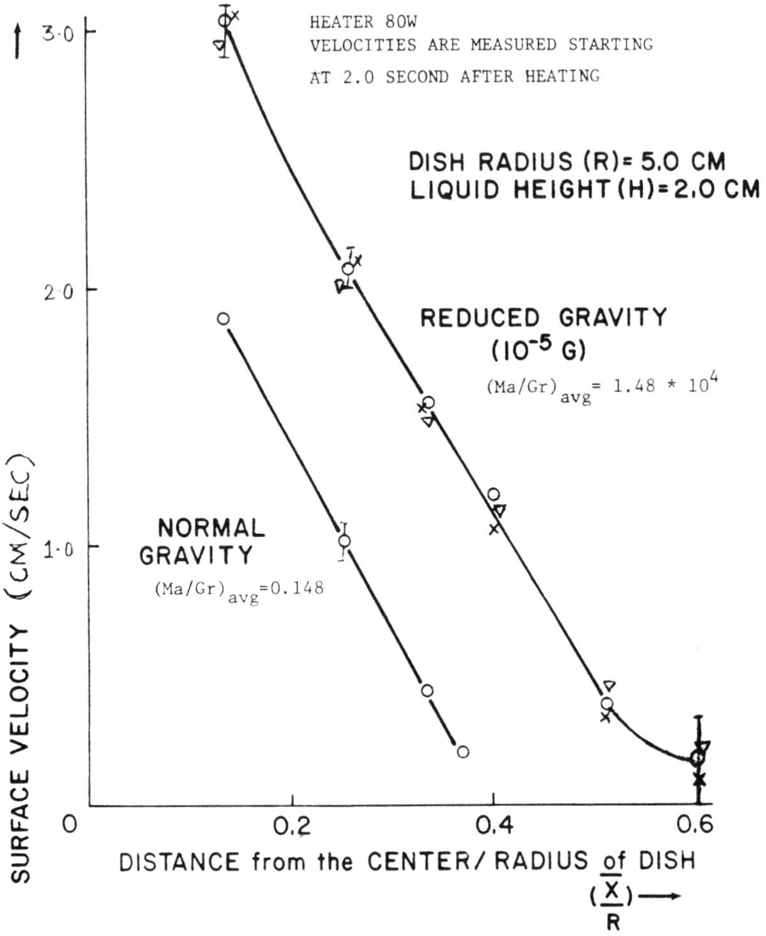

Fig. 14 Surface velocities.

a very thin film on the surface is pulled away from the heater at a velocity of about 3 cm/sec because of the induced surface-tension gradient. No motion could be observed around 3 cm away from the center of the dish, where the surface-tension gradients were zero.

In the interior of the liquid, a two-way motion was observed, and a boundary layer formed close to the free surface (Fig. 15). Outside the boundary layer, all of the liquid was moving toward the center, with a velocity of the order of 1.0 mm/sec. It was remarkable to see so much motion in such a short time produced solely by the surface tension. Note also that the induced flow is not confined to the region of the free surface but penetrates the entire depth of the liquid.

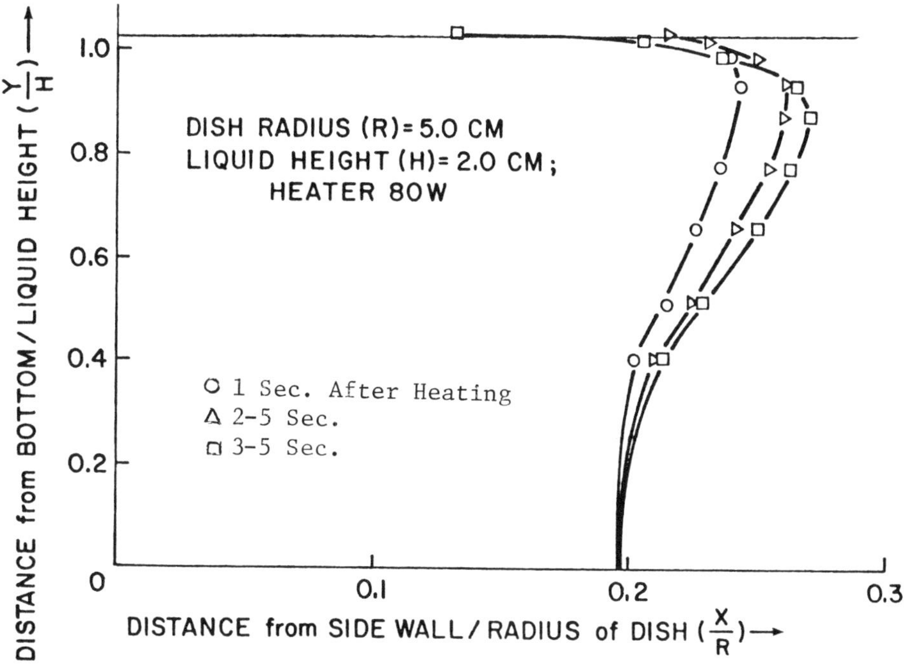

Fig. 15 Surface-tension-induced velocity profiles (reduced gravity).

The associated surface temperature profiles are given in Fig. 16.

Velocity profiles observed near the center in a normal gravity environment are shown in Fig. 17. Comparison of the results indicates that the surface velocities were considerably higher under reduced-gravity conditions (Fig. 14). In the interior of the liquid, the boundary layers near the free surface were thicker at 1 g than at reduced gravity. It is thus clear that the surface tension at reduced gravity can generate significant flows that are somewhat similar to those due to buoyancy at normal gravity.

Unstable Convection

When a fluid layer is heated from below, it is found that a cellular flow pattern develops when the temperature gradient exceeds a critical value. This motion is referred to as Bernard cells. Such motions can be obtained merely due to the thermal instability previously described. However, when a free surface is present, the motion has been shown[43] to be due to surface tension. The theory of such surface-tension-induced motions was developed further in Ref. 38.

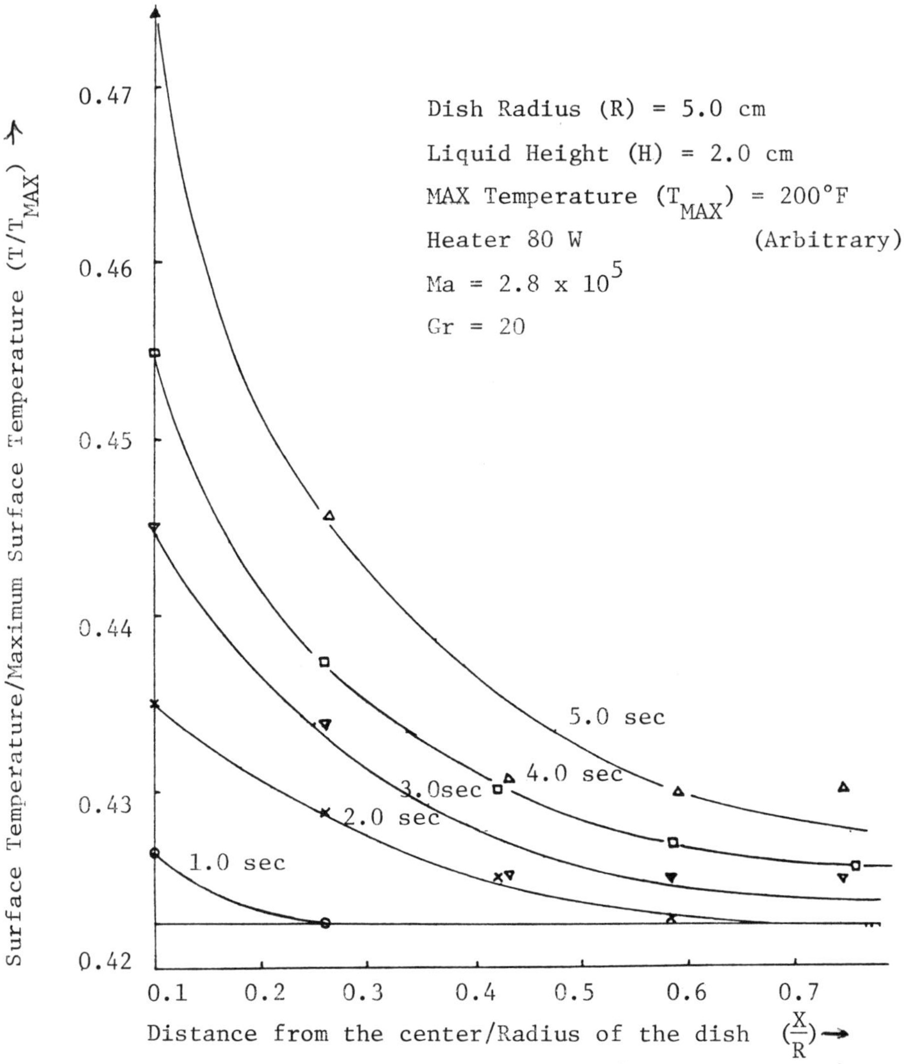

Fig. 16 Surface temperature distribution (reduced gravity).

Experiments performed on the flights of Apollo 14 and 17[1-3,5] indicated that Benard cells are obtained in reduced-gravity environments and that, as in a normal gravity environment, a critical temperature gradient first must be exceeded. Other experiments like the one just described are necessary to investigate surface-tension convection comprehensively, viz., to find the effect of container aspect ratio, sidewall "wettability," and thermal conditions on the resulting flow patterns and temperature distributions.

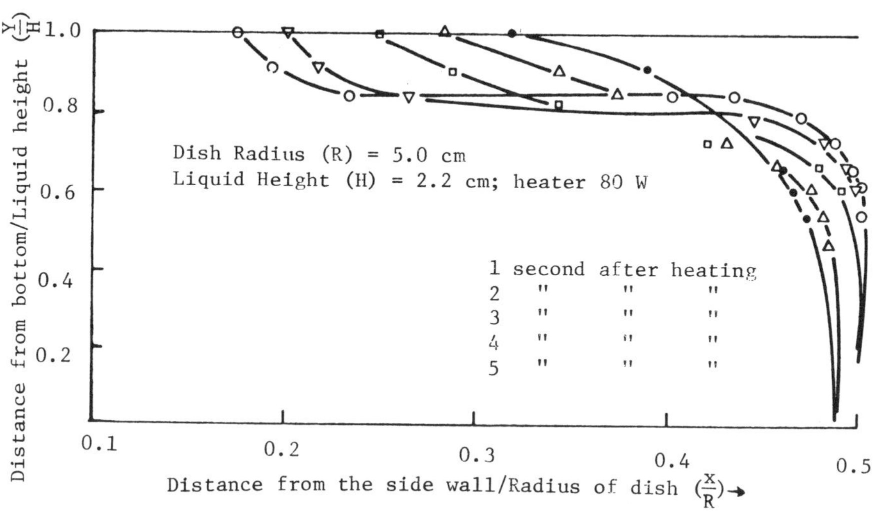

Fig. 17 Velocity profiles (normal gravity).

Some direct reduced-gravity observations have been obtained for the convection phenomena discussed to date. There are, in addition, other mechanisms possible for generating fluid motions under reduced-gravity conditions. These will be described now but not as comprehensively.

Thermoacoustic Convection

Independent of gravity, thermal volume expansions can act as the driving force for convection. Rapid heating of a confined fluid causes rapid local expansions, which, in turn, generate pressure waves. These pressure waves produce a convective motion, which can increase heat transfer greatly relative to conduction and also can cause mass and chemical species transport. This provides a mechanism for enhancing or suppressing convective motion at low gravity by controlling the heating rate. Thermoacoustic convection in a reduced-gravity environment has been studied theoretically[44,45]. Significant reduced-gravity thermoacoustic convection in gases is predicted when the heating rates are sufficiently high. For the example treated in Ref. 44, it was found that at normal gravity the gravity-driven convection is so strong as virtually to overshadow the thermoacoustic effects. The two types of convection are of comparable magnitudes at about 10^{-3} g_o. At this level, the temperature profiles are a hybrid between the buoyancy-dominated 1-g and the thermoacoustic 0-g cases.

No experimental evidence of this phenomenon has, as yet, been demonstrated. Some further insight to this phenomenon could be obtained from relatively small-scale experiments. The apparatus could consist of closed rectangular and circular containers filled with such gases as carbon dioxide and helium. Heaters would be in the walls (for cylindrical ones, e.g., at one end). The sidewall would be insulated and the other end cooled to maintain ambient temperature. The heaters would have to be able to produce rapid heating at a variety of controlled and measured rates. The first phase of this research should define the heating rates required to generate thermoacoustic convection. This must be done for a variety of geometrical configurations and aspect ratios because the pressure wave reflections are important. Quantitative relations between the heating rate and resulting convection then should be obtained. Some steady-state conditions are attained quickly, and each experiment would require only a few minutes. Ground-based experiments should be performed to guide space experiments.

Phase-Change Convection

A shrinkage usually occurs during solidification because the density of the solid usually is higher than that of the liquid and, hence, occupies a smaller volume. This volume reduction results in a flow of liquid toward the solidifying interface. Such flows also are generated by nonequimolar reactions, such as occur in vapor deposition crystal growing. Pressure pulses can accompany such flows and, thereby, influence the nature of the material. Analyses of this phenomenon are presented in Refs. 46 and 47. Some speculation concerning the influence of phase-change convection on space experiments in presented in Ref. 5.

Thermosolutal Convection

If a thermal gradient is imposed on a solution, its components will migrate, so that a concentration gradient will be established. This is called the Soret effect. Usually the heavier species migrate to the warmer region and the lighter species to the cooler region. If these gradients are normal to the gravitational force (conventional convection), the unusual phenomenon known as "salt fingers" occurs, in which columns of cold fresh water rise and columns of saltier hot water descend[48]. Other unexpected results are obtained if the gradients are parallel to the gravity vector (unstable convection). The Soret effect has been used for separation processes, but it is relatively inefficient in the absence of natural convection because of back diffusion. Laminar convection improves the separation. On Earth, however, to maintain laminar convection, the flow passages have to be quite narrow. In a reduced-gravity environment, however, laminar convection could be obtained with larger flow passages, and, thus, larger samples could be processed. In such a case, the low-gravity environment is used to control rather than to eliminate convection. Thus, thermosolutal convection at reduced gravity appears to be a promising and beneficial phenomenon.

To gain an understanding of these unusual phenomena, research is necessary to delineate the many flow and transfer processes that occur when temperature and concentration gradients exist simultaneously. Most existing work on this topic relates to configurations in which the gradients are aligned with the gravity vector, either opposed to it or in the same direction. Since numerous convection modes are possible, as discussed earlier, future research also should treat configurations in which the gradients are transverse to the gravity vector. This work also would be relevant to some crystal-growing techniques.

Convection Due to Electric and Magnetic Fields

Electric and magnetic fields induce body forces (such as gravity) so that they can generate convection and phase separation similar to those in a gravitational field. Whereas in a gravitational field convection is generated by density differences, in an electrical field the flow is generated by differences in electrical conductivity and by differences in susceptibility in a magnetic field. The electrical conductivity and magnetic susceptibility are temperature dependent, so that temperature differences usually are required to obtain the flows. Both conventional and unstable types of convection are possible with such fields. These phenomena have not been explored or exploited fully in the space program.

Coupling Phenomena

It should be noted that two or more forces (such as gravity and surface tension) and gradients (such as temperature and concentration) can occur in a given body of fluid. In a sense, thermosolutal phenomena are examples. Their combined action can be such that a given mode of convection is reinforced, annulled, or altered. What little work that has been done on problems of this type pertains to very specific situations, and the results are not generalizable or predictable.

Summary

The various types of reduced-gravity convection can be categorized as follows:

Acceleration-field dependent: a) thermal convection, b) solutal convection, c) g jitter convection, and d) thermo-solutal convection.

Independent of acceleration field: a) surface-tension convection, b) thermoacoustic convection, c) phase-change convection, and d) convection due to electric and magnetic fields.

Coupled or combined convection.

Acknowledgment

This work was supported under NASA Grant NAS8-31802.

References

[1] Grodzka, P.G. and Bannister, T.C., "Heat Flow and Convection Demonstration Experiments Aboard Apollo 14," Science, Vol. 176, May 1972, pp. 506-508.

[2] Bannister, T.C., "Heat Flow and Convection Demonstration (Apollo 14)," NASA TM X-64735, March 1973.

[3] Bannister, T.C., Grodzka, P.G., Spradley, L.W., Bourgeois, S.V., Hedden, R.O., and Facemire, B.R., "Apollo 17 Heat Flow and Convection Experiments," Final Data Analysis Results, NASA TM X-64772, July 1973.

[4] Grodzka, P.G., "Types of Natural Convection in Space Processes: Summary and Report," HREC-5577-4, CMSC-HREC TR D306350, Jan. 1973, Lockheed Missels and Space Co., Huntsville Research & Engineering Center.

[5] Grodzka, P.G. and Bannister, T.C., "Natural Convection in Low-g Environments," AIAA Paper 74-156, 1974.

[6] Ostrach, S., "Natural Convection in Enclosures," Advances in Heat Transfer, Vol. 8, Academic Press, New York, 1972, Chap. 3.

[7]Ostrach, S., "Laminar Flows with Body Forces," Theory of Laminar Flows: High Speed Aerodynamics and Jet Propulsion, edited by F.K. Moore, Vol. 4, Princeton University Press, Princeton, N.Y., 1964.

[8]Ostrach, S. and Pnueli, D., "The Thermal Instability of Completely Confined Fluids Inside Some Particular Configurations," Transactions of the American Society of Mechanical Engineers, Vol. 85, Ser. C. Nov. 1963.

[9]Sherman, M. and Ostrach, S., "Lower Bounds to the Critical Rayleigh Number in Completely Confined Regions", Journal of Applied Mechanics, Vol. 34, Ser. E. Feb. 1967.

[10]Hart, J.E., "Stability of Flow in a Differentially Heated Inclined Box," Journal of Fluid Mechanics, Vol. 47, 1971.

[11]Hart, J.E., "A Note on the Structure of Thermal Convection in a Slightly Slanted Slot," International Journal of Heat and Mass Transfer, Vol. 16, 1973.

[12]Ostrach, S., "Role of Analysis in the Solution of Complex Physical Problems," Proceedings of the Third International Heat Transfer Conference, Vol. 6, Aug. 1966.

[13]Ostrach, S., "Stable and Unstable Confined Natural Convection," Proceedings of the First Mechanical Engineering Congress, 1976, Pahlavi University, Iran.

[14]Samuels, M.R. and Churchill, S.W., "Stability of a Fluid in a Rectangular Region Heated from Below," AIChE Journal, Vol. 10, 1967.

[15]Davis, S.H., "Convection in a Box: Laminar Theory," Journal of Fluid Mechanics, Vol. 30, 1967.

[16]Catton, I., "Convection in a Closed Rectangular Region: The Onset of Motion," Journal of Heat Transfer, Vol. 92, 1970.

[17]Jennings, P.A. and Sani, R.L., "Some Remarks on Thermal Convective Instability in Completely Confined Regions," Journal of Heat Transfer, Vol. 94, 1972.

[18]Catton, I. and Edwards, D.K., "Effect of Side Walls on Natural Convection between Horizontal Plates Heated from Below;", Journal of Heat Transfer, Vol. 89, 1967.

[19]Heitz, W.L. and Westwater, J.W., "Critical Rayleigh Numbers for Natural Convection of Water Confined in Square Chlls with L/D from 0.5 to 8," Journal of Heat Transfer, Vol. 93, 1971.

[20]Edwards, D.W. and Catton, I., "Prediction of Heat Transfer by Natural Convection in Closed Cylinders Heated from Below," International Journal of Heat and Mass Transfer, Vol. 12, 1969.

[21]Catton, I., "Effect of Wall Conduction on the Stability of a Fluid in a Rectangular Region Heated from Below," Journal of Heat Transfer, Vol. 94, 1972.

[22]Unny, T.W., "Thermal Instability in Differentially Heated Inclined Fluid Layers," Journal of Applied Mechanics, Vol. 94, 1972.

[23]Hollands, K.G.T. and Konicek, L., "Experimental Study of the Stability of Differentially Heated Inclined Air Layers," International Journal of Heat and Mass Transfer, Vol. 16, 1973.

[24]Clever, R.M., "Finite Amplitude Longitudinal Convection Rolls in an Inclined Layer," Journal of Heat Transfer, Vol. 95, 1973.

[25]Ozoe, H., Sayama, H., and Churchill, S.W., "Natural Convection in an Inclined Square Channel," International Journal of Heat and Mass Transfer, Vol. 17, 1974.

[26]Ozoe, H., Yamamoto, K., Sayama, H., and Churchill, S.W., "Natural Circulation in an Inclined Rectangular Channel Heated on One Side and Cooled on the Opposing Side," International Journal of Heat and Mass Transfer, Vol. 17, 1974.

[27]Ozoe, H., Sayama, H., and Churchill, S.W., "Natural Convection in an Inclined Rectangular Channel at Various Aspect Ratios and Angles -- Experimental Measurements," International Journal of Heat and Mass Transfer (to be published).

[28]Chin, J.H., Donaldson, J.O., Gallagher, L.W., Harper, E.Y., Hurd, S.E., and Slatterlee, H.M., "Analytical and Experimental

Study of Liquid Orientation and Stratification in Standard and Reduced Gravity Field," LMSC. 2-05-64-1, July 1969, Lockheed Missiles & Space Co., Palo Alto, Calif.

[29]Forester, C.K., "Pressurized Expulsion of Non-isothermal Single-Phase Cryogen," MSC Cryogenic Symposium Papers, MSC - 04312, May 1971.

[30]Batchelor, G.K., "Heat Transfer by Free Convection across a Closed Cavity between Vertical Boundaries at Different Thmperatures," Quarterly Journal of Applied Mechanics., Vol. 12, 1954.

[31]Rice, R.A., "Apollo 14 Flight Support and Systems Performance," MSC Cryogenic Symposium Papers, MSC - 04312 May 1971.

[32]Fineblum, S.S., Haron, A.S., and Saxton, J.A., "Heat Transfer and Thermal Stratification in the Apollo 14 Cryogenic Oxygen Tanks," MSC Cryogenics Symposium Papers, MSC - 04312, May 1971.

[33]Conway, B.A., "Development of Skylab Experiment T-013 Crew/Vehicle Disturbance," NASA TN D 6584, Jan. 1972.

[34]Richardson, P.D., "Effects of Sound and Vibrations on Heat Transfer", Applied Mechanics Review, Vol. 20, March 1967, pp. 201-217.

[35]Pak, H.Y., Winter, E.R.F., and Schoenals, R.J., "Convection Heat Transfer in a Confined Fluid Subjected to Vibration Augmentation of Convective Heat and Mass Transfer," edited by A.E. Bergles and A.L. Webb, American Society of Mechanical Engineers, New York, 1970, p. 158.

[36]Gershuni, G.Z., Zhukhovitskii, E.M., and Iurkov, I.S., "On Convective Stability in the Presence of a Periodically Varying Parameter," PMM, Vol. 34, March 1970, pp. 470-480.

[37]Spradley, L.W., Bourgeois, S.V. and Lin, F.N., "Space Processing Convection Evaluation: G-Jitter Convection of Confined Fluids in Low Gravity," AIAA Paper 75-695, 1975; also published elsewhere in this volume.

[38]Pearson, J.R.A., "On Convection Cells Induced by Surface Tension," Journal of Fluid Mechanics, Vol. 4, 1958, pp. 489-500.

[39]Nield, D.A., "Surface Tension and Buoyancy Effects in Cellular Convection," Journal of Fluid Mechanics, Vol. 19, 1974, pp. 341-352.

[40]Scriven, L.E. and Sternling, C.V., "On Cellular Convection Driven by Surface-Tension Gradients," Journal of Fluid Mechanics , Vol. 19, 1974, pp. 320-340.

[41]Birikh, R.V., "Thermocapillary Convection in a Horizontal Layer of Fluid," Journal of Applied Mechanics and Technical Physics, March 1966, pp. 69-72.

[42]Babskiy, V.G., Skolvskaya, I.L., and Sklovskiy, Y.B., "Thermocapillary Convection in Weightless Conditions," Space Studies in the Ukraine, No. 1: Space Materials Studies and Technology," edited by G.S. Pisarenko, Nankova Domka, Kieve, 1973, pp. 121-131.

[43]Black, M.J., "Surface Tension as the Cause of Benard Cells and Surface Deformation in a Liquid Film," Nature, Vol. 178, Sept. 22, 1956, pp. 650-651.

[44]Spradley, L.W. and Churchill, S.W., "Buoyancy and Pressure Driven Thermal Convection in a Rectangular Enclosure," Journal of Fluid Mechanics.

[45]Larkin, B.K., "Heat Flow to a Confined Fluid in Zero Gravity," Progress in Astronautics and Aeronautics: Thermophysics of Spacecraft and Planetary Bodies, Vol. 20, 1967, pp. 819-833.

[46]Chambre, P.L., "On the Dynamics of Phase Growth," Quarterly Journal of Mechanics and Applied Mathematics, Vol. 9, 1956, pp. 224-233.

[47]Horvay, G., "Freezing into an Undercooled Melt Accompanied by Density Change," Proceedings of the U. S. National Congress of Applied Mechanics, Vol. 2, June 1962.

[48]Yih, C.S., "Some Results of the Non-Oscillation of Salt Fingers," Physics of Fluids, Vol. 13, Dec. 1970, pp. 2907-2911.

CRYSTAL GROWTH IN A REDUCED GRAVITY ENVIRONMENT

J. R. Carruthers*
Bell Laboratories, Murray Hill, N. J.

Abstract

The growth of crystals is achieved through the precise control of heat and mass flows during the appropriate phase transformation. The interaction of these flows, in turn, with the compositional segregation processes at the growing crystal-fluid interface is discussed to provide a basis for understanding both the advantages and disadvantages of growing crystals in space. The four main features of reduced gravitational levels which will be considered are the containerless handling of melts, the reduction of density-gradient driven flows, the reduction of sedimentation (and Stokes flow), and the elimination of hydrostatic pressure gradients.

I. Introduction

Crystals are prepared by the controlled nucleation and growth of highly ordered solids from highly disordered fluid phases. Since such crystals usually are prepared for specific applications, it is necessary to produce the necessary properties by exercising some degree of control over the shape, size, composition, and defect structure during their growth. Of these qualities, compositional control is by far the most important, and this paper will focus on those aspects of crystal growth processes which affect the crystal composition over dimensions ranging from the micron scale to the macroscopic size of the crystal itself.

II. Segregation Processes During Crystal Growth

At thermodynamic equilibrium, the solubilities of various components in any crystal growth system will differ

---

Presented as Paper D.4.2 at the COSPAR Symposium on Material Sciences in Space, Philadelphia, Pa., June 9-10, 1976.

*Head, Crystal Growth and Glass Research and Development Department.

between the solid and fluid phases. These phase relationships are known for many systems and usually also pertain to a moving growth interface because of the slow growth rates employed. However, the redistribution of these components, which occurs at an advancing growth interface, leads to a diffusion-controlled mass flow in the fluid adjacent to the interface. This segregation process is influenced by any convective processes in the fluid for a range of conditions where the diffusion distance D/R (where D is the fluid diffusion coefficient and R is the crystal growth rate) is larger than the convectively produced diffusion boundary-layer thickness δ_D. A tutorial review of these conditions may be found in Ref. 1 for crystal growth from melts. Similar considerations apply to crystal growth from the vapor phase.

III. Convective Processes in Crystal Growth Systems

In crystal growth, temperature and/or compositional gradients are used to constrain the position and shape of the growth interface as well as to prevent uncontrolled nucleation elsewhere in the growth system. In a 1-g environment, these gradients will result in density gradients, which, in turn, will generate fluid flow when not aligned in the direction of g. Such uncontrolled natural convection can, in many instances, influence compositional segregation processes at the growth interface as discussed in the previous section. Because the convection is uncontrolled, both spatially and temporally, the composition of the growing crystal cannot be controlled reproducibly. There have been many attempts in crystal growth systems both to eliminate natural convection (by maintaining all density gradients to be vertically stabilizing only) and also to override it with forced convection. Although both of these solutions are successful to some degree, there are associated problems such as container incompatibility and growth transients (respectively) which still remain.[2] Other more sophisticated specific techniques have been used to eliminate natural convection flows on Earth such as the use of static magnetic fields across melts of metals and semiconductors, and the use of magnetic field gradients across paramagnetic fluids.[3]

IV. Uniqueness of Materials Processing in a Reduced Gravity Environment

The availability of a reduced gravity environment for extended periods of time in Earth-orbit laboratories has stimulated interest in its utilization for new materials processing techniques. To date, four areas have been identified which define the uniqueness of reduced gravity for materials processing:

1) Containerless handling of liquids to suppress unwanted container reaction or interaction. Areas of interest here include the reduction of contamination during crystal growth, the thermodynamic study of reactive materials at high temperatures, studies of liquid-solid nucleation phenomena, and the preparation of reactive glasses such as new metallic glasses and oxide glasses containing BaO and CaO.

2) Elimination of natural convection flows arising from thermally or compositionally induced density gradients in fluids. Such flows on Earth are important during compositional segregation in crystal growth and solidification processes because of the creation of nonuniform diffusion boundary layers as well as because of transient segregation due to the temperature and velocity fluctuations associated with unstable flows. Although such flows can be attenuated to a large extent on Earth by previously mentioned techniques, the reduced gravity environment offers somewhat greater flexibility because of the containerless aspect.

3) Elimination of sedimentation and Stokes flows such as those occurring during the preparation of phase separating glasses, multiphase monotectic solidification, the equi-axed zone formation in ingot solidification, vapor-liquid bubbling to promote reaction and mixing, and the casting of some composite material combinations that have large density differences.

4) Elimination of hydrostatic pressure and its influence on phase equilibria (liquid-vapor triple point phenomena and liquid-liquid critical point phenomena).

However, each of these areas possesses an additional set of phenomena not normally encountered or of importance in an Earth gravity environment. For reference purposes, the advantage and disadvantages of the four aspects just mentioned are shown in Table 1 and discussed in detail below.

The use of containerless processing techniques will mean that liquid shape changes and associated flows may arise from many possible sources, including 1) shape instabilities from static or rotational considerations as studied on Skylab in science demonstrations, 2) vibrational oscillations due to constraining acoustic or electromagnetic force fields or transmittance through the growing crystal, 3) solidification flows due to solid-liquid density changes and meniscus shaping requirements, 4) drop coalescence, and 5) capillary

Table 1 Advantages and Disadvantages of Various Aspects of Space Processing of Materials

Space environment use for materials processing	Advantages	Disadvantages
1) Containerless handling of liquids	Container contamination avoided; thermodynamic study of reactive materials at high temperature; studies of liquid-solid nucleation phenomena possible; preparation of new reactive phases and amorphous solids made easier; stable length of liquid floating zones increased	Need for position control of drops with external force fields; surface tension-gradient driven convection possible; liquid shape changes will induce convection in liquid
2) Reduction of density-gradient driven flows	Mass transport by diffusion alone results in uniform macrosegregation in grown crystals; elimination of time-dependent convection phenomena and microsegregation striation in grown crystals	Heat transfer by thermal conduction alone in melts produces undesirable crystal-melt interface shapes; constitutional supercooling instabilities more favored in convectionless melts; bulk mixing of melts not possible; other sources of uncontrolled convection may become dominant
3) Reduction of sedimentation and Stokes flows (of solids and bubbles in melts)	Controlled monotectic solidification possible; microphase separation possible in glasses; reduction of equi-axed zone formation in ingot solidification; preparation of uniformly dispersed composite materials	Elimination of bubbles in melts very difficult

flows due to wetting/dewetting phenomena of contained melts (such as used to date in space experiments).

Very little quantitative work has been performed on such configurations and ground-based research is needed to study these problems. Science demonstrations on Skylab indicated that the vorticity generated by coalescing and oscillating drops decayed quite quickly and that, in fact, very little mixing occurred in the drop for quite large oscillation amplitudes. In addition to liquid shape changes, containerless melts also may be subject to surface tension-gradient driven (Marangoni) flows, although much ground-based work is needed to ascertain whether such melt surfaces conform to the theoretical boundary conditions used to date. Preliminary indications from space flight experiments to date would indicate that such agreement does not exist. Another problem of concern in reduced gravity processing is the achievement of compositional uniformity in melts and the elimination of unwanted bubbles: two processes that occur naturally in 1-g.

The reduction of density-gradient driven natural convection in low-gravity environments leads to a consideration of other sources of residual fluid motion which may become dominant. It is important to understand that only very slow flows may influence mass transport in crystal growth systems significantly but will exert no influence on the overall heat transport in the systems. Consequently, natural convection arising from the variation of fluid properties other than density with temperature and concentration must be considered at reduced gravity. Flows from surface tension gradients (thermocapillary convection) already have been mentioned. Variations in other fluid properties such as viscosity, thermal conductivity, and thermal expansion will generate slow flows. Such fluid properties are known to contribute non-Boussinesq terms to the Navier-Stokes flow equations for thermal convection at 1-g and to alter the flow stability criteria.[4-6] Although not studied, their influence at reduced g in generating fluid vorticity may be very important. Other sources of uncontrolled convection may arise in gases from pressure gradients due to chemical reactions, to low-level g-jitter[7] (variations of 10^{-3} g may be common in spacecraft at average levels of 10^{-4} to 10^{-3} g), and to boundary-layer thermal transient contributions (such as thermoacoustic convection).[8]

The elimination of sedimentation and Stokes flows in liquids at low g has implications in particular for the behavior of bubbles in such liquids. Therefore, questions of bubble nucleation, migration, coalescence, stability, incorporation, and elimination are all of importance in reduced gravity melt processes as opposed to Earth gravity processes and should be studied carefully in a ground-based research program.

V. Future Prospects for Crystal Growth in Space

Many different types of crystal growth experiments have been both proposed and performed for space flight. All experiments are basically 1-g processes that have been adapted for a reduced gravity environment to study the differences in the grown crystals with g-level. (One exception was the undirectional solidification of a molten sessile drop of indium antimonide on Skylab III.) Although these experiments were of great interest, they did not utilize fully the unique aspects of a reduced gravity environment and therefore will not lead to the scientific insight required to generate new and innovative processing technology. At the present time, there has been no major discovery or finding that would justify singling out any one material or process for extensive further investigation leading to a commercial application.

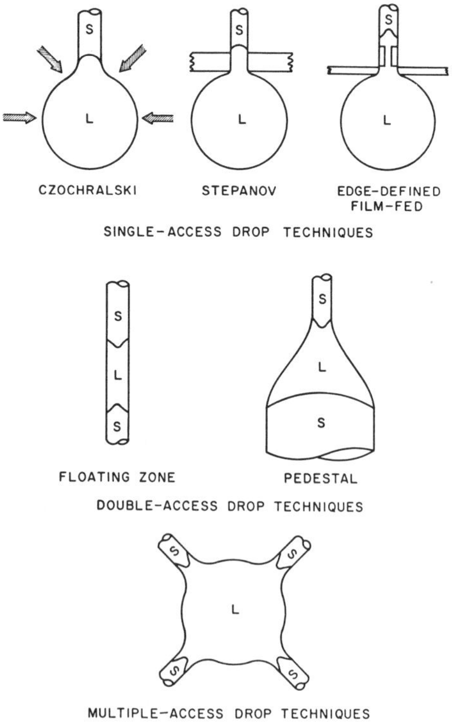

Fig. 1 Schematic classification of melt crystal growth processes on Earth in terms of the degree of confinement.

In fact, some experiments have been performed in space which can be done equally well on Earth. In addition, many space crystal growth experiments were performed without adequate ground-based support research programs and with inadequate characterization of the space-grown crystals in postflight analysis.

Some ideas of rather crude crystal growth techniques that more fully utilize the reduced gravity environment are shown in Fig. 1 (from Ref. 9).

In this classification, the degrees of access to a containerless molten drop are shown. In addition, instead of a liquid drop, a liquid shell with a central gas bubble can be employed. Such a shell possesses a mechanically stiffer resistance to external vibrations.

Lastly, many different ground-based experiments have been suggested in this overview which are required in support of detailed investigations of crystal growth in a reduced gravity environment. These include studies of the static behavior of liquid surfaces, fluid dyanmics at low g-levels, surface tension measurements and contact angle phenomena in melt systems of interest, bubble dynamics, and phase equilibria studies of highly reactive systems that possess container problems at Earth gravity. Other areas should be committed to similar study as they become identified in future space flight.

References

[1]Carruthers, J. R., "Crystal Growth from the Melt," Treatise on Solid State Chemistry, edited by N. B. Hannay, Vol. 5, Plenum Press, New York, 1975, p. 325.

[2]Carruthers, J. R., and Witt, A. F., "Transient Segregation Effects in Czochralski Growth," Crystal Growth and Characterization, edited by R. Ueda and J. B. Mullin, North Holland, Amsterdam, 1975, p. 107.

[3]Carruthers, J. R., "Thermal Convection Instabilities Relevant to Crystal Growth from Liquids," Preparation and Properties of Solid State Materials, edited by R. A. Lefever and W. R. Wilcox, Dekker, New York, 1976.

[4]Somerscales, E. F. C., and Dougherty, T. S., "Observed Flow Patterns at the Initiation of Convection in a Horizontal Liquid Layer Heated from Below," Journal of Fluid Mechanics, Vol. 42, July 30, 1970, p. 755.

5
Davenport, I. F., "Variable Fluid Properties in Benard Convection," The Physics of Fluids, Vol. 16, December, 1973, p. 2346.

6
Davenport, I. F., and King, C. J., "The Onset of Natural Convection from Time-Dependent Profiles," International Journal of Heat and Mass Transfer, Vol. 17, January 1974, p. 69.

7
Spradley, L. W., Bourgeois, S. V., and Lin, F. N., "Space Processing Convection Evaluation: G-Jitter Convection of Confined Fluids in Low Gravity," AIAA Paper 75-695, May 1975, Denver, Colorado, also published elsewhere in this volume.

8
Spradley, L. W., Bourgeois, S. V., Fan, C., and Grodzka, P. G., "A Numerical Solution for Thermoacoustic Convection of Fluids in Low Gravity," CR-2269, May 1973, NASA.

9
Carruthers, J. R., "The Application of Drops and Bubbles to the Science of Space Processing of Materials," International Colloquium on the Science of Liquid Drops and Bubbles, edited by D. J. Collins, 1976, Jet Propulsion Lab., Pasadena, California.

ELECTROPHORESIS

M. Bier *

Veterans Administration Hospital and University of Arizona,
Tucson, Ariz.

Abstract

The phenomenology of electrophoresis has been reviewed with particular emphasis on the role of gravity. The many ground based techniques for electrophoresis are based on the need either to circumvent the effects of gravity to prevent convection, or to utilize gravity for fluid stabilization through artificial density gradients. The microgravity environment of orbiting spacecraft provides a new alternative for preparative electrophoresis, by avoiding the need for either of the above two approaches. The contributions of ground based electrophoresis to biology and medicine have been placed into context with further advances potentially realizable from a space electrophoresis facility. This has to be viewed primarily as a unique national research facility, which may yield significant advances in biomedical knowledge and its technological utilization. Primary objectives are increased resolution and throughput for separation of living cells and biomacromolecules.

Introduction

Electrophoresis is defined as the transport of electrically charged species under the influence of a direct current electrical field. Most materials in aqueous solution or suspension acquire an electrical charge due to ionization of their functional groups, ion adsorption, or other more complex phenomena, and are therefore attracted by electrodes of opposite polarity. The charged species

---

This work was supported in part by the NASA Contract NAS8-29566.

*Research Biophysicist and Visiting Research Professor.

may be simple ions, complex macromolecules or colloids, or even particles, such as living cells, emulsion droplets, clay, etc. Their migration velocity in unit electrical field is referred to as their electrophoretic mobility and is a complex function not only of their electric charge, but also of their molecular size, shape, and hydration, as well as the dielectric characteristics of the solvent. As a result, electrophoresis is capable of providing a high degree of characterization of individual ionized species, which is most important for macromolecular systems and living cells, where chemical structure parameters are difficult to determine.

Based on this uniqueness of information provided by electrophoresis, a number of applications have been developed. To categorize them in their broadest outlines, these are: 1) identification and characterization of an ionized species; 2) determination of the quantitative composition of a complex mixture; 3) actual isolation of components of a mixture, separation being achieved on the basis of differences in transport rates.

A multitude of techniques and instruments have been developed for the exploitation of the basic phenomenon of electrophoresis.[1,2] For some applications the minutest sample is sufficient, and microscopic techniques have been developed.[3-5] At the other extreme, a few large industrial installations have been constructed, although such applications are generally lagging.[6]

The most important applications of electrophoresis are in molecular biology and medicine. In biology, it has contributed to the advancement of our knowledge of proteins more than any other laboratory technique. Its impact originated with Tiselius[7] who first demonstrated the electrophoretic complexity of human blood proteins and received for it the Nobel prize. More recently, electrophoresis led to a new branch of human genetics, the study of the inherited variabilities of blood proteins. In medicine, electrophoresis offered the first clue to the primary cause of sickle cell anemia by demonstrating the presence of an abnormal hemoglobin in sickled red blood cells and has been widely used for the diagnosis of this disease. It is also the method of choice for the diagnosis of a variety of other acquired and inherited protein-linked diseases, such as multiple myeloma, agammaglobulinemia, Waldenstrom macroglobulinemia, etc. Electrophoresis also is used for the detection of lipoproteinemias, the earliest indicator of possible development of atherosclerosis, which is a primary cause of heart disease. In short, electrophoresis is an essential tool of modern medicine, widely used in such diverse areas as nutrition, cancer research, immunology, etc.

Because of these achievements in the protein field, the techniques also have been extrapolated to a broad spectrum of substances of high or low molecular weight, covering practically the entire range of organic and inorganic chemistry.[8,9] The importance of electrophoresis in this field has been overshadowed, however, by various chromatographic procedures. Most significant for the space-processing program is that electrophoresis is also applicable to characterization and separation of living cells.[3-5] Although cell electrophoresis historically preceded protein electrophoresis, it is nevertheless still in its infancy, largely due to a variety of technical difficulties, some of which, at least are gravity dependent.[10-12]

Within the scope of the space processing program, electrophoresis was one of the first processes clearly identified as possibly benefiting from a microgravity environment. The primary reason for it is that gravity cannot be ignored in electrophoresis, and, consciously or unconsciously, in all electrophoretic techniques one tries either to circumvent or to utilize the effects of gravity. Equally important is the significant potential socioeconomic importance of a space facility for electrophoresis. The premise that the process may benefit from a micro-gravity environment has been confirmed in pilot experiments conducted aboard Apollo 14 and 16,[10-12] Skylab,[13] and the recent Apollo-Soyuz flight.[14]

Theoretical Considerations

Most materials, when dissolved in polar media, particularly in water, will spontaneously acquire an electrical charge. For the proper understanding of electrophoresis one needs to consider the origin of these charges, and their implications. All proteins and many other biomacromolecules contain as an integral part of their molecular structure ionizable functional groups which will dissociate as a function of pH of the aqueous medium. As the groups are both acidic (carboxylic, imidazole, phosphoric and sulfonic acid groups) and basic (primary and tertiary amines), proteins are amphoteric in nature and will acquire a positive charge in acid media and a negative charge in basic. The pH at which the net charge due to ionization is zero is called the isoionic point. It may not coincide with zero electrophoretic mobility, because of possible adsorption of free ions, such as Na^+ or Cl^-, and this pH of zero net charge is called the isoelectric point. Ion adsorption is also responsible for the charge exhibited by many hydrophobic surfaces, such as oil droplets or air bubbles. Most adsorption effects are usually due to anions, and detergents because of their sizable hydrophobic residue, are adsorbed particularly strongly. Cations are more hydrated, as a rule, and therefore less likely to be adsorbed by hydrophobic surfaces.

Other colloidal particles may acquire charge by virtue of unequal dissolution of their ionic constituents. Thus, for example, colloidal silver iodide may acquire a negative charge in presence of an excess of free iodide ions, and a positive charge in presence of an excess of silver ions. Hydroxyl and hydrogen ions play a similar role for metal oxides and hydroxides, and such ions are known as the potential-determining ions. Glass usually is negatively charged because of trace solubilization of surface cations.

In electrophoresis and other electrokinetic phenomena one is not concerned only with the net charge of the particles, but also with charge distribution in their immediate surrounding. Proteins and other colloidal particles, including of course cells, are much larger and carry higher charges than small ions thus creating in their immediate surrounding an ionic environment of their own. The theory of the electric double layer deals with the structure of the boundary between two phases, considering it a layer of finite dimensions, rather than as a mathematical plane. If ions of one sign are an integral part of or are adsorbed by one of the phases, free small ions of the opposite sign will be attracted by the resulting electrical field, and will accumulate preferentially near the phase boundary, assuring the electrical neutrality of the total system. These small ions of opposite polarity will still be subject to Brownian movement, and the fixed charges of one phase and the mobile charges of the other constitute the electrical double layer. Thus, the resulting electrical potential will vary with the distance from the surface of the particle, and can be defined as the work necessary to bring a unit charge of the same sign from infinite distance to a given point in the neighborhood of the particle.

Of particular importance for electrophoresis is the potential at the effective shear surface of the particles, the so-called electrokinetic or zeta potential, ζ. The shear surface does not correspond to the actual physical surface of the particle itself, because of a strongly adsorbed hydration shell of solvent molecules. The various models for the structure of the electric double layer and the zeta potential have been reviewed in depth by Overbeek.[15]

The zeta potential cannot be measured directly but can be calculated only on the basis of the theories of the electric double layer. Electrophoretic mobility is most often used for these calculations, and for small particles the Huckel relation is used

$$\mu = U/E = \epsilon\zeta/6\pi\eta$$

where U is the observed migration velocity, E the applied electric field, ϵ the dielectric constant, and η the viscosity. For larger particles, such as cells, the Helmholtz-Smoluchowski equation is mostly used

$$\mu = U/E = \epsilon\zeta/4\pi\eta$$

the difference between the preceding two expressions having been reconciled by Henry and others.[15]

The existence of the zeta potential causes not only migration of the charged particles, but also a certain amount of liquid flow as the liquid is polarized in the neighborhood of any charged surfaces. This flow is referred to as electroosmosis, and it is most pronounced if the charged surface are immobilized, such as at the walls of the vessels or in porous plugs. Electro-osmotic flow is usually in the direction opposite to that of electrophoresis, and may present problems in some electrophoretic techniques. It can be used also for determination of the zeta potential, the velocity of electro-osmotic flow, v, being given by

$$v = E\epsilon\zeta/4\pi\eta$$

Classification of Experimental Techniques and Role of Gravity

Electrophoretic separations are based on differential rates of electrical transport in the bulk of the liquid phase and are not concerned with reactions at the electrodes. Differences in transport rates alone, however, may not suffice for optimal separation of all components in a mixture, as some components may have comparable or overlapping mobilities. Thus, electrophoresis alone is not a high resolution technique unless a second discriminating parameter is superimposed upon the transport process. This is accomplished by creating a discontinuity or gradient in the properties of the medium in which electrophoresis is carried out. These criteria permit the following recognition of four electrophoretic modalities:

Zone electrophoresis: this is the oldest form of electrophoresis, where separation is carried out in a homogeneous medium, buffer electrolytes providing a background of small molecular weight ions. In human serum it typically gives five clearly identifiable protein fractions. Though not a high resolution method, it still finds wide usage particularly in medical diagnostic applications.

High density gel electrophoresis: much higher resolution is obtained if an element of molecular sieving is superimposed on electrophoresis. This is achievable with high-density gels, where the effective gel pore size approximates the dimensions of the protein species to be separated. Two such systems are in common use: polyacrylamide gels (PAGE) and starch gels. In such gels serum proteins separate into some 20 to 25 clearly identifiable fractions.

Isoelectric focusing: in isoelectric focusing a continuous pH gradient is generated within the electrophoretic medium, and the protein fractions become immobilized at the pH corresponding to their isoelectric point. The pH gradient is generated electrophoretically within the system by incorporating into the buffer a complex mixture of amphoteric salts (ampholines), possessing a nearly continuous spectrum of components of different isoelectric points. Resolution obtainable in isoelectric focusing is comparable to that of high density gels, and these two techniques are used in most advanced protein analyses.

Isotachophoresis: is characterized by a discontinuous buffer system, where the sample is introduced at the interface between a high mobility leading buffer and a low mobility terminator. This system has not received much attention for protein analysis but is of interest as a preparative method because of its high capacity.[16, 17]

The preceding four modes in electrophoresis are compatible with a number of different experimental techniques or instruments.[1, 2, 18] These were developed to answer a wide array of specific needs in analytical or preparative applications. From the point of view of the readers of this volume, it is interesting to note that all techniques of electrophoresis have evolved around the need to cope with effects of gravity. In free fluids, gravity can cause convective flows if density gradients are present, and density gradients are unavoidable in electrophoresis because of concentration and temperature gradients. Concentration gradients arise due to the presence of the sample to be fractionated, and temperature gradients are caused by the need to dissipate the Joule heating. Any uncontrolled convection could, of course, remix fractions in the process of being separated by the electric current.

Two basic modes of natural convection are recognized. Conventional convection is generated immediately by a density gradient that is normal to the gravitational vector. Such a situation will occur in vertical columns with a radial temperature gradient, which is a geometry prevailing in most electrophoretic instruments. Unstable convection can occur when the density gradient is parallel to, but opposite in direction to the gravity vector. The onset of this fluid motion depends strongly on the geometry of the vessel and does not start until a critical value of density gradient is exceeded, but once convection starts it usually causes greater mixing than conventional convection. For this reason, this configuration is usually avoided in electrophoresis.

The most valuable criterion, therefore, for the classification of various experimental techniques in electrophoresis is according to the means employed to cope with the potential problems of fluid convection:

1) All convective flow is suppressed if the electrophoretic process is carried out within capillary pores of gels, packed beds of fine granules, or membranes. Such anticonvective supporting media do not prevent molecular transport by electrophoresis, but suppress all convective fluid flows. The pore size has to be, of course, larger than or at least comparable to the dimensions of the migrating particles. This principle of convection control is compatible with all four electrophoretic modalities, and a variety of methods and instruments have been developed for membrane zone electrophoresis, isoelectric focusing, high density gel electrophoresis, and isotachophoresis. These techniques fulfill all of the needs for analytical and micropreparative electrophoresis of proteins, and no foreseeable advantage is to be gained by going to a microgravity environment. It is unfortunate that the principle is not applicable to large particles, such as cells, and that the scaling

up of instruments to commercially significant quantities proved to be as yet impossible.

2) Free fluids can be stabilized very effectively against convection if a stable density gradient is generated within the system, using an electrically neutral solute, such as sucrose. The imposed gradient must be steeper than any possible gradient engendered by the electrophoretic process. Density stabilization is used most often for micropreparative separation of proteins by isoelectric focusing. In principle, it is also applicable for zone electrophoretic separation of cells, but this use is too recent [19] to have received thorough evaluation.

3) Most electrophoretic separations are carried out in batch operations, but for preparative purposes a continuous mode would appear to be preferable. A continuous flow apparatus was developed by Hannig,[20] and stabilization of the fluid against convection is obtained by confining it to a thin film, less than 1 mm in thickness, formed between two parallel plates. The apparatus is mainly suited for zone electrophoresis and therefore offers limited resolution. It is therefore of little use for proteins, but it is the best method currently available for separation of cells. Operation of such an instrument in a microgravity environment would permit increasing the thickness of the fluid film, resulting in better resolution and higher throughput. A prototype of such an instrument has been tested as part of the Apollo-Soyuz mission,[21] and other modifications of the concept have been proposed.[22] The convection problems of continuous flow instruments have been studied in some details.[22,23]

4) Stabilization can be also obtained in narrow bore tubes, rotating around their horizontal axis. Since the gravity vector is constantly changing in direction no sedimentation or convection occurs.[24,25] These instruments are the closest gound based analogue of the static column electrophoresis instruments used in Apollo missions.[12, 14]

5) Rotational stabilization is also achievable by a superimposition of electrical and magnetic fields. Such an instrument was developed by Kolin [26] but is not yet commercially available. Its performance is therefore difficult to assess.

6) Finally, electrodecantation, electrophoresis-convection, and forced-flow electrophoresis utilize gravity-caused convection as

part of the separating process. Convection is maximized by allowing migrating species to accumulate against a semipermeable membrane. These are the only techniques applicable on a truly large, industrial scale but provide only two fractions separating electrically charged from electrically neutral species.[27]

7) A purely analytical technique is microscope electrophoresis, where migration of individual particles is directly observed under a microscope.[3-5] It is of particular importance for cell electrophoresis, having provided the bulk of information on this subject. Several modifications of this system are currently in various stages of development, but, unfortunately, none have preparative capabilities. In none of them is convection a major problem, as one deals with highly dilute suspensions and small instrument dimensions.

8) Orbiting spacecraft have provided the ultimate approach to eliminate the effect of gravity. This microgravity environment provides a unique environment which is not mimicked by any of the foregoing enumerated stratagems. The full impact of this approach for electrophoresis has yet to be evaluated, but the pilot experiments have substantiated the early promises.[10-14]

From the foregoing enumeration, it can be seen that there are a variety of approaches to control the effects of gravity which can be utilized to advantage under the proper circumstances. Each of the preceding methods has its own advantages and limitations, and none has yet fulfilled all of the demands of electrophoreticists. On an analytical level, one has satisfactory methods for both proteins and cells, and nothing much is to be gained from a microgravity environment. On a preparative level, electrophoresis has been disappointing, and no attempts to scale protein electrophoresis to commercially significant production rates have as yet succeeded. The paradoxical situation has therefore evolved where electrophoresis is the ultimate test for the purity and quality control of all purified proteins, whereas none of them are actually manufactured by the electrophoretic process. The reason for it is not theoretical but only a limitation in throughput of existing equipment.

Electrophoresis of Living Cells

Because of its nondestructive nature, electrophoresis is one of the few separative methods applicable to living cells. Nevertheless, in comparison to proteins, cell electrophoresis is only in its infancy. Most of the techniques and instruments developed for protein electrophoresis are not applicable, and cell electrophoresis has remained the province of a few highly specialized laboratories. One of the merits of the NASA program is that it has focused the attention of a number of scientists here and abroad on this long-neglected field. At present, cell separation is the main objective of NASA's space electrophoresis facility.

Basic knowledge in this field is sorely needed. Although there are a multitude of analytical electrophoretic methods applicable to proteins, until quite recently there was only one method suitable for cell electrophoresis. This technique involves direct visual microscopic measurement of electrophoretic migration velocity of individual cells and has remained essentially unchanged for over 50 years.[3-5] It is an inherently slow and unreliable method, burdensome and tedious for the observer. As a result, although there is adequate information on some normal cell populations, such as red blood cells and lymphocytes, there are almost no reliable data on changes of cell properties in most clinical or pathologic conditions. This situation is intolerable, since the present state-of-the-art would readily permit computer-assisted automation of the microscopic method, resulting in rapid accumulation of important basic data on cell mobilities in health and disease. It is hoped that, through NASA sponsorship, such an instrument will soon become available. Other alternatives to more rapid accumulation of data involve the measurement of the Doppler effect caused by migrating particles under laser illumination.[28,29] Both of these two types of instruments are operable in the presence of gravity, but at zero gravity their scope of application would be extended to larger cells, characterized by rapid sedimentation in a normal gravity field. Moreover, such instruments will be essential for the space facility, to provide real time information on the quality of separation achieved in space in the preparative instruments.

Similar considerations prevail in preparative electrophoresis. Several techniques have been developed, including thin-film free-flow electrophoresis,[20] stable-flow electrophoresis,[30] electromagnetophoresis,[26] and rotationally stabilized instruments,[24,25] but most have remained almost exclusively in the hands of their original developers. This is largely due to their complexity and the paucity of basic analytical data, which are indispensable in pinpointing the most important areas of preparative application. Moreover, the throughput of the instruments is limited and their resolution less than optimal.

There are numerous areas of medicine and biology where cell separation would be desirable. Some data are already available on peripheral blood cells, spermatozoa, bacteria, viruses, and cells derived from bone marrow, spleen, lymph nodes, kidneys, and other organs. Major current interest is focused on lymphocytes, as these cells are directly involved in the immune mechanism and thereby control such diverse responses as resistance to cancer, rejection of transplanted kidneys and other organs, autoimmune diseases, lymphocyte neoplasias, etc.

Cell electrophoresis has also been explored as a diagnostic tool for certain forms of cancer. Bone marrow transplantation might be greatly aided by availability of pure cell lines. The same situation prevails in numerous areas of tissue culture, used in growth of various viruses and preparation of biologicals. A preliminary experiment on the separation of kidney cells for the purpose of increased production of biologicals has already been carried out as part of the ASTP mission.[14] If present results were to be confirmed, this could lead to large-scale production of the enzyme urokinase and some other biologically active proteins of considerable medical importance.

Conclusions

The term "electrophoresis" comprises a great variety of techniques, having in common the principle of molecular or particle separation on the basis of their electrical properties. The applications of the phenomenon have been manifold and have been of importance in diverse areas of modern biology and medicine. Although eminently successful in ground based work, electrophoresis is limited in quantities of samples it can separate, due to problems related directly or indirectly to gravity. Its limitations are most pronounced when applied to living cells, but it is just this application which is currently of greatest interest. Biologists have only begun to look into functions of specific cells and have recognized the importance of cell subpopulations in many diverse areas.

A space facility for electrophoresis will overcome the limitations imposed by terrestrial gravity but will not overcome all of the problems inherent in electrophoresis. These are, mainly, electro-osmosis and the dissipation of the heat generated by the electric field. The NASA program has already led to excellent coatings to prevent electro-osmosis, whereas the need for heat dissipation will continue to impose limits on the actual size of equipment. It is also not excluded that, once the dominant force of gravity is eliminated, disturbances in fluid stability may originate from weaker forces, such as surface tension.

The prospective space electrophoresis facility has to be considered as primarily a unique research tool, which eventually may evolve into a processing plant. Its success will depend primarily on the skill of its designers in optimizing its performance, for electrophoresis in space has no characteristics inherently different from ground based electrophoresis, except the potential advantages of increased throughput and/or resolution. As no single technique or apparatus has answered all of the requirements of ground-based electrophoresis, one can also expect that more than one space apparatus will be required. These may be directed towards the optimization of either throughput or resolution, there being usually a tradeoff between these two factors.

It is certain that the space electrophoresis facility will have an impact on our understanding of cell biology. The potential economic value of cell separations is, at present, difficult to evaluate. The facility may provide valuable diagnostic services, purify cells for direct cell therapy for treatment of immune deficiencies, or improve selection of cells for tissue culture production of biologicals and vaccines.

In the protein field, if significant increase of throughput is realized, its research and commercial applications are easier to foresee. These may comprise preparations of purified materials for research purposes or for actual theraputic usage. It could yield, for instance, improved preparation of selected components of human plasma, such as clotting factors. Human blood is a unique national resource in short supply, even though in the United States alone over 9,000,000 yearly donations are collected.[31] No realistic dollar value can be ascribed to it, and optimal utilization is imperative. Even scarcer and more valuable in both economic and medical terms are many protein or peptide hormones, derived from pituitary, hypothalamus, blood and other organs. Some of them can be synthesized. Purification of either the natural or the synthetic products may benefit from electrophoresis. Finally, a great number of enzymes and isozymes are used in research, for diagnostic purposes, or in industry. An adequate facility for preparative fractionation of these materials would find immediate widespread usage.

References

[1]Bier, M., _Electrophoresis Theory, Methods and Applications_, Academic Press, New York, Vol. I and II, 1959 and 1967.

[2]Shaw, D. J., _Electrophoresis_, Academic Press, New York, 1969.

[3]Abramson, H. A., Moyer, L. S., and Gorin, M. H., _Electrophoresis of Proteins_, Hafner Publishing Co., New York, 1964.

[4]Ambrose, E. J., _Cell Electrophoresis_, Little, Brown and Co., Boston, Mass., 1965.

[5]Brinton, C. C. and Lauffer, M. A., "The Electrophoresis of Viruses, Bacteria, and Cells, and the Microscope Method of Electrophoresis", _Electrophoresis_, Vol. I, edited by M. Bier, Academic Press, New York, 1959, pp. 427-492.

[6]Bier, M., "Electrophoresis as an Industrial Process" _Water - 1971_, AIChE Symposium Series No. 124, Vol. 68, 1972, pp. 84-93.

[7]Tiselius, A., _Trans. Faraday Soc._ Vol. 33, 1937, p. 524.

[8]Clotten, R. and Clotten, A., _Hochspannungs Elektrophorese_, Georg Thieme Verlag, Stuttgart, Germany, 1962.

[9]Wieland, T., "Applications of Zone Electrophoresis", _Electrophoresis_, Vol. I, edited by M. Bier, Academic Press, New York, 1959, pp. 493-530.

[10]Bier, M. and Snyder, R. S., "Electrophoresis in Space at Zero Gravity" AIAA Paper No. 74-210, January 1974, Washington, D.C.

[11]Bier, M. et al., "Role of Gravity in Preparative Electrophoresis" _Proceedings 3rd Space Processing Symposium, Skylab Results_, NASA Marshall Space Flight Center, Alabama, 1974, pp. 729-755.

[12]Snyder, R. S. et al., "Free Fluid Particle Electrophoresis on Apollo 16," _Separ Purification Methods_, Vol. 2, 1973, pp. 259-282.

[13]Bier, M., Hinckley, J. O. N., and Smolka, A. J. K., "Potential Use of Isotachophoresis in Space," _Protides Biological Fluids_, Vol. 22, edited by H. Peeters, Pergamon Press, New York, 1975, pp. 673-678.

[14]Allen, R. E. et al., "Electrophoresis Technology - Experiment MA-011," Preliminary Science Report on the Apollo-Soyuz Test Project, NASA Report TM X-58173, February 1976, pp. 20-1 to 20-23.

[15]Overbeek, J. Th. G. and Wiersema, P. H., "The Interpretation of Electrophoretic Mobilities," Electrophoresis, Vol. II, edited by M. Bier, Academic Press, New York, 1967, pp. 1-52.

[16]Kopwillem, A. et al., "Serum Protein Fractionation by Isotachophoresis using Amino Acid Spacers," Journal of Chromatography, Vol. 118, 1976, pp. 35-46.

[17]Baumann, G. and Chrambach, A., "Gram-Preparative Protein Fractionation by Isotachophoresis," Proceedings of the National Academy of Science USA, Vol. 73, 1976, pp. 732-726.

[18]Bier, M., "Electrophoresis," An Introduction to Separation Science edited by B. L. Karger, L. R. Snyder and C. Horvath, Wiley, New York, 1973, pp. 497- 526.

[19]Griffith, A. L., Catsimpoolas, N., and Wortis, H. H., "Electrophoretic Separation of Cells in a Density Gradient," Life Sciences, Vol. 16, 1975, pp. 1693-1702.

[20]Hannig, K., Methods in Microbiology, edited by J. R. Norris and D. W. Robbins, Academic Press, New York, 1971.

[21]Hannig, K. and Wirth, H., "Electrophoresis Experiment - Experiment MA-014," Preliminary Science Report on the Apollo-Soyuz Test Project, Nasa Report TM X-58173, February 1976, pp. 21-1 to 21-16.

[22]Bier, M., Smolka, A. J. K., Kopwillem, A., and Ostrach, S., "Preparative Electrophoresis in Zero Gravity," Journal of Colloid Interface Science, Vol. 55, 1976, pp. 197-207.

[23]Ostrach, S., "Convection in Continuous-Flow Electrophoresis," preprint - personal communication.

[24]Hjerten, S., Free Zone Electrophoresis, Almquist and Wiksells Boktryckeri AB, Uppsala, 1967.

[25]Bier, M., patent pending.

[26]Kolin, A., "Electromagnetophoresis," Journal of Chromotography, Vol. 17,1965, pp. 532-537.

[27]Bier, M. "Preparative Electrophoresis without Supporting Media" Electrophoresis Vol. I, edited by M. Bier, Academic Press, New York, 1959, pp. 263-316.

[28]Ware, B. R., "Electrophoretic Light Scattering," Advances in Colloid Interface Sciences, Vol. 4, 1974, p. 1.

[29]Uzgiris, E. E. and Kaplan, J. H,, "Protein Coated Electrodes," Review of Scientific Instruments, Vol. 45, 1974, p. 120.

[30]Mel, C., "Electrophoretic Interaction Studies by the Stable-Flow Free-Boundary Method," Science, Vol. 132, October 28, 1960, pp. 1255-1256.

[31]Ness, P. M., and Pennington, R. M., "Plasma Fractionation in the United States," Journal of the American Medical Association, Vol. 230, 1974, pp. 247-250.

CAPILLARY PHENOMENA IN MICROGRAVITY

J.M. Haynes*

University of Bristol, Bristol, England

Abstract

The general conditions for the static capillary equilibrium of a fluid interface and for the stability of such equilibrium are well known. Their quantitative usefulness so far has been limited, however, to certain rather simple situations. The possibility of conducting experiments in Spacelab under conditions of microgravity will enable studies to be made of systems hitherto intractable to mathematics and at the same time unsuited to the neutral buoyancy technique of Plateau. In addition, some of the proposed space-processing experiments involve complex problems of capillarity and fluid dynamics, for the solution of which model experiments in microgravity are proposed.

Introduction

The study of capillary phenomena has proceeded for over 250 years. The development of the subject has been motivated as much by its inherent scientific interest (and, in particular, its fundamental relationship to intermolecular forces) as by its relevance to many different technologies. Today, the growth of interest in the new technology of space processing raises a number of novel capillary problems. At the same time, the opportunity to conduct experiments in the virtual absence of gravity forces now offers an approach to some of the basic problems that have remained unsolved for so long.

"Capillarity" might be defined as the science of curved interfaces, since most of its manifestations are attributable

---

Presented as Paper D.3.2 at the COSPAR Symposium on Materials Sciences in Space, Philadelphia, Pa., June 9-10, 1976.

* Lecturer in Physical Chemistry, School of Chemistry.

to the hydrostatic pressure difference that must exist across a curved surface subjected to uniform tension, as a condition of its mechanical equilibrium. [From the thermodynamic viewpoint, the extent of such an interface might be regarded as a more natural variable than its curvature. Configurations of high surface-to-volume ratio are, however, usually associated with correspondingly high values of the curvature (the principal exception being that of thin liquid lamellae, which, while having zero interfacial curvature, are at the same time sufficiently different in nature as to be considered separately from the topic of capillarity).] This pressure difference ΔP is given by the Laplace equation

$$\Delta P = \sigma C \tag{1}$$

where σ is the surface (or interfacial) tension, and the mean curvature C is defined by

$$C = (1/r_1) + (1/r_2) \tag{2}$$

Here, r_1 and r_2 are the principal radii of curvature of the surface. In considering liquid/vapor interfaces, a radius of curvature conventionally is given a positive sign if the corresponding center of curvature lies in the liquid phase. Thus, for a convex liquid drop, both radii are positive and so, therefore, is ΔP, indicating that the hydrostatic pressure inside the liquid is greater than that in the surrounding phase. [It is possible for r_1 and r_2 to be opposite in sign (anticlastic surfaces), as we shall see. If, in addition, the radii are equal in magnitude, then the mean curvature defined by Eq.(2) will be zero. Such a surface nevertheless may be extended very much if r_1 and r_2 are small; this kind of surface, which possibly may exist in certain porous solids, could constitute a more important exception to the definition of capillarity given previously.]

It is this pressure difference between the phases that is responsible for almost all of the phenomena of capillarity, ranging from the retention of water by soils and the replacement of crude oil by other fluids in reservoir formations to the condensation of vapors in porous solids and the shapes of liquid drops and bubbles. Capillary effects are vital to the functioning of plants and animals, and they play a central role in certain meteorological phenomena. Thus, the longstanding interest in this subject seems to be justified fully.

Capillary Equilibrium and its Stability

Most problems in capillarity reduce to a description of an equilibrium interfacial configuration subject to specified constraints and an investigation of the stability of such an equilibrium. In the absence of external fields such as gravity, the pressure within a bulk fluid at rest must be uniform; the quantity ΔP in the Laplace equation therefore must be uniform everywhere within a capillary system subject to similar conditions. Since the interfacial tension also must be uniform at equilibrium, it follows that equilibrium capillary configurations must be surfaces of uniform mean curvature, or homoclastic surfaces. The family of radially symmetric homoclastic surfaces (unduloid, nodoid, and catenoid) has been known for a long time (see, e.g., Ref.1 and earlier sources quoted therein), but any description of the infinite variety of homoclastic surfaces of lesser symmetry, whose existence is demonstrated so readily with soap films, remains intractable to mathematics.

The shapes of capillary surfaces influenced by gravity, as observed terrestrially in sessile and pendent drops and bubbles, are susceptible to analysis only if they have an axis of rotational symmetry parallel to the direction of the gravitational acceleration.[2] Once again, the geometry of less symmetrical configuration is unknown.

As a general capillary system, let us consider two fluids and a solid in mutual contact (Fig.1). In the absence of external fields, the fluid/fluid interface must be homoclastic, and, in addition, whether subject to gravity or not, it must meet the solid surface in a fixed angle θ (measured through fluid 1), given by Young's equation

$$\cos\theta = (\sigma_{s2} - \sigma_{s1})/\sigma_{12} \tag{3}$$

It then can be shown thermodynamically[3] that an equilibrium interfacial configuration corresponds to an extreme value of the effective area, A^{eff}, defined by

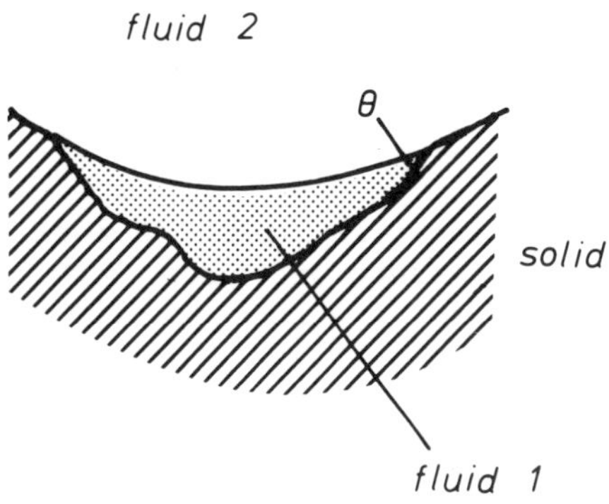

Fig.1 Configuration of general capillary system consisting of two fluids and a solid.

$$A^{eff} = A_{12} - A_{s2}\cos\theta \tag{4}$$

where A_{ij} denotes the area of the ij interface. The effective area obeys the geometrical relationship (first obtained by Gauss)

$$dA^{eff}/dV_1 = C \tag{5}$$

where V_1 is the volume of fluid 1.

If fluid 1 is taken to be a pure liquid and fluid 2 its vapor, then a further condition of equilibrium is given by the Kelvin equation

$$(RT/v_\ell)\ln p/p^o = \sigma_{12}C \tag{6}$$

in which p^o is the saturated vapor pressure, at the temperature T, of the liquid (of molar volume v_ℓ) when the liquid/vapor interface is of zero mean curvature, and p is its value at the same temperature when the curvature is C. R is the gas constant. Thus, p is raised or lowered according to whether C is positive or negative.

As well as knowing whether a given configuration is an equilibrium one or not, it is important to decide whether the equilibrium is stable, metastable, neutral, or unstable. Again, the effective area provides a useful criterion, since it also can be shown[3,4] that the hydrostatic equilibrium described by Eq.(1) is stable (or metastable) to small deformations (Laplace stability) only if

$$(\partial^2 A^{eff}/\partial\eta^2)_{T,V_1} > 0 \tag{7}$$

where V_1 is the volume of fluid 1, and η is a parameter describing the shape of the configuration. On the other hand the vapor pressure equilibrium described by Eq.(6) is stable (or metastable) to microscopic evaporation and condensation processes (Kelvin stability) only if

$$(\partial^2 A^{eff}/\partial V_1^2)_{T,\eta} > 0 \tag{8}$$

Thus, for total stability, the effective area must be a local minimum as regards variations in both volume and shape. The inequalities (7) and (8) are reversed for unstable equilibria, and equalities hold good for neutral equilibria. For some configurations, such as a spherical liquid drop, inequality (7) is satisfied, whereas (8) is not: a fact with important consequences in meteorology. In general, since viscous flow is usually a more rapid transport mechanism than evaporation and condensation, the two types of stability often may be considered separately in practice.

These methods may be applied quantitatively to radially symmetrical homoclastic surfaces in the absence of external fields and have provided the basis for a theory of capillary condensation.[5,6] Figure 2 illustrates some of the radially

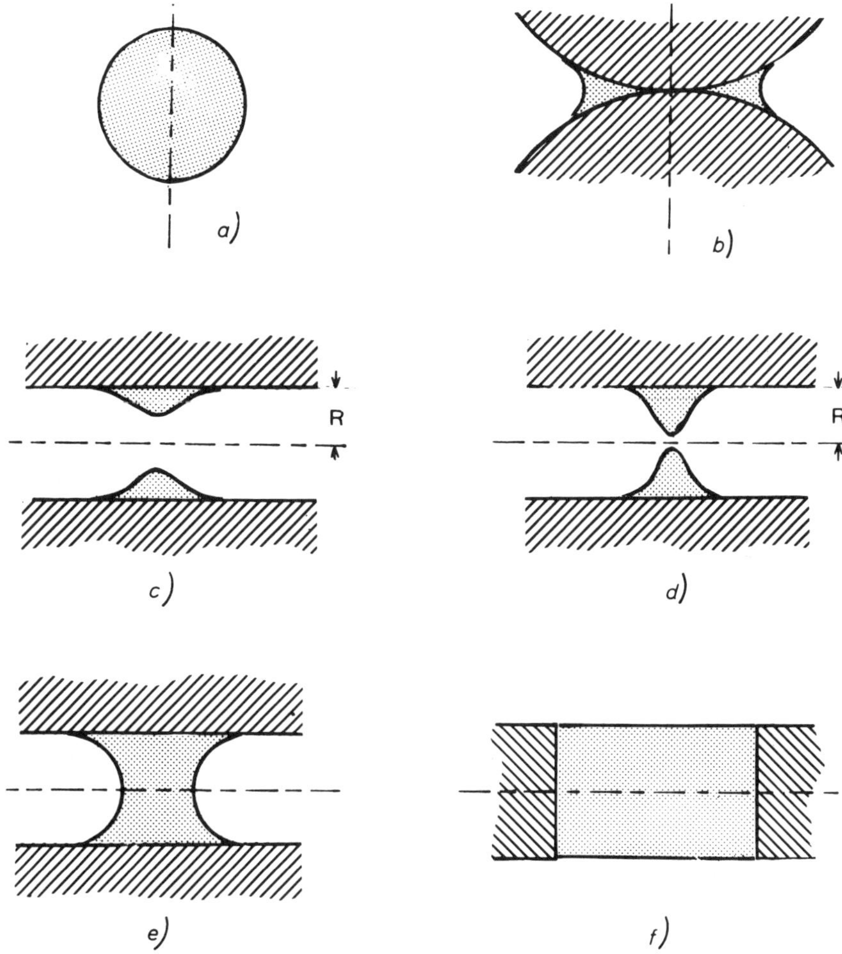

Fig.2 Examples of homoclastic configurations with rotational symmetry. The liquid phase is stippled, and the solid (where present) is hatched; the broken lines indicate axes of symmetry. a) spherical drop; b) nodoid; c) unduloid I, with $C > -1.4114/R$; d) unduloid II, with $C < -1.4114/R$; e) spherically capped thread; and f) cylinder.

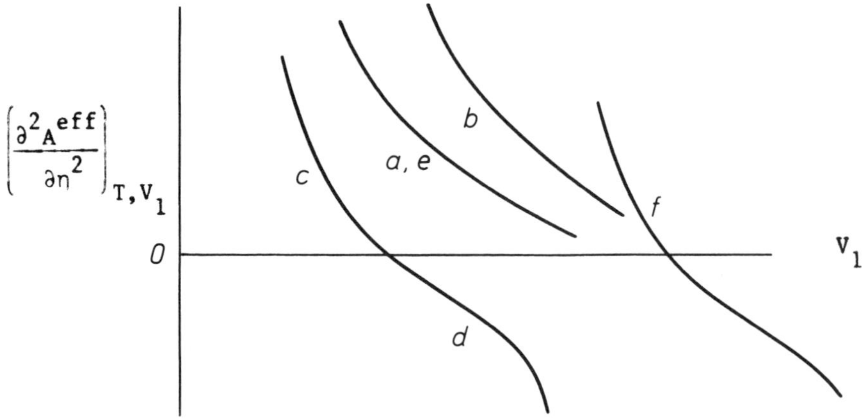

Fig.3 Laplace stability of configurations illustrated in Fig.2 (schematic).

symmetrical homoclastic surfaces, whereas Figs. 3 and 4 show schematically the conditions for their Laplace and Kelvin stability.

Under the action of gravity, a more involved minimization is needed,[4] but this still can be performed numerically for surfaces having an axis of symmetry in the g direction.[7,8]

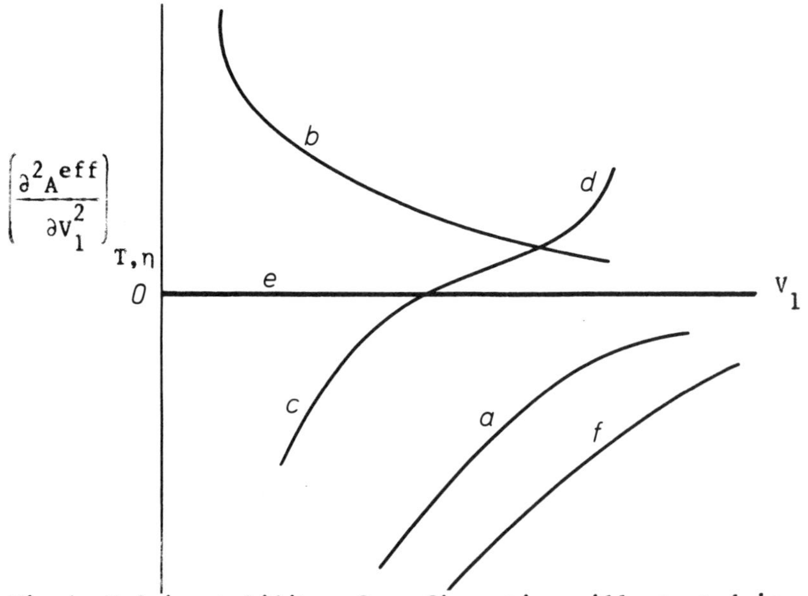

Fig.4 Kelvin stability of configurations illustrated in Fig.2 (schematic).

Capillarity in Microgravity

In practice, capillary effects are often of the greatest importance in systems of small dimensions, where interfacial curvatures become large. Many natural capillary phenomena (e.g., in porous media) therefore occur in the effective absence of gravity. Although this has fortunate consequences insofar as it simplifies their mathematical description, it produces two serious disadvantages for the experimentalist. The first and most obvious difficulty is that of making accurate observations on physically small systems. In some cases, this can be overcome simply by improving existing techniques. A more serious problem concerns interactions in the vicinity of lines of intersection of phase boundaries: the so-called "three-phase zone", within which the macroscopic contact angle is determined by submicroscopic interactions. The experimentalist wishing to explore such interactions is faced here with a dilemma: in large systems, gravity effects overwhelm adsorption forces at any range accessible to study, but in small systems the necessarily high interfacial curvatures have the same effect. The only possible solution appears to be to study large systems, of low interfacial curvature, in zero (or greatly reduced) gravity.

The desirability of studying capillarity in reduced gravity was recognized clearly just over a century ago by J.A.F. Plateau. Using pairs of immiscible liquids of equal density, he was able to form physically large fluid interfaces that were unaffected by gravity, and he and later workers thus were able to investigate some previously insuperable problems of capillarity. There are, however, several important conditions in which Plateau's neutral buoyancy method cannot be applied profitably because of the choice of fluids which it imposes. Such circumstances include the following: 1) dynamic systems, in which the viscosity ratio between the phases cannot be chosen at will; 2) systems in which the contact angle between the fluid interface and a solid must be controlled and reproducible; and 3) investigations directed at measurements of intermolecular forces at phase boundaries, for which a large density difference between the phases is desirable, and for which chemically simple, single-component systems are required.

Under such circumstances, alternative methods of removing the effects of gravity must be sought. Plateau no doubt would count himself fortunate if he were alive today, with access to the facilities provided by drop towers, parabolic aircraft trajectories, sounding rockets, and orbiting spacecraft.

There have been a number of experimental suggestions in the field of capillarity within the Spacelab program. These aim at the production of large interfaces, either to overcome problems of scale or to provide a combination of low curvature with low gravity in order to accentuate intermolecular force effects. They also involve conditions in which Plateau's neutral buoyancy method is inappropriate for one or more of the reasons given.

Capillary Phenomena in Space Processing

In addition to experiments designed to investigate specific capillary problems by exploiting the microgravity environment of Spacelab, there are many aspects of the materials-processing program, involving the manipulation of fluids, in which capillary phenomena must be considered, often in association with other quite intricate problems of fluid dynamics. In particular, the maintenance of stable molten zones during crystal growth experiments poses some novel problems, in which the following factors must be taken into account:

1) The fluid zone is rotating (usually steadily) about its axis. It thus is subjected to a radial acceleration, which may, for large zones, be substantial.

2) It also is subjected to other accelerations, random in direction and magnitude, arising from spacecraft attitude control, crew movements, and so on.

3) The surface tension may be nonuniform because of the existence of gradients both of impurity concentration and of temperature in the axial direction.

4) In addition, fluid flows may be generated by composition and temperature gradients normal to the axis of the rotation.

5) The fluid zone may be bounded by polygonal, or otherwise noncircular, contact lines where it meets the neighboring solid phases.

Thus, although the zone profile will, in the first instance, be dependent on the feed rate and on the solidifcation rate in the grown crystal, its stability may be influenced not only by the usual capillary constraints of length-to-diameter ratio for a given profile, but also by any of the preceding factors. Some of these produce effects that increase with increasing dimensions of the molten zone, whereas for others the converse is expected to be true. In some cases, the absence of gravity may lead to dominance by phenomena that are insignificant in terrestrial gravity, and it is not always possible to model these effects using the neutral buoyancy technique of Plateau, for the reasons given in Sec.3. For example, the so-called "C-mode" instability, first observed in a Skylab demonstration experiment, has not been reproduced in Plateau experiments, presumably because it is suppressed by having an outer phase of viscosity comparable to that of the rotating zone.

For these reasons, a program of model experiments has been proposed, to be performed in a fluid physics module, which, it is hoped, will form part of the first Spacelab payload. The module will enable the complicating factors listed previously to be reproduced in a controlled manner and their influence on the equilibrium and stability of a rotating fluid zone to be studied in detail; it may, in addition, incorporate facilities for other experiments on fluid interfacial behavior. The planned program of experiments will provide results of both technological and basic scientific value which cannot be acquired in any other way.

References

[1]Maxwell, J.C., "Capillary Action," Encyclopaedia Britannica, 9th ed., 1876.

[2]Padday, J.F., "The Profiles of Axially Symmetric Menisci," Philosophical Transactions of the Royal Society, Vol. A269, 1971, pp. 265-293.

[3]Everett, D.H. and Haynes, J.M., "The Thermodynamics of Fluid Interfaces in a Porous Medium, Part I. General Thermodynamic Considerations," Zeitschrift für physikalische Chemie (Neue Folge), Vol.82, 1972, pp.36-48.

[4]Haynes, J.M., "Capillary Instabilities in 1 g and 0 g," Proceedings of the Second European Symposium on Material Sciences in Space, European Space Agency Special Publication 114, 1976, pp. 467-471.

[5]Everett, D.H. and Haynes, J.M., "Model Studies of Capillary Condensation, Part I. Cylindrical Pore Model with Zero Contact Angle," Journal of Colloid and Interface Science, Vol.38, 1972, pp. 125-137.

[6]Everett, D.H. and Haynes, J.M., "The Thermodynamics of Fluid Interfaces in a Porous Medium, Part II. Capillary Condensation

Surface Area and Pore Size Distribution Determination, and Hysteresis," Zeitschrift für physikalische Chemie (Neue Folge), Vol.97, 1975, pp. 301-312.

[7]Padday, J.F. and Pitt, A.R., "The Stability of Axisymmetric Menisci," Philosophical Transactions of the Royal Society, Vol. A275, 1973, pp. 489-528.

[8]Boucher, E.A., Evans, M.J.B. and Kent, H.J., "Capillary Phenomena. II. Equilibrium and Stability of Rotationally Symmetric Fluid Bodies," Proceedings of the Royal Society, Vol. A349, 1976, pp. 81-100.

POSSIBLE APPLICATION OF CONTROLLED PROCESSES IN SPACE TECHNOLOGY

R. F. Ganiev, V. F. Laptchinsky, and A. S. Okhotin

Space Research Institute, Academy of Sciences, Moscow, USSR

Abstract

In some cases it is expedient to produce different materials under zero-gravity conditions with the use of controlled processes. One of the most acceptable controlled processes is nonlinear oscillations. Their use in the processes of substance crystallization and for the production of composite materials will allow the structure and the properties of these materials to be controlled. This paper gives the theoretical foundations for using nonlinear oscillations in the various processes of space technology. The results of experimental investigations of these processes under zero-gravity conditions which have been obtained by means of the model substances and the model installations, are analyzed. The recommendations for the applications of the controlled processes to space technology are considered.

I. Introduction

This paper deals with the scientific investigations of multiphase media dynamics (bodies with liquid, solid, and gaseous inclusions) in zero-gravity or almost-zero-gravity conditions for the case of controlled external disturbances, in particular, vibrations; emphasis is made on practical problems of space technology. Some results of the studies also constitute a subject of the paper. Studies of the problem of controlled technological processes in space were caused mainly by the following two circumstances:

1) Since the conditions of "pure" weightlessness are not easy to attain in practice and space objects almost always suf-

---

Presented as Paper D.3.3 at the COSPAR Symposium on Materials Sciences in Space, Philadelphia, Pa., June 9-10, 1976.

fer from all kinds of external disturbances, the technological processes of reprocessing materials in a liquid state carried out in space can differ radically from those assumed for the perfect ("pure") weightlessness. Thus, for instance, when materials, uniformly reinforced by various inclusions and composite materials, are fabricated, external disturbances destroy the uniformity of a material in the process of its crystallization. Apparently without controlling actions, these processes are hardly realizable in space, since disturbances, if present, do not allow stationary stability of liquid mixtures to be attained, including those with gaseous and solid inclusions. To solve such problems, specific forms of motion of liquid media and impurities should be sought for which dynamic stability of mixtures could be insured.

2) A somewhat opposite problem sometimes may arise in space, that is, a problem of separating different phases. That is inevitable, for instance, if problems arise of degassing or cleaning the liquid or metal melts from alien inclusions. One of the possible and efficient ways of solving those problems lies, as we see it, in applying external actions, including, in particular, periodic disturbances, such as vibration, ultrasound, and alternating electric and magnetic fields. According to preliminary theoretical and experimental investigations, controlled periodic disturbances also can be used successfully to solve another problem of practical importance, i.e., how liquids and liquid metals can be held and transported in weightlessness. All of this allows a conclusion to be made that the possibility of applying controlled processes in space technology is a topical problem worthy of further studies; obviously as important and scientifically interesting as it is, this problem has not yet been studied thoroughly. Theoretically, the analysis of controlled, including vibrational, technological processes leads to the studies of multiphase media dynamics subjected to periodic disturbances. Technological problems of liquid metals mixing, degassing, retaining, and so on, in weightlessness, can be formulated mathematically as problems of stability of equilibrium states or periodic motions of multiphase media under periodic disturbances.[1-3] This provides an adequate picture of conditions of two-phase medium transport or of liquid degassing, as well as directed transport or steady confinement of liquid metals in weightlessness.

As for experimental studies, the still high cost of experiments onboard the orbital space objects should be taken into account, and it will be reasonable for the first stages of these studies to simulate, in terrestrial conditions, some of the properties of space environment, in particular, short-period weightlessness, where it is possible. In doing so, two methods usually are used: that of a free-falling capsule with the objects studied, and space vehicles maneuvering along Keplerian trajectories.[4-7] In the first case, a near-zero-gravity state is insured for several seconds, and in the second case, for several dozen seconds. The latter method is preferable for experiments where external actions are applied, since corrections can be made quickly in the experimental procedure by way of changing external disturbance parameters, and time is sufficient for transient processes to attenuate.

It is not easy to carry out such experiments, using the free-falling capsule method, because of time shortage and the long inertia of processes in liquid media. Moreover, to identify most general features and phenomena inherent to the class of objects under consideration, in our opinion, it is reasonable to use model liquids and materials in the initial stages of the studies. This substantially facilitates experiments, and particularly so in specific conditions.

Given below are some of the basic results of such investigations in the case of short-period weightlessness.[4] To this effect, a small-sized vibrational setup has been developed that produced, measured, and photographed controlled periodic motions for models studied over a sufficiently wide range of vibration amplitudes and frequencies.

The objective of the experiment was to study dynamics of multiphase media, i.e., liquids with solid particulates and gas bubbles subjected to controlled periodic disturbances. Here attention was drawn mainly to the studies of the stable equilibrium states and motions of systems under consideration, in particular, to the study of resonance modes. Transparent cylindrical sheaths were used as models with model liquids and inclusions. Some of the results of the completed experimental program are analyzed below; their possible applications in space technology are mentioned.[2-4]

II. Vibrational Mixing and Formation of Periodic Layered Structures in Near-Zero-Gravity Conditions

When experiments were carried out to study processes of immiscible media mixing in weightlessness conditions, a phenomenon was taken into account which is observed on the Earth. Its idea is that vertical (longitudinal) vibrations of a cylindrical sheath, partially filled with two immiscible liquids (water and capacitor oil), are accompanied by sub-

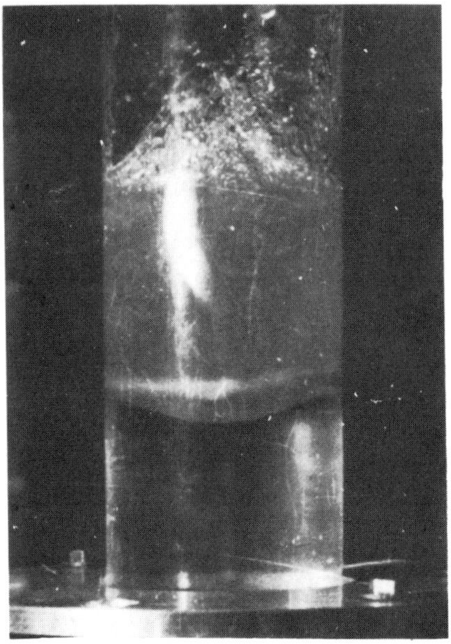

Fig. 1 Vibrational mixing and formation of periodic layered structures.

harmonic oscillations of the media interface and by very intensive destruction of the free surface (Fig. 1) over a specific, fairly narrow range of excitation frequencies. At other excitation frequencies, with a constant amplitude, the processes if any, are less intense. It is only natural to assume that it is in this particular frequency range that most effective mixing of liquids can be expected. In this case, in fact, fast

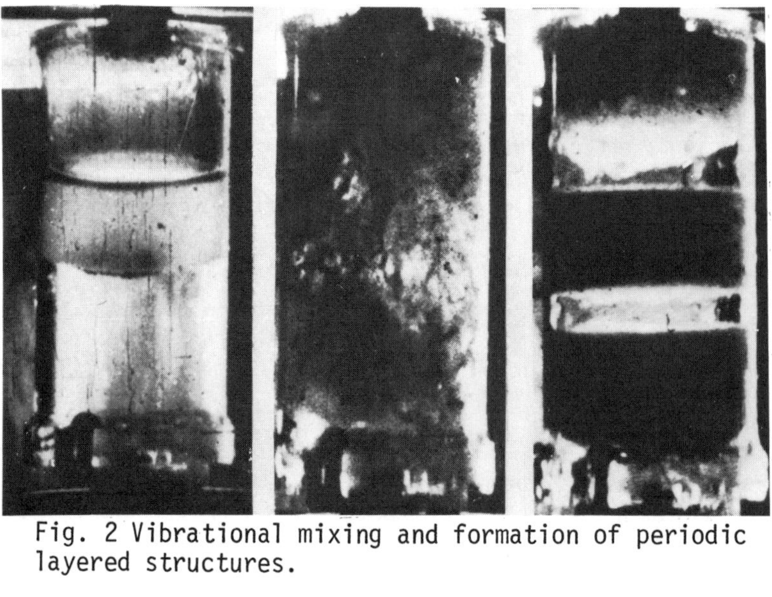

Fig. 2 Vibrational mixing and formation of periodic layered structures.

mixing of immiscible media is observed in near-zero-gravity conditions, that is, air, capacitor oil, and water. Figure 2a shows the model under study when there is no external excitation. If vibrations are superposed, intensive destruction of the free surface is observed, and the oil quickly develops vertical motion directed deep inside which reaches the interface and destroys it, thus giving rise to the process of immiscible media mixing. Along with this, the air over the free surface is being captured, which finally results in the formation of foamy water-oil suspension (Fig. 2b). Here, solid particles, which prior to mixing had been on the water-oil interface, became "almost uniformly" distributed over the whole bulk of the mixture. As assumed, the quality of mixing sharply degrades with external excitation frequency changing; that is, it is a resonance phenomenon. The chaotic motion of the mixture, with excitation parameters kept constant, is a steady-state process, and it exists until the weightlessness mode switches off. If, after the complete mixing of media the external excitation frequency is raised, it will bring about new forms of motions and mechanical equilibrium of the system. First, discontinuities and clots appear in suspension which have become seen more and more clearly with growing frequency; then, at a certain instant, suspension disintegrates into strata (stratification is observed in suspension), and a stable periodic configuration forms with alternating layers of suspension and air (Fig. 2c). It should be mentioned that in this case, as well as after the process of mixing is completed, solid particles are dispersed, "almost uniformly" in suspension layers. The resulting configuration is stable only over a narrow frequency range; with excitation frequency changing, the layers start oscillating, which eventually disrupts the structure. Furthermore, suspension layers start smearing, i.e., lose their stability, if external excitation is removed after the formation of the structure.

III. Motions of Gas Bubbles and Drops of Liquid Metals in Oscillating Liquid Media in Conditions of Low or Zero Gravity

The subject of this series of experiments was to study whether it was possible to control motions of gas bubbles and liquid metal drops by controlling periodic disturbances. It is known that, if a liquid partially filling a cavity moistens its walls, then gas or vapor present over the free surface in the initial conditions will form a bubble in weightlessness (Fig. 3a).[5] The solution of many applied problems poses a question as to how such a bubble behaves if subjected to external disturbance; of great interest here is the study of equilibrium states and relative motions of liquid and gaseous phases. When experiments were carried out for gravity values sufficiently

Fig. 3 Motions of gas bubbles and drops of liquid metals in oscillating liquid media.

near to zero, an already well-known phenomenon of capillar hop[8] was observed which for a long time was a subject of our studies.

If a vessel was filled with a liquid, the bubble moved periodically between the lid and the bottom of the vessel, pushing off from them in turn. If a vessel contained several immiscible liquids, a bubble was pushed off from their interfaces. When the system was subjected to periodic disturbances, pulsations of the bubble's surface were generated (Fig. 3b). Of main interest is the interaction of such pulsations with the vibrating liquid, which often gives rise to monotone translation of bubbles.

Similar phenomena also were observed in the studies of dynamics of liquid metal (Hg) drops in a vibrating liquid (Fig. 3c). There, when an external excitation frequency coincided with the pulsation frequency of a drop, monotonous unidirectional motion of the latter was observed because of its interaction with a vibrating liquid. Obviously, such disturbances may be used to solve problems related to transporting and retaining liquids and liquid metals in weightlessness. It should be mentioned that during these experiments the behavior of systems studied depended on residual aircraft overloadings, mainly random in their character (Fig. 4). This fact complicated experimental data processing. Apparently it will be reasonable in the future to put systems and objects under study into the capsules soaring inside the aircraft.

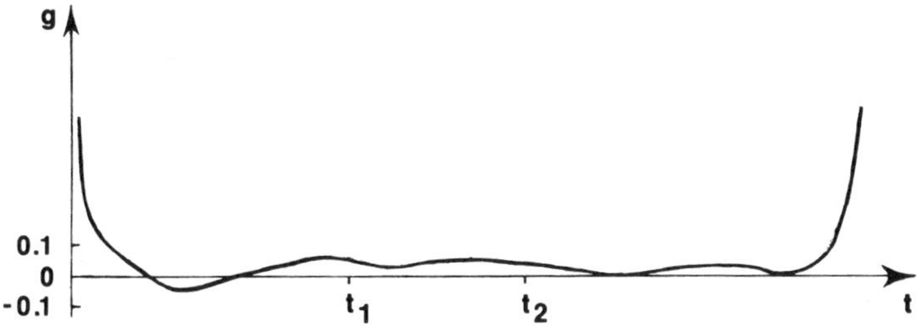

Fig. 4 Aircraft accelerations.

IV. Studies of Degassing Processes in Near-Zero-Gravity Conditions

Degassing liquids and metal melts in weightlessness constitutes one of the most topical problems of space technology. In weightlessness, a buoyant force does not exist; hence numerous gas or vapor bubbles remain suspended in liquid media, which often has negative implications. For instance, if metals are welded in weightlessness, weld seams have many gaseous pores that adversely affect their strength and reliability.

Therefore, experiments on degassing liquids in weightlessness were carried out, with the phenomenon observed on the Earth, that of gas bubbles' localization if subjected to vibrations, taken into account. Similar phenomena also were observed in weightlessness. If the system was subjected to high-frequency (about 1000 Hz) vibrations, intense release of diluted gas was observed, as well as its localization, a sort of a swarm of bubbles near the vessel bottom (Fig. 5). With a growing amount of localizing gas, the swarm buoyancy also grew. Then, if a small positive residual overloading acts upon the system, the swarm comes onto the surface at a certain instant when the Archimedean force exceeds the vibrational forces that sustain gas equilibrium.

After this, a new swarm originates near the bottom of the vessel, and so on. That is a stationary periodic process; and it is on until weightlessness exists, i.e., liquid degassing continues. Besides if the external excitation frequency is being changed gradually after swarm formation, this can be instrumental in transporting the swarm vertically. If the excitation frequency grows, it is moving toward the free surface; if the former decreases, the swarm is moving downward to the bottom of the vessel. Although the experiments used a model liquid (water with high content of diluted gas), the effects discussed obviously can be regarded as a basis for developing techniques of liquid metal cleaning from gaseous inclusions.

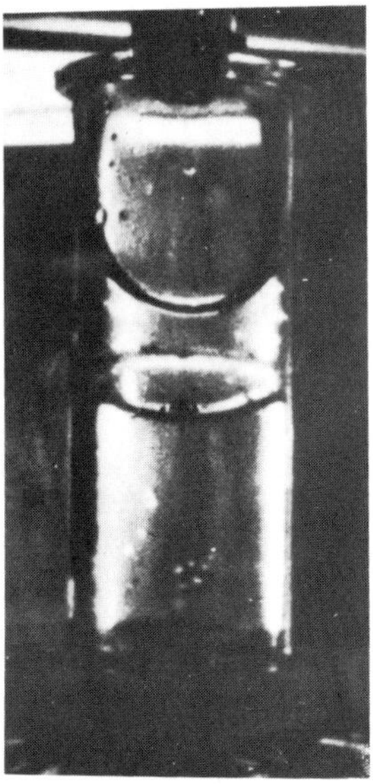

Fig. 5 Bubble formation.

Hence a conclusion can be drawn, from the summary of the experimental studies discussed, that, according to the program carried out, a number of new vibrational effects have been identified. Many of them can be recommended for further use in developing controlled processes in space technology:

1) Thus, for example, the phenomenon of resonant mixing of several liquid media, immiscible on Earth, and of stable periodic structures' formation can be recommended to be used in fabricating materials with unique characteristics (foamy materials, composite, layered materials, etc.) in space.

2) Effects of monotone unidirectional motions of liquid metal drops and big gas bubbles can be recommended to be used for performing controlled relative transport of various phases in weightlessness.

3) The new facts about localization and controlled transport of gas bubbles in vibrating media can be recommended to be used in solving the problems of degassing liquids and liquid metals in space.

Together with this, the aforementioned yields a conclusion that further studies and development of the scientific basis of mechanics of controlled space-technological processes are topical, expedient, and promising. Hence both theoretical and experimental studies to this end should be carried out on a larger scale.

References

[1]Ganiev, R. F. and Ukraniskii, L. E., "Dynamics of a Systems Vibration," Soviet Thought, Kiev, USSR, p. 167.

[2]Ganiev, R. F., Puchka, G. N., Ukraniskii, L. E., and Tsapenko, A. S., "On Nonlinear Vibration Effects with Gases of Varied Media," Sixth International Symposium on Nonlinear Acoustics, Moscow, USSR, 1975.

[3]Ganiev, R. F. and Tsapenko, A. S., "On the Dynamics of Fluids with Excitable Vibration -- A Problem of Mathematical Physics and Oscillation Theory," Ivanovo, Vol. 3, 1975.

[4]Ganiev, R. F., Daniza, V. D., and Tsapenko, A. S., "On the Behavior of Liquid Sodium Metal Conditional to Interdependence of Vibration Process," Dan (State Academy of Sciences), USSR, Series A, Vol. 4, 1976, pp. 329-332.

[5]Belyakov, I. T. and Borisov, U. D., "Technology and Cosmos," Maminostrenie, Moscow, USSR, 1974, p. 290.

[6]Paton, B. E., et al., "Conditions for Existence of the Technological Process in the State of Free Space," Cosmic State as an Ultimate Resort, Vol. I, 1973, pp. 7-12.

[7]Paton, B. E. and Kubasov, V. N., "Concerning Metallic Alloys in Space," Automatic Welding, Vol. 5, 1970, pp. 7-12.

[8]Popov, V. I., "On the Capillary Experiments "PRIJHKOV" of Bubbling Gas upon the Transitional System of Liquid to Gas Independently," Aerodynamic, Electrodynamic and Aeromechanics of Flight, Kiev, USSR, 1973, p. 75.

INTERFACE PHENOMENA AND TRANSPORT PROCESSES UNDER REDUCED GRAVITY

G.S.R. Sarma*

DFVLR,
Freiburg i.Br., Federal Republic of Germany

Abstract

Earlier space missions as well as related theoretical work have shown that under reduced gravity conditions the interfacial free energy gradients easily can lead to convective currents, which, in turn, affect the heat- and mass-transfer processes across these interfaces, causing changes in bulk properties as well. Since such convection can affect many of the manufacturing processes under consideration adversely, it is necessary to investigate the conditions under which the tendency can be controlled. The author's earlier studies on the interaction of interfacial waves with magnetic and centrifugal fields suggest such control possibilities. In view of the use of rotation in certain terrestrial crystal growth techniques, some of the more recent results of the author on barodiffusion of species in a rotating binary mixture also are discussed with reference to possible interpretation in the Spacelab context.

Nomenclature

Dimensional quantities

d = fluid layer (film) average thickness
g = acceleration due to gravity (terrestrial value used in parameter estimations in Ref. 18)
h = heat-transfer coefficient at interface in Marangoni convection problem

---

Presented as part of Paper D.3.4 at the COSPAR Symposium on Materials Sciences in Space, Philadelphia, Pa., June 9-10, 1976.

*Scientific Associate, Institut für Strömungsmechanik, Abteilung Angewandte Mathematik und Mechanik.

p_o = representative pressure
r = radius of rotating tube
B = applied magnetic induction field
D = diffusion coefficient of the minor component in the binary mixture
K = thermal conductivity
M = molecular weight of component in binary mixture
T = temperature
W_o = average velocity for thin-film flow in a tube
γ = electrical conductivity of fluid in film flow
$\varkappa$ = thermal diffusivity of fluid
λ = disturbance wavelength
μ = dynamic viscosity
ν = kinematic viscosity
ρ = density
σ = surface tension
Ω = angular velocity

Dimensionless quantities

Bd = $(M_2-M_1)\mu\Omega_o/M_2p_o$, barodiffusion number
Cr = $\mu\varkappa/\sigma d$, crispation number
Ha = $B.d.\sqrt{(\gamma/\mu)}$, Hartmann number
Ma = $|d\sigma/dT|\left[(T_w-T_o)d/\mu\cdot\varkappa\right]$, Marangoni number
Nu = $(h\cdot d)/K$, Nusselt number
R = dimensionless radial distance (reference length = $\sqrt{\nu/\Omega_o}$)
Re = $(W_o\cdot d)/\nu$, Reynolds number
S = Ω_∞/Ω_o, relative rotation parameter
Sc = ν/D, Schmidt number
$\mathcal{R}$ = $3\Omega^2 r/g$, centrifugal parameter
$\mathcal{S}$ = $(\sigma/\rho)\left[3/g\nu^4\right]^{1/3}$, surface tension parameter
α = $2\pi d/\lambda$, dimensionless wave number
ζ = dimensionless axial distance from disk (reference length = $\sqrt{\nu/\Omega_o}$)
Δ = $1/\{1+\left[(Re\cdot\tau)/2\right]\}$, gas-pressure parameter for thin-film flow in a rotating tube with a core-gas flow
τ = (interfacial shear)$/\rho W_o^2$, dimensionless interfacial shear for thin-film flow in a rotating tube with a core-gas flow

The broad heading was chosen as a working title during the early stages of defining an area of fluid dynamic study as part of a DFVLR scientific support program to serve the needs of the Spacelab experiments in particular and those of the user community in West Germany in general. The details of such cooperative activity are still at an incipient stage. Hence I shall present here three specific examples drawn from my other work to illustrate some general observations of possible relevance to some space manufacturing and processing ideas under consideration.

The advantages and challenges of the space environment and the broad goals of technology in space to attain better compositional, structural, and/or process control, to a degree hitherto unattainable under terrestrial conditions, have been presented elsewhere[1-3]. A status report on some of the individual studies by various groups in Germany is to be found in Refs. 4-6.

It now is well established that convection flows can be induced by gradients of interfacial free energy, also generally known as surface tension, when suitable gradients of temperature and/or concentration (in the case of a many-component system) are present. Thermocapillary convection indeed has been confirmed in many earlier space experiments[7-10], and a recent numerical study of a zone melting configuration[11] neglecting gravity shows results that indicate that this type of convection can lead to significant compositional changes in the melt even when the applied temperature gradients are very low. Such flows due to nonuniform interfacial tension and their perceptible effects are well known in the chemical engineering literature[12,13].

In Fig. 1, we see the much-quoted theoretical results[14] on a simplified problem of this type, namely, the onset of thermocapillary convection, also called the Marangoni convection, in a layer of fluid of thickness d bounded on one side by a thermally conducting solid wall and on the other by an ambient fluid whose presence is accounted for thermally through an effective heat-transfer coefficient h(T). For the purposes of our discussion later, the details of the tempera-

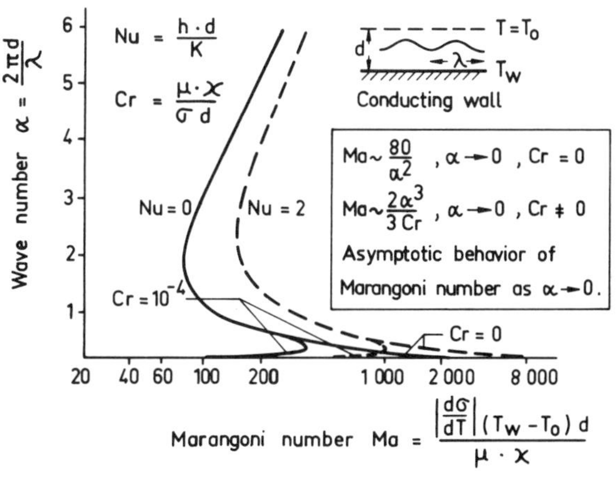

Fig. 1 Neutral stability curves for Marangoni convection at a conducting wall.

ture profiles and the heat-transfer mechanism in the ambient fluid are not essential.

We see that when the crispation number Cr (parameters are defined on the respective figures and also in the Nomenclature) is set equal to zero, then there exists a minimum critical Marangoni number Ma_c below which the fluid layer is stable with respect to Marangoni convection. This is true whether the heat transfer at the interface is zero (Nusselt number Nu = 0) or not (Nu $\neq$ 0). This was the result originally derived by Pearson[15] on the assumption that the interface does not deform, i.e., remains plane. By allowing interface perturbations[14], we see that even for very small Cr (which are realistic) such convection indeed can set in at all Ma, i.e., all temperature gradients, for instance, although the corresponding disturbance wave number tends to zero with decreasing Ma. In view of this inherent destabilizing influence due to the presence of the interface, which is rather well known to the fluid dynamicists, we have to look for possible stabilizing influences, because, when gravity is absent, such convection will presumably be just as deleterious as the buoyancy convection on Earth.

From the foregoing, it is plausible to anticipate that, if we can hold the fluid interface plane, i.e., prevent it from becoming wavy, then the minimum critical Marangoni number for this configuration can be reinstated. Based on our previous studies on such interfacial waves, we suggest the possible use of magnetic fields in the case of electrically conducting fluids and rotation in a suitable form.

An example of the use of magnetic fields to control such waves is indicated[16] by the results on Fig. 2. In this study,

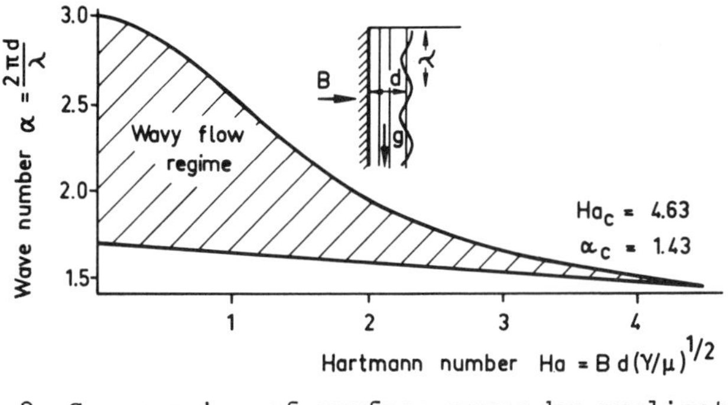

Fig. 2 Suppression of surface waves by application of magnetic field.

we investigated the influence of the application of a transverse magnetic field to an inherently unstable gravity-capillary wavy flow on a vertical wall also known as the Kapitza wave. By generalizing Kapitza's approach, we obtained the conditions under which such surface wave solutions are possible to within the limits of the approximations employed. As the Hartmann number Ha is increased, i.e., as the applied magnetic field is increased, say, the range of admissible disturbance wave numbers $\alpha = 2\pi d/\lambda$ decreases. And beyond Ha = 4.63, such surface waves cannot exist insofar as the approximations and assumptions of the analysis hold. Such fields seem to be in the feasible range.

Thus we see a possibility of reviving a minimum critical Marangoni number for a layer of fluid against variable surface tension effects that dominate under reduced gravity conditions. It may be emphasized here as well as in the next example to be shown that we are not concerned primarily here with the actual destabilizing mechanism, which happens to be gravity in the investigations mentioned which were concerned with other prototype situations[17]. Here we wish to point out only the possibility of controlling such an interfacial instability once the tendency is present, whatever the origin.

In a similar vein we show in Fig. 3 the results of our stability analysis[18] on the stabilizing influence of rotation on the interfacial waves in a thin-film flow in a vertical rotating tube with a core-gas flow. Without rotation $\mathcal{R} = 0$, the neutral stability curve on the α-Re (Reynolds number of the film flow) plane passes through the origin. It is well known that such a vertical film flow becomes wavy even at very low flow rates and ultimately breaks up. But, with the appli-

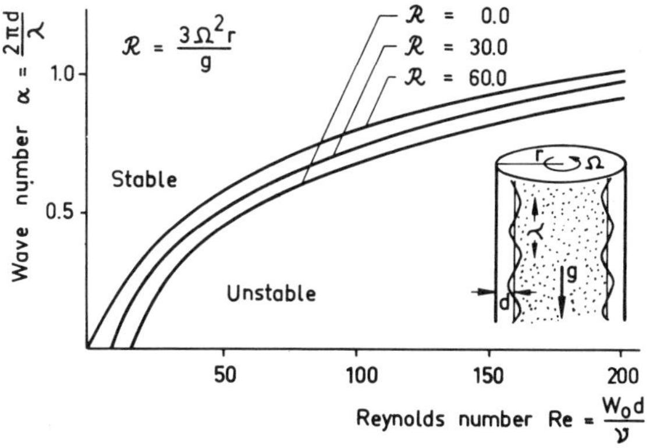

Fig. 3 Stabilization of thin-film flow through rotation.

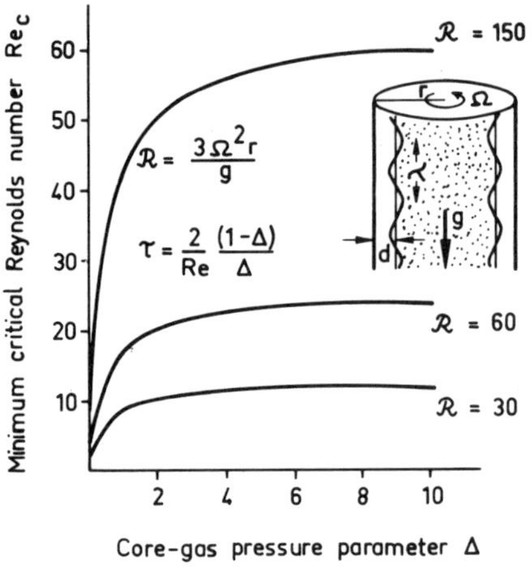

Fig. 4 Variation of Re_c with $\mathcal{R}$ and Δ for thin-film flow in a vertical rotating tube with a core-gas flow.

cation of rotation $\mathcal{R} \neq 0$, a minimum critical Re = Re_c is introduced below which the flow is stable against all interfacial waves of finite wavelength, and this critical Re_c increases with increasing rotation. We show in Fig. 4 the Re_c as a function of the centrifugal parameter $\mathcal{R}$ and the core-gas pressure parameter Δ, which is a measure of the interfacial shear exerted by the core-gas on the interface. Under reduced gravity conditions, this shear can serve as the driving mechanism for the film flow. Although gravity was taken as primary in Ref. 18, we did allow for this additional feature with space applications in view[17]. We see that in each case, for all Δ, the influence of rotation is to introduce and to increase a lower limit of stability against long wave perturbations of the interface. It can be shown that the short waves are damped out by surface tension and viscosity in this configuration. In Fig. 5, we show the influence of the surface tension on the stability characteristics of this configuration. Here again we see that increasing surface tension parameter $\mathcal{s}$ does decrease the domain of instability, but, unlike rotation, surface tension cannot introduce a minimum critical Re for all $\alpha \neq 0$.

Thus, subject to other constraints on the actual configurations under study, rotation and magnetic fields can be considered for controlling the tendency toward unwanted effects due to interfacial waves as typified by the simple case of surface tension convection, which seems to be a potential difficulty in certain space processing operations.

In certain terrestrial techniques of crystal growth, the use of rotation is rather well established[19-24], and its use

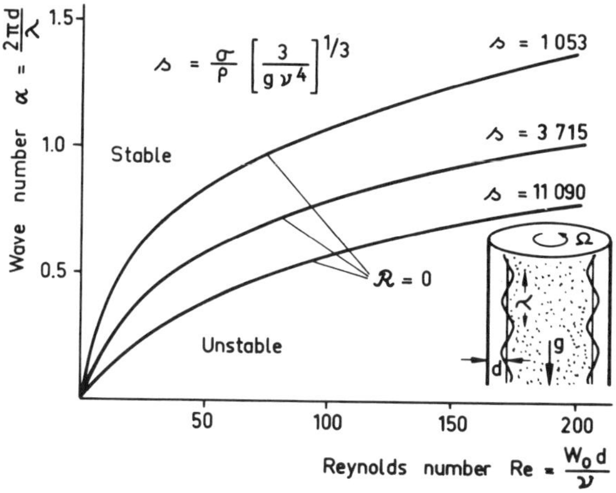

Fig. 5 Influence of surface tension on the stability of thin-film flow in a vertical rotating tube with a core-gas flow.

also is under consideration in space[3,19]. Here the use of rotation is motivated by the desire to achieve thermal symmetry, good stirring action, homogenization of the melt, etc., but the interaction of rotation and thermal gradients, together with the associated compositional changes, despite its great practical interest, does not seem to have been investigated fully, in view of its complexity. If buoyancy-driven convection is absent, as may be achieved in space experimentation, we can associate compositional changes either with temperature gradients (Soret effect), with a pressure gradient, or with an externally applied concentration gradient in the constituting species of the fluid. The species distribution then is governed by the three diffusional mechanisms, the last of which is generally dominant, but the others can become important under special circumstances. The Soret effect already has been suggested[8,9] as a possible means of separating small particles of like mass on the basis of the Clusius-Dickel column under reduced gravity conditions. Although normally small, barodiffusion due to pressure gradients has been utilized successfully in separating mixtures of particles with small relative mass difference, especially in the gas centrifuge in recent years. In that context, we investigated the species distribution in an isothermal rotating binary mixture[25] over a rotating disk. An analogous flow situation prevails in the crystal growth techniques mentioned earlier when the crystal and the melt in the crucible are rotated, in general at different angular velocities. As far as the growth interface is concerned, the angular velocity just outside the boundary layer at the crystal is some effective core velocity rather than the actual crucible velocity[26,27]. Furthermore, the buoyancy convection effects can, in principle, be ignored

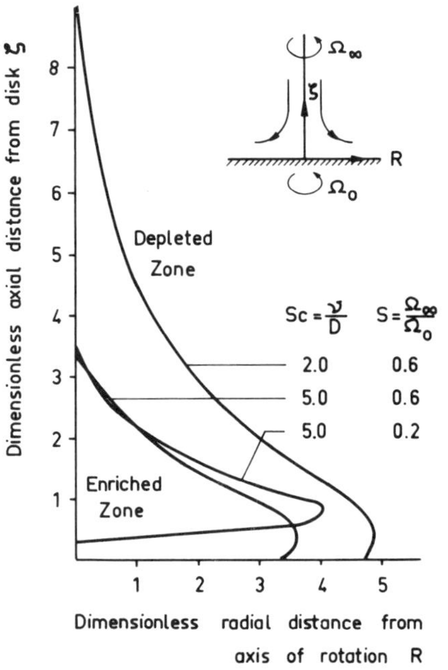

Fig. 6 Barodiffusion of solute in a rotating binary mixture over a rotating disk.

under space conditions, as was in fact done in our analysis. Although the analogy perhaps is not far-fetched, we must recognize that the prevailing temperature and concentration gradients can play significant roles in the ultimate analysis of the complete species distribution problem. Thus barodiffusion only can be an additional contributing factor in the crystal growth configuration. However, the point of showing the results[25] on Fig. 6 is to illustrate the effect of such small driving forces on the composition of a binary mixture subjected to rotational fields.

The results in Fig. 6, in a way, isolate the small but significant separative action due to the pressure gradients in the configuration. The curves, when rotated about the axis of rotation (ζ axis), generate surfaces of revolution, inside which there is a zone of enrichment of the rarer and lighter component in the binary mixture relative to the mixture far from the disk. Outside the surfaces, the mixture is depleted in this component. First of all, the result indicates the radial variation of composition, in addition to the usually assumed axial variation. A quantitative measure of the barodiffusion effect is a small parameter Bd (in the definition subscripts 1, 2 denote the lighter and heavier components respectively) that may be interpreted as the product of the relative mass difference of the species in the binary mixture and the ratio of the dynamic pressure variation to a typical pressure in the axial zone of interest. The case of crystal rotating faster than the crucible is represented in Fig. 6.

We notice from Fig. 6 that, when $S = \Omega_\infty/\Omega_0$ is small, there is only a depleted layer near the growth surface, whereas at higher values of S there is an enriched layer near the axis. The Schmidt number $Sc = \nu/D = 5$ seems to be representative of silicon melts with aluminium impurity and also of InSb with tellurium impurity[11], systems considered in the relevant literature[24]. Since the effect mentioned is proportional to the relative mass difference, we may anticipate that it will be more pronounced in the InSb-Te system than in the Si-Al

References

[1]Wuenscher, H. F., "Manufacturing in Space," Astronautics & Aeronautics, Vol. 10, Sept. 1972, pp. 42-54.

[2]Bredt, J. H. and Montgomery, B. O., "New Challenges for Industry," Astronautics & Aeronautics, Vol. 13, May 1975, pp. 22-41.

[3]Battrick, B. T. and Duc, N. T. (eds.), Processing and Manufacturing in Space, Proceedings of European Space Research Organization Symposium, March 1974, Frascati, Italy.

[4]Status-Seminar Spacelab-Nutzung, May 1975, Schliersee, Federal Republic of Germany.

[5]Zimmermann, P., "Systemtechnische Betrachtungen von Spacelab-Nutzlasten der Disziplin Werkstoff-Forschung und Verfahrenstechnik," Raumfahrtforschung, Vol. 20, Jan. 1976, pp. 27-31.

[6]"370 Vorschläge für deutsche Spacelab-Experimente," Umschau, Vol. 75, Sept. 1975, pp. 533-535.

[7]Bourgeois, S. V. and Barshears, M. R., "Fluid Dynamics and Kinematics of Molten Metals in the Low Gravity and Environment of Skylab," AIAA Paper 74-205, Jan. 30 - Feb. 1, 1974, Washington D. C.

[8]Grodzka, P. G., "Types of Natural Convection in Space Manufacturing Processes," Summary Rept. LMSC-HREC TR-D-306350, 1973, Lockheed Missiles & Space Co. and Huntsville Research and Engineering Center, Huntsville, Ala.

[9]Grodzka, P. G. and Bannister, T. C., "Natural Convection in Low-g Environments," AIAA Paper 74-156, Jan. 30 - Feb. 1, 1974, Washington, D. C.

[10]Bannister, T. C. and Grodzka, P. G., "Heat Flow and Convection Demonstration Experiments Aboard Apollo 14 and Apollo 17," XXIV Congress of the International Astronautical Federation, Oct. 1973, Baku, USSR.

[11]Chang, C. E. and Wilcox, W. R., "Inhomogeneities Due to Thermocapillary Flow in Floating Zone Melting, Journal of Crystal Growth, Vol. 28, Jan. 1975, pp. 8-12.

[12]Sawistowski, H., "Interfacial Phenomena," Recent Advances in Liquid-Liquid-Extraction, edited by C. Hanson, Pergamon Press, Oxford 1971, pp. 293-366.

[13]Kenning, D. B. R., "Two Phase Flow with Nonuniform Surface Tension," Applied Mechanics Reviews, Vol. 21, Nov. 1968, pp. 1101-1111.

[14]Scriven, L. E. and Sternling, C. V., "On Cellular Convection Driven by Surface Tension Gradients: Effects of Mean Surface Tension and Surface Viscosity," Journal of Fluid Mechanics, Vol. 19, July 1964, pp. 321-340.

[15]Pearson, J. R. A., "On Convection Cells Induced by Surface Tension," Journal of Fluid Mechanics, Vol. 4, Sept. 1958, pp. 489-500.

[16]Lu, P.-C. and Sarma, G. S. R., "Magnetohydrodynamic Gravity-Capillary Waves in a Liquid Film," The Physics of Fluids, Vol. 10, Nov. 1967, pp. 2339-2344.

[17]Stone, J. R., Gray, V. H., and Gutierrez, O. A., "Forced-Flow-Once-Through-Boilers," SP-369, 1975, NASA.

[18]Sarma, G. S. R., Lu, P.-C., and Ostrach, S., "Film Stability in a Vertical Rotating Tube with a Core-Gas Flow," The Physics of Fluids, Vol. 14, Nov. 1971, pp. 2265-2277.

[19]Wenzl, H., Mika, K., Müller-Krumbhaar, H., and Uelhoff, W., "Kristallzucht im Weltraum," Kernforschungsanlage Jülich, Bericht Nr. 1182, April 1975.

[20]Capper, P. and Elwell, D., "Crucible Rotation and Crystal Growth in the Czochralski Geometry," Journal of Crystal Growth Vol. 30, Oct. 1975, pp. 352-356.

[21] Cockayne, B., Chesswas, M., and Gasson, D. B., "Facetting and Optical Perfection in Czochralski Grown Garnets and Ruby," Journal of Materials Science, Vol. 4, May 1969, pp. 450-456.

[22] Wald, F. V. and Bell, R. O., "Natural and Forced Convection During Solution Growth of CdTe by the Travelling Heater Method," Journal of Crystal Growth, Vol. 30, Aug. 1975, pp. 29-36.

[23] Kobayashi, N. and Arizumi, T., "Computational Analysis of the Flow in a Crucible," Journal of Crystal Growth, Vol. 30, Sept. 1975, pp. 177-184.

[24] Jindal, B. K., Karelin, V. V., and Tiller, W. A., "Impurity Striations in Czochralski Grown Al-Doped Si Single Crystals," Journal of the Electrochemical Society, Vol. 120, Jan. 1973, pp. 101-105.

[25] Sarma, G. S. R., "Barodiffusion in a Rotating Binary Mixture over an Infinite Rotating Disk," Journal of Applied Mathematics and Physics (ZAMP), Vol. 26, May 1975, pp. 337-345.

[26] Carruthers, J. R. and Nassau, K., "Non Mixing Cells Due to Crucible Rotation During Czochralski Crystal Growth,", Journal of Applied Physics, Vol. 39, Nov. 1968, pp. 5205-5214.

[27] Carruthers, J. R. and Grasso, M., "Studies in Floating Liquid Zones in Simulated Zero Gravity," Journal of Applied Physics, Vol. 43, Feb. 1972, pp. 436-445.

GRAVITATIONAL EFFECTS ON COMBUSTION

A. L. Berlad*

State University of New York, Stony Brook, N.Y.

Abstract

Virtually all combustion phenomena of fundamental or practical interest are characterized by spatial nonisothermality. In a nonzero-gravitational field, resulting body forces give rise to natural convection processes that may or may not have an important effect on combustion phenomena of interest. In some cases these effects may be trivial, and in others, crucial. This paper examines various prominent combustion phenomena with regard to the effects of gravity on normal (g=1) experimental observations, observational differences to be expected for g=0 (space-based) experimentation, and the possible scientific and technological values to be derived from such space-based research.

I. Introduction

The central scientific questions in combustion embrace the broad fields of single- and two-phase combustion; steady, unsteady, and oscillatory combustion; flame structure and stability; flame initiation and extinction; and composition and pressure limit phenomena. Combustion experiments, aimed at addressing these questions, generally are carried out under normal gravitational conditions (g=1) in Earth-based laboratories. Free convective energy and mass transport processes frequently obscure or transform the underlying g=0 combustion phenomena. Current combustion theory finds the representation of the roles of multiply coupled transport (free convection-condution-radiation) and chemical kinetic processes generally

---

Presented as Paper No. D.3.6 at the COSPAR Symposium on Materials Sciences in Space, Philadelphia, Pa., June 9-10, 1976. This work was supported by NASA Grant NSG 3051 through the NASA Lewis Research Center.

*Professor of Engineering.

intractable. Thus we generally are employing substantially truncated combustion theory in the interpretation of g=1 combustion experiments.

Accordingly, a most compelling basis for space-based combustion studies (g=0) derives from unsatisfied scientific and societal needs for combustion information that Earth-based laboratories have not provided. Under reduced gravitational conditions, we can create stable, uniform arrays of combustible drops and particulates and then study their combustion behavior under (natural) convection-free conditions; we can attribute any asymmetries to the burning of a single particle or liquid drop to reasons other than "gravity"; we can discard the confusing requirement of distinguishing between observed "upward" and "downward" flame propagation without analytically describing their fundamental differences; we can assess the energy and mass transport mechanisms that influence flame oscillation and extinction phenomena in more systematic and tractable terms; the entire area of high-pressure combustion and extinction phenomena, so significant in current energy conversion and safety technologies, can be studied from a fundamental perspective. This paper reviews the effects of gravitational conditions on combustion phenomena and examines the necessity and utility of space-based experimental combustion studies in providing fundamental insights to problems of fundamental and applied importance.

II. Observation and Interpretation of Combustion Phenomena at Normal (g=1) Gravitational and (g=0) Conditions

A. Premixed Gaseous Flame Propagation and Extinction Limits

The most frequently made combustion observations involve the rates of "steady-state" flame propagation supported by a premixed gaseous medium. At g=1, quasisteady flames are observed as multidimensional flames propagating in long tubes, or as "flat" or "conical" flames stabilized on the lips of tubular burners. For a given size, shape, and temperature of apparatus, there exist limits of ambient temperature, pressure, fuel-oxidant ratio, and diluent concentration beyond which quasisteady flame propagation is not possible.[1-7] Beyond these extinction conditions, quasisteady flames cannot be established on burners or caused to propagate through long tubes. Reflecting the importance of heat-loss mechanisms (from flame to environment), the size, shape, and temperature of the experimental apparatus influence the extinction conditions. Special names have come into use for special extinction conditions. Flammability limits generally refer to the critical values of fuel-lean (or fuel-rich) composition, which, for a

5-cm-i.d. tube and a pressure of 1 atm, correspond to quasi-steady flame extinction. Quenching limits generally refer to the critical values of apparatus size which correspond to flame extinction. Pressure limits refer to critical lower (or upper) values of ambient pressure which correspond to flame extinction. It now is known that these various experimentally determined extinction limits are not independent. Figure 1[8,9] shows how pressure, quenching, and flammability limits represent special cases of a multidimensional extinction limit

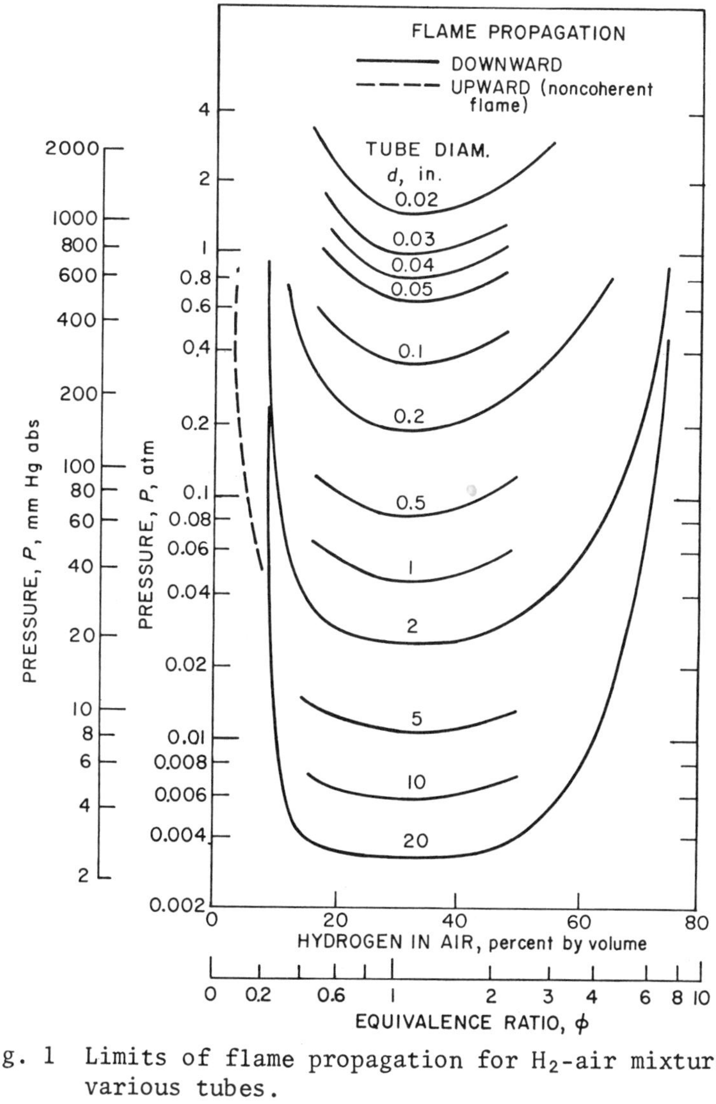

Fig. 1 Limits of flame propagation for H_2-air mixtures for various tubes.

diagram defined by the thermochemical and physical parameters of the problem.

A number of theories attempt to interpret these flame propagation and extinction data. Details and emphases vary, but certain central assumptions are shared. Quasisteady flame propagation is taken to be nonadiabatic, and losses of heat (and reactive species) from flame to finite-sized apparatus necessarily results. These loss mechanisms necessarily limit quasisteady flame propagation and prescribe extinction limits.

Gravitational effects influence observed premixed flame propagation and extinction phenomena in a number of ways. The nonuniform temperature-composition-density field of a flame is subject to gravitationally imposed body forces. These gravitational effects enter both as a mechanism important to flame structure and as a loss mechanism. Accordingly, flame propagation and extinction data (for g=1) can be affected substantially by "free convective effects." Striking examples of the effects of gravity on flame propagation and extinction include the following:

1) At g=1, upward flame propagation may be characterized by a flame propagation mode, flame structure, flame speed, and lean extinction limit different from those found for downward flame propagation. This is strikingly illustrated for the case of hydrogen-air flames,[8] where noncoherent upward flame propagation is observed in the neighborhood of the "lean limit" but not observed for downward propagation.

2) Convectively induced "noncoherent flames" as well as "flame balls" are observed for upward flame propagation, as the characteristic size of flame apparatus is increased.[3,10,11]

3) At g=1, convectively related multidimensional flame shapes (structures) are observed for hydrogen-air, methane-air, carbon monoxide-air, and other common/uncommon combustible systems. Diversity of flame shapes, structures, and propagational modes (oscillatory vs nonoscillatory, coherent vs noncoherent) is particularly common in the neighborhood of extinction limit conditions.

4) Upward flame propagation (at g=1) sometimes is associated with substantially incomplete combustion. Lovachev[3] and Markstein[12] have examined these phenomena in terms of flame front stability. These two analyses differ, but "free convective" processes are operative in either approach.

Despite the observed multidimensionality of (g=1) flame propagation and extinction phenomena, current "complete" theories of flame propagation and extinction are one-dimensional and ignore gravitational effects. Table 1 indicates that only a few simplified theories attempt to include free convective effects.

It follows, then, that flame propagation and extinction theories that may be applicable to (g=0) conditions have not been measured against g=0 data. As theories that ignore free-convective effects, they may not be applicable to observations made at g=1. For the g=1 observations that are influenced convectively, the truncated theories appear inadequate.

Thus, to establish the necessary theoretical bases for an understanding of flame propagation and extinction limits on a range $g \geq 0$, it is necessary that the observational facts be established on this range. For $g<1$, these observations are unavailable. It appears reasonable to expect that, once theory and observation can be brought together for g=0 (the simplest case theoretically, and the most unperturbed case experimentally), the inclusion of gravitational effects in "complete theories" of ($g>0$) flame propagation and extinction will be facilitated.

B. Premixed Two-Phase Flame Propagation and Extinction Limits

Flame initiation, propagation, and extinction processes supported by homogeneous mixtures of (premixed) finely divided combustible particulates (solid or liquid) in an oxidizing gaseous atmosphere are thought to be partly analogous to the previously discussed single-phase combustion phenomena.[16-18] That is, there are transport phenomena for which theoretical approaches, as well as experimental observations, closely parallel premixed gaseous systems. There may be support for this point of view for rarified clouds of particulates. For high-density clouds/arrays of particulates, array smoldering, initiation, fire-spread, and extinction processes are substantially different phenomena.[19,20] Nevertheless, that free convection influences the experimental observations of these phenomena (g=1) is either well established[5,19-22] or (in some cases) cannot be ruled out now. A broad range of combustible solids (e.g., cellulosic materials, corn starch, coal, synthetic fibers, lycopodium dust) and liquids (hydrocarbons, etc.) and oxidizing gases support these phenomena.

The differences between g=0 and $g>0$ two-phase combustion are thought to derive from body-force effects on heat and mass

Table 1. Premixed gaseous flames: quasisteady flame propagation and extinction limit analysis[a]

References	Losses	Dimensionality considered			Transport properties considered		
	Nonadiabatic	Multi-dimensional	1-dimensional or others	1-dimensionalized	Free convection	Radiation	Molecular conduction of heat & mass
Hirschfelder and Curtiss[6]	—	—	X	—	—	—	X
Spalding[7]	X	—	—	X	—	—	X
Berlad[13] and Yang[14]	X	—	—	X	—	X	X
Levy[15]	—	—	X	—	X	—	—
Lovachev[10]	—	—	X	—	X	—	—

[a] — Consideration absent in theory; X consideration provided in theory.

transfer. Thus, for example, arrays of large numbers of porous, solid, small fuel elements support combustion phenomena in a coupled manner. The coupling mechanisms include free-convective particle-gas and gas-boundary transport processes. Additional transport mechanisms include particle-particle and particle-gas radiative transport, molecular transport, and the radiation-conduction mechanisms coupling the gaseous medium losses to the boundaries.

Unfortunately, "complete" predictive theories of two-phase "homogeneous" flame propagation are largely undeveloped. The situation is aggravated by the fact that quasisteady flame propagation through "homogeneous clouds" of combustible particulates cannot be studied (at g=1) in a manner that is analogous to that employed for premixed gases. This experimental fact derives from the following:

1) Prior to the initiation of combustion experimentation, the physical and chemical characteristics of the combustible medium must be characterized.

2) A spatially uniform, unburned particle density, size distribution, and gas composition must be established and maintained prior to and during flame propagation and extinction measurements.

3) For gravitationally influenced systems, "gravitational settling" precludes the establishment of a uniform, quiescent particle cloud, either before or during experimentation. Where vigorous mixing techniques are used[23] to establish fairly uniform clouds (e.g., Fig. 2), substantial secondary flow patterns are established which correspond to complex, unknown transport of heat and mass.

For larger combustible particles (solids or liquids) in a gas, at g=1, some observers[16] report cases of clouds of burning (liquid) drops for which flame propagation is ascribed to the burning of individual (flame-surrounded) drops, with no apparent burning occurring in the interdroplet space. Such a flame-transport mechanism is strikingly different from one in which a cloud is taken to act collectively. Nevertheless, for $g \neq 0$, "free convection" and "gravitational settling" are essential processes to be considered.

Thus we find, for the case of flame propagation through clouds of particulates, at g=1, 1) that experimental homogeneity of a two-phase, quiescent particle-gas mixture is unobtainable (gravitational settling); 2) that unburned reac-

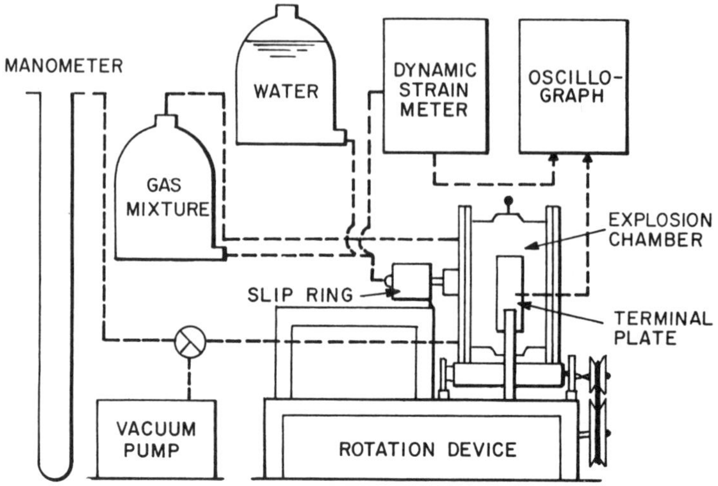

Fig. 2 Schematic of Ishihama and Enomoto[23] two-phase (rotating) explosion test apparatus.

tants have time-dependent characteristics; 3) that there exist convectively influenced flame transport and propagation mechanisms, made apparent through the substantial differences between observed upward and downward flame propagation characteristics; and 4) that particle-gas and gas-boundary heat-loss mechanisms are influenced convectively and ill-defined experimentally.

The identification of current (g=1) experimental difficulties suggests the important impact of obtaining experimental particle-gas combustion data in space. In a space environment (g≃0), 1) "settling" does not defeat our ability to create and maintain a uniform cloud of unreacted particles prior to and during a combustion experiment; and 2) "free convection" does not affect the flame microstructure (in the neighborhood of individual particles) or the flame macrostructure (gas-cloud-wall interactions).

From an experimental point of view, planned g=0 flame propagation studies promise an initially quasisteady gas-particle cloud (characterizable combustion system) and reproducible experimental results. Although we have been discussing flame propagation and extinction phenomena, similar implications obtain for other combustion studies aimed at delineating 1) particle-cloud autoignition temperatures; and 2) critical particle concentration or oxygen index for autoignition, spark ignition, flame propagation speed, flame shape, and flame structure, homogeneous "oscillatory" phenomena having long characteristic times.

Data (for g=0) will provide a more meaningful set of experimental bases for our understanding of two-phase combustion processes. They permit the construction, testing, and verification of theoretical formulations that are simpler and more tractable than those to be required (ultimately) by (g=1) experimentation. Together, a body of (g=0) data and suitable theory may be built upon for subsequent (g>0) studies aimed at addressing the multiplicity of effects which derive from gravitationally induced processes.

C. Combustion Phenomena in Nonflowing Single-Phase Systems

A large variety of combustion phenomena are observed experimentally in nonflowing, premixed combustible systems. For premixed gaseous systems (observed at g=1), these phenomena include the classic "homogeneous slow reaction," "autoignition" or "explosion," "cool flame", and other oscillatory combustion processes, as well as phenomena characterized as "multistage ignition" and "unsteady combustion." Experiment and theory for such nonflowing systems have been reviewed previously.[24]

In all of the aforementioned phenomena, transport of heat and mass play crucially definitive roles.[24] Criticality conditions for "autoignition" involve thermal interactions (as well as free radical interactions) with apparatus walls. "Cool flame," "thermokinetic," or purely "kinetic" oscillations involve similar wall interactions. As experimental apparatus sizes are increased, "free convective" transfer of heat and mass can dominate the other transport processes and render experimental observations (at g=1) difficult or impossible to interpret. For a modest-sized apparatus (of diameter) in which combustible self-heating is sustained, the Rayleigh number variation with hydrocarbon-oxygen stoichiometry is shown in Fig. 3, for a ΔT of 1°K. For many thermokinetic oscillations or autoignition phenomena, ΔT values of one to two orders of magnitude higher are encountered.[24] Inasmuch as critical Rayleigh numbers for free-convective onset are of the order $\leq 10^3$, it follows that, at g=1, 1) substantial free convective effects are encountered for highly exothermic processes and/or in large apparatuses, and/or at high pressures; 2) current theory[24] of autoignition and/or oscillatory combustion generally does not incorporate free convective effects; and 3) as a result of the experimental and theoretical shortcomings just noted, combustion data in nonflowing gaseous media are studied incompletely and represented inadequately.

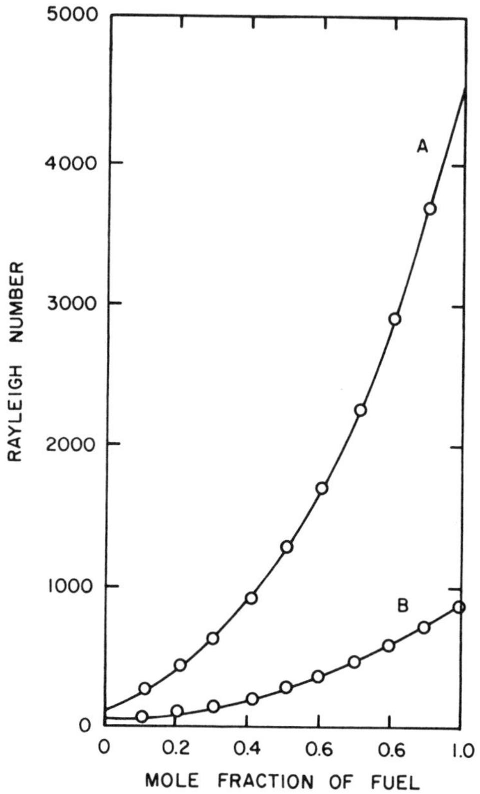

Fig. 3 The variation of Rayleigh numbers for a difference of 1°K between the center and wall of the reaction vessel. Curve A: 200 Torr = p_T for iso-octane/oxygen; curve B: 100 Torr = p_T for n-heptane/oxygen.

These facts may be illustrated through examination of the one-dimensionalized (simplified) forms[24] of the conservation equations generally taken to be appropriate to these systems:

$$\rho c_v \frac{\partial T}{\partial t} = \frac{d}{dx_1} \lambda \frac{dT}{dx_1} + \frac{dI}{dx_1} + \sum_{j=1}^{r} R_j \Delta_j - L_2 \quad (1)$$

$$\frac{\partial c_i}{\partial t} = \frac{d}{dx_1} D \frac{dc_i}{dx_1} + \sum_{j=1}^{r} \dot{c}_{ij}''' - L_{D,2} \quad (2)$$

where c_i is the number of moles (per unit volume) of the ith chemical species, for i = 1, 2, . . ., n; $\dot{c}_{ij}'''$ is the molar rate of production (per unit volume) of the ith chemical species by the jth kinetic process, where j = 1, 2, . . ., r; c_v is specific heat at constant volume; D is the diffusion coefficient; I is the local (thermal) radiative flux density; k_j is the rate constant for the jth kinetic process; L_2 is the loss function (for a two-dimensional system) in the x_2 direction; R_j is the molar reaction rate corresponding to the species and energy release rate specified by Δ_j; T is absolute temperature; Δ_j is the molar heat of reaction for the jth unidirectional reaction; and λ is thermal conductivity.

Clearly, (1) and (2) take no specific account of free convective effects, even though transport of heat and mass are essential processes under consideration. In fact, it is clear that (1) and (2) are more appropriate to a g=0 situation than to a general g>0 set of experimental conditions.

The role of heat and mass transport in the determination of oscillatory combustion processes is illustrated with the aid of (g=1) data[25] employed to construct Fig. 4. Involved in the theory of kinetic oscillations for CO-O_2 reactions[24-27] is the

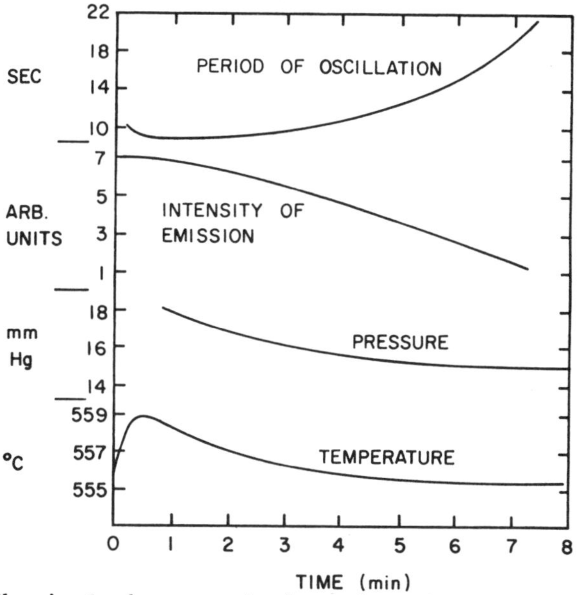

Fig. 4 Physical characteristics of typical oscillatory run (CO-O_2 reaction). RV1, T_i = 554.3°C, P_i = 18.8 torr. Intensity of emission is the maximum oscillograph height of each flash in arbitrary units.[25]

transport of O atoms to walls. Inasmuch as this time-dependent process is almost isothermal during a given cycle, neglect of free convective processes (at g=1) appears justified and leads to calculated trajectories[27] such as those illustrated in Fig. 5. Current theory and experiment suggest that this (CO-O_2) oscillatory process should be virtually unaffected by gravitational field. No g=0 confirmation of this has been made.

For thermokinetic oscillations, heat transfer to walls plays a major role,[28,29] and the reaction process (hydrocarbon-oxygen) is known experimentally to be highly nonisothermal. Nevertheless, theory[29] at g=1 appears to ignore the role of free convective effects on the oscillatory stability limits and on the oscillatory trajectories associated with the thermokinetic oscillations. For these thermokinetic processes, substantial Rayleigh numbers may be encountered,[28-32] and substantial differences between g=0 and g=1 observations may be expected. For completely analogous reasons, ignition delays, multiple ignitions, etc., in closed systems also may be characterized by large Rayleigh numbers and free convective effects at g=1.

D. Combustion Phenomena in Nonflowing Two-Phase Systems

In Sec. II.B, the roles of "gravitational settling" and "free convection" in g=1 experimentation were discussed. For

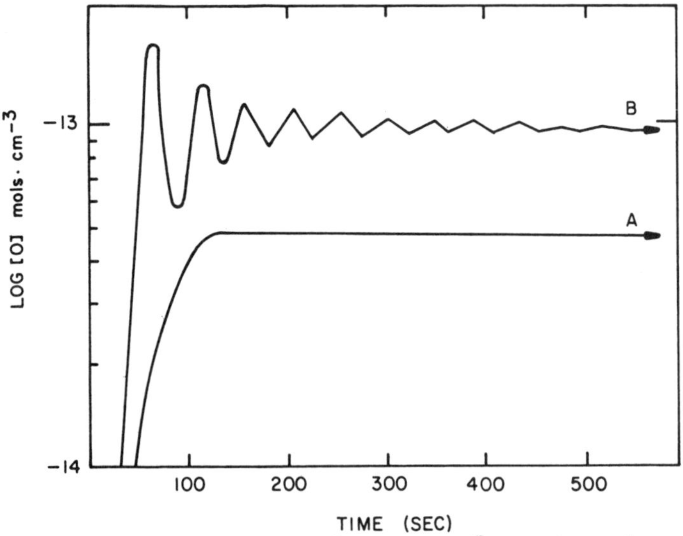

Fig. 5 Trajectories of O atoms in an inactive kinetic state.[27]

nonflowing two-phase systems, the same physical processes complicate the experimental results. Theory, conceptually simpler than flame propagation theory, still is useful deficiently to a representation of g=1 observations. Consider the elements of a simple (thermal) particle-cloud autoignition theory. Such a theory may be constructed[30] along lines that closely parallel those developed for pure gas-phase processes. The thermokinetic stability[24] of a cloud is described in terms of the kinetic (heat release) processes in the neighborhood of a typical particle, the heat and mass transfer rates in the neighborhood of a typical particle, and the collective heat-transfer processes involving the two-phase cloud and the boundaries. Accordingly, two energy conservation equations are written, one for the particles and one for the gaseous medium. These take the form[30]

$$m_p c_p (dT_p/dt) = S_p[\dot{q}''_p - \alpha_1 (T_p - T_g) - L_r] \tag{3}$$

$$m_g c_g (dT_g/dt) = S_p[N\alpha_1 (T_p - T_g) + (1 - \delta_g)L_r] - \alpha_2 S(T_g - T_\infty) \tag{4}$$

where m_p is particle mass; M_p is the summed mass of all particles; M_g is the total mass of gas in the system; c_p is particle specific heat at constant volume; c_g is gas specific heat at constant volume; T_p is characteristic particle temperature; T_g is characteristic gas temperature; S is the surface area of container boundaries; S_p is the surface area of a particle; N is the number of particles; α_1 is the particle-gas heat-transfer coefficient; α_2 is the gas-container heat-transfer coefficient; L_r is radiative loss rate per particle; and δ_g is optical transmissivity of gas.

One may employ the method of the phase plane[24,30,31] to deduce the appropriate criticality conditions for cloud autoignition. It is clear that α_1 and α_2 are functions of the Grashof number and may become particularly different from the molecular transport limiting values as particle sizes become larger and as the apparatus (cloud) size becomes larger, given a normal (g=1) gravitational field.

Although kinetic data are not as available as one would hope, calculations of autoignition conditions for metallic clouds have been carried out. Results for zirconium oxidation are shown in Fig. 6. For a total particle mass of 1 g (M_p) and a particle size of 1 μ, the free convective effects (for g=1) implicit in α_z are substantial. Figure 6 results imply that 1) gravitational effects on particle-cloud autoignition

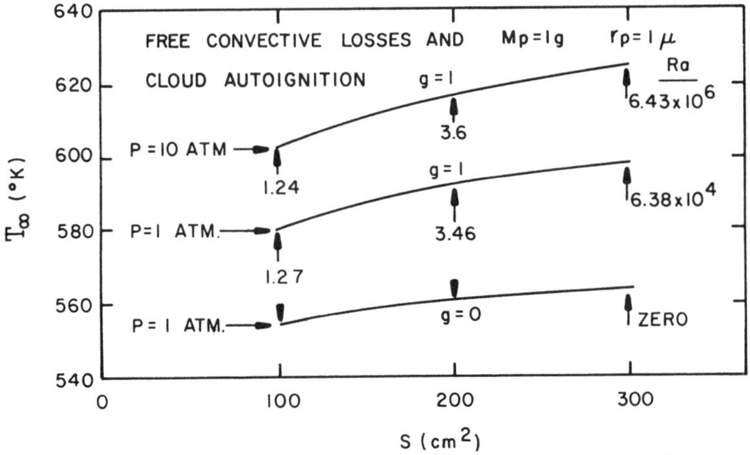

Fig. 6 Oxidation of zirconium clouds.[30]

phenomena can be substantial; 2) high-pressure flame propagation and extinction (as well as autoignition) for both gas phase and particle cloud flames may be changed dramatically for g=0 environments (consistent with the data and analyses given by Lovachev[3] in discussing high-pressure extinction of pure gas phase flames); and 3) high-pressure combustion studies (at g=1) may be so convectively dominated as to inhibit importantly our ability to study the other flame processes (which appears to be the case for single-phase as well as two-phase systems).

E. Diffusion Flame Phenomena in Flowing Systems

The (g=0) literature pertaining to laminar gas diffusion flames has been reviewed previously.[5] Particularly interesting are the results[33] that show the transient behavior of laminar gas jet diffusion flames as (g=1) conditions are transformed (at the NASA Lewis Research Center, Drop Tower Facility) to (g=0) for several seconds. Figures 7 and 8, taken from Ref. 33, show how either extinction or a different diffusion flame structure results in the transformation from (g=1) to (g=0).

An extensive analytical study[34] of axisymmetric laminar-jet diffusion flames provides good agreement for (g=1). Careful comparison with (g=0) data awaits more extensive observation of flame structures under conditions of weightlessness.

Recent studies by Lavid and Berlad[35] examine the effect of gravity for cases where the buoyant force is transverse to

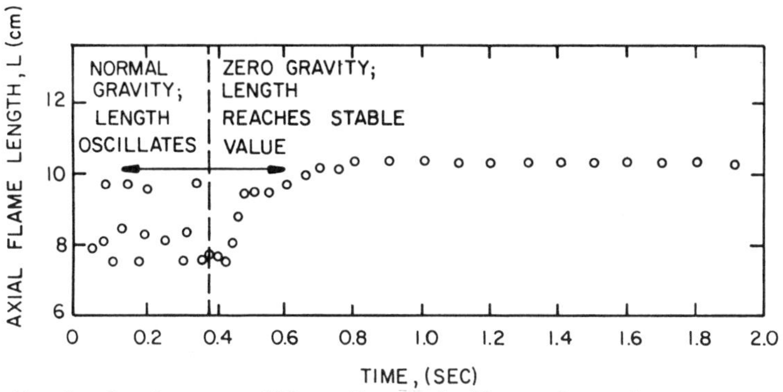

Fig. 7 Typical time profile of axial flame length upon entry into weightlessness.[33]

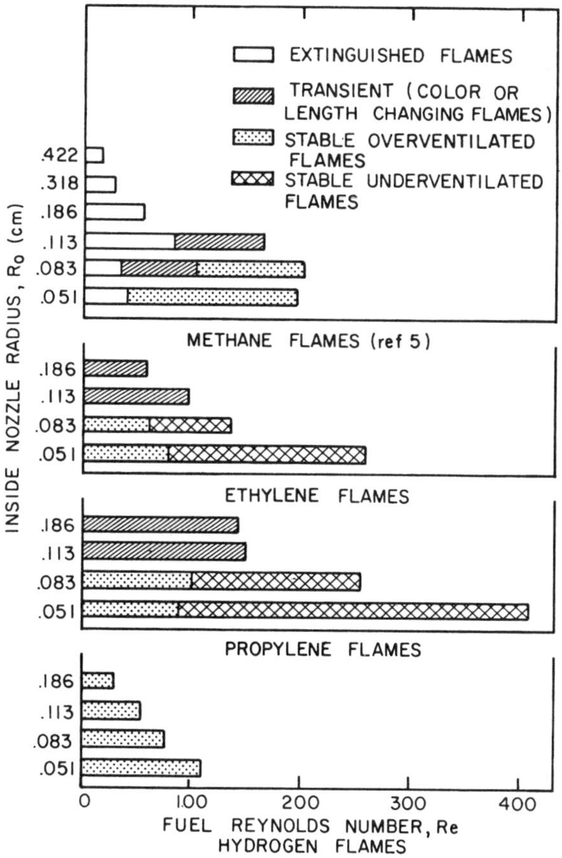

Fig. 8 Flame conditions encountered in zero gravity as function of flow.[33]

the flow direction, in boundary-layer flow. It is concluded that buoyancy does play an important role in boundary-layer diffusion flames. For fuel injected at (or through) the surface of a flat plate and burning in an oxidizing boundary-layer flow, these results prescribe 1) the acceleration of the boundary-layer flow (velocity overshoot), and 2) a decrease in the flame "standoff" distance for g=1.

The assumed flow model is indicated in Fig. 9, and the "velocity overshoot" results (calculated) are indicated in Fig. 10 ("aiding flows" correspond to a flat plate facing upwards, and "opposing flows" corresponds to a flat plate facing downwards). Results show that local boundary-layer flow is accelerated (aiding flows) or decelerated (opposing flows) relative to the corresponding gravity-free forced convection flow. Although theoretical predictions are in agreement with currently available experimental data,[36] zero-g studies needed for full evaluation of these analyses are not available.

There exists a great diversity of possible combustible flow (premixed or unpremixed) systems. Data and analyses available to date indicate that gravitational effects are to be expected. The zero-g data necessary to establish a baseline for such future studies currently are not available.

III. Avenues of Combustion Experimentation at Reduced Gravitational Conditions

For single- and two-phase combustible systems, gravitationally induced body forces result in natural convective processes, which, in turn, modify the underlying (g=0) combustion

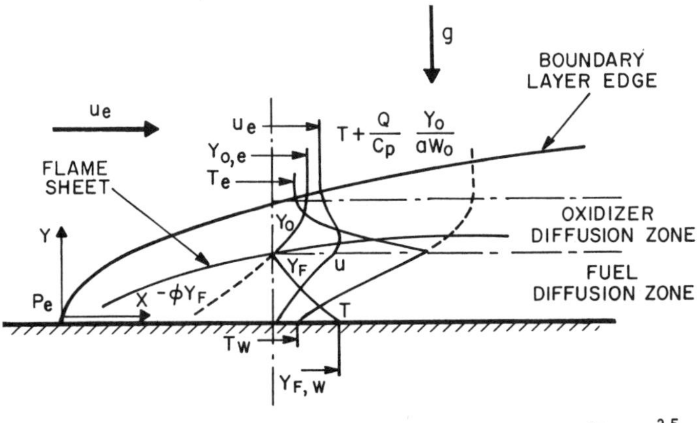

Fig. 9 Diffusion flame boundary-layer flow.[35]

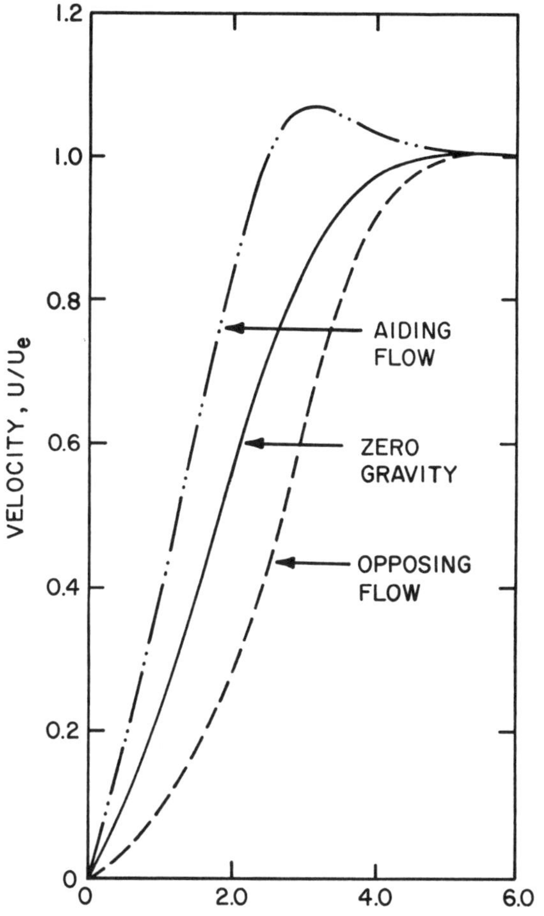

Fig. 10 Boundary-layer thickness η.[35]

phenomena. This fact generally engenders the following situation:

1) There is a set of observed experimental results, characteristic of Earth-bound reality, in which free convection plays a significant (frequently dominant) role.

2) There is a literature of highly truncated theoretical approaches to the representation of g=1 combustion phenomena. Typically,[5] either real chemical kinetic rate processes are ignored (taken to be infinitely fast), or free convective effects are ignored (taken not to exist).

3) Where free convective effects are taken not to exist (in a theoretical representation), the corresponding g=0 experimentation has not been performed. Accordingly, there generally is no basis for comparison of the most rudimentary theory (g=0) with the most uncomplicated combustion phenomena (g=0).

4) In the absence of verified g=0 experiment and theory, the systematic incorporation of g>0 experimental data, and development of associated theory, is inhibited severely. It is evident that a) appropriate g=0 experimental data would permit direct comparison of complete (convection-free) theory with experiment; and b) complete, verified, convection-free theory then may be used as a basis for the development of more acceptable (more complete) combustion theory for g>0 conditions. In particular, our understanding of the all-important (g=1) data would be enhanced greatly.

Facilities, current and anticipated, for combustion experimentation at reduced gravitational conditions include drop towers, special aircraft, and the forthcoming Space Shuttle Laboratory.[5] Although drop tower facilities have played an important role (e.g., Refs. 5 and 33) in previous g<1 experimentation, they impose severe limitations on the size and time scales for combustion experimentation. Typically, experiments in drop towers are limited to time scales of less than 5 sec and total space allowances (including auxiliary instrumentation) of less than 5 ft. Many important combustion experiments cannot be executed properly under these conditions. These include[5] such important phenomena as autoignition of single-phase and two-phase combustibles, thermokinetic oscillations and cool flames, flame propagation and extinction in single-phase and two-phase combustible systems, stability and structure of smoldering arrays of particulates, high-pressure flame propagation and extinction processes, and others. The small times available for drop tower experimentations are particularly limiting.

The Space Shuttle Laboratory offers a boxcar-sized facility for long-time (hours/days) combustion experimentation. One may list the diverse areas of combustion experimentation where pivotal observations are needed, which have not been obtainable otherwise: 1) autoignition for large (and/or high-pressure) single-phase (or two-phase) premixed combustible systems; 2) single (or two-phase) premixed flame propagation and extinction limits over a range of apparatus size and pressures; 3) noncoherent flame propagation; 4) upper pressure limit combustion phenomena and ignition, propagation, and extinction phenomena in the neighborhood of upper pressure limits; 5) cool flames in large premixed gaseous systems; 6) burning and extinction of individual drops or particles, over large pressure ranges; 7) two-phase combustion phenomena involving large liquid-gas or solid-gas interfaces; 8) radiative ignition of solids and liquids; 9) pool burning and flame propagation over liquids; 10) flame spread and extinction over solids; 11) smoldering of solid combustibles, and the associated transition to flaming (or extinction); 12) laminar gas jet combustion; 13) coupling (or decoupling) of convectively induced turbulence involved in various combustion phenomena; and 14) transient responses of combustible systems to time variations in gravitational field strengths.

The preceding tabulation of needed Space Shuttle experimentation is extensive. No less extensive is the corresponding theory and analysis. The anticipated experimental observations will guide and facilitate the development of verifiable theory, for $g=0$ as well as for $g>0$.

References

[1]Lewis, B. and Von Elbe, G., Combustion, Flames and Explosions of Gases, Academic Press, New York, 1961.

[2]Coward, H. F. and Jones, G. W.,"Limits of Flammability of Gases and Vapors," Bull. 503, 1952, U. S. Bureau of Mines.

[3]Lovachev, L. A., Babkin, V. S., Buner, V. A., V'Yun, A. V., Krivulun, V. N. and Banatov, A. N., "Flammability Limits: An Invited Review," Combustion and Flame, Vol. 20, April 1973, p. 259.

[4]Anon. Rep. 130, 1957, NACA.

[5]Berlad, A. L., Huggett, C., Kaufman, F., Markstein, G., Palmer, H. B., and Yang, C. H., "Study of Combustion Experiments in Space," CR-134744, Nov. 1974, NASA.

[6]Hirschfelder, J. O., Curtis, C. F., and Bird, R. B., The Molecular Theory of Gases and Liquids, Wiley, New York, 1954.

[7]Spalding, D. B., Some Fundamentals of Combustion, Academic Press, New York, 1955.

[8]Drell, I. L. and Belles, F. E., "Survey of Hydrogen Combustion Properties," Rep. 1383, 1958, NACA.

[9]Potter, A. E., Jr. and Berlad, A. L., "The Effect of Fuel Type and Pressure on Flame Quenching," Sixth Symposium (International) on Combustion, Reinhold Publishing Corp., New York, 1957, p. 27.

[10]Lovachev, L. A., "Theory of the Propagation Limits of a Flame in a Gas," Akademii Nauk SSSR, Doklady, Vol. 193, July 1970, p. 570 (English), p. 634 (Russian).

[11]Strehlow, R. A., Fundamentals of Combustion, International Textbook Co., Pennsylvania, 1968.

[12]Markstein, G. H., Nonsteady Flame Propagation, AGARDograph 75, Pergamon Press, New York, 1964, pp. 9-12.

[13]Berlad, A. L. and Yang, C. H., "A Theory of Flame Extinction Limits," Combustion and Flame, Vol. 4, December 1960, p. 325.

[14]Yang, C. H., "Burning Velocity and the Structure of Flames Near Extinction Limits," Combustion and Flame, Vol. 5, June 1961, p. 163.

[15]Levy. A., "An Optical Study of Flammability Limits," Proceedings of the Royal Society (London), Vol. A283, January 1965, p. 134.

[16]Mizutain, Y. and Ogasawara, M., "Laminar Flame Propagation in Droplet Suspension of Liquid Fuel," International Journal of Heat and Mass Transfer, Vol. 6, June 1965, p. 921.

[17]King, M. K., "Prediction of Laminar Flame Speeds in Boron-Oxygen-Nitrogen Dust Clouds," XV Symposium (International) on Combustion, 1974, p. 467.

[18]Mason, W. E. and Wilson, M. J. G., "Laminar Flows of Lycopodium Dust in Air," Combustion and Flame, Vol. 11, June 1967, p. 195.

[19]Pagni, P. J. and Peterson, T. G., "Flame Spread Through Porous Fuels," XIV Symposium (International) on Combustion, 1973, p. 1099.

[20]Berlad, A. L. and Krishna, C. R., "Transport Mechanisms in Fire Spread and Extinction," Clay Preston Butler Conference on Experimental Methods in Fire Research, edited by A. M. Kanury and N. J. Alvares, 1975, Stanford Research Institute.

[21]DeRis, J., Kanury, A. M., and Yuen, M. C., "Pressure Modeling of Fires," XIV Symposium (International) on Combustion, 1973, p. 1133.

[22]Markstein, G. H. and DeRis, J., "Upward Fire Spread Over Textiles," XIV Symposium (International) on Combustion, 1973, p. 1085.

[23]Ishihama, W. and Enomoto, H., "New Experimental Method for Studies of Dust Explosions," Combustion and Flame, Vol. 21, October 1973, p. 177.

[24]Berlad, A. L., "Thermokinetics and Combustion Phenomena in Nonflowing Gaseous Systems: An Invited Review," Combustion and Flame, Vol. 21, October 1973, p. 275.

[25]McCaffrey, B. J. and Berlad, A. L., "Some Observations on the Oscillatory Behavior of Carbon Monoxide Oxidation," Combustion and Flame, Vol. 26, February 1976, p. 77.

[26]Yang, C. H. and Berlad, A. L., "Kinetics and Kinetic Oscillation in Carbon Monoxide Oxidation," Journal of the Chemical Society, Faraday Transactions I, Vol. 70, September 1974, p. 1661.

[27]Yang, C. H., "On the Explosion, Glow and Oscillation Phenomena in the Oxidation of Carbon Monoxide," Combustion and Flame, Vol. 23, September 1974, p. 97.

[28]Gray, P., Jones, D. T., and MacKinven, R., "Thermal Effects Accompanying Spontaneous Ignition in Gases," Proceedings of the Royal Society (London), Vol. A325, November 1971, p. 175.

[29]Yang, C. H. and Gray, B. F., "On the Slow Oxidation of Hydrocarbon and Cool Flames," Journal of Physical Chemistry, Vol. 73, October 1969, p. 3395.

[30]Berlad, A. L. and Krishna, C. R., "Gravitational Effects on the Autoignition of Particle Clouds," Eastern States Section, The Combustion Institute, November 1975, Upton, N.Y.

[31]Yang, C. H. and Gray, B. F., "The Determination of Explosion Limits from a Unified Thermal and Chain Theory," XI Symposium (International) on Combustion, The Combustion Institute, Philadelphia, Pa., 1967, p. 1099.

[32]Fine, D. H., Gray, P., and MacKinven, R., "Thermal effects Accompanying Spontaneous Ignition in Gases: I. An Investiga-

tion of the Heating Effects which Accompany the Rapid Admission of Inert Gas to an Evacuated Vessel," Vol. A316, April 1970, p. 223; also "Thermal Effects Accompanying Spontaneous Ignition in Gases: II. The Slow Exothermic Decomposition of Diethyl Peroxide," Vol. A316, April 1970, p. 241; also "Thermal Effects Accompanying Spontaneous Ignition in Gases: III. The Explosive Decomposition of Diethyl Peroxide," Vol. A316, April 1970, p. 255.

[33]Haggard, J. B. and Cochran, T. H., "Hydrogen and Hydrocarbon Diffusion Flames in a Weightless Environment," TN D-7165, Feb. 1973, NASA.

[34]Edelman, R. B., Fortune, O., and Weilerstein, G., "Analytical Study of Gravity Effects on Laminar Diffusion Flames," CR-120921, Feb. 1972, NASA.

[35]Lavid, M. and Berlad, A. L., "Gravitational Effects on Chemically Reacting Laminar Boundary Layer Flows over a Horizontal Flat Plate," XVI Symposium (International) on Combustion, Aug. 1976, Cambridge, Mass.

[36]Hirano, T., Iwai, K., and Kanno, Y., "Measurements of the Velocity Distribution in the Boundary Layer over a Flat Plate with a Diffusion Flame," Astronautica Acta, Vol. 17, October 1972, p. 811.

INSTABILITIES OF INTERFACES
AND INTERFACIAL CONVECTION

R. Brückner*

Institut für Nicht-Metallische Werkstoffe,
Technische Universität, Berlin, Federal Republic of Germany

Abstract

Local and temporal disturbances of the equilibrium of boundary surfaces lead to instabilities, which act as boundary surface energy equilibration processes in liquids and melts and cause boundary surface convection and give rise to new instabilities by hydrodynamics coupling. The material transport under these conditions is much greater than under diffusion conditions and can exceed the material transport of the density and thermal convection. From a general point of view, the characteristic instabilities and equilibration processes systematically are dealt with qualitatively and, when expresions are available, quantitatively. Density instabilities, as one of an important category of disturbances, are excluded under 0-g conditions, which give rise to hydrodynamic consequences other than under 1-g conditions.

1. Introduction

Normally in the absence of forced external convection (also in the absence of normal gravity) mass transfer through an interface is determined by diffusion or reaction processes. This is always the case in the range of low concentrations. Here an undisturbed homogeneous interface during mass transfer generally can be assumed. This is still the case even if an external forced convection is maintained on both sides of the interface (convective diffusion).

Presented as Paper D.3.6 at the COSPAR Symposium on Materials Sciences in Space, Philadelphia,Pa., June 9-10,1976.

*Prof. Dr.-Ing.; Nonmetallic Anorganic Materials.

If the differences in the concentration of the transfered substance are high, or in the case of mass transfer of typical surface active substances, even small disturbances can lead to fluctuations in the concentration and can lead to inhomogeneities in the boundary surface or interface tension.[1,2,3] These disturbances give rise to boundary surface energy equilibration processes, and in the case of fluid boundary surfaces these are combined with flow movements in the immediate neighborbood of the boundary surfaces because of the final friction. The most striking and technically the most important consequence of boundary surface convection is that, through the hydrodynamic movements started by the boundary surface energy, there is a considerable increase in the material exchange caused otherwise by genuine and convective diffusion or reaction. This applies both to the materials exchange at liquid interfaces and to the materials transport in corrosion processes. Boundary surface convection or interfacial convection at liquid/liquid, liquid/gaseous, and in some cases also liquid/solid phase boundaries can be divided, in principle, into the equilibration processes at inhomogeneous interfaces and their elementary processes and into the instabilities (disturbances) of the boundary surface homogeneity leading to these inhomogeneities and their mechanisms.

2. Principles of the Equilibration Processes of Interfacial Convection

If a drop of a liquid is brought in contact with a flat surface of a second liquid that is immiscible with the drop, a process will start which is called "spreading process". When the drop has the lower surface tension (or surface energy), the spreading pressure commonly is positive, and the drop is spreading to a thin film. When the drop has the greater surface tension, the spreading pressure commonly is negative, and the drop will contract to a lens or will keep the form of a lens: $p_{sp} = \sigma_1 - (\sigma_2 + \gamma_{1,2}) \gtrless 0$.

If, however, both liquids are miscible or soluble (partly or completely), an additional more or less violent process occurs (Fig. 1), because all parameters of the spreading pressure change with time.[1] In an element of volume on the three-phase line, the approximate equilibrium between the vectors σ_1, σ_2, and $\gamma_{1,2}$ is disturbed; because the amount and the direction toward σ_2 are increased by the exchange of both substances, σ_1 becomes smaller with time (right-hand side of Fig. 1), and vice versa (left-hand side of Fig. 1). For ener-

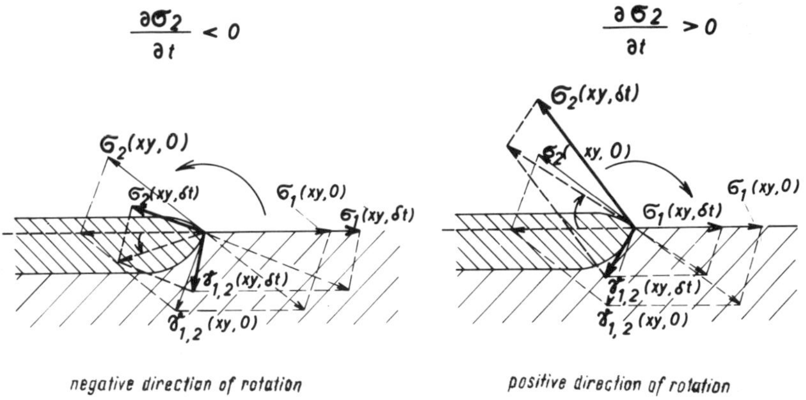

Fig. 1 Mechanism of development of swirling. Left: negative direction of rotation. Right: positive direction of rotation.

gy reasons, $\gamma_{1,2}$ becomes smaller in any case by the exchange of the liquids. As a result, a rotation is started whose direction depends largely on whether in the course of the exchange of substances σ_2 becomes larger (right-hand side) or smaller (left-hand side). The diagrammatic presentation in Fig. 1 can, or course, be understood only in the sense of a virtual displacement. The boundary surface tensions arising as forces are released only at the place where the three boundary surface energies compete in their efforts to restore equilibrium. The swirling produced in this way brings new unmixed substances to the three-phase line, so that the average angular velocity increases until the boundary forces depending on the concentration and the supply of substance are in dynamic equilibrium with the forces of viscosity and inertia. With increasing equilization of the concentrations, the average angular velocity becomes smaller again after some time as a result of smaller differences of the actual surface tensions. As a rule, negative direction of rotation is accompanied by negative spreading pressure, which means that contraction and positive direction of rotation (clockwise at the right of the feed point) are accompanied by positive spreading pressure.

Two examples for illustrating the fundamental mechanism are given. Figure 2 shows a drop of water on acetic acid in a small curette. Direction of rotation right of the feed point is anticlockwise, with negative spreading of swirling, because $\sigma_{water} > \sigma_{acetic\ acid}$. Figure 3 shows a drop of dioxane on nitrobenzene. Direction of rotation right of the feed point is

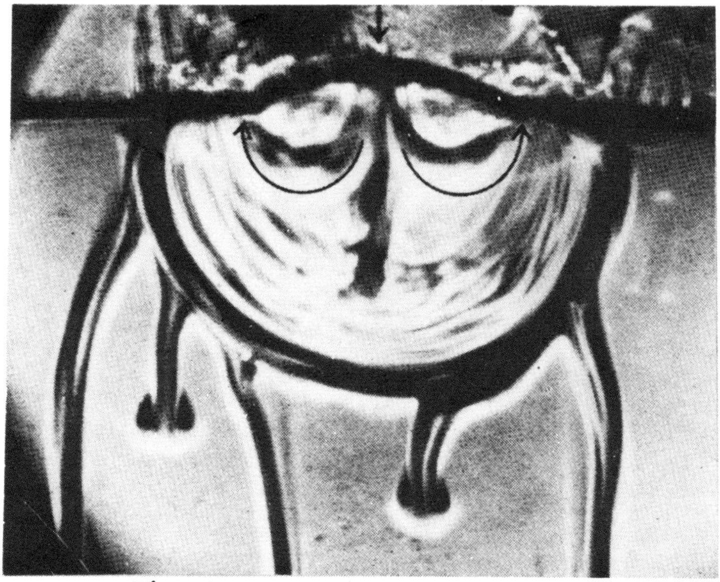

Fig. 2 A drop of water on acetic acid. Direction of rotation right of the feed point anticlockwise, negative, and negative spreading of swirling.

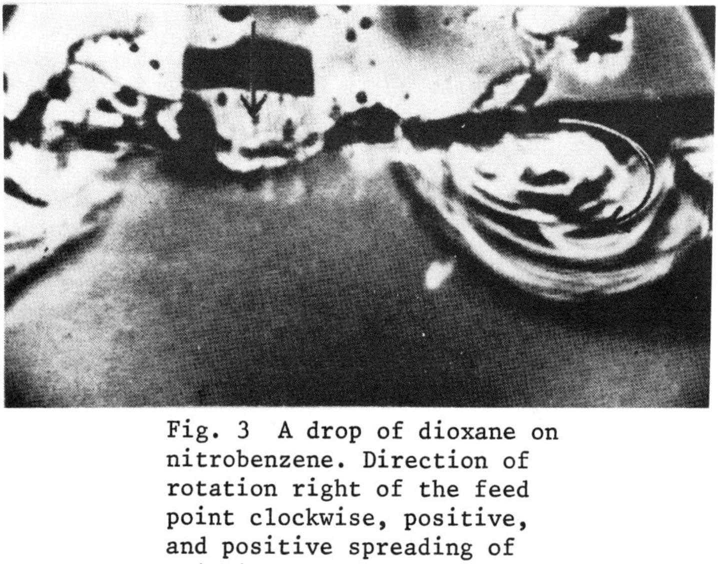

Fig. 3 A drop of dioxane on nitrobenzene. Direction of rotation right of the feed point clockwise, positive, and positive spreading of swirling.

clockwise, with positive spreading of swirling, because $\sigma_{dioxane} < \sigma_{nitro}$.

All possible variations of spreading and swirling phenomena of miscible and partly miscible liquids are summarized in Fig. 4: in cases I to V, liquid 1 is immiscible with liquid 2; in cases I to IV, liquid 3 is miscible with liquid 1 but immiscible with liquid 2. Always when the interfacial energy is increased by liquid 3, negative spreading and negative rotation of swirling occur (cases II and IV); when the interfacial energy is lowered by liquid 3, positive spreading and positive rotation of swirling occur (cases I and III). In Case V, liquid 3 is miscible with liquid 1 and 2, and

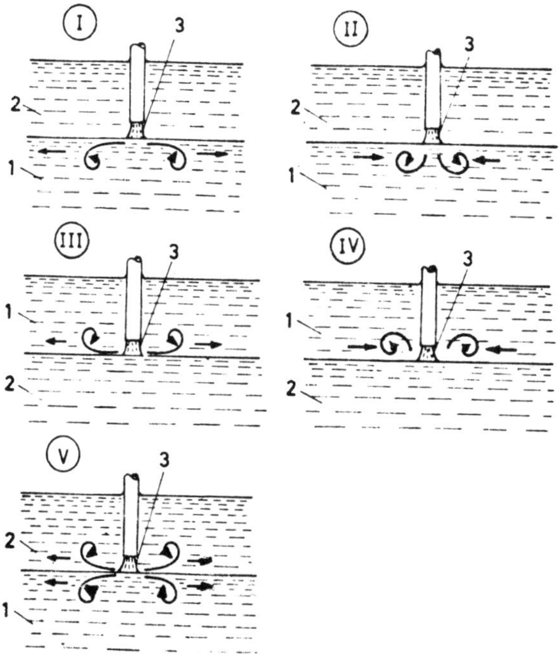

Fig. 4 Possible variations of spreading and swirling phenomena at two-phase ternary boundaries of miscible and partially miscible liquids. Case I to V: liquid 1 is immiscible with liquid 2. Case I to IV: liquid 3 is miscible with liquid 1 but immiscible with liquid 2. Case V: liquid 3 is miscible with liquid 1 and 2.

positive spreading and positive rotation of swirling are produced on both sides of the phase boundary. The counter part of case V does not exist because only a decrease of the interface energy is possible when liquid 3 is soluble in liquids 1 and 2. As a rule, spreading-effects combined with swirling effects are possible at two-phase boundaries with three or more substances partly or completely soluble in one or in both phases[3].

If a third liquid soluble in two phases is dissolved in one phase at the beginning of the experiment, then, stimulated by concentration fluctuations (creation of ternary boundaries) and strengthened by instability of density, it passes through the interface into the other phase, forming many statistically distributed swirlings having a reciprocal effect on each other, with positive spreading pressure and positive direction of rotation; an example is given in Fig. 5: transfer of acetic acid from amyl alcohol (from above) into water (beneath the interface); there are two momentary pictures in different enlargements and different places and times. The process continues until the concentrations corresponding to the distribution coefficients are reached.

With curved boundary surfaces, the capillary pressure is changed according to the Laplace equation, in addition to the discussed mechanisms. For example in Fig. 6, a jet of acetic acid comes into contact with a drop of chlorobenzene which is under water. Because of the local reduction in the capillary pressure, the boundary surface is deformed outwards, and if there is a sharp and sudden disturbance through the jet of acetic acid this can lead to the constriction of drops (dispersion)[4]. The counterpart (local increase in the capillary pressure) will lead to deformation of the drop inwards. In addition to the dispersion mechanism, emulsifying takes place, which, because the solubility limit of chlorobenzene in the inhomogeneous actic acid/water solution is exceeded, is brought about by swirling during the rapid convective diffusion of the acetic acid in the water (small droplets in Fig.6).

The possible equilibration processes of inhomogeneous boundary surfaces discussed here are summarized in Fig. 7. An inhomogeneous boundary surface should be understood here to mean one with boundary surface tension variable with place and/or time or one with free boundary surface energy.

3. Instabilities

The homogeneity of a boundary surface can be disturbed in many ways. But the principle is always the same and con-

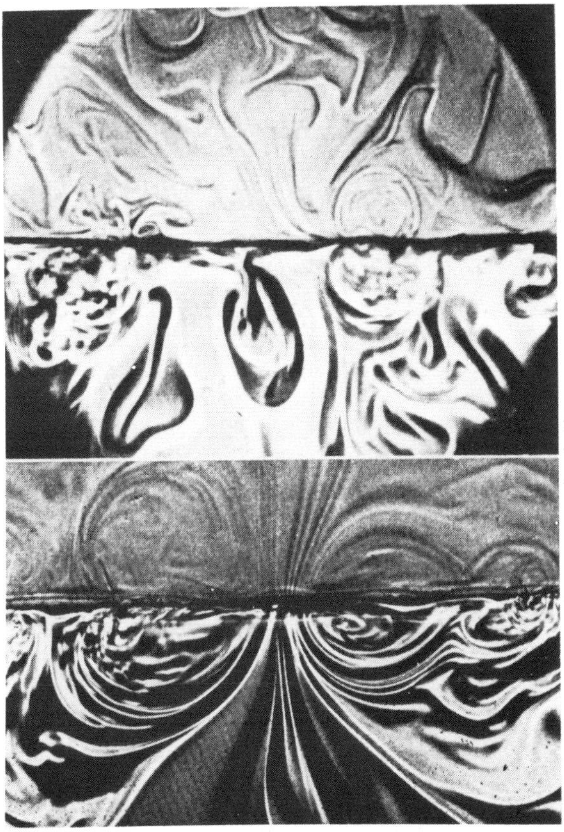

Fig. 5 Transfer of acetic acid through the boundary surface amyl alcohol plus acetic acid/water (below). Top figure approximately actual size, bottom figure magnified approximately four times.

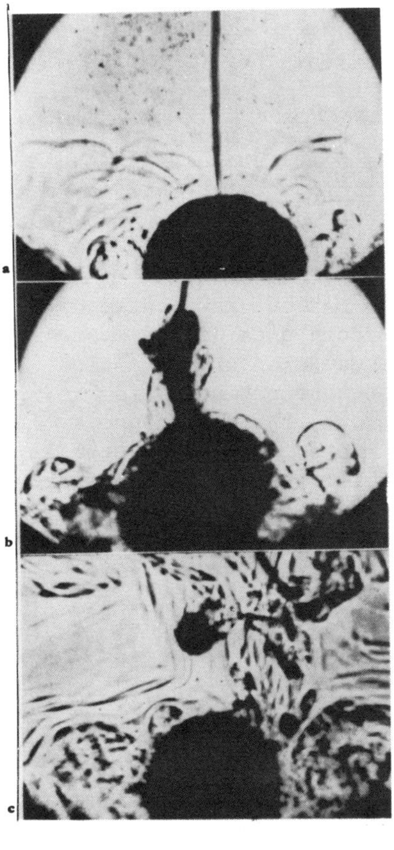

Fig. 6 Eruption of a drop of chlorobenzene under water after impact by a jet of acetic acid: a) spreading and swirling; b) swelling out of boundary surface of the drop; c) constriction of chlorobenzene drop (dispersion) and emulsifying of the swirlings (small drops) by distribution of the acetic acid in the water.

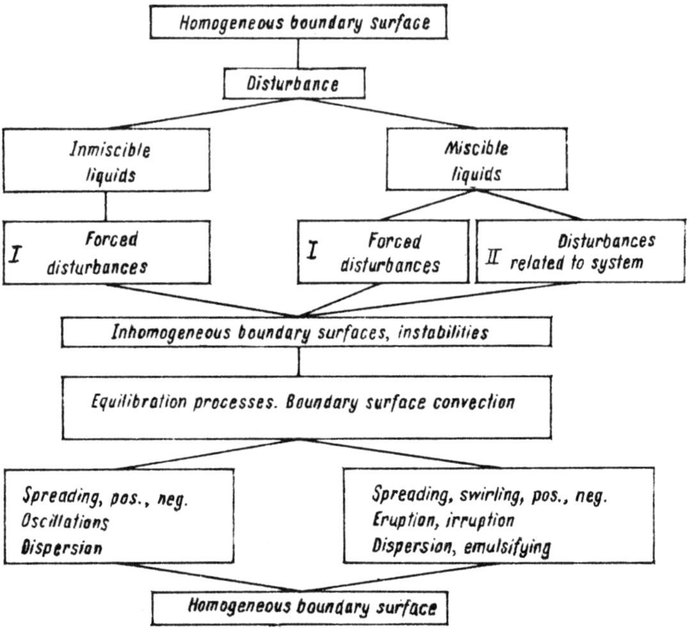

Fig. 7 Equilibration processes of inhomogeneous boundary surfaces.

sists generally of lacal differences being produced in the boundary surface tensions. The larger this difference is, then, in general, the more intensive are the equilibration movements described before.

In the following, a distinction may be drawn between disturbances within the system and those outside the system, and in individual cases it may be a question of convention what is to be considered as belonging and not belonging to a system. According to Table 1, therefore, the disturbances leading to equilibration processes (interfacial convection) should be devided into forced instabilities and instabilities related to the system [3]. From these instabilities, especially of interest are those in relation to the COSPAR meeting which are free from gravity, which means those that still will act under 0-g conditions.

3.1. Forced Instabilities

A. Ternary Boundary Lines and Quaternary Angles (Multiphase Boundaries). Two phases can form an interface. Three phases can form ternary boundary lines and four phases quaternary angles. When there are more than four phases or components, only those three or four components that show the greatest differences in the boundary surface tensions and possess the least viscosity have any effect. The most frequent prerequisite for interfacial convection is formed by two-phase ternary component boundaries. The third component has a disturbing effect in many ways, as will be seen from Table 1:

a) There are drops on a flat or curved boundary surface, as was the case in the fundamental experiments of Fig. 2 and 3.

b) There are gas bubbles or liquid drops through a boundary surface or through a diffusion layer. Arround the gas

Table 1 Instabilities for boundary surfaces

I) Forced instabilities		
A)	a) Drops on a flat or curved boundary surface b) Gas bubble through boundary surface or diffusion layer c) Local adsorption d) Local chemical reaction	A) Ternary boundary layers
B)	e) Local heat transfer f) Heat source, negative source (reaction)	B) Temperature differences
C)	g) Electrical fields	C) Electrocapillarity
II) Instabilities related to the system		
D)	h) A priori ternary boundaries i) Displacement of solution j) Uneven boundary surface, drops, bubbles	D) Ternary boundary layers
E)	k) $\Delta\varrho$ in liquid-liquid mass transfer l) $\Delta\varrho$ in adsorption, condensation m) $\Delta\varrho$ in desorption, evaporation o) $\Delta\varrho$ in reaction	E) Instabilities of density
F)	Heat transfer	F) Temperature diffusion
G)	Hydrodynamic diffusion instability	G) Viscosity, diffusion

bubble, swirling and spreading effects will occur as soon the gas bubble or the drop penetrates the boundary or diffusion layer.

c) Ternary boundaries are obtained also with local adsorption or desorption of a gas or vapor from a liquid boundary surface and are the more precise the greater $\Delta\sigma$ is and the quicker the mass transfer takes place (adsorption or desorption of acetone or alcohol in or from water by forced convection in the gas phase).

d) By local chemical reaction or decomposition a new formation of material can take place with changed boundary surface tensions, as is the case, for example, with basic acid trimethylester on the surface of water. (The methyl alcohol produced causes spreading and swirling in the same way as under point a.)

B. Temperature Differences. e) If local heat is removed from a surface by evaporation of a substance (e.g., blowing of air from a capillary on an ether surface), the surface tension generally is increased (reduced in the case of liquid sulphur), and boundary surface convection is produced. This process plays a large part in destillation.

f) In mixing processes with thermal and chemical decomposition or in chemical reactions, heat sources or negative sources can be obtained and can produce unstable boundary surfaces in addition to the ternary boundaries described before under point a, c and d (e.g., camphor on water).

C. Electrical Fields. g) Through the phenomena of electrocapillarity, electrical fields can lead to inhomogeneities in interfacial tensions similar to those in the previous examples. In addition to boundary surface convection resulting from differences in boundary surface tensions produced by electrical potential [explained by the equation of Helmholtz-Lippmann: $c = -\partial\sigma/\partial\psi$; $\sigma = f(\psi)$; c is surface carrier density], a current also is produced by increased mobility of ions in the boundary layer.

3.2. Instabilities Related to the System

D. Ternary Boundary Layers. h) A priori ternary boundaries are produced by a dissolving solid at the surface of the dissolving liquid or at the boundary of two overlying or underlying solutions. A fluid ternary boundary is formed (solution/diffusion layer/gas phase or solution/diffusion Layer/second liquid phase), which is renewed continually by dissolutions. This process produces an erosion of the solid at the level of the surface or boundary surface.

i) The erosion process can be intensified if displacement of a solution during the dissolving process is produced as, for example, dissolving of a common salt crystal in a 50% alcohol or acetone water solution (Fig. 8).

j) Under zero-gravity conditions, uneven boundary surfaces, drops, and bubbles play an important part. In addition to the interface convection phenomena, changes of the capillarity pressure have to be taken into consideration. This will lead to impulses and oscillations of the boundary surfaces and in some cases to eruptions and even to dispersion, as already described by Fig. 6.

E. Density Instabilities. These are very numerous under 1-g conditions and are of no interest under 0-g conditions. However, for diffusion experiments in liquid systems, it should be proved whether density instabilities of any kind of Table 1 perhaps lead to boundary surface convection if the 0-g condition is not maintained exactly and if deviations occur during the diffusion experiments. For example, one kind of diffusion experiments is possible only under 0-g conditions: the chemical diffusion or the mass transfer of a component with the density greater than the densities of the two solvent phases. Also, there are many diffusion problems for which the direction of the diffusion process is not all the same or all different. In all of these cases, the experiments should be proved to be free of boundary surface convection.

Fig. 8 Preferred corrosion of NaCl crystal at the liquid level by boundary surface convection as a result of displacement of the solution as a local interfacial instability.

F. Heat Transfer with and Especially without the Effect of Gravity. Only local heat transfer without the effect of gravity is of interest for boundary surface convection if it is produced from reactions related to the system. The interfacial convection will be, in principle, similar to the effects described already under B of Table 1.

G. Hydrodynamic Diffusion Instability. This is a very interesting instability for all gravity cases, for 1-g as well as for 0-g conditions. We consider a two-phase system with one component soluble in both phases A and B. If the mobility of the solute is greater in phase B than in A, then the material transport takes place more quickly in B than in A. If the mass transfer is in the direction from A to B, the development of boundary surface convection is possible. This is the case when the diffusion coefficient $D_B > D_A$ and the kinematic viscosity $\nu_B < \nu_A$ and if at the same time the boundary surface tension between A and B decreases with increasing concentration of the third component[5] : $d\sigma/dc < 0$. This form of instability should be considered as analogous to the condition for density instability (E), where for dynamic reasons the free boundary surface convection also depends on the direction of mass transfer, because the mass transfer in the direction from B to A does not lead to free boundary surface convection.

4. Consequences and Applications

From the previous sections, it can be seen immediately that material transport takes place much more quickly under boundary surface convection conditions than under pure diffusion conditions. Even under conditions of forced convection, the effect of boundary surface convection is still quite noticeable in many cases.

Only one example may be given: the transfer of ammonium tetrarhodanide cobaltate from moving drops of an aqueous ammonium rhodanide solution into pure methyl isobutyl Keton[6]. Figure 9 indicates the cobalt concentration remaining in the drops in relation to the contact time. Curves 1 to 5 show increasing rhodanide concentration. The boundary surface convection, and thus the quantity of cobaltate being transfered, increases by the same proportion. (Addition of 2.5 % of dodecyl benzene sulphate, as in curves 3a and 5a, reduces the speed of mass transfer!) Evaluation of the experiments shows that the mass transfer coefficient remains constant only in the case of very small rhodanide concentrations (curve 1, right-hand side,) whereas for the other experiments it is dependent largely on the contact time. This shows that,

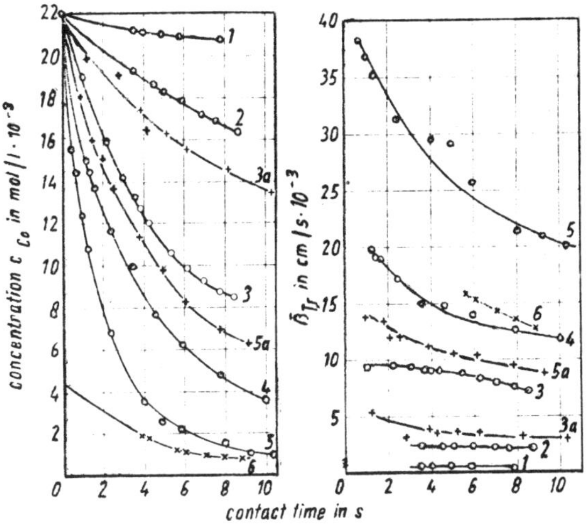

Fig. 9 Left: transfer of a solute from drops with solution 1 into solution 2 as a function of contact time and increasing concentration of solution 1 (curves 1 to 5). Right: mass transfer coefficient, calculated from the curves to the left.

despite the forced convection of the movement of the drops at the beginning of the measuring series 5, roughly 60 times the material transfer can be obtained through the effect of boundary surface convection compared with pure diffusion.

In many mixing and mass transfer or mass extraction experiments, boundary surface convection will be a helpful tool, in addition to forced convection. This is true under conditions with and without the effect of gravity. On the other hand, boundary surface convection should be eliminated for pure diffusion experiments in fluid systems, because even under zero-gravity condition this effect can lead to errors from case to case, when aforementioned instabilities are not regarded. Therefore, the various conditions of boundary surface convection should be studied under zero-gravity conditions, so that density instabilities can be excluded which are very troublesome during the study of various other instabilities and their accompanying conditions, from which principle examples have been given.

References

[1] Brückner, R., "Instationäre Grenzflächenvorgänge zwischen mischbaren Flüssigkeiten," Naturwissenschaften, Vol. 47, Heft 16, 1960, p. 371. "Instationäre Grenzflächenvorgänge zwischen partiell mischbaren Lösungen," ibid., p. 372.

[2] Scriven, L.E. and Sternling, C.V., "The Marangoni Effects," Nature, Vol. 187, July 1960, pp. 186-188.

[3] Brückner, R., "Mechanismen und Systematik der Elementarvorgänge der Grenzflächenkonvektion," Kolloid-Zeitschrift und Zeitschrift für Polymere, Vol. 222, Heft 1, 1968, pp. 39-50.

[4] Brückner, R., "Grenzflächenenergetische Ausgleichsprozesse bei Stoffaustauschvorgängen," Glastechnische Berichte, Vol. 34, Heft 9, 1961, pp. 438-456.

[5] Sternling, C.V. and Scriven, L.E., "Interfacial Turbulence: Hydrodynamic Instability and the Marangoni Effect," AIChE Journal, Vol. 5, December 1959, pp. 514-523.

[6] Fritz, W. and Popova, T., "Grenzflächeninstabilitäten und Geschwindigkeit beim Stoffdurchgang von Ammonium-Tetrarhodanokobalt(II) zwischen Wasser und Methylisobutylketon," Chemie-Ingenieur-Technik, Vol. 42, November 1970, pp. 1004-1009.

GRAVITATIONAL DYNAMICS OF BIOSYSTEMS:
SOME SPECULATIONS

J. O. Kessler*
University of Arizona, Tucson, Ariz.

and

M. Bier†
Veterans Administration Hospital, Tucson, Ariz.

Abstract

The response of organisms to gravity is generally discussed in terms of hypotheses involving sedimentation and other static effects. This paper considers several complex, inhomogeneous fluid-containing systems that are intended to model some possible dynamic effects of gravity on biosystems. It is shown that the presence of gravity may result in modified long range transport, concentration oscillations, and broken symmetries. The magnitude of density-gradient-driven convective transport times, and their ratios to diffusive transport times, are calculated for cell dimensions of six different plant varieties. The results indicate that further investigation of gravitational convection effects may be realistic in some cases and is definitely not in others. The results of this paper should aid in the planning of "zero-gravity" experiments concerning plant geotropism and bio-materials processing.

Presented as paper D.3.7 at the COSPAR Symposium on Materials Sciences in Space, Philadelphia, Pa., June 9 - 10, 1976. Performed with the partial support of NASA Grant NAS8-29566. We wish to acknowledge A. Gibson's help with the helianthus measurements, and helpful conversations with A. H. Brown, R. Kilkson, and B. Zinn. J. O. Kessler also would like to express his special appreciation to G. W. Swan for many illuminating discussions relating to the biological oscillator problem.
*Professor of Physics.

†Research Biophysicist and Visiting Research Professor, University of Arizona.

Introduction

This paper discusses several hypothetical mechanisms by which gravity may interact with living organisms or other complex dynamic systems that include fluids or are embedded in fluids. The well-known "direct" effects of gravity, such as segregation by density, maintenance of pressure gradients and modification of fluid contours in competition with surface tension will be omitted almost entirely. The topics presented involve mainly "indirect" effects, in the sense 1) that they are dynamic, driven by energy dissipation characteristic of systems situated in a gravitational field, and 2) that there is an essential involvement in some feedback loop of the system.

It is hoped that the models presented here will stimulate further thought and research concerning gravitation-related effects in biology and that new insights will be generated concerning fundamental aspects of the techniques that may be projected for future utilization of the space environment in the "processing" of biological materials. We have already seen in this Symposium, and previously, a number of advances in materials science -- practical results and fundamental understanding -- provided by "zero-g." These advances relate to separation efficiency in electrophoresis and to a better understanding and improved practice of crystal growth. An extension to living bio-materials seems appropriate at this time.

Basic Effects of Gravity

The gravitational field $\underline{g}$ is conservative; $\underline{g}$ cannot be an energy source for a localized cyclic process. The effect of $\underline{g}$ on chemical affinities is minute; if $\underline{g}$ is to affect chemical or biochemical kinetics, the effect must be indirect. But gravitation does provide the stage for life: a pressure reservoir, a definite location for the phases of matter in the environment, a polar symmetry axis and a floor to push against. Life probably could not have developed without the reduction in the dimensionality of space that $\underline{g}$ provides. The aggregation of the component parts of proto-organisms and their eventual nutrition must have required large, simply connected surfaces that tend to collect and absorb matter from the three dimensional continuum.

Another aspect of $\underline{g}$ is related to food supply and cleansing. In a fluid environment, a small organism may pursue its food by swimming and leave its waste products behind: an energetically costly process. Or it may wait for diffusion,

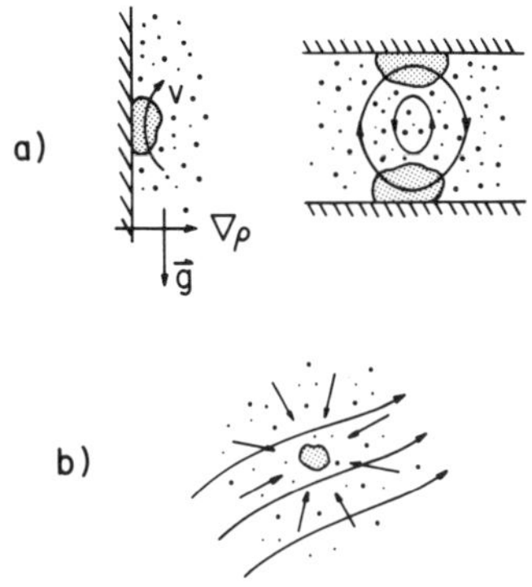

Fig. 1 The Feeding and cleansing of organisms. a) An organism attached to a surface bounding a convecting fluid. b) A free organism in the fluid stream. Transport is diffusion-limited. The dots symbolize suspended matter of significance to the organism.

adequate for well-dispersed metabolites such as O_2 or CO_2 but involving delays that may be too long. If the organism is attached to a surface, and if the fluid environment convects, due to the presence of g and suitable density gradients resulting from environmental energy fluxes, all that the organism need do is to remain attached and wait. This effect is summarized symbolically in Fig. 1. Active living systems depend on transport. Externally, they require the delivery of nutrients, the removal of wastes and the maintenance of a reasonably stable thermochemical environment. Internally, controlled transport of matter and energy is crucial.

The indirect influence of g on organisms is related to the dominance, or ranking, of various transport processes. Given the chemical possibility of life (or for that matter any reaction, such as the growth of crystals), it still is necessary to bring the reactants to the site of reaction. In the laboratory, we have stirring machines. In nature, transport is provided by diffusion, convective motion due to surface tension gradients, peristaltic movements, and gravitationally mediated convection. These effects are "indirect," from the point of view of the chemical affinities, but of the utmost importance if transport is rate-limiting (Fig. 2).

The indirect effects of g therefore should be marked especially in systems that depend most strongly on transport, i.e., systems undergoing rapid growth. Embryos where stabilizing redundant control loops are not yet fully developed, quickly growing portions of plants, or parts of plants in which rapid growth is latent should be particularly appropriate objects for investigation. The question of dominance among long-range transport mechanisms is implicit throughout this

Fig. 2 Transport as the rate-limiting step in a chemical reaction. a) Assuming different densities of the reactants, gravity produces convective mixing. The reaction rate is eventually determined by k, k_- and the average concentrations. b) In the absence of gravity, the reaction rate is limited by diffusive transport of the reactants through the product phase. The graph sketches the time dependence of the product concentration C(•), assuming infinite supply of reactants A(+) and B(-).

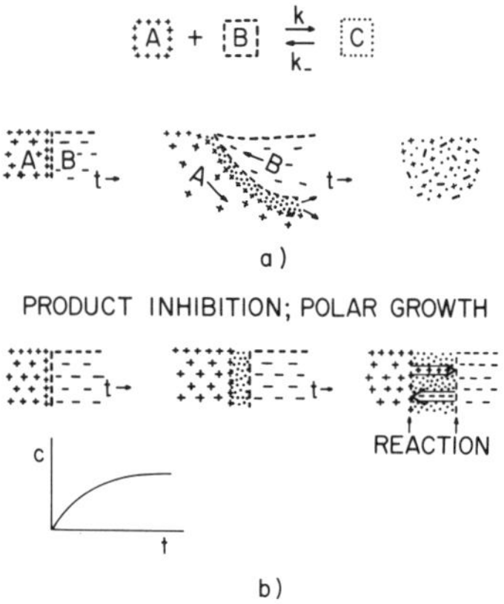

paper. The competition between diffusion and convection is treated explicitly in part of the paper; other effects, such as those due to surface tension gradients, are ignored. Some of the symmetry properties of g-mediated transport are dealt with, since these properties potentially provide one of the best "handles" for future investigations.

A Preliminary Example

This section presents a gravitationally mediated mechanism that does not relate to convective transport. The model depends on static effects (segregation and buoyant symmetry axis) and dynamic effects (buoyant motion, chemical reaction, reactant collection, interface motion in response to shear stress). It is conceivable, but not very likely, that this model may be related to some natural migrations of unicellular organisms. Without doubt, it is an excellent example of complex gravitational feedback effects.

Consider, first, an object possessing an inhomogeneous distribution of mass. Then gravity provides a polar symmetry axis: the object will float upright. If the fluid containing the object has a segregated vertical property, such as temperature or chemical concentration, and if the object's surface has a gradient of surface properties, the gravitationally induced polar symmetry and object positioning may facilitate or inhibit interactions. Such interactions may change the mean density of the object, resulting in motion.

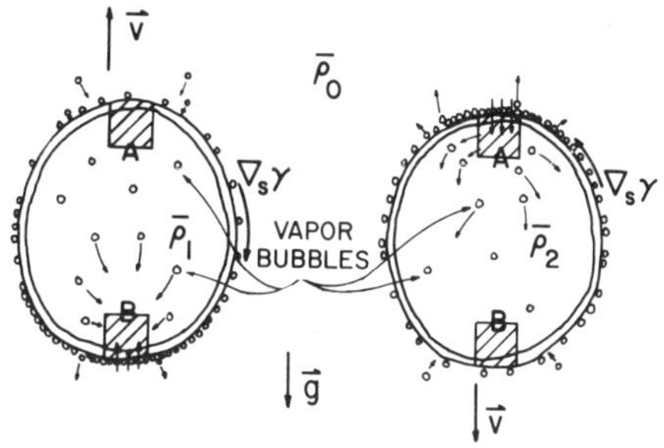

Fig. 3 Active Cartesian diver, a chemical/ mechanical buoyant oscillator. γ is the concentration of surfactant; the surface gradient is $\nabla_S\gamma$. Organelle A tends to emit vapor bubbles (interior open circles) into the diver when γ is large in its vicinity, whereas under the same conditions B absorbs them. The velocity of the diver is $\underline{v}$, the gravity field is $\underline{g}$. When the mean density $\bar{\rho}_i$ of the diver exceeds $\bar{\rho}_o$, the density of the ambient fluid, as at left, $\underline{v}$ is downward, and conversely. The surfactant is symbolized by open circles at the periphery of the diver and in its surround. The $\underline{v}$-dependent loss or gain of surfactant (as in Ref. 1) is symbolized by small arrows.

Figure 3 depicts a somewhat more complex situation where a dilute solution containing an object that is neutrally buoyant on the average does not exhibit significant gradient properties over the object's dimension. Let the solute tend to adsorb on the object's surface and interact with organelles located at the poles of the interior, so that a net amount of gaseous phase is emitted or absorbed within the object, depending on which organelle is in the vicinity of the greater surfactant concentration. Since[1] the surfactant tends to be more concentrated at the rear of a small moving object than at the front, relative to its velocity $\underline{v}$, oscillatory motion of the object along the $\underline{g}$ axis may ensue.

If the described motion is stable only within definite limits, a gravitationally mediated catastrophe can result. The effect may be visualized in terms of an active Cartesian diver that acts as an oscillating messenger between the upper and lower strata of its container. Such a diver may "stick" at the top or bottom of its container if its internal gas volume exceeds upper or lower limits. Normally, "rescue" is effected by changing the ambient atmospheric pressure. In the present situation it would require production or absorption of gas by chemical reaction.

It is evident that, in this example, gravity is of no direct importance. It does not enter into the chemical reaction or in the adsorption of surfactant. Gravity does result in chemical and mechanical feedback that facilitates or inhibits reaction and thus, in an indirect way, it is the whole show. Without gravity, no dynamical effects would occur.

Broken Symmetry and Nonlinear Effects

One of the best known concrete examples of a g-mediated transport effect is Bénard convection.[2] When the temperature dependence of surface tension becomes important the effect is known as "Bénard-Marangoni." In the arrangement of Fig. 4, two heat reservoirs are connected through a black box and a heat-flux-sensing device that transmits a signal to an external observer. Unknown to the outside observer, the black box contains a thermally expanding viscous fluid. If $g = 0$, the temperature difference $\Delta T = T_2 - T_1$ produces an average heat flux $j_q = \lambda \Delta T$. Let g increase slowly. Above a certain threshold,[2] convection begins; the heat flux rises markedly and continues to do so. The criterion for onset of convection is proportional to $g\Delta T$, therefore at constant g, the threshold may be reached at sufficiently high ΔT. The observer infers that heat transport is a nonlinear effect, i.e. that λ is a function of g and ΔT. Although the gravitational field does not itself transport anything, it crucially influences the observed kinetics.

The experiences of another experimenter, located within the black box (Fig. 5), are even more remarkable. Let this observer have approximately the same density as the fluid, and let him be connected flexibly (by a chain) to an interior wall of the box. Since he is neutrally buoyant, he never gets to know about g, but he certainly can observe the streaming motion when it occurs. If the fluid contains identifiable suspended particles, he can use his environment as a clock or as a source of nourishment when g is on. Without g, or below threshold, this observer's surroundings are static, except for Brownian motion. Beyond threshold, he observes a qualitative g-related breaking of the symmetry of his environment, whereas the external experimenter observes substantial quantitative effects only. Furthermore, the tethered interior observer in the convecting environment directly relates to other interior points via the convection stream: his sphere of influence is delocalized; he may communicate with other entities attached elsewhere in the cell. The time lags or phase shifts of this communication channel depend on the rate of

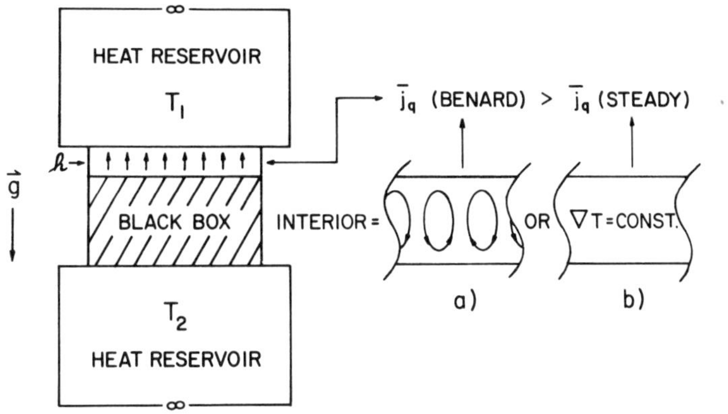

Fig. 4 Heat conduction through a black box. The fluid-containing black box separates two heat reservoirs, with constant temperatures $T_1 < T_2$ and $T_2 - T_1 = \Delta T$. A heat flux meter h is interposed. In the indicated gravitational field g, and for sufficiently large $g\Delta T$, an external observer measures the average heat flux $\bar{J}_q$(Bénard). For lower values of $g\Delta T$ the flux is $\bar{J}_q$(steady) $<$ $\bar{J}_q$(Bénard). The Bénard velocity field is illustrated schematically in Fig. 4a; it is absent in Fig. 4b.

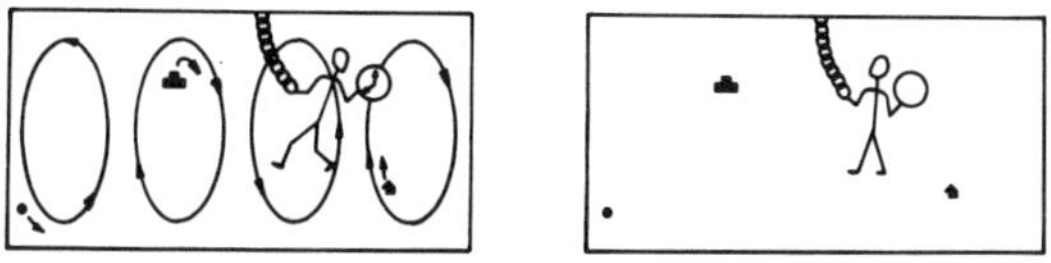

a) BENARD CONVECTION b) STEADY

Fig. 5 Heat conduction through a black box, seen from within. A neutrally buoyant observer flexibly connected to an interior wall experiences a) dynamic and b) static environments. The static or moving odd objects and velocity field of the fluid symbolize the interaction possibilities discussed in the text. The convective dissipative structure implies a direction and scale for time.

convection which is a function of the magnitude of g and ΔT and on the shape of the box.

If the observers, internal and external, find all of the phenomena described, whereas an additional measurement indicates that $g = 0$, they must conclude that not g, but another mechanism, operates. This mechanism may be temperature-dependent surface tension. Qualitatively similar convective effects are obtained,[2] but with different thresholds in ΔT and certain other characteristics. Conversely, given a convective effect of significance, the observer can decide on the fundamental cause or measure the separate determinants by setting $\underline{g} = 0$ in a space experiment.

It should be noted that this symmetry-breaking effect requires both a gravitational field and thermal or chemical energy dissipation. The situation differs fundamentally from the non-cyclic one in which potential energy of an anisotropic mass is decreased by re-orientation of the mass in a $\underline{g}$ field. In that case the asymmetry exists already. In Bénard convection, it is created by the natural tendency of dissipation to rise, with the concomitant creation of structure.[3] Perhaps g-mediated effects of this sort are important in the development of the complex structure of simple organisms; chemical reactions that produce density gradients would be required in addition to, or replacing, the heat dissipation introduced here.

Returning to the example, one also may consider what happens in the pure Bénard case if $\underline{g}$, or the arrangement of the experiment, is rotated by 90°. This simple change results in the destruction of the threshold effects. If $\underline{g}$ and the imposed density gradient are not parallel, there always will be some convection, with the results discussed above.

Convection-Diffusion Competition in a Cell Reactor

The context of the following section is "geotropism" and "biological oscillators." The basic gravitational phenomenon is taken as convection within a relatively open cell. Non-gravitational cytoplasmic streaming is ignored in the model system. It may be superposed when required. The convective flow is assumed to be due to a density gradient within a relatively open cell, in the no-threshold geometry. To avoid an excessive number of nonlinearities, and to permit the use of a simple steady state heat flow analogy, the rather unrealistic assumption is made that the density gradient within the cell results from the passage of a steady flux of inert molecules through the cell boundaries. The flux of molecules is supposed due to a suitable array of sources and sinks outside the cell. The resultant steady toroidal convective stream of cell fluid is assumed to transport chemical reactants. These assumptions imply a characteristic transport time, governed by the density gradient and cell properties. If convection were assumed to be driven by gradients of reactants, the transport time would vary in addition to the other effects to be discussed.

The postulated model again features gravity in a central but "indirect" role, in the sense that the convective motion crucially affects the chemical kinetics of some cellular synthetic process(es) by providing a supply of reactant at a localized reaction site ("reactor") and by delivering feedback information to a membrane-gate that determines the admission of reaction facilitators (enzymes, hormones) and/or reactants.

Figure 6 represents a hypothetical elongated upright cell containing a mobile fluid. The gate organelle 0(1) controls the input of a substance S(1). Approximately half a cell perimeter away, the substance S(1) can undergo chemical change in the reactor organelle 0(2) where the products also

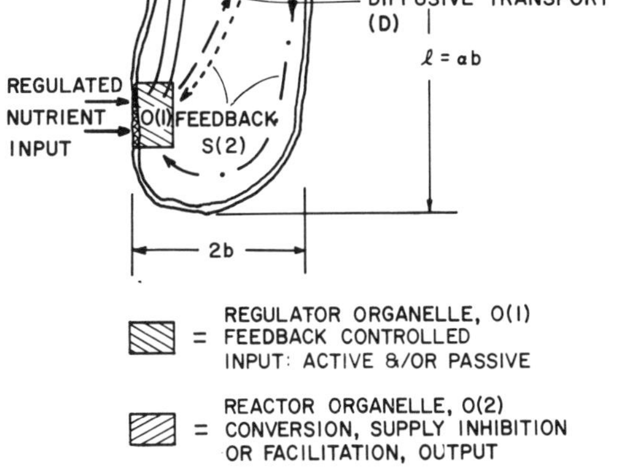

TRANSIT TIMES, O(1) ⇌ O(2):

DIFFUSION: $L_D \approx \ell/3 \approx \sqrt{Dt_D}$; $t_D \approx \ell^2/9D$

CONVECTION: $L_C \approx \ell \approx |\bar{v}|t_C$; $t_C \approx \ell/|\bar{v}|$

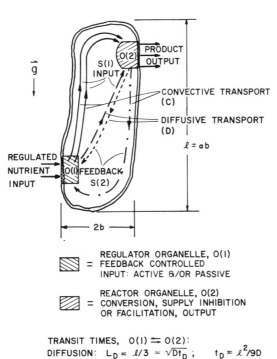

Fig. 6 Convection/diffusion limited active cell reactor. Explanation in text. L_i and t_i are characteristic lengths and times.

are exported. Organelle (2) produces a substance S(2) that provides feedback information to O(1). The amount of S(2) emitted is related to the concentration of S(1) at O(2). The substance S(2) may be identical with S(1) (unreacted fraction), or it may be an enzyme or hormone.

S(1) and S(2) move between O(1) and O(2) by diffusion and convection. The convective stream is assumed to result from a density gradient across the cell, perpendicular to g. In a general situation, this density gradient may result from the presence of S(1) and S(2), or from other solutes, not named specifically. The density must be lower at the left of the figure for the indicated location of O(1) and O(2); this symmetry choice is arbitrary.

Assuming convection with average velocity $|\overline{v}|$, the convective transit time t_c, between O(1) and O(2), is $t_c \approx \ell/|\overline{v}|$, where ℓ is the height, or approximate half-perimeter of the cell, and $\ell >> b$. The characteristic distance for diffusion L_D has been set arbitrarily at $L_D \approx \ell/3$; thus the diffusive transit time $t_d \approx \ell^2/9D$, where D is the diffusivity. The convective and diffusive transport processes compete. If the ratio t_c/t_d is large (small cells), diffusion determines the rate, and there can be no g-effect, and conversely.

Figure 7 indicates the simplified model discussed in the introduction to this section. The formulas are estimates derived from an idealized case of convection due to an imposed temperature gradient. The original source[4] considers the x and z dimensions infinite (but $\Delta\rho$ replaces $\overline{\rho\beta\Delta T}$). The present adaption uses the finite height to derive the period of the circulation but ignores the finite x dimension. The errors in this procedure are expected to be unimportant compared to uncertainties in the parameter estimates.

The convective transport time in this model is then

$$t_c = (48\mu/g\Delta\rho) \times (\ell/b^2)$$

where μ is viscosity, $\Delta\rho$ the density difference across the cell, g the acceleration due to gravity, ℓ the cell height, and b the half-width. The convection/diffusion time ratio is

$$t_c/t_d = (48\mu\ell/gb^2\Delta\rho) \times (9D/\ell^2)$$

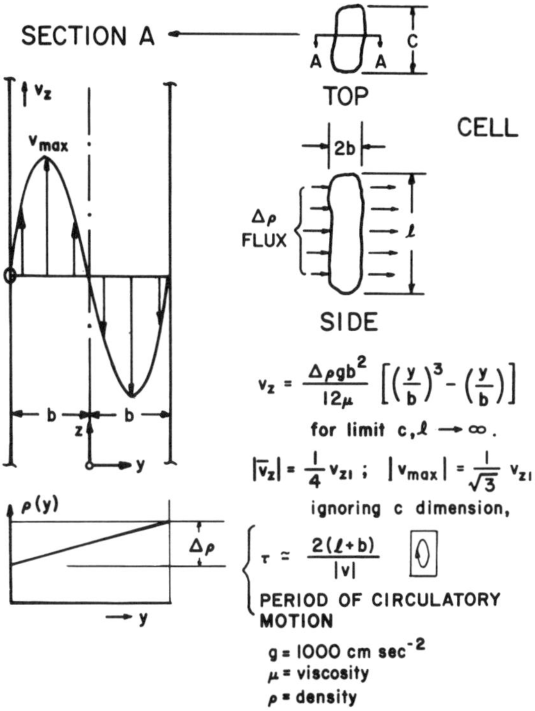

Fig. 7 Model for calculating convective transport velocity. The local velocity is v_z; the average velocity, determined by integration is $|\bar{v}_z|$; $v_{z1} = gb^2\Delta\rho/12\mu$. Section A is the schematic figure presented in Ref. 4. The density gradient is indicated below the section, and g is downward.

Assuming, for concreteness, that $\mu = 1$ cp. (as in Ref. 12; but Ref. 5 reports data for falling amyloplasts which imply viscosity values ranging from 5 to 200 cp), $g = 1000$ cm-sec^{-2}, $\Delta\rho = 0.1$ g-cm^{-3}, and $D = 10^{-6}$ cm^2-sec^{-1} (protein diffusion constants range from 0.7 to 12 x 10^{-7} cm^2-sec^{-1}; for sucrose in water, $D \approx 5 \times 10^{-6}$),[6] these equations result in

$$t_c = 5 \times 10^{-3} \ (\alpha/b) \text{ sec}$$

and

$$t_c/t_d = 5 \times 10^{-8} \ (1/\alpha b^3)$$

where $\alpha = \ell/b$ and b is in centimeters. If one further assumes that $\alpha = 10$ and $b = 10^{-3}$ cm = 10 μm, $t_c = 50$ sec

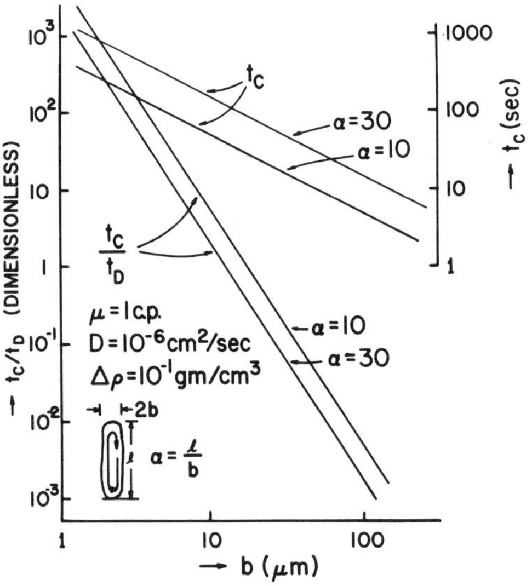

Fig. 8 Nomogram. Plot of convective transit time t_c (scale at right of figure) and the ratio of convective to diffusive transit times t_c/t_d vs cell dimension b and two choices of aspect ratio α.

and $t_c/t_d = 5$. Figure 8 has been constructed to provide a convenient graphical summary.

This model now must be tested with a realistic and representative set of α and b parameters. If cases can be found where $t_c/t_d \leqslant 1$ and t_c is of the order of a biological oscillation period one may infer that the model could have some applications.

Numerical Estimates

Geotropism has been correlated with the sedimentation of "statoliths" within certain cells of growing plants.[7,8] (The authors apologize to the many researchers whose work has been omitted from this short review. Summaries may be found in Refs. 5, 7, 8, 15, 21 and 22.) The causal chain remains obscure (see, for instance L. J. Audus, p. 137, Ref. 9, and p. 212, Ref. 10). It has been proven that the geotropic response requires intact root and shoot tips and that auxin transport is involved in at least some cases. A connection has been demonstrated between geotropism and the normal oscillations about the vertical axis of *Helianthus* hypocotyls (p. 35, Ref. 7). It seems likely that this effect involves turgor pressure variations[9] as well as growth effects. (Turgor pressure is the hydrostatic pressure in the sap of soft plant tissues.) The growth of reaction wood only in those appropriately stressed circumferential portions of woody plants which are not parallel to $\underline{g}$[8] implies that latent gravity sensors exist in nonapical active tissues, possibly the phloem sieve tubes or cells associated with them. Finally, geotropism is well known in *Phycomyces*,[10] a large single-cell organism (also see p. 65, Ref. 7).

The preceding catalogue of effects has been used in picking the examples listed in Table 1. The phloem sieve-tube dimensions are scaled from illustrations in a standard reference text.[12] Evidently, *Cucurbita* phloem exhibits a t_c/t_d range that seems outside the limits of this model; i.e. it is unlikely that g-mediated convection could compete with diffusion. Considering the well-known growth of that plant this result is reasonable. *Eucalyptus* and *Vitis*, on the other hand, are within range. *Vicia faba* root tip cell dimensions[13] exhibit a t_c/t_d value that seems out of line for the model presented here, unless the diffusivity to be entered into the equation relates to a macromolecule. Similar root-tip dimensions occur in *Lepidium sativum*.[5] The *Helianthus* hypocotyl lengths were approximately 4 cm overall. The data are the results of 24 measurements by A. Gibson. The t_c/t_d value is within range. t_c is much shorter than observed macroscopic geotropic reaction times (p. 35, Ref. 7).

The final entry in the table, *Phycomyces*, involves a much larger cell. It is difficult, from the literature (Refs. 10 and 11, and p. 65 of Ref. 7) to decide on the dimensions to be used in the calculation. The quoted figures result from the taking as 1 mm the order of magnitude of the length of the elongating portion of the stem. (The elongation occurs over 2-3 mm,[10] but is a strong function of the distance from the sporangium.) Other possible numerical choices of ℓ are indicated by the inequality signs.

The duration of the observed geotropic transient response is in the range 300 - 600 sec,[14] which compares well with the calculated value of 500 sec entered in Table 1. It may be necessary to include convection in the ambient atmosphere, which controls transpiration, to make a more valid comparison.

Table 1 Cell dimensions and transport times[a]

	α	b, cm^{-3}	t_c,sec	t_c/t_d
I) Phloem				
Cucurbita				
Immature	10	0.25	200	320
Mature	10	0.7	71	14
Eucalyptus	32	1	150	1.5
Vitis	16	2.5	32	0.2
II) Root cap				
Vicia faba	6.5	1	32.5	7.7
(various cell types)	12.7	0.9	70	5.4
	22	0.6	180	10.5
III) Hypocotyl, six days old, *Helianthus annuus*.				
Pith	4.3 to 9.4	3.9 ± .2	55 to 121	.019 to .009
Cortex	4.2 to 6.0	2.8 ± .5	75 to 107	.054 to .038
IV) Single cell				
Phycomyces	≥ 100	1	≥ 500	≤ 0.5

[a]See text for sources of dimensions. Equation parameters: $D = 10^{-6}$ cm^2-sec^{-1}, $\mu = 1.0$ cp, $\Delta\rho = 0.1$ g-cm^{-3}. Cell half-width = b; length = αb; t_c is the convection time for a cell half-perimeter; t_d is the diffusion time diagonally across the cell.

The calculation results summarized in Table 1 imply 1) that intracellular, gravitationally mediated convective transport may compete with diffusive transport in some types of cells of some plants; and 2) that there is no chance in many other cases. Summarized more simply, the numbers say that this type of convection can compete with diffusion only in sufficiently large cells; the size requirement is, however, not excessive. There is no evidence, in any case, that the geotropic mechanism must be identical in all cells; in fact, the evidence is to the contrary.[8]

Some Possible Consequences of g-Mediated Convective Transport

In what way might this type of convection be significant at some stage in the life cycle of a cell, a small group of cells, or a plant? To avoid subjunctive phrases, g-mediated convection will be assumed in the following discussion, along with the elongated cell geometry and asymmetric disposition of the gate and reactor organelles.

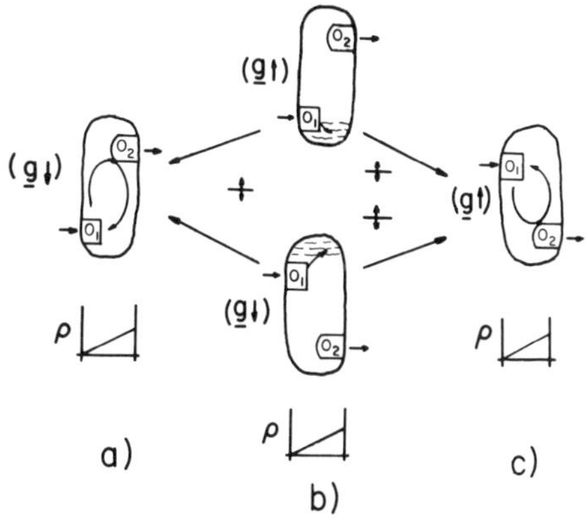

Fig. 9 g-determined polarity of transport processes and reflection symmetry. a) Standard configuration. 0_1 and 0_2 are controlled input and reactor/output organelles. The arrow indicates a convective supply/feedback loop. b) Either the position of the organelles (bottom figure) or the direction of g (top figure) has been reflected in the central plane. Convective transport stops and is replaced by sedimentation. c) Simultaneous reflection of the organelles and g restores convective transport. The transitions a) → b) and c) → b) are geotropic sensing mechanisms. If the organism containing the illustrated cell depends on convective transport in that cell, a) and c) represents polar transport.

A. Geotropism

1. Polarity. See Fig. 9 and its caption. The broken reflection symmetry is a qualitative geotropic sensor and possible morphogenetic determinant. The diagrams in Fig. 9 assume that, contrary to the model assumptions in the previous sections, S(1), the substance entering at O(1), reduces the density and drives the convective stream. If, as before, the density gradient is due to another substance that is not involved in the O(1) $\leftrightarrows$ O(2) sequence, a single reflection (Fig. 9b) has no effect on the process, and there is no polarity mechanism. In the latter case, polarity sensitivity is restored if the fundamental cellular process requires three cyclical sequential steps, $\rightarrow$ O(1) $\rightarrow$ O(2) $\rightarrow$ O(3) $\rightarrow$ O(1) $\rightarrow$. The practical application of this discussion concerns the difference between Clinostat and true freefall or zero-g experiments. The convective transport, nonlocal feedback theory presented here implies that there are cases where these methods are not equivalent. Experimentally observed cases of non-equivalence have been reported.[15]

2. Angular Dependence. If the long axis of a cell is slightly tilted with respect to g, the transport time t_c will change, whereas t_d remains invariant; there also may be mixing effects. This is a quantitative geotropic sensor.

3. Catastrophic Angular Dependence. If the long axis of the type of cell considered in this section is tilted until it is approximately orthogonal to g, there will be no convection, only density segregation. The threshold for Bénard convection (see Fig. 4) probably would not be reached. The elimination of convective control may be involved with the generation of reaction wood.

4. Statoliths. Any large objects interposed in the convective stream would tend to inhibit convection and/or to occlude one or another of the active organelles. The latter idea is, of course, not original.

B. Oscillations

The past decade has seen a steadily increasing rate of experimental and theoretical work on oscillatory biological and biochemical effects that occur, or may occur, on a microscopic continuum or cellular level. The focus of the more abstract investigations has been the search for complex chemical reaction schemes, usually involving one or more catalytic or autocatalytic steps, which exhibit more than one steady-state set of reaction coordinates. The latter condition results in the possibility of instabilities, oscillations, and bifurcations within a well-stirred reactor. The inclusion of diffusive source/sink conditions in the rate equations reduces the nonlinearity required in the chemical reaction scheme.[16,17]

Another type of research has concerned itself with the characteristics of oscillations that are actually observed in experiments and with their possible governing reaction schemes. In the case of glycolytic oscillations, for instance, there has been great progress, including the demonstration that the oscillation frequency can be entrained by a time-varying reactant supply.[18,19] A different type of investigation, of macroscopic mechanical oscillations, has been mentioned previously (see p. 35, Ref. 7). The *g*-mediated convective transport model discussed in this paper may be connected with cellular bio-oscillations as in the following.

1. Entrainment. If a naturally oscillating chemical reaction happens to take place in the organelle 0(2), and if the rate of convective supply of reactants is related to the *g*-mediated dimensional period t_c [or to $t_c t_d/(t_d + t_c)$], one may expect entrainment of reaction oscillations of the type reported by Hess et al.[18,19] If such an effect takes place it would be a "clock" where the "resonant element" is the transport circuit of the cell. This resonant element might prove to be less affected by temperature changes or slow variations of reactant concentrations than a well-stirred chemical reaction. On the other hand, variations in the *g* axis may result in substantial frequency changes. Frequency stability of a bio-clock may or may not be "desirable."

2. Convective Nonlinearity. Assume that a given oscillatory chemical reaction should occur for proper operation of some organism. If the chemical reaction that takes place is insufficiently nonlinear by itself, a convective transport supply term in the reactant rate equation(s) can produce the required nonlinearity. This can be seen from the fact that this additive term depends at least on $x_i g\Delta\rho \sim x_i(\underline{r})[x_j(\underline{r}') - \bar{x}_j]g$, where $\underline{r}$ and $\underline{r}'$ are spatial coordinates, x_i and x_j are concentrations of chemical species, i may or may not equal j, and $\bar{x}_j$ is an average value. This concept is very similar to the one involved in reaction-diffusion oscillations,[16] except that the nonlinearity introduced is of higher order.

3. Intrinsic Oscillations Due to Delayed Control. The *g*-mediated convection model presented here oscillates even

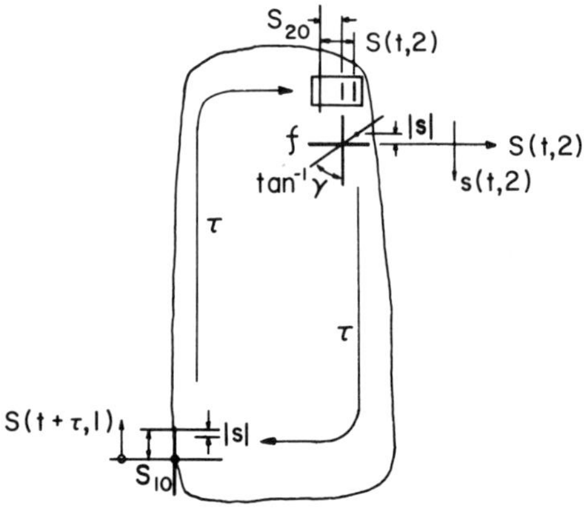

$$S(t,2) = S_{20} + S(t-\tau,1)$$
$$S(t,1) = S_{10} + s(t-\tau)$$
$$s(t) = -1/\gamma\left[S(t,2) - S_{20}\right]$$

Fig. 10 Model of time-delayed feedback controlled concentration oscillator. The control increment is $s(t)$, the input reference level is S_{10}, and the control level is S_{20}. The gate organelle $O(1)$ is in the lower left corner, $O(2)$ is in the upper right.

without any chemical reaction, if one assumes a time-delayed control circuit between $O(2)$ and $O(1)$. Assume that the substance S requires a time τ_1 to travel from $O(1)$ to $O(2)$ and that the control substance s requires an additional time τ_2 to reach the gate $O(1)$. Furthermore, let there be a controlling transfer function f, such that f regulates the input or export of S at $O(1)$, depending on some "conditions" at $O(2)$. For illustrative purposes, the simplest choice of the "condition" at $O(2)$ is the amount of S present there, and the simplest choice of f is linear, around a reference level. The location of the organelle possessing the transfer function property is chosen as $O(2)$. The transfer function communicates with $O(1)$ via s, which takes the place of the previously defined $S(2)$. For simplicity, $\tau_2 = \tau_1 =$ constant. Figure 10 summarizes the model.

The governing equations for S are

$$S(t,2) = S_{20} + S(t - \tau,1)$$

$$S(t,1) = S_{10} + s(t - \tau)$$

$$s(t) = -(1/\gamma)\left[S(t,2) - S_{20}\right]$$

where the second term in the parentheses indicates location, (i.e., $S(t - \tau,i)$ is $S(1)$ at location i, at time $t - \tau$), S_{20} and S_{10} are reference levels at $0(2)$ and $0(1)$, and $-(1/\gamma)$ is the absolute magnitude of the slope of the transfer function. These equations may be combined to give

$$S(t + 2\tau,2) = S_{10} + S_{20}(1 + 1/\gamma) - (1/\gamma)S(t,2)$$

and a similar equation for $S(t,1)$.

Assuming fixed τ and γ, the solutions of the equations are

$$S(t,2)=S_{20}+S_{10}(1+\frac{1}{\gamma})^{-1}+\gamma^{-t/2\tau}\sum_{0}^{\infty}\left\{A_n\cos\frac{(2n+1)\pi t}{2\tau}+B_n\sin\frac{(2n+1)\pi t}{2\tau}\right\}$$

$$S(t,1)=S_{10}(1+\frac{1}{\gamma})^{-1}+\gamma^{-(t-\tau)/2\tau}\sum_{0}^{\infty}\left\{A_n\sin\frac{(2n+1)\pi t}{2\tau}-B_n\cos\frac{(2n+1)\pi t}{2\tau}\right\}$$

If any perturbation is applied to the constant solution, $S(t,i)$ begins oscillations with unchanging amplitude for $\gamma = 1$, and growing or decaying amplitude for $\gamma < 1$ and $\gamma > 1$, respectively. The oscillation period of the fundamental wave is $T = 4\tau$. Such solutions also could have been obtained from two coupled first-order differential equations, but with less insight into the basic effect of the transport/control delay times.

Figure 11 illustrates a solution of this type but for the slightly more complex transfer function shown. This function was used to demonstrate both growing and stable behavior. The perturbation P was chosen so as to make all other aspects of the figure, and especially the phase plane diagram, as simple as possible. The basic oscillating behavior does not depend on the type of perturbation applied.

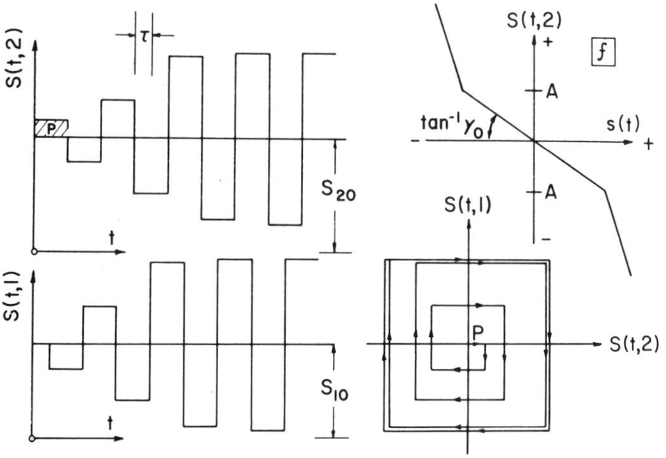

Fig. 11 Concentration oscillations resulting from time-delayed gate control. A transfer function f with segments of differing slopes relates S(t,2) to S(t,1) via the increment s(t). This particular f is used to illustrate growing oscillations at small amplitude and a stable cycle at larger ones. The phase plane diagram of S(t,1) vs S(t,2) also is shown. The perturbation P is applied to S(t,2) for a duration 2τ, i.e., two delay times. Before P, $S(t,2) = S_{20}$ and $S(t,1) = S_{10}$. The slope of the inner segment of f is γ_0.

The growing-amplitude case of the simplest model, with $\gamma < 1$, is of special interest. Evidently, at some stage the amplitude will be limited by "other effects," which, in this context, may be expected to have biological significance.

One may infer that, given suitable external reservoirs, the transport control time delays may serve to "drive" biological oscillators, eliminating the need for special oscillating chemical reactions. Since controlled gating effects are well known in biology (interplay of passive and active transport), this observation may be of considerable significance.

If a reaction, such as $-dS/dt = S/\tau'$, is included in the equations, solutions may still be found but their properties are much more complex. The solutions also oscillate in that case, as will be discussed elsewhere.[20]

Returning to the problem of indirect _g_ effects, the preceding discussion implies that in appropriate cases _g_ may have a remarkable effect. If indeed the transport delay time τ is equal to or related to t_c, the magnitude of g would enter into the determination of the biological oscillator frequency! Such an effect has been suggested by some experiments;[15a] its absence is inferred from others.[15c,23]

Johnsson's analysis of the geotropic response of sunflower hypocotyls in relation to their natural circumnutations about the vertical (p. 35, Ref. 7 and Ref. 23b) also involves a delay time, but in the very different context of the whole-plant response function. It is very interesting that his theory also gives $t_o = T/4$, where t_o is the overall delay and T is the period of natural oscillations. Furthermore, his experimental results indicate a similar relationship, with an offset to shorter times. Typical delay times were of the order of 30 min. It must be remembered, however, that t_o is averaged over many cells and cellular processes, it is the time delay between whole-plant stimulation and response, whereas the t_c and τ delays discussed in this paper involve one cell.

Summary

Some specific ways in which the presence or absence of gravity may affect the dynamics of living systems have been described. Most of the hypothetical model mechanisms presented depend on the indirect effects of convection in general; they therefore may have significance beyond the gravity-effects context. This may be summarized as follows:

1) The role of the gravitational field in the environment of organisms was discussed in terms of the static and dynamic collection and transport of nutrients and waste products. The frequently observed affinity of micro-organisms for surfaces, and the efficient growth of colonies thereon, may be related to their original evolution and their rate of metabolism in such an environment. The discussion of these effects was relatively short compared to the rest of the paper; it may, nevertheless, be of importance in arriving at fundamental insights relating to the processing or culture of biological materials under reduced gravity conditions.

2) The effect of gravitational convective mixing on chemical and biochemical kinetics was discussed.

3) A free-floating mechanical-chemical oscillator was described. In the biological context, the model may relate to vertical migrations of phytoplankton.

4) The well-known Bénard convection, driven by heat flux in the presence of gravity, was used to show that the co-presence of gravity and dissipation may result in a) system nonlinearity, b) symmetry breaking, c) the establishment of a time scale, d) the establishment of communication means within closed fluid systems, e) changes in the metabolism of organisms fixed to internal walls of the fluid container, and f) on-off g-direction sensors.

5) Using the idea of continuous convection, as in the case where there is a density gradient perpendicular to g, a model for a biochemical "cell" reactor was constructed. The model assumes that two (there could be more) organelles, with feedback, are active in chemical syntheses and the import and export of reactants. The relative magnitudes of diffusive and gravitationally convective transport times were calculated.

6) Table 1 gives the results of the foregoing cell model for the actual dimensions of various plant materials. The figures imply that convective transport may be more important than diffusive transport in some cases. Some of the calculated transport times are of reasonable magnitude. The case of *phycomyces* matches observations. The table suggests experiments relating cell parameters (dimensions, viscosity, chemical composition, etc.) with observed streaming or oscillating effects in intact systems.

7) Having shown that the numerical estimates for the convective cell reactor model are not unreasonable, geotropic sensing mechanisms were discussed. A mechanism for polarity suggests that experiments be done which search for differences between actual freefall and freefall simulated by time-averaging the direction of g in a Clinostat. Experiments quoted in the literature imply that such a difference indeed may exist. Further verification in controlled satellite experiments would tend to confirm the significance of g-mediated convection. Another experiment suggested in this part would involve a direct search for a convective g-sensor in the process of reaction-wood formation.

8) It was then shown that any convecting cell reactor with feedback may oscillate even in the absence of local chemical oscillations. This fact may be of general significance in biological systems. If the convection is wholly or partly g-mediated, one would expect the oscillation frequency of biological clocks in simple systems to depend on the direction and intensity of g. It is relatively easy to construct

clinostat or 0-g experiments to examine this conclusion, providing the "right" clock can be found. The model also predicts the relationship between the biological clock's period and the feedback/supply delay time within the cell.

References

[1]Levich, V. G. and Krylov, V. S., "Surface-Tension-Driven Phenomena," Annual Review of Fluid Mechanics, Vol. 1, Annual Reviews, Palo Alto, Calif., 1969, p. 293; also Ivanova, S. V. and Popel', A. S., "Motion of a Drop in a Viscous Liquid under the Action of an Insoluble Surface-Active Substance," Izvestiya Akademii Nauk SSSR, Mekhanika Zhidkosti i Gaza, March-April 1974, p. 63.

[2]Chandrasekhar, S., Hydrodynamic and Hydromagnetic Stability, Oxford University Press, London, 1961; also Koschmieder, E. L., "Bénard Convection," Advances in Chemical Physics, edited by I. Prigogine and S. A. Rice, Vol. 26, Wiley, New York, 1974, p. 177.

[3]Prigogine, I., Introduction to Thermodynamics of Irreversible Processes, third edition, Wiley, New York, 1967, pp. 126, 127.

[4]Bird, R. B., Stewart, W. E. and Lightfoot, E. N., Transport Phenomena, Wiley, New York, 1960, pp. 297 - 300.

[5]Larsen, P., "Gravity Sensing by Plants," Life Sciences and Space Research XI, COSPAR 1972, Akademie Verlag, Berlin, 1973, p. 141.

[6]Mahler, H. R. and Cordes, E. H., Biological Chemistry, Harper and Row, New York, 1966.

[7]Gordon, S. A., and Cohen, M. J., Gravity and the Organism, University of Chicago Press, Chicago, Ill., 1971.

[8]Leopold, A. C., and Kriedemann, P. E., Plant Growth and Development, McGraw-Hill, New York, 1975.

[9]Scheld, H. W., private communication, March 1976.

[10]Bergman, K., Burke, P. V., Cerdá-Olmedo, E., David, C. N., Delbrück, M., Foster, K. W., Goodell, E. W., Heisenberg, M.,

Meissner, G., Zalokar, M., Dennison, D. S., and Shropshire, W., "Phycomyces," Bacteriological Reviews, Vol. 33, March 1969, p. 99.

[11]Tobias, C. A., Risius, J., and Yang, C.-H., "Biophysical Considerations Concerning Gravity Receptors and Effectors Including Experimental Studies on Phycomyces Blakesleeanus," Life Sciences and Space Research XI, COSPAR 1972, Akademie Verlag, Berlin 1973, p. 127.

[12]Esau, K., Plant Anatomy, Wiley, New York, 1965.

[13]Jensen, W. A., "Morphological and Biochemical Analysis of the Early Phases of Cellular Growth in the Root Tip of Vicia Faba," Experimental Cell Research, Vol. 8, June 1955, p. 506.

[14]Dennison, D. S., "Tropic Responses of Phycomyces Sporangiophores to Gravitational and Centrifugal Stimuli," Journal of General Physiology, Vol. 45, September 1961, p. 23.

[15]a) Gordon, S. A., "Effect of Free Fall on Higher Plants," Life Sciences and Space Research XI, COSPAR 1972 , Akademie Verlag, Berlin, 1973, p. 155; b) Brown, A. H., Chapman, D. K., and Liu, S. W. W., "A Comparison of Leaf Epinasty Induced by Weightlessness or by Clinostat Rotation," BioScience, Vol. 24, September 1974, p. 517; c) Brown, A. H., Dahl, A. O., and Chapman, D. K., "Morphology of Arabidopsis Grown under Chronic Centrifugation and on the Clinostat," Plant Physiology, Vol. 57, March 1976, p. 358; d) Brown, A. H., Dahl, A. O., and Chapman, D. K., "Limitation on the Use of the Horizontal Clinostat as a Gravity Compensator," preprint, NASA Contractor's Report NULTST-1, August 1975.

[16]Goldbeter, A., and Caplan, S. R., "Oscillatory Enzymes," Annual Review of Biophysics and Bioengineering, Vol. 5, Annual Reviews, Palo Alto, Calif., 1976, p. 449; also Chance, B., Ghosh, A. K., Hess, B., and Pye, E. K., Biological and Biochemical Oscillators, Academic Press, New York 1973.

[17]Glansdorff, P., and Prigogine, I., Thermodynamic Theory of Structure, Stability and Fluctuations, Wiley-Interscience, London, 1971.

[18]Boiteux, A., Goldbeter, A., and Hess, B., "Control of Oscillating Glycolysis of Yeast by Stochastic, Periodic, and Steady Source of Substrate: A Model and Experimental Study," Proceedings of the National Academy of Sciences, USA, Vol. 72, October 1975, p. 3829.

[19]Hess, B., "Oscillations in Biochemical and Biological Systems," Bulletin of the Institute of Mathematics and Its Applications, Vol. 12, January 1976, p. 6.

[20]Kessler, J. O., "Time Delay Oscillators in Bio-Systems" (In preparation).

[21]Hoshizaki, T., "Influence of Gravitational Forces on Plants," Environmental Biology and Medicine, Vol. 2, No. 2, 1973, p. 47.

[22]Juniper, B. E., "Geotropism," Annual Review of Plant Physiology, Vol. 27, Annual Reviews, Palo Alto, Calif., 1976, p. 385.

[23]a) Brown, A. H. and Chapman, D. K., "Nutations of Sunflower Seedlings on Tilted Clinostats," preprint, NASA Contractor's Report NUTANG-1, June 1976; also b) Brown, A. H. and Chapman, D. K., "Effects of increased g-Force on Nutation of Sunflower Hypocotyls," preprint, NASA Contractor's Report NUTFOG 2, July 1976.

DROP DYNAMICS IN SPACE

T.G. Wang,* M.M. Saffren,* and D.D. Elleman*

Jet Propulsion Laboratory, California Institute of Technology, Pasadena, Calif.

Abstract

Experiments to study the dynamics of liquid drops are being planned to be performed in the weightless environment of Spacelab. The liquids will range from superfluid helium through ordinary liquid to molten metals and glasses. The experiments will be conducted in a chamber now being developed which utilizes the forces and torques produced by acoustic waves excited within the chamber. None of the currently available facilities (drop towers, sounding rockets, or zero-g aircraft flights) can provide a sustained weightless environment, since the resulting zero-g periods are from 3 sec. to 5 min. Spaceflight, however, will provide weightlessness for periods of one week, or more, allowing truly laboratory-like experiments to be conducted on free liquid drops and bubbles. In this paper we discuss both the drop dynamics experiments proposed for Spacelab and the acoustic chamber: its operation and current testing for these and other experiments.

I. Drop Rotation and Oscillation Phenomena (DROP) Experiment

A. Introduction

The theory of the dynamics of a free drop has been well studied in the approximation that dynamic quantities deviate linearly from a resting drop. With special exceptions to be discussed below, there is no nonlinear theory of the dynamics of a fluid drop. Not only are definitive experiments for the

---

Presented as Paper D.4.3 at the COSPAR Symposium on Materials Sciences in Space, Philadelphia, Pa., June 9-10, 1976. The authors wish to thank I. Rudnick (UCLA) and D.J. Collins, P.V. Mason, E.E. Olli (all of the Jet Propulsion Laboratory) for their excellent help and suggestions.

*Senior Scientist.

large-amplitude behavior of fluid drops lacking, but there are few definitive experiments even for linear behavior. This is a consequence of the limitations involved in conducting experiments in an Earth laboratory, including insufficient droplet sizes for accurate observation and perturbing effects due to the method of suspending the droplets.

The proposed drop dynamics experiments will utilize the unique zero-g environment provided by the orbiting Space Shuttle to investigate the dynamics of a free drop. The results of the proposed experiments will be used to verify existing theory and to provide insight for further theoretical development. The deficiencies of the existing theory, which disregards viscosity, internal flows, virtual mass, and other parameters, are exemplified by the differing results of Plateau's system of two immiscible fluids[1] and the Skylab science demonstrations.[2] A more detailed description of these two experiments is given in Sec. II. Aside from fundamental interest, a better physical understanding of the behavior of the dynamics of free liquid spheroids is required in many areas of science and technology.

B. Scientific Objectives

1. Equilibrium Figures of a Rotating Drop. A rotating fluid in its equilibrium state can sustain no internal flow and therefore rotates as a rigid body. When subject to gravity and contained in a vessel, at any angular velocity, the free liquid interface (meniscus) assumes a parabolic shape. When free from gravity and the host medium, however, the fluid mass can assume various shapes (axisymmetric, triaxial, or multi-lobed), depending on the angular velocity. The proposed experiments will determine the stable equilibrium shape of a rotating drop of fluid as a function of its angular velocity, as well as the angular velocities at which there is a qualitative change of drop shape (the bifurcation points) and the critical angular velocity at which the rotating drop fissions. A more detailed listing of experiment objectives will follow.

Theories on the equilibrium shapes of rotating fluids began in the 17th century with Newton's[3] investigations on the shape of the rotating earth. The extensive theory that developed postulated that a rotating fluid is held together by self-gravitation. Plateau, however, in observing ordinary rotating fluid drops suspended in a neutral buoyancy tank and held together by their surface tension, found that his experiments were in rough qualitative agreement with the theory of that time, except for one remarkable difference: one of the stable configurations for a rotating drop was toroidal, which was not generally thought to be an equilibrium shape for a self-gravitating drop. That it is, in fact, an equilibrium figure for rotating liquid drops held together by surface tension was shown theoretically more than seventy years later when Rayleigh[4] and Appell[5] investigated droplets symmetric about the rotation axis. The stability of the simple axisymmetric shapes awaited study by Chandrasekhar[6] and even today the stability of the toroidal and nonaxisymmetric shapes remains virtually unexplored both theoretically and experimentally.

Observation of the behavior of a rotating drop held together by surface tension goes beyond simply testing the existing theory. This theory has in fact been embedded in a grander theory which at one extreme embraces fluid masses held together by their gravity, modeling the stars, and at the other extreme embraces uniformly electrically-charged fluid masses, modeling atomic nuclei[7]. Consequently, any deviation in the observed behavior of ordinary liquid drops from their predicted behavior would call into question the more all-embracing theory of equilibrium figures of fluid masses. Conversely, agreement between observed behavior and theoretical predictions would suggest strongly a unified theory of the dynamics of fluid masses. The observed behavior of ordinary liquid drops then would help to frame the theory of their dynamics, and this theory, in turn, could be extended into the astronomical and nuclear realms. This is one of the ultimate aims of the two proposed sets of experiments. The experiments on rotation and oscillation are precursors to future experiments in which the oscillation of rotating drops will be studied and in which the drops are electrically charged, electrically conducting, dielectric, non-Newtonian, or superfluid; and where external fields are applied (electric, magnetic, electromagnetic, acoustic, or thermal). In addition, it is envisaged that multiple-drop experiments will be performed in which the interactions of free drops can be observed, and these experiments will be based, of course, on what has been learned previously about single-drop behavior in externally controlled fields.

The following discussion presents the current theory of the equilibrium shapes of a rotating fluid drop held together by its surface tension. Rayleigh[4] was the first to calculate the axially symmetric equilibrium shapes. These calculations were extended by Appel,[5] who presented a more detailed and elegant description, thus opening the discussion of the dynamics of the shape change and the stability of these shapes. Chandrasekhar[6] made a definitive study of the stability of the simply connected axisymmetric shapes and, in addition, obtained the frequencies of their small-amplitude oscillations. Ross[8,9] extended the previous work on drops to "bubbles": fluid drops less dense than the surrounding medium. Gans[10] has examined the small-amplitude oscillations about equilibrium shapes of compressible fluids. The equilibrium shape of a drop containing a bubble was discussed by Bauer and Siekmann,[11] whereas Bohme et al. studied the shape of a rotating dielectric drop in an electric field.[12] Finally, Swiatecki,[7,13] by inserting the theory of the equilibrium shapes of surface-tension drops into the more general theory, was able to give a fairly complete semiquantitative description of the stability of shapes for

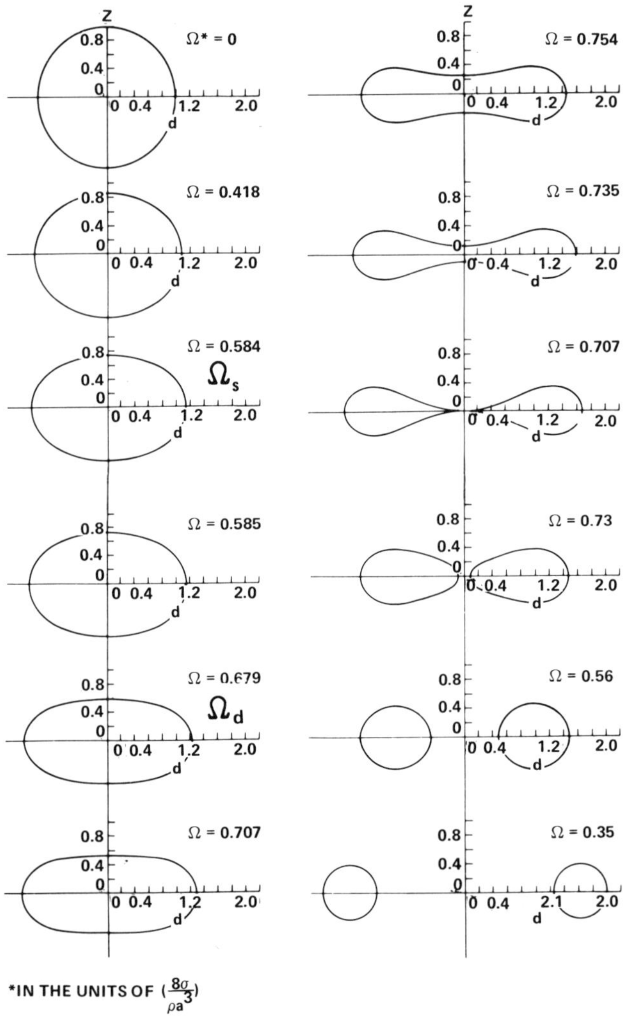

Fig. 1 Axisymmetric equilibrium shapes (to pinch-off).

such drops as a function of their angular momentum, including a discussion of metastable shapes that he calls "saddle-point" shapes.

The axisymmetric equilibrium shapes (see Fig. 1) are described conveniently as a function of the dimensionless angular velocity measured in units of the fundamental oscillation frequency of the resting drop $\Omega = \omega/(8\sigma/\rho a^3)^{1/2}$, where ω is the rotational angular velocity, σ is the surface tension, a is the equatorial radius, and ρ is the density. When $\Omega<0.7071$, there are always two equilibrium shapes; the one of lower energy is simply connected, whereas the other is toruslike. For $\Omega = 0.7070$, there appears an additional "collapsed" shape in which zero thickness at the center yields a "figure-eight" cross section. For $0.7071<\Omega<0.73$, there are two toruslike shapes but still two simply connected shapes. When $\Omega = 0.73$, there is only one toruslike shape but still two simply connected shapes. (Appell[5] and Ross[8] disagree on the number of toroidal shapes for $\Omega<0.7071$.) The toruslike shapes are lost once $\Omega> 0.73$, and when $\Omega = 0.7540$ there remains only one simply connected shape; this is the greatest angular velocity that an axisymmetric equilibrium shape can have.

The only detailed study of the stability of the equilibrium figures was made by Chandrasekhar[6] but only for the simply connected shapes. He showed that for $\Omega = 0.584$ the drop can deform, without changing its energy, to another shape not having rigid body rotation; thus the original shape is unstable. He presumes that the stable equilibrium shapes become nonaxisymmetric for $\Omega = 0.584$. This presumption is based on an analogy with what is known to occur for a liquid mass held together by self-gravitation. There the stable equilibrium figures are true ellipsoids below a critical angular velocity and triaxial ellipsoids above.

As shown in Fig. 2, at $\Omega = 0.584$ (the bifurcation point), the secular stability passes from the sequence of axisymmetri-

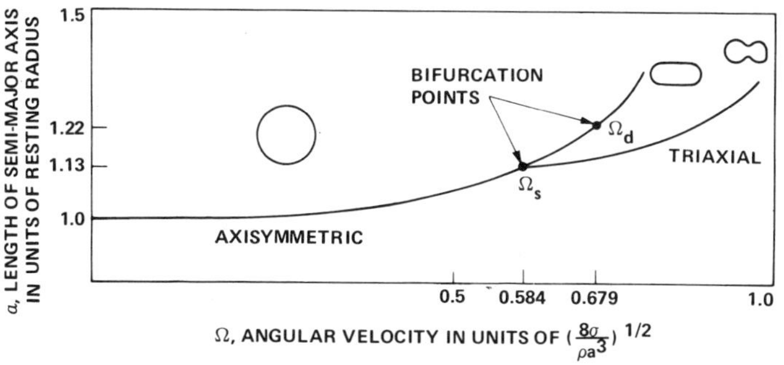

Fig. 2 Bifurcation points.

cal shapes to triaxial shapes. Berringer and Knox[14] have calculated that for the surface-tension drops the triaxial shapes are not ellipsoids, but the stability of the toroidal shapes has received no definitive treatment. However, the results of Wong[15] on the toroidal shapes of charged liquid drops suggests that these equilibrium shapes may be "saddle-shapes": shapes stable against deformations that preserve the axial symmetry but unstable against others, such as varicose deformations, against which fluid jets are unstable (the Rayleigh instability). The triaxial equilibrium saddle-shapes were calculated by Pik-Pichak.[16]

The neutral buoyancy experiments of Plateau[1] on the shapes of rotating liquid drops are in qualitative accord with the transition from axisymmetric to triaxial shape as described theoretically by Chandrasekhar.[6] However, Plateau showed that at high angular velocity the drop first rotates nonrigidly, and a toroidal shape then is obtained which becomes a rigidly rotating figure, indicating that the toroidal shape is indeed stable. However, this conclusion was called into question by very recent experiments by the authors at JPL which showed that, if the drop is of the less viscous fluid rather than the more viscous as it was in Plateau's original experiment, the toroidal shape is not stable, pinching off as does a liquid jet.

The Skylab experiments on rotating drops[2] yielded the "pinched" triaxial shapes resembling "dog-bones." In one experiment a dog-bone shape fissioned; it was not clear if this was a result of the particular dog-bone being a saddle-point shape, or if it was the result of an internal flow or slight oscillation within a stable shape close to the limit of stability which may have converted it to a saddle-shape when the extra energy was added to the rigid body's fluid motion.

It is very important to note that Plateau's and JPL's systems of two immiscible fluids and the Skylab experiments yielded different results at the same angular velocities. The immiscible systems showed both axisymmetric and non-axisymmetric instabilities; i.e., toroidal, "curlicue", and multi-lobed shapes. The Skylab experiment, however, showed only the one non-axisymmetric instability, the dog-bone shape. On the other hand, the results were reversed in experiments on cylindrical liquid columns rotating about their axes. Neutral buoyancy experiments carried out by Carruthers[17] showed the instability of such columns always to be axisymmetric, whereas the Skylab experiment on rotating liquid columns showed the instabilities to be non-axisymmetric[17]. However, the axisymmetric instabilities were recovered on Skylab once the fluid was made sufficiently viscous.

Observation of the "curlicue" shapes in the laboratory may have been due to the effect of "added mass" (also know as virtual mass or hydrodynamic mass); i.e., in an immiscible system, a triaxial drop nonaxisymmetric about the rotation axis will entrain adjacent portions of the surrounding liquid (Fig. 3). The consequence of this added mass is to modify the pressure drop severely across the droplet interface. In the limit that the adjacent fluid moves rigidly with the droplet, the pressure drop vanishes since the density difference of the two fluids vanishes. In this extreme, the portions of the droplet that extend into the added fluid will tend to assume a spherical shape to minimize the surface energy. (See Fig. 3.)

In weightlessness, the added mass effect becomes negligible because the ratio of the density of two fluids can be chosen to be three orders of magnitude less than unity. Thus, it appears that viscosity and virtual (added) mass effects strongly limit the validity of neutral buoyancy experiments. In fact, their effects on the flows in rotating fluids may make otherwise stable shapes unstable, and vice versa (e.g., the "spin-up" effect associated with Ekman boundary layers).[18] These problems can be studied experimentally only in the true weightlessness afforded by space flight where the viscosity and the density differences of the two liquids can be chosen freely.

2. Large-Amplitude Oscillation of a Liquid Drop. In contrast to the problem of a rotating drop, a reasonably complete theoretical formulation of small-amplitude dynamics of freely suspended liquid drops under the influence of surface tension forces has been well developed.[19-24] An extensive review of the theoretical work has been given by Chandrasekhar, and a large variety of experimental tests have been conducted to verify and support this theoretical work. The experimental procedures fall into three general categories: the liquid drop is suspended in a neutral buoyant media; the drop is supported

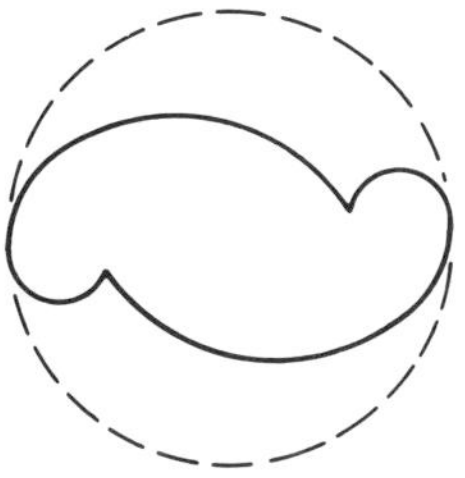

Fig. 3 "Curlicue" shape. The solid lines indicate the shape obtained by Plateau and JPL. The dotted lines suggest the "boundaries" of the added host liquid.

by a vertical gas flow; or the drop falls through a gas or vacuum. All of these methods suffer various limitations that have made a detailed quantitative comparison of theory and experiment limited in scope.

At the present time, there is no adequate theory for large-amplitude oscillations of liquid drops, nor have the criteria for rupture or coalescence of liquid masses and the transition region between the high-viscosity and low-viscosity regions been developed. However, Foote[25] and Alsonso[26] have simulated with computer calculations the motion of a drop undergoing large amplitude oscillation.

In 1879, Lord Rayleigh conducted one of the first investigations on the behavior of an oscillating liquid drop about its spherical equilibrium shape. He limited his study to the case where the oscillations were axisymmetric and assumed that the internal motions were described by a potential flowfield. He did not include viscous effects. The results of Rayleigh's investigations can be expressed by a series of expansion of Legendre polynominals:

$$r = a_0 + \Sigma a_n P_n (\cos \theta) \tag{1}$$

where r is the radial coordinate, ρ is the polar angle measured from the pole of the drop, and the coefficients a_n are functions of time. In solving for a_n in Eq. (1), it is necessary to limit the oscillations to small amplitudes, $a_n << a_0$. It can be shown that, if $a_n \cong \cos \omega_n t$, then $\omega_n^2 = n(n-1)(n+2)$ $(\sigma/\rho a^3)$, where σ is the surface tension, ρ is the density of the liquid, and a is the equilibrium spherical radius. Note that n=0 and n=1 correspond to rigid body motions. The fundamental mode of oscillation is given by n = 2. The period for the fundamental mode is given by $\tau_2 = 2\pi\sqrt{\rho a^3/8\sigma}$. For a 2.5-cm-diam water drop where ρ = 1 g/cm^3 and σ = 75 dyn/cm, the period would be τ_2 = 0.36 sec for the fundamental mode, τ_3 = 0.19 for n=3, and τ_4 = 0.12 for n=4.

Foote[25] has made extensive computer calculations of Rayleigh's equation and has dropped the restriction of the calculations to small amplitudes. The results of Foote's calculations are shown in Fig. 4 for the cases of n=2, 3, and 4. In all cases, the drop is started in motion at time T=0 in the deformed shape with the internal flows at zero. The time is measured in units of π rad, so that at T=1 the drop has gone through one-half of a cycle. Even at large amplitudes, the calculated shape of the drop appears to have the approximate shape observed in experiments.[25] A detailed comparison with

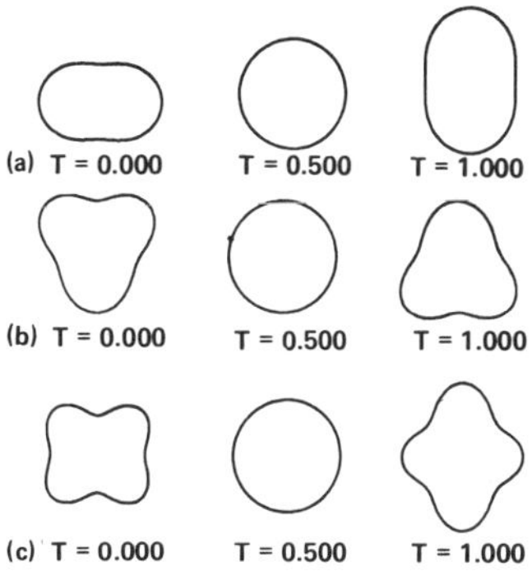

Fig. 4 Fundamental modes of oscillation. (The axial ratio is 1.7 at the maximum distortion.) a) n=2; b) n=3; c) n=4 .

experimental data[25] is not possible because the quality of the data is limited by the experimental techniques that are now available. It also should be pointed out that the Rayleigh solutions are probably true only for amplitudes corresponding to T from 0.375 to 0.625.[25]

In the analysis that has been discussed so far, viscous effects have not been included. Lamb[20] has shown that for small viscosity the only effect on the oscillating spherical drop is the gradual damping of the amplitude of the oscillation. The normal mode frequency is not affected by the viscosity. The decay of the amplitude A can be shown to be given by $A = A_0 e^{-\beta_n t}$, where A_0 is the initial amplitude of the oscillation of the drop and β_n is given by $\beta_n = [(n-1)(2n+1)\nu]/a^2$, where ν is the kinematic viscosity of the liquid, and a is the radius of the drop. For a drop of water 2.5 cm in diameter with $\nu = 0.014$ cm^2/sec oscillating in fundamental mode n = 2, then $\beta = 0.045$. Thus, a free oscillating drop would decay to 1% of its initial amplitude in 102 sec.

Chandrasekhar[24] has shown that aperiodically damped motion of the drop is possible for the fundamental mode if $\omega_n a^2/\nu$ is less than 3.69 cm^2/sec. Therefore, a drop 0.023 cm in radius or smaller would experience aperiodic motion. Prospertti[27] has found that a drop that is initially critically damped should have an aperiodic decay for a short time and a damped oscillation motion at a later time. He implies that the effective damping factor first increases and then decreases with time. These predictions have yet to be verified by experiment.

In contrast to the case of small viscosity where ω_n is independent of viscosity, Happel[23] and Chandrasekhar[24] have shown that, for a system controlled by gravitational forces, as $\nu \to \infty$ the normal-mode oscillation can be given by $\omega = \omega_n^2 \, [(2_n + 1)/2(n-1)(2n^2+4n+3)] \, (a^2/\nu)$, where a is the radius of the sphere, and ν is the kinematic viscosity.

Foote has noted from his computer calculations that the drop spends more time in the prolate configuration than in the oblate (57% vs 43%). Montgomery[28] has made vertical wind-tunnel measurements on drops and has observed a similar behavior. However, it is not clear how much effect the air streaming around the drop has on this unequal distribution of time in the prolate and oblate shapes. The calculations show that at small amplitudes the drop spends an equal amount of time in the two configurations.

Another feature of the computer calculations is that the period of oscillation is not constant with large-amplitude oscillations but shows an increase in the period as the amplitude is increased. For a large oscillation in which the ratio of major to minor axis is 1.7, the fundamental frequency increases approximately 9% for an ellipsoidal drop. If the calculation is done for a Rayleigh-shaped drop, the predicted increase is about 5%.

Montgomery's[28] experiments on small drops agrees qualitatively with these computer calculations. The computations show a rather smooth change in the increase of the period with increasing amplitude of the oscillation. The calculations do not account for any turbulent flow within the drop which one might expect to find at large-amplitude oscillations. This turbulent flow might manifest itself as a break in the curve of period vs. amplitude as one enters the turbulent flow region.

As the drop oscillations grow to larger amplitudes, a point is reached when drop fission is possible. A considerable amount of theoretical work on charged drops has been stimulated by nuclear physicists' attempts to model nuclear fission with the behavior of a charged drop. Diehl[29] has calculated the ternary fission for the liquid-drop model and has shown that there are two modes of fission, the prolate mode that has axial symmetry and the oblate mode. Alonso[26] has calculated the binary fission case and finds that the neck connecting the two sections becomes very elongated and eventually develops a long thin neck that will not pinch off until it has extended to virtually no width. It has been hypothesized that the pinch-off actually is initiated by a surface fluctuation in the neck. Thompson and Swiatecki conducted a neutral buoyant experiment on polarized drops and observed the thin-necking. In addition, from their data it appeared that the drop attempted fission in the prolate ternary mode.

The liquid drop can undergo another type of oscillation that has received little attention to date. That is the so-called running wave, which for the fundamental frequency is the superposition of fundamental oscillations along the x and y axes $\pi/2$ out of phase with one another. A careful investigation of film taken by the astronauts on Skylab of oscillating drops seems to indicate that this type of oscillation indeed was stimulated. A more detailed investigation of this type of behavior is needed, particularly in the large-amplitude regions. One then could determine if the running wave is still a superimposition of the fundamental modes.

As one can see, there has been extensive theoretical work done on small-amplitude oscillation and a considerable number of computer calculations on large-amplitude oscillations and fission processes. Unfortunately, the experimental work needed to back up these calculations, even though extensive, has been limited by various experimental constraints.

The experimental techniques used to date fall into four general categories. The first technique is the suspension of a liquid drop in a viscous neutral buoyant medium.[30-34] However, the energy dissipation mechanism for a droplet oscillating within another fluid of appreciable density has been shown by Miller and Scriven[30] to be significantly different from the case in which the second fluid has negligible density. Also, it was pointed out by Park and Crosby[35] that the interfacial tension is modified by the presence of the second medium.

The second technique involves the suspension of a liquid droplet in gas currents or electrical fields.[28] Unfortunately, experiments with droplets in air or electrical fields generally have been limited to drop sizes in the millimeter diameter range, where it has been difficult to obtain accurate quantitative information for comparison with hydrodynamic theory.[35] In addition, the oscillations in a column of gas supporting the drop may create forced vibrations in the drop.[33]

The third technique involves drops in free-fall through a gas or vacuum, such as the experiments carried out in the NASA MSFC 400-ft drop tower. These experiments have shown that it is possible to obtain accurate data on shap oscillations of liquid masses deployed in sizes in the centimeter to several centimeter diameter range when the liquids are deployed under carefully controlled conditions with relatively low internal vorticities[36]. Unfortunately, good quantitative resolution in terms of fundamental modes has not been obtained because of the very short (3-sec) experiment times available.

Recently, Skylab astronauts have demonstrated the capability of performing drop dynamics experiments in space. Although

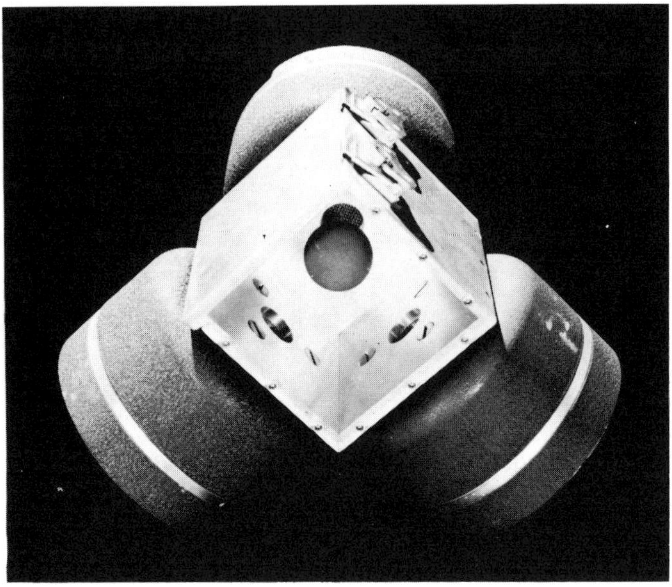

Fig. 5 Acoustic chamber.

those experiments were carried out in uncontrolled and unrestrained conditions, the results already have stimulated a great deal of interest both in the scientific community and in the public.[2] This discussion emphasizes the need for a quantitative experiment on oscillation of drops which is free from all of the defects just mentioned.

II. Apparatus

Figure 5 shows one of the laboratory prototypes of the triaxial acoustical levitation resonance chamber[37] which will be used to position and control large liquid drops in zero-g environments. The chamber itself is nearly cubical, with inside dimensions of 11.43 x 11.43 x 12.70 cm, which are the x, y, and z faces, respectively. Three acoustic drivers are fixed rigidly to the center of three mutually perpendicular faces of the chamber. During operation of the chamber, each driver excites the lowest-order standing wave along the direction that the driver faces. In a resonant mode, the ambient pressure is maximum at the nodes of the velocity wave and minimum at the antinodes. Consequently, there is a tendency for introduced liquids and particles to be driven toward the antinodes, where they collect and remain until excitation ceases.

Calculation of the acoustic pressure on the drop is simplified by the fact that the characteristic impedance of the liquid $\rho_\ell c_\ell$ is very much greater than that of the gas ρc: $\rho_\ell c_\ell$ ($\sim 10^5$ cgs)/ρc ($\sim$40 cgs)/$\simeq 10^3$ where ρ_ℓ and ρ are the density of liquid and gas, respectively, and c_ℓ and c are the sound velocity of liquid and gas, respectively. Because of this impedence mismatch, the acoustic power in the drop is three orders of magnitude smaller than in the gas and is negligible. This simplifies the expression for the radiation pressure $\langle \Delta P \rangle$, which is time-independent and is given at the boundary by

$$\langle \Delta P \rangle = \overline{(P^2/2\rho c^2)} - (1/2)\rho\ \overline{(\vec{U}^2)} \quad (2)$$

where P is the excess acoustic pressure, $\vec{U}$ is the gas particle velocity, and the bar over a quantity denotes the time average of the quantity. Eq. (2) is the Bernoulli equation,[37-39] which gives the acoustical perturbation on the ambient pressure from its quiescent value.

The pressure profile in our system can be derived as follows. The velocity potential ϕ of the wave in the chamber can be expressed as

$$\phi = \phi \cos(k_x x)e^{i\omega_x t} + \phi_y \cos(k_y y)e^{i\omega_y t} + \phi_z \cos(k_z z)e^{i\omega_z t},$$

where $\phi_{x,y,z}$ are the complex velocity potential amplitudes of standing waves of frequency $\omega_{x,y,z}$ and wave number $k_{x,y,z}$. The particle velocity U, by definition, is $\vec{U} = \nabla\phi$. The pressure is given by $P = -\rho\dot{\phi}$. Figure 6 shows the resulting expression [Eq. (2)] for the radiation pressure with only one of the three

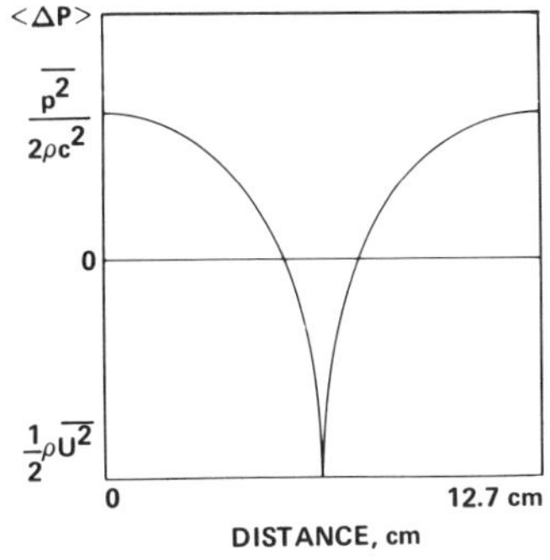

Fig. 6 Theoretical pressure profile in the chamber. $\langle \Delta P \rangle = \overline{P^2}/2\rho c^2 - (1/2)\rho\,\overline{U^2}$, where $P = P_0 \cos(kx)e^{i\omega t}$ and $U = U_0 \sin(kx)e^{i\omega t}$.

drivers on ($\phi_x = \phi_y = 0$). The node is a plane ($z = \ell_z/2$), becoming a point when all three are turned on. The profile of Fig. 6 has been verified experimentally. Because this is a three-dimensional system with independent control on each dimension, it has a great deal of versatility. It can position a drop acoustically and then manipulate it; for example, it can induce drop oscillation and/or rotation.

III. Operation of the Chamber

A. Rotation and Oscillation Experiments

In the following discussion, we discuss the operating characteristics of the acoustic chamber necessary to perform rotation and oscillation experiments. Assume that the sample to be studied is a 1.25-cm-radius (a) water droplet, the residual acceleration is 10^{-1} cm/sec^2 (10^{-4} g), and the quality factor (Q) (defined as $\omega/2\Delta\omega$) of the acoustic chamber is ~25:

1) Newton's equation for the motion of a water drop in an acoustic pressure field is $\int\langle\Delta P\rangle\, n_x\, dA = \rho_\ell\cdot 10^{-4}g\cdot(4/3)\pi a^3$. In the limit of ka << 1, this has been calculated by King[40] to be $(P^2/2\rho c^2)\sin 2\,kx\cdot 2\pi a^3\cdot k\cdot(5/6) = \rho_\ell\cdot(4/3)\pi a^3\cdot 10^{-4}g$. For a sphere 2.5-cm diam, and of density 1 g/cm^3, the corresponding minimum acoustic pressure required to position the drop is $P \simeq 10^3$ dyn/cm^2 $\simeq$ 134 dB, where the decibels are measured against the reference effective pressure (2×10^{-4} dyn/cm^2). For a 50% efficient compression driver, less than 0.2 W of electrical power is needed to provide the required acoustic pressure. It is worth pointing out that, at this acoustic pressure level, the surface tension force (F_s) that acts on the water drop is two orders of magnitude larger than the acoustic force (F_A): $F_s/F_A = (\sigma\cdot 2\pi r)/(\int\langle\Delta P\rangle\cdot\hat{n}_x\cdot dA) \sim 100$.

2) If the amplitude of the foregoing 134-dB acoustic wave is modulated at a given frequency ω_0, the drop experiences a modulated force $F_0 = \int\langle\Delta P\rangle\, n_x\, dA$ = (~1 dyn). When ω_0 matches the normal oscillation modes of the drop given by $\omega_n^2 = n(n-1)(n+2)(\sigma/\rho a^3)$, the amplitude A of the oscillation, assuming potential flow inside the drop, can be as large as $|A| = |F_0/(i\omega_0 M_\ell\cdot\beta_n)|$ = (~1 cm), where β_n is the damping constant of the nth mode of the drop, and M_ℓ is the mass of the drop. Since the drop radius itself is 1.25 cm, this modulation force is sufficient to drive the drop into large-amplitude oscillation at least at the fundamental frequency. However, a higher power modulation is required for higher modes because of the increase in damping. That there is, in fact, sufficient power to do this has been demonstrated in KC-135 flights, where the prototype was able to shatter a water drop of 1.25-cm

radius in less than 1 sec while operating at the fundamental frequency.

3) If the phase between the two orthogonal 134-dB waves on the x and y axes is locked with 90^0 phase shift, this will produce a torque that spins the drop. In the asymptotic limit, the drop will achieve a rotational velocity of 23 rad/sec, exceeding the maximum rotational velocity (10.1 rad/sec) required for this experiment. However, in order to spin up the drop at a constant acceleration, the acoustic power must ramp up as the square root of the rate. The power setting and the rate of increase will have to be determined after the liquid has been selected. We have demonstrated the rotation capability in our laboratory with a 1.25-cm radius styrofoam ball levitated in a 155-dB sound field, as presented in Fig. 7. Spinning up of a 1-cm-diam water droplet also has been shown in KC-135 flights.

B. Operation of the Chamber at Extreme Temperatures

Experiments to be performed in future space flights, will be extended beyond those on room-temperature droplets. These future experiments will require the manipulation and control of liquid helium droplets and of molten metal droplets and glass. In this section, we describe laboratory tests of the chamber which demonstrate the feasibility of operation at such temperatures:

1) For the acoustic chamber to operate and function properly between these extreme temperature limits, it must be able to maintain resonance at all times. In fact, the resonant frequencies f_n of the chamber are

$$f_n = (nC_o/2\ell)\sqrt{T/273} \tag{3}$$

where C_o is the velocity of sound at 0^oC, ℓ is the physical dimension of the chamber, n is an integer, and T is the ambient temperature of the chamber in degrees Kelvin. An automatic

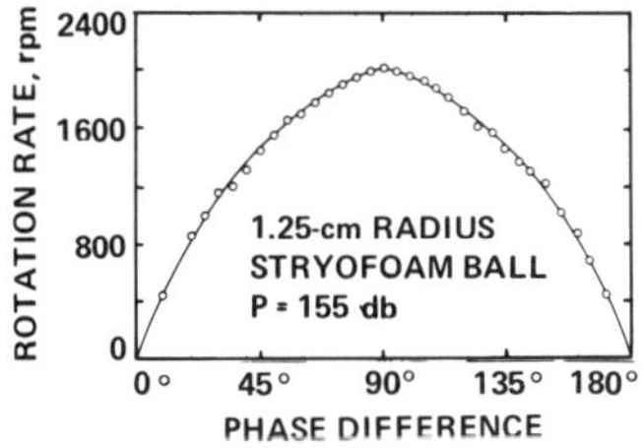

Fig. 7 Rotational rate as a function of phase difference.

frequency control to maintain resonance despite temperature excursions within the chamber has been developed. The heart of this control is a phase-locking loop. The complex displacement X for a system undergoing forced oscillation is $X = (-j\, Fe^{j\omega t}) / \omega[R_m + j\,(\omega m - s/\omega)]$, where F is the driving force, R is the resistance, m is the mass, and s is the "spring" constant. Without solving the real part of this equation, one easily can see that a resonance occurs where $\omega m = s/\omega$; the complex displacement X lags the driving force by 90°. This is a well-known property of acoustical systems. The principle of phase locking is to monitor the driving frequency so that the input signal has 90° phase lead with respect to the acoustical signal inside the chamber at all times. At the present time, we do not have at our disposal acoustical drives that will operate at the high temperatures at which we wish to test the automatic frequency controller. Consequently, the variation of high temperatures within the chamber was simulated by mixing helium gas with air to vary in time the resonant frequency in the chamber. The resonant frequencies f_n of the chamber are

$$f_n = (nC_o/2\ell)\sqrt{\rho_o/\rho} \tag{4}$$

where C_o is the velocity of sound in air, ρ_o is density of air, and ρ is the density of the air and helium mixture. One easily can see from Eqs. (3) and (4) that a decrease in the density of the mixture will simulate an increase in the temperature of the chamber. In the test, helium gas was bled into the chamber while a styrofoam ball was levitated. The purpose of the test is to see how fast the servo loop can track the change in resonant frequency as the "temperature" is varied. The test was conducted by changing the gas in the chamber from 100% air through intermediate mixtures to a 100% helium composition. This variation in gas density and the resulting change of velocity of sound simulated a change of temperature from 25° to $\sim 2000^oC$. The fundamental resonance frequency of the chamber thus varied from 1.5 to 4.2 kHz during the simulated temperature rise. The automatic controller was able to vary the driver frequency to match the change in the chamber's resonance frequency, and measurements of the chamber's pressure profile indicated that the profile maintained its original pattern throughout the test. The most significant portion of the test was the demonstration that the levitated sphere located at the center of the chamber remained at this position throughout the test with no measured motion or oscillation. This indicated that no unwanted oscillation was occurring in the servo system.

2) Another test is the operation of the chamber at a highly nonuniform temperature. In a zero-g environment,

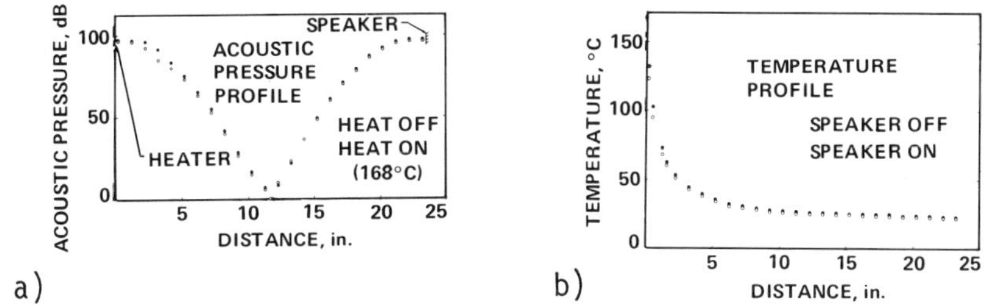

Fig. 8 a) Acoustic profile; b) temperature profile.

gravitation-induced convection is absent, leading to inefficient heat transfer from a molten drop positioned in the chamber to the wall. Consequently, the temperature around the droplet can be much higher than at the wall. The questions that we must answer are as follows: 1) Will this extreme temperature gradient affect the sound intensity profile? 2) What will the acoustic wave do to the temperature gradient? The test apparatus was a glass cylinder 60.76 cm long and 15.78 cm i.d. At its upper end, a disk heater plate of the same diameter was fitted into the cover. A speaker was mounted in the lower opening. The temperature and sound intensity profiles were determined first independently and then simultaneously. The results are shown in Figs. 8a and b. Figure 8a) plots the measured acoustic pressure as a function of distance with and without the heater. It shows that resonance was not perturbed by the temperature gradient. Figure 8b) compares the temperature profiles with and without the speaker. It shows that the acoustic field slightly improved the heat conductivity of gas without much alteration of the shape of the profile. We conclude from these tests that temperature gradients resulting from molten material being positioned will not affect the positioning capability of the chamber. Likewise, the acoustic field will not significantly modify temperature gradients, which would affect the melting and solidification of the material being positioned.

3) A very convenient method of testing the purity of ultrapure metals is to measure the resistivity of the metal at low temperatures. The resistivity measurements could be made by using eddy-current-induction techniques on a levitated sample that would obviate the necessity of placing electrical leads on the sample. Measurements of this type often are conducted at temperatures below 2°K. At the other end of the temperature scale, the determination of the purity of ultrapure metals requires that the chamber perform at a temperature below 2°K. One anticipated use of the acoustic levitation furnace is the growth of ultrapure single crystals with a minimum of crystal defects. It would be convenient to be able to grow and

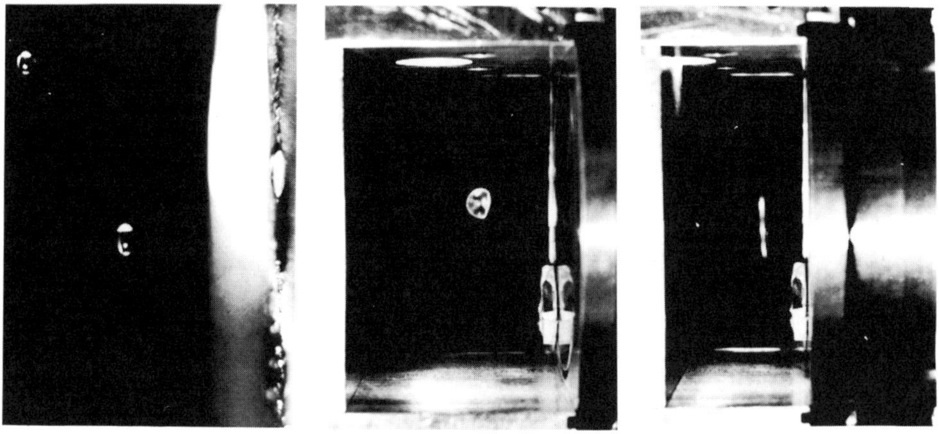

a) b) c)

Fig. 9 Acoustically levitated substances: a) water droplets; b) glass sphere; c) metal plate.

test the crystal in the same chamber. This type of handling of the material would reduce inadvertent contamination of the sample greatly and eliminate the possibility of producing defects in the crystal through additional handling when transferring from the furnace to another separate test chamber. The combined furnace/test chamber has the added advantage of reducing the time needed to conduct purity tests on the samples. It therefore was decided to conduct exploratory tests on the acoustic levitation chamber at these low temperatures to ascertain any difficulties in operation of the chamber at these reduced temperatures. Preliminary tests were carried out at $1.8^{o}K$, and the results indicated that the acoustic pattern did not show any significant deviatiations from room-temperature operation.

4) To provide an understanding and engineering design of the flight experiments, it is desirable to study the melting and solidification process under the influence of acoustic fields in an Earth laboratory. A high-power acoustic chamber that is capable of levitating liquid droplets, glass beads, and metal plates, as shown in Fig. 9, has been developed in our laboratory. The capability of the new chamber will be used to make feasibility studies of containerless materials processing in the laboratory. Initial tests will be conducted with low-melting organic materials, which have the advantages of low density and ease of handling. If these experiments are successful, later tests may be conducted on low-melting metals.

References

[1]Plateau, J., "Experimental and Theoretical Researches on the Figures of Equilibrium of a Liquid Mass Withdrawn from the Action of Gravity," (1863). The Annual Report of the Board of Regents of the Smithsonian Institution, GPO, Washington, D.C. pp. 270-285.

[2]Gibson, E.G., "Skylab Fluid Mechanics Demonstrations," International Colloquium on Drops and Bubbles, Proceedings, Aug. 29-31, 1974, Pasadena, Calif. (to be published).

[3]Chandrasekhar, S., Ellipsoidal Figures of Equilibrium, Yale University Press, New Haven, Conn., 1969.

[4]Rayleigh, Lord, "Equilibrium of Revolving Liquid under Capillary Forces," Philosophical Magazine, Vol. 28, 1914, p. 161.

[5]Appell, P., Traite de Mecanique Rationelle, Vol. 4, Gauthier-Villars, Paris, 1932, Part 1, Chap. IX.

[6]Chandrasekhar, S., "The Stability of a Rotating Liquid Drop," Proceedings of the Royal Society, Vol. 286, 1965, p. 1.

[7]Cohen, S., Plasil, F., and Swiatecki, W.J., "Equilibrium Configurations of Rotating Charged or Gravitating Liquid Masses with Surface Tension. II.," Annals of Physics, Vol. 82, 1974, p. 557.

[8]Ross, D.K., "The Shape and Energy of a Revolving Liquid Mass Held Together by Surface Tension," Australian Journal of Physics, Vol. 21, 1968, pp. 823-835.

[9]Ross, D.K., "The Stability of a Rotating Liquid Mass Held Together by Surface Tension," Australian Journal of Physics, Vol. 21, 1968, pp. 837-844.

[10]Gans, R.F., "On the Poincare Problem for a Compressible Medium," Journal of Fluid Mechanics, Vol. 62, Pt. 4, 1974, pp. 657-675.

[11]Bauer, H.F. and Siekmann, J., "On the Shape of a Rotating Fluid System Consisting of a Gas Bubble Enclosed in a Liquid Globe," Zeitschrift fur angewandt Mathematik und Physik, Vol. 22, 1971, pp. 532-542.

[12]Böhme, G., Johann, W., and Siekmann, J., "Note on a Differential Equation of Electrohydrodynamics," Acta Mechanica, Vol. 20, 1974, pp. 303-307.

[13]Swiatecki, W.J., "The Rotating, Charged or Gravitating Liquid Drop, and Problems in Nuclear Physics and Astronomy," International Colloquium on Drops and Bubbles, Proceedings, Aug. 29-31, 1974, Pasadena, Calif. (to be published).

[14]Berringer, R. and Knox, W.J., "Liquid-Drop Nuclear Model with High Angular Momentum, "Physics Review, Vol. 121, 1961, p.1195.

[15]Wong, C.Y., "Toroidal and Spherical Bubble Nuclei," Annals of Physics, Vol. 77, 1973, pp. 279-353.

[16]Pik-Pichak, G.A., J. Exptl. Theoret. Phys. (U.S.S.R.) Vol. 34 p. 341, 1958, translated in Soviet Phys. JETP Vol. 34, p. 238, 1958. J. Exptl. Theor. Phys. (U.S.S.R.) Vol. 42, p. 1294, 1962, translated in Soviet Phys. JETP Vol. 15, p. 897, 1962. J. Exptl. Theor. Phys. (U.S.S.R.) Vol. 43, p. 1701, 1962, translated in Soviet Phys. JETP Vol. 16, p. 1201, 1963.

[17]Carruthers, J., "The Application of Drops and Bubbles to the Science of Space Processing of Materials," International Colloquium on Drops and Bubbles, Proceedings, Aug. 29-31, 1974, Pasadena, Calif. (to be published).

[18]Greenspan, H.P., Theory of Rotating Fluids, Cambridge University Press, Cambridge, Mass. 1968.

[19]Lamb. H., "On the Oscillations of a Viscous Spheroid," Proceedings of the London Mathematical Society, (1), Vol. 13, 1881, pp. 51-56.

[20]Lamb, H., Hydrodynamics, 6th ed., Cambridge University Press, Cambridge, Mass., 1932, pp. 473-639.

[21]Rayleigh, Lord, The Theory of Sound, Dover Publications, New York, 1945, pp. 371-375.

[22]Reid, W.H., "The Oscillations of a Viscous Liquid Drop," Quarterly of Applied Mathematics, Vol. 18, 1960, pp. 86-89.

[23]Happel, J. and Brenner, H., Low Reynolds Number Hydrodynamics, Prentice-Hall, Englewood Cliffs, N.J., 1965, p. 62.

[24]Chandrasekhar, S., Hydrodynamics and Hydromagnetic Stability, Oxford University Press, London, 1961.

[25]Foote, G.B., "A Theoretical Investigation of the Dynamics of Liquid Drops," Ph.D. Thesis, 1971, Univ. of Arizona.

[26]Alonso, C.T., "The Dynamics of Colliding and Oscillating Drops," International Colloquium on Drops and Bubbles, Proceedings, Aug. 29-31, 1974, Pasadena, Calif. (to be published).

[27]Prosperetti, A., "On the Oscillations of Drops and Bubbles in Viscous Liquids," International Colloquium on Drops and Bubbles, Proceedings, Aug. 29-31, 1974, Pasadena, Calif. (to be published).

[28]Montgomery, D.N., "Collisional Phenomena of Uncharged Water Drops in a Vertical Electric Field," Ph.D. Thesis, 1968, Univ. of Arizona.

[29]Diehl, H. and Greiner, N., "Ternary Fission in the Liquid Drop Model," Physics Letters, Vol. 45B, 1973, p. 35.

[30]Miller, C.A. and Scriven, L.E., "The Oscillations of a Fluid Droplet Immersed in Another Fluid," Journal of Fluid Mechanics, Vol. 32, Pt. 3, 1968, pp. 417-435.

[31]Valentine, R.S., Sather, N.F., and Heideger, W.J., "The Motion of Drops in Viscous Media," Chemical Engineering Science, Vol. 20, 1968, pp. 719-729.

[32]Davis, T.V. and Hagdon, D.A., "An Investigation of Droplet Oscillations During Mass Transfer," Proceedings of the Royal Society, Vol. A243, 1957, p. 492.

[33]Chomiak, J., "Oscillations of a Viscous Liquid Drop in a Turbulent Gas," Fluid Dynamics Transactions, Vol. 1, Macmillan, New York, 1964.

[34]Narasinga Rao, E.V.L., Kumar, R., Kuloor, N.R., "Drop Formation Studies in Liquid-Liquid Systems," Chemical Engineering Science, Vol. 21, 1966, pp. 867-880.

[35]Park, R.W. and Crosby, E.J., "A Device for Producing Controlled Collisions between Pairs of Drops," Chemical Engineering Science, Vol. 20, 1965, p. 39.

[36]Carruthers, J., Private Communication.

[37]Wang, T.G., Saffren, M.M., and Elleman, D.D., "Acoustic Chamber for Weightless Positioning," AIAA Paper 74-155, 1974.

[38]Landau, L.D. and Lifshitz, E.M., Fluid Mechanics, Pergamon, New York, 1959.

[39]Westervelt, P.J., "Scattering of Sound by Sound with Applications," Finite Amplitude Wave Effects in Fluid, Proceedings of the 1973 Symposium, 1973, Copenhagen.

[40]King, L.V., "On the Acoustic Radiation Pressure on Spheres," Proceedings of the Royal Society, Vol. A147, 1934, pp. 212-240, London.

NATURAL CONVECTION IN LOW-g ENVIRONMENTS

Philomena G. Grodzka*
Lockheed Missiles & Space Company, Inc., Huntsville, Ala.

and

Tommy C. Bannister†
Marshall Space Flight Center, Huntsville, Ala.

Abstract

In low-g environments, convective driving forces other than gravity can be of comparable or predominant importance. Very little is known presently about the nature of convection in low-g environments. Data from recent space experiments, equipment performances during spaceflight, and computer studies have begun to fill the knowledge gap about the nature and vigor of convection in low-g environments. The present paper reviews the findings to date. Convections driven by steady low-g accelerations, g-jitter, internal thermal volume expansions, surface tension and interfacial tension, electric field, and liquid/solid phase change are covered. Convection associated with boiling, however, is not considered. Implications for space processing operations are also discussed.

I. Introduction

Natural convection is the spontaneous fluid flow caused by temperature and solutal concentration gradients in conjunction with a number of possible driving forces. Among these possible driving forces are various accelerations (including gravity), surface tension (vapor/liquid interface), interfacial tension (liquid/liquid interface), electric fields, magnetic fields, and internal molecular forces. Once started convection can profoundly alter internal thermal and solutal

---

Presented as Paper 74-156 at the AIAA 12th Aerospace Sciences Meeting, Washington, D.C., January 30 - February 1, 1974.

*Staff Scientist.
†Physicist.

profiles in a fluid. Processes involving phenomena in which heat and mass transport are an integral part, such as crystallization, solidification, electrophoretic migration, and Soret diffusion, therefore, can be profoundly affected by convection.

Non-gravity-driven convection has not been studied as extensively as gravity-driven convection. The reason for this is that gravity is usually the dominant driving force for convection on earth and thus has received most of the attention. Fortunately, during the Apollo 14, 16 and 17 and Apollo-Soyuz spaceflights it was possible to conduct a number of experiments on natural convection. These experiments along with data from other sources and a number of computer studies have begun to fill the knowledge gap about the nature and vigor of convection in low-g environments. The major portion of this paper is devoted to reviewing the findings to date in the area of low-g natural convection. Convections driven by steady low-g accelerations, g-jitter, thermal volume expansions, surface tension and interfacial tension, electric fields, and liquid/solid phase change are covered. Convection associated with boiling, however, is not considered. The implications of the findings on low-g natural convection for space processing operations are also discussed.

II. Convection-Driven by Steady Low-g Accelerations

On earth a constant gravity acceleration of 980 cm/sec^2 (one-g) is experienced by bodies. In a spacecraft both constant and varying accelerations occur to varying extents depending on the mission phase. Steady g-levels result from spacecraft rotation, gravity gradients, solar wind and solar pressure. Varying g-levels result from engine burns, attitude control maneuvers, and onboard vibrations from machinery or astronaut movement. Varying g-levels have been called g spikes, disturbance environments, or g-jitter. Convection caused by g-jitter can be significant in low-g environments. The topic of g-jitter convection is discussed in the next section. Steady accelerations associated with several mission conditions range from about 10^{-4} g to about 10^{-9}g in earth orbit.

Convection can be of significant vigor in certain situations even at the 10^{-8} g-level or lower. Consider the two cases of heat addition to a fluid as shown in Fig. 1. In the side heating case, flow begins as soon as a temperature gradient develops. In the heating from below case, however, the fluid remains immobile until a certain critical temperature

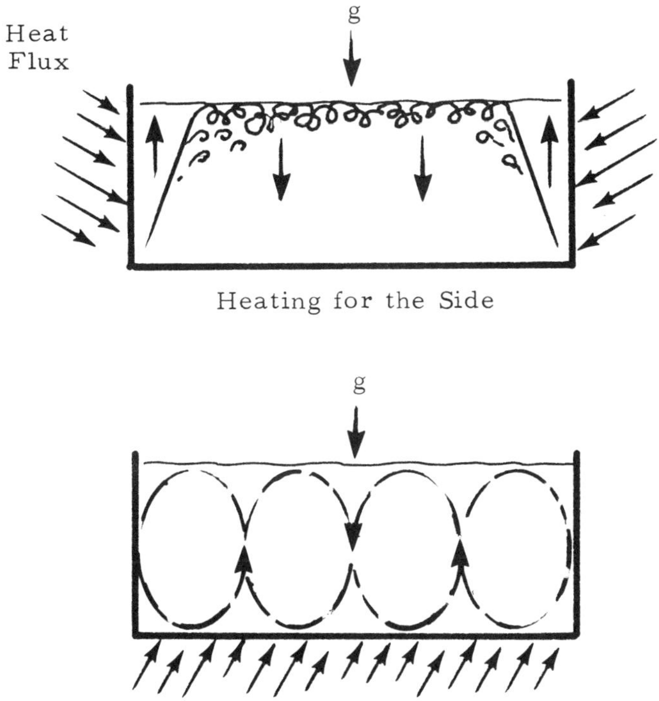

Heating for the Side

Heat Flux

Heating from Below

Fig. 1 Convection dependence on heating direction.

gradient is established through the layer of fluid. Comparable sketches can be drawn for the removal of solute from the side or bottom boundaries (assuming, of course, that removal of solute from a volume of fluid decreases the density of the volume). In the side heating case, convective flow is slow enough so that the heat transfer rate does not differ appreciably from pure conduction until a certain critical temperature gradient is attained. The subject of critical conditions will be discussed shortly. The point to be made here is that in the side heating case some degree of convection is inescapable. Although the vigor of convective flow in the side heating case can be attenuated by low-g environments and the heat transfer rates made not to differ appreciably from the pure conduction case, mass transfer rates can still be affected appreciably. In low-g processes such as crystal growth from solution, therefore, the vigor of low-g convection needs careful consideration.

One of the chief parameters of gravity-driven convection is the dimensionless number known as the Rayleigh number, Ra. The Rayleigh number represents a weighed ratio of the buoyancy to viscous forces and is defined by the following relationship

$$Ra = \frac{g\,\beta\,\partial T/\partial y\,d^4}{\nu\kappa}$$

where g is gravity acceleration, β volumetric expansion coefficient, $\partial T/\partial y$ relevant temperature gradient, d characteristic length, ν kinematic viscosity, and κ thermal diffusivity. A comparable number for buoyancy generated by concentration gradients is called the solutal Rayleigh number. For a few special cases the value of the Rayleigh number which must be exceeded before convection will begin (critical value) are known. For example, for the case of slowly heating from below an infinite layer of fluid confined on top and bottom, convection will begin when the value of the Rayleigh number exceeds 1708. For a special case of side heating, a critical Rayleigh number of 500 L/d (L cell height, d cell width) applies.[1] If the critical value of the Rayleigh number is known for the situation of interest one can change the boundary conditions (scaling) for the purpose of controlling convection. The dependence of the Rayleigh number on the fourth power of the significant cell dimension, however, means that the size of the containers used in low-g environments cannot be too much larger than in a one-g environment if the effects of convection are to be avoided. A review of research on gravity-driven convection in enclosures for the cases of rectangular cavities and horizontal circular cylinders has appeared recently.[2] It may be well to caution, however, that using convection parameters defined for earth processes to scale operations for low-g environments can be extremely risky if done unthinkingly.

During the last four Apollo flights a number of pressure and temperature measurements in the cryogenic gas storage tanks were taken. The flight data were compared to the results of a number of computer models of low-g convection in these tanks. The studies were undertaken to ascertain that natural convection would provide an adequate mixing mechanism to avoid undesirable temperature stratification. Prior to Apollo 14 forced convection provided by mixing fans was used to avoid the stratification problem. After the Apollo 13 incident, however, the fans were removed. An intensive and extensive program of flight support activity occurred prior to the Apollo 14 flight including not only computer modeling but also a number of ground performance and simulation tests [3]. Flight support activity for subsequent missions was reinforced by the Apollo 14 flight data. The mathematical and simulation models developed for the Apollo 14 oxygen storage tanks are quite complex and include rather complicated boundary conditions. Also the properties of supercritical oxygen are highly temperature dependent, to a degree not matched by fluids in the subcritical condition. The technical results of the flight support activity, therefore, are quite specific for the Apollo tanks. Nevertheless some of the results are of general interest. These are briefly summarized as follow: The vigor of natural convection in the Apollo tanks in low-g environments is of sufficient vigor to obviate the need for forced convection.[4] Large thermal gradients exist along the heater and are a strong function of the gravity level [4]. Data from the Apollo 14 flight show increased convection vigor, as would be expected, with increase in rotation rate [5]. The rotation rates for which data were obtained were 1 and 3 RPH. The Apollo 14 data also indicate that convection persists for quite a long time after rotation from 3 RPH is stopped. Stoppage from a rotation rate of 1 RPH, however, results in little persistent fluid motion.[5]

III. g-Jitter Convection

Data from the Apollo 14 and 17 heat flow and convection experiment [6,7,8,9], as well as temperature and pressure data from the Apollo 15 cryogenic tanks [10,11] show that g-jitter can result in convection of significant vigor even in relatively small containers. As indicated in the preceding section, varying g-levels or g-jitter results from engine burns, attitude control maneuvers, and onboard vibration from machinery and astronaut movement.

To gain a better understanding of how g-jitter affects heat transfer, time-temperature curves for the Apollo 14 radial heating experiment configuration were calculated by computer assuming a g-jitter of 10^{-3} g with a frequency of 0.5 per sec.[6] The results are shown in Fig. 2. The flight, constant 10^{-3} g, and conduction curves are shown for comparison. It can be seen that the g-jitter curve falls somewhat below the constant g-curve, bringing it closer to the flight curve. The shape of curve, however, still does not bend as the flight curves are observed to bend. An interesting aspect of the g-jitter curve, however, is that the curve is not actually as straight as is presented in Fig. 2. A definite undulatory character is just becoming evident. One of the most striking features of the Apollo 14 data was the presence of long period oscillations in the time-isotherm curves. It is most probable

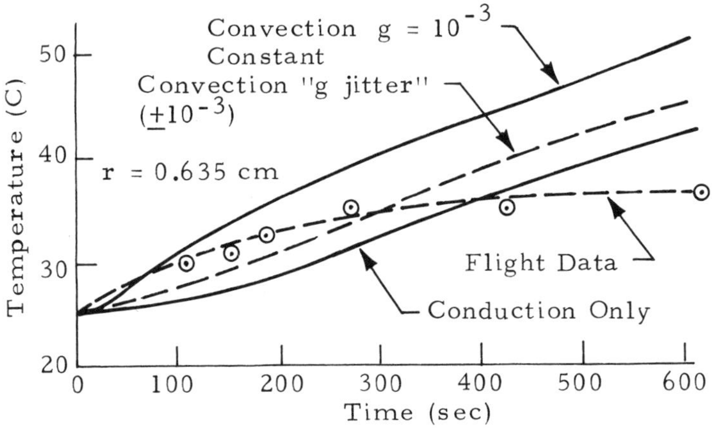

Fig.2 Curves calculated by assuming various g levels and Apollo 14 radial cell data.[6]

that if precise vibration data, including apparatus rotation oscillations, were available, a calculated time-temperature curve could duplicate more closely the observed Apollo 14 curves. Another interesting facet of g-jitter is that when g-jitter is coupled with a superimposed steady g-field, the steady g-field exerts a damping effect on the fluid motions caused by g-jitter.[12]

During an extravehicular activity period the Apollo 15 spacecraft heater temperatures in the cryogenic oxygen tank were observed to decrease markedly. A detailed analysis of this period was conducted[10, 11]. Vehicle accelerations caused by cabin venting and astronaut movement were input into a computer program and resultant heater temperatures and tank pressures calculated. From a comparison of the calculated data with the flight data it was concluded that accelerations resulting from planned and unplanned oxygen venting from the command module and astronaut movement caused the observed heater temperature changes. Venting of the cabin atmosphere caused rapid increases in accelerations from the range of 10^{-7} to 10^{-4} g.

IV. Thermoacoustic Convection in Low-g

Thermal volume expansions per se can cause two kinds of flow: bulk and acoustical. In enclosed containers bulk fluid flow caused by thermal volume expansion would not be expected to result in much convection in the cases of ordinary liquids and gases. The situation for supercritical cryogenic gases, however, is apparently different. A mathematical model in which the gravity level is taken as zero and only thermally induced motions are considered showed that fluid flow is significant when the amount of oxygen in the tank is large. A high degree of temperature stratification, however, resulted in all cases.[13] The results of the model are in fair agreement with the Apollo 14 flight data during attitude hold conditions. Although bulk flow may be of some concern for liquids which are not constrained in all directions, i.e., levitated liquids or liquids contained in open vessels, acoustical flow will probably be the flow of most general interest.

In the absence of gravity, a mechanism for acoustical convection consists of the following. A suddenly heated wall causes adjacent flow to expand. This sudden expansion sets up an acoustic wave which propagates into the fluid. Given a sufficient heat rate, certain container dimensions, and dissipative mechanisms, a thermoacoustic vibration can be sustained as long as the appropriate boundary conditions are maintained. The conversion of heat energy into acoustic energy was discovered and defined by Sondhauss in 1850. The phenomenon of the conversion of thermal energy into acoustic energy is now called the Sondhauss effect. In open or closed containers thermoacoustic waves can convect considerable heat from the heated side. Rayleigh was the first to give a correct physical criterion for the occurrence of spontaneous thermoacoustic oscillations. His criterion is[14]: "If heat be given to the air at the moment of greatest condensation or be taken from it at the moment of greatest rarefactions, the vibration is encouraged." In closed containers thermoacoustic convection will usually damp out after a short time. Under certain conditions, e.g., heat applied to one end of a long, closed pipe while the other end is cooled, thermoacoustic convection can become a sustained fluid motion.

"Singing" tubes are well known to workers dealing with liquid helium. The "singing" occurs in tubes connecting a liquid helium reservoir to ambient temperature. It has been observed that "singing" can increase the evaporation rate of liquid helium by a factor of one thousand.[15] That is to say, the heat pumped by the oscillations can be as much as a thousand times the conduction heat transfer rate. A number of studies both theoretical and experimental have appeared in the area of "singing" helium tubes.[16] A smaller number of theoretical studies have directly addressed the problem of thermoacoustic convection in low-g environments.[17, 18, 19] These studies predict significant low-g thermoacoustic convection in gases when heating rates are sufficiently high. In a sample case where the wall temperature is increased instantaneously to a value which is twice the initial Rankine temperature, the thermoacoustic mechanism is shown to cause significant low-g convection.[18] The sample problem also shows, somewhat surprisingly, that at one-g the vigor of gravity-driven convection is so strong as to almost completely mask the effects of thermoacoustic convection. Gravity and thermoacoustic convection became of comparable vigor at the 10^{-3} g-level. The internal temperature profiles at 10^{-3} g are a hybrid between the buoyancy dominated 1-g case and the thermoacoustic dominated 0-g case. Experimental confirmation of one computer code [18] has recently been obtained on a cryogen system.

V. Surface Tension-Driven Convection in Low-g Environments

Surface tension-driven convection occurs quite readily in low-g environments as has been demonstrated in a number of space experiments. The findings in this area are summarized under the headings cellular convection and non-cellular convection.

Cellular Convection: When a thin layer of oil, containing suspended aluminum particles to render the flow pattern visible, is heated on the ground, a pattern of hexagonal cells is observed (Fig. 3). The cell centers are liquid upflows, and the cell peripheries are downflows. The cells in the hex-

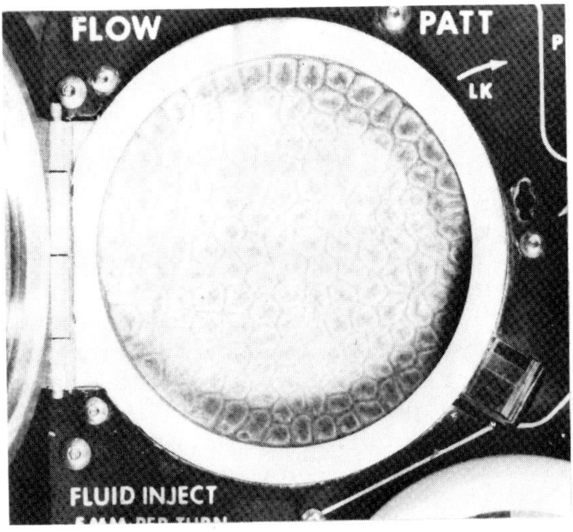

Fig. 3 Bénard cells generated in ground test.

agonal pattern are called Bénard cells after Henri Bénard who studied the phenomenon in 1900.[20] Lord Rayleigh subsequently developed a theory of cellular convection which accounted for the Bénard cells on the basis of an unstable density gradient.[21] Although Rayleigh's theory included a satisfactory explanation of some of the features of cellular convection when surface tension is not a factor, as in the case of a fluid layer contained between two rigid plates, the convection observed by Bénard was subsequently shown to be driven by surface tension, not gravity.[22] A theory of cellular convection caused by surface tension gradients was subsequently developed by Pearson.[23]

An increasing number of recent papers [24-27] have been concerned with the role of both gravity and surface tension in cellular convection. It is generally agreed that, in liquid layers thicker than about 4 mm, gravity is the chief determinant of such aspects of cellular convection as the thermal gradient at which convection begins and the shape of the resultant cells. Surface tension usually dominates in liquid layers less than 4 mm thick. The hexagonal pattern is generally associated with the convection driven by surface tension and a roll pattern with convection driven by gravity. There exists, however, uncertainties concerning the magnitude of the thermal gradients required for the onset of convection and the resultant flow pattern when gravity and surface tension forces are of the same magnitude. There is also some question about the possibility that gravity somehow is a necessary ingredient in cellular convection. The existing uncertainties are difficult to clear up in experiments on the earth because, of necessity, they must always be conducted in 1-g conditions.

In the flow pattern experiments conducted aboard the Apollo 14 spacecraft [8, 9] a layer of oil containing fine aluminum flakes to render flow visible was heated electrically from below on a circular, uncovered dish with a diameter of 7.30 cm. The cellular flow pattern which developed as the result of heating was photographed on motion-picture film. The gravity level at the time of the experiments, calculated from spacecraft rotation rates, was less than 10^{-6} g. The cellular convection observed in the Apollo 14 flight experiment showed conclusively that cellular convection can be caused by surface tension alone. The Apollo 14 experiment further showed that, as in 1-g, a critical value of the temperature gradient must be exceeded before cellular convection is initiated. Furthermore, a polygonal cellular pattern was seen as the preferred pattern in a thin liquid layer of uniform thickness.

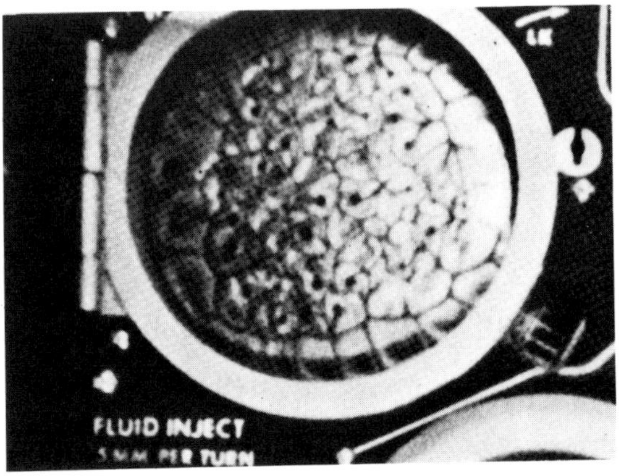

Fig.4 Cellular convection observed in Apollo 17 test.

Similar flow pattern experiments were conducted aboard Apollo 17.[6, 7] An example of the data obtained is shown in Fig.4. The data showed that the sizes of the observed surface tension cells compared quite well with the values predicted by Pearson's linear analysis of surface tension-driven cellular convection.[23] The experiments further showed that the surface tension-driven cellular convection occurs at lower temperature gradients in low-g environments than in 1-g environments. The easier convection onset in low-g than in 1-g was surprising because Nield's linear analysis of cellular convection [25] which considers the coupling between surface tension and gravity predicts that surface tension and gravity reinforce each other strongly. Furthermore, Nield's analysis has received experimental verification in one-g.[28] A number of explanations for the surprising Apollo 17 result were considered. It was finally concluded that the formation of large surface tension-driven cells which tend to be the same size as those caused by gravity is hindered by gravity. Smaller sized surface tension-driven cells, however, reinforce gravity-driven cells. The occurrence of a critical condition for convection onset in the Apollo 17 case is the result of the influence of the retaining side walls. Data were also obtained from the Apollo 17 experiments on the flow patterns at the onset of the convection in low-g. Both rolls and cells were observed, an observation somewhat at variance with the somewhat general belief that rolls are associated with gravity-driven convection and cells with surface tension-driven convection.

Non-Cellular Convection: Several direct observations of non-cellular, surface tension-driven flows in various fluids in low-g have been reported.[29] Inferred evidence for surface and interfacial tension-driven convection has also been presented.[30]

VI. Electrohydrodynamics in Low-g

A number of potential space manufacturing processes depend on the use of an electric field and electrically conducting water as the fluid medium. Among these potential space processing candidates may be listed electrophoretic separations, electrolysis separations, electrocrystallizations, and electrosyntheses. As indicated previously electric fields represent a possible driving force for fluid flow. Electrohydrodynamic effects, therefore, may be a complication in any process employing electric fields in conjunction with fluid media. Electrically-driven fluid flow can be classified either as electroosmotic or electroconvection. Electroosmosis depends on the presence of an electrical double layer. Electroconvection requires electrical inhomogeneities within the fluid. In the Apollo 16 electrophoresis demonstration fluid flows were observed which probably were caused by electroosmotic effects.[31] Electroconvection has been studied previously in electrically insulating fluids. Some recent work by Dr. James R. Melcher of the Massachusetts Institute of Technology, however, indicates that electroconvection may also occur under special circumstances in aqueous, electrolyte solutions.

VII. Phase Change Convection in Low-g

When a liquid freezes the solid formed usually has a somewhat higher density than the liquid and hence a smaller volume. This shrinkage on freezing causes a corresponding fluid flow in the liquid; liquid flows toward the solidifying interface. Depending on the speed of crystallization, a number of fluid flow phenomena can occur. Acoustical disturbances, cavitation effects, grain size transitions, and various types of segregation effects in alloys are some of the phenomena attributed to phase change convection.[32-35] Some inferred evidence was found for phase change convection in a number of flight experiments.[29, 30]

VIII. Controlling Convection in Space

In this section the implications of the information presented in the preceding discussion for space processing operations are considered. First of all with regard to convection driven by gravity or steady g accelerations, some degree of convection is inescapable even in low-g environments if the thermal or solutal gradient is oriented perpendicular to the g gradient, i.e., a side heating case. From the preceding discussions it should be quite clear, however, that the Rayleigh number is at best an approximate guide to specifying the kinds and magnitudes of gravity-driven convection except in a few very special cases. Convective velocities calculated from formulas derived for idealized situations must be viewed, therefore, as approximate first cuts until shown otherwise.

With regard to the non-gravity-driven convections, all of the ones studied so far, i.e., g-jitter, surface tension, thermoacoustic, electro-osmosis and electroconvection, and phase change, appear to be more vigorous in low-g environments than in a one-g environment. Gravity on earth either produces convection which overshadows the other types or generates a stabilizing effect. Any contemplated space processing operation which has boundary conditions which might result in one of the non-gravity types of convection, therefore, should be studied carefully. All of which is not to say that convection cannot be suppressed in low-g environments. The Apollo 17 radial and lineal heating experiments showed that convection could indeed be suppressed, almost totally given the right boundary conditions. The preceding should rather serve to indicate situations where non-gravity convections might arise and how they can be controlled.

IX. References

[1] Eckert, E.R.G., and Carlson, W.O., "Natural Convection in an Air Layer Enclosed Between Two Vertical Plates with Different Temperatures," International Journal of Heat Transfer Vol. 2, 1961, pp. 106-120.

[2] Ostrach, S., "Natural Convection in Enclosures," in Advances in Heat Transfer, Vol. 8, Editors, J.P. Hartnett and T.F. Irvine, Jr., Academic Press, New York, 1972, pp. 161-227.

[3] MSC Cryogenics Symposium Papers, MSC-04312, presented at NASA-Manned Spacecraft Center, Houston, Texas, 20-21 May 1971.

[4] Rice, R.A., "Apollo 14 Flight Support and System Performance," MSC-04312, MSC Cryogenic Symposium Papers, 20-21 May 1971.

[5]Fineblum, S.S., Haron, A.S., and Saxton, J.A., "Heat Transfer and Thermal Stratification in the Apollo 14 Cryogenic Oxygen Tanks," MSC-04312, MSC Cryogenics Symposium Papers, 20-21 May 1971.

[6]Bannister, T.C., Grodzka, P.G., Spradley, L.W., Bourgeois, S.V., Hedden, R.O., and Facemire, B.R., Apollo 17 Heat Flow and Convection Experiments, Final Data Analyses Results," NASA TM X-64772, 16 July 1973.

[7]Grodzka, P.G., and Bannister, T.C., "Heat Flow and Convection Experiments Aboard Apollo 17," Science, Vol. 187, 1975, pp. 165-167.

[8]Grodzka, P.G., Fan, C., and Hedden, R.O., "The Apollo 14 Heat Flow and Convection Demonstration Experiments; Final Results of Data Analysis," LMSC-HREC D22533, Lockheed-Missiles & Space Company, Huntsville, Ala., September 1971.

[9]Grodzka, P.G., and Bannister, T.C., "Heat Flow and Convection Demonstration Experiments Aboard Apollo 14," Science, Vol. 176, 5 May 1972, pp. 506-508.

[10]Barton, J.E., and Patterson, H.W., "Post-Flight Analysis of the Apollo 15 Cryogenic Oxygen System," Boeing Company Report D2-1189422-1, 15 December 1971.

[11]Barton, J.E., and Patterson, H.W., "Apollo Oxygen Tank Stratification Analysis — Final Report," Report D2118406-2, Vol. 2, Boeing Company, Huntsville, Ala., 31 January 1972.

[12]Pak, H.Y., Winter, E.R.F., and Schoenals, R.J., "Convection Heat Transfer in Contained Fluid Subjected to Vibration," In Augmentation of Convective Heat and Mass Transfer, A.E. Bergles and A.L. Webb, eds., ASME, New York, 1970, p. 148.

[13]Suttles, J.T., and Smith, G.L., "Stratification Calculations in a Heated Cryogenic Oxygen Storage Tank at Zero Gravity," MSC-04312, MSC Cryogenics Symposium Papers, 20-21 May 1971.

[14]Rayleigh, Lord, "The Explanation of Certain Acoustical Phenomena," Nature, London, Vol. 18, 1878, p. 319.

[15]Wexler, A., in Experimental Cryophysics, Edited by F.E. Hoare, et al., Butterworths, London, 1961, p. 155.

[16]Clement, J.R., and Gaffney, J., "Thermal Oscillation in Low-Temperature Apparatus," Advances in Cryogenic Engineering, Vol. 1, 1954, pp. 302-306.

[17]Spradley, L. W., "Thermoacoustic Convection of Fluids in Low Gravity," Paper presented at the 12th AIAA Aerospace Sciences Meeting, 30 January-1 February, Washington, D.C., 1974.

[18]Spradley, L. W., and Churchill, S. W., "Buoyancy and Pressure Driven Thermal Convection in a Rectangular Enclosure," Journal of Fluid Mechanics, Vol. 70, 1975, pp. 705-720.

[19]Larkin, B.K., "Heat Flow to a Confined Fluid in Zero Gravity," Progress in Astronautics and Aeronautics, Vol. 20, 1967, pp. 819-832.

[20]Bénard, H., "Les Tourbillous Cellulaires," Annals of Chemical Physics, Vol. 23, 1901, pp. 72-144.

[21]Rayleigh, Lord, "On Convection Currents in a Horizontal Layer of Fluid when the Higher Temperature is on the Under Side," Philosophical Magazine, Vol. 32, (ser. 6), 1916, p. 529.

[22]Black, M. J., "Surface Tension as the Cause of Bénard Cells and Surface Deformation in a Liquid Film," Nature, Vol. 178, 22 September 1956, pp. 650-651.

[23]Pearson, J.R.A., "On Convection Cells Induced by Surface Tension," Journal of Fluid Mechanics, Vol. 4, 1958, pp. 489-500.

[24]Koschmieder, E. L., "On Convection Under an Air Surface," Journal of Fluid Mechanics, Vol. 30, 1967, pp. 9-15.

[25]Nield, D.A., "Surface Tension and Buoyancy Effects in Cellular Convection," Journal of Fluid Mechanics, Vol. 19, 1964, pp. 341-352.

[26]Scriven, L.E., and Sternling, C. V., "On Cellular Convection Driven by Surface-Tension Gradients," Journal of Fluid Mechanics, Vol. 19, 1964, pp. 321-340.

[27]Smith, K. A., "On Convective Instability in Liquid Pools Heated from Below," Journal of Fluid Mechanics, Vol. 24, 1956, pp. 401-414.

[28]Palmer, H. J., and Berg, J. C., "Convective Instability in Liquid Pools Heated from Below," Journal of Fluid Mechanics, Vol. 47, 1971, pp. 779-787.

[29] Bourgeois, S. V., and Brashears, M. R., "Fluid Dynamics and Kinematics of Sphere Forming Aboard Skylab II," paper given at AIAA 12th Aerospace Sciences Meeting, Washington, D.C., 30 January-1 February 1974.

[30] Grodzka, P. G., and Bourgeois, S. V., "Fluid and Particle Dynamic Effects in Low-g," LMSC-HREC TR D306402, Lockheed Missiles & Space Company, Huntsville, Ala., January 1973.

[31] Synder, R.S., "Electrophoresis Demonstration on Apollo 16," NASA TM X-64724, November 1972.

[32] Glicksman, M. E., "Dynamic Effects Arising from High-Speed Solidification," Acta Metallurgica, Vol. 13, 1965, pp. 1231-1246.

[33] Mehrabian, R., Keane, M., and Flemings, M. C., "Interdendritic Fluid Flow and Macrosegregation; Influence of Gravity," Metallurgical Transactions, Vol. 1, 1970, pp. 1209-1220.

[34] Chambre, P. L., "On the Dynamics of Phase Growth," Quarterly Journal of Mechanics and Applied Mathematics, Vol. 9, 1956, pp. 224-233.

[35] Horvay, G., "Freezing into an Undercooled Melt Accompanied by Density Change," Proceed. U.S. National Congress of Applied Mechanics, Vol. 2, Berkeley, Calif., 18-21 June 1962.

FLUID DYNAMICS AND KINEMATICS OF MOLTEN METALS IN THE LOW-GRAVITY ENVIRONMENT OF SKYLAB

S. V. Bourgeois* and M. R. Brashears+
Lockheed Missiles & Space Company, Inc., Huntsville, Ala.

Abstract

The response of molten metals to mechanical and thermal driving forces in nominal and microgravity is analyzed both theoretically and experimentally. The magnitude and transient behavior of internal fluid circulations, surface deformations, and globule trajectories and their effects on solidification in the Skylab electron beam sphere-forming and metals-melting experiments are determined. The theoretical approach consists of dimensional analysis of the governing differential equations. Experimental aspects include evaluation of specimens from terrestrial, KC-135 research aircraft, and actual Skylab tests and analysis of high-speed movies taken during the melting processes. Several gravity-induced variations and gravity-independent results were predicted successfully based on expected differences and similarities in fluid dynamics.

I. Introduction

The M551 and M553 experiments were conducted in the M512 materials processing in space facility aboard Skylab

---

Presented as Paper 74-205 at the AIAA 12th Aerospace Sciences Meeting, Washington, D.C., 30 January - 1 February 1974. This work supported by NASA contracts NAS8-27015 and NAS8-28729. We sincerely thank T.C. Bannister, E.A. Hasemeyer, and R.M. Poorman of NASA-MSFC, the latter two of whom were the principal investigators for these Skylab experiments. We also are grateful to C.M. Hung, M.G. Klett, J.H. McDermit, and S.J. Robertson of Lockheed-Huntsville for their consultation and assistance with some of the calculations. We gratefully acknowledge this support.

*Scientist Associate-Research, Space Processing Group.

+Scientist Associate-Research, Fluid Mechanic Applications Group.

during June 1973 by Astronaut Charles Conrad. The M12 facility consisted of a spherical processing chamber, approximately 40 cm in diameter, in which several experiments were performed, specifically the M551 metals-melting and M553 sphere-forming experiments. The electron beam in the M512 unit was operated between 50 to 80 mA at 20 kV. A vacuum environment was created by venting the chamber directly to outer space.

The M551 metals melting experiment consisted of a rotating metal disk mounted perpendicular to the electron beam (eb) heat source with the eb impingement point located 6 cm from the center of rotation. The velocity of the beam relative to the impingement point was 1.61 cm/sec with a corresponding radial acceleration of $5.09(10)^{-4}$g. The eb was focused to approximately 0.15 cm diam. The three materials used in the experiment were 2219 aluminum, 321 stainless steel and tantalum. The thickness of the material varied with angular position around the disk. During the continuous weld portion of each disk, both full and partial penetration of the disk was achieved by using a constant power input but a varying disk thickness. For each disk, the continuous weld was followed by a dwell portion. In the dwell portion of the weld, the disk was stationary while the eb impinged on the thick segment of the disk, thus creating a large molten pool. The eb then was shut off and the pool allowed to solidify.

The primary objective of the M551 experiment was to study the melting and solidification of metals in reduced gravity. A second objective was to evaluate the eb process as a joining and cutting technique applicable to assembling and repairing structures in space.

The M553 experiment consisted of two 15-specimen indexing pinwheels mounted perpendicular to the eb. With each discrete rotation of the pinwheel, a new cylindrical specimen was positioned in the path of the eb. As the specimen melted, the hardware was designed to allow for deployment of the resulting liquid spheres, with the ensuing free-float time giving rise to a containerless solidification in the vacuum chamber. Three specimens were designed to be retained. Specimens consisted of Ni, Ni-1% Ag, Ni-30% Cu, and Ni-12% Sn.

The basic objective of the M553 sphere-forming experiment was to determine the effects of reduced gravity on fundamental solidification phenomena. In particular, the density difference between components (e.g., nickel and tin) should not lead to sedimentation problems, and specimens may be cast from the melt without using containers or molds to allow homogeneous nucleation.

The primary goals of the studies reported herein were to establish the expected low-gravity variations of terrestrial vs space processing and to optimize the experiments within the constraints of existing hardware. This included delineating the magnitude and pattern of the molten metal flow for both terrestrial and space processing conditions. From a knowledge of the convective differences and other differences between terrestrial and space processing, the effects on grain structure and properties were predicted.

During the course of the investigation, all process phenomena were considered with emphasis on the fluid dynamics of the molten metal. This was accomplished by establishing all expected variations in terrestrial vs space processing occurring as a result of 1) the dominance of capillary motion (insteady of gravity-induced flow; 2) minimal segregation (sedimentation; and 3) a decrease in hydrostatic pressure gradient. All these mechanisms are hydrodynamical in nature; thus gravity has no direct affect on grain structure or any other properties of the solidified material. The gravity effects occur as a result of differing fluid motion. This is exemplified further by the following discussion.

Sedimentation

This effect may be significant whenever heterogeneous mixtures exist in fluids, such as in monotectic, dispersed-particle, or fiber-reinforced composite casting. Denser immiscible materials will tend to settle, unless colloidal or electrostatic attractions interfere. Also, in supercooled melts, segregation of freshly formed nuclei by gravity would affect the final grain structure. Nonmetallic inclusions, gas bubbles, and voids, which usually exist in melts, also are distributed nonuniformly by gravity.

Convection

In terrestrial processing, gravity is the primary driving force for the convection of contained fluids when they are subjected to thermal concentration gradients. Temperature gradients arise from external heating and cooling, whereas concentration gradients usually are produced internally (Soret effect and solute rejection at freezing interfaces that leads to "consitutional supercooling"). These two gradients can produce density gradients large enough to induce buoyancy-driven flow. This fluid motion affects the temperature and concentration profiles within the fluid. This subsequently alters the shape and rate of movement of the freezing interface, because the kinetics of freezing depend on the local temperature and concentration. The degree of mixing caused by convection may be large enough to change the rate of solidification from kinetic to heat transfer or diffusion controlled, which could alter the grain structure drastically. Examples of this convective effect on the transitions from planar to cellular or dendritic growth, from columnar to equiaxed eutectic structures, and from unidirectional to colonied or banded eutectic structures, are cited frequently in the literature. Another effect of gravity-driven convection on solidification processes is that the bulk fluid movement, if rapid enough, can break delicate dendrite arms and thereby alter final grain structure. Furthermore, interlamellar spacing in eutectic growth and dendrite arm spacing are dependent on cooling rate, which is a strong function of convection.

Hydrostatic Pressure

A body of fluid in a gravity field sustains a vertical pressure gradient, as the bottom fluid must support the weight of the upper fluid. This pressure gradient distorts the shape of liquids on Earth because the shape of a liquid surface is determined by the surface tension and the internal hydrostatic pressure (and adhesion, if the liquid wets a solid surfact). Distorted drops of liquid will result in nonsymmetrical solids upon freezing.

Details of theoretical and experimental analysis techniques utilized to assess these M512 materials processing experiments are given elsewhere.[1, 2] The summary and conclusions of these analyses are presented in the following sections.

II. Summary of M553 Analyses

A summary of the most significant predictive results found are given below.

1) The following physical forces are operative on the M553 specimens during eb melting and solidification: gravity/acceleration, surface tension, Lorentz (beam current), electrostriction, magnetostriction, electrostatic charges, solidification shrinkage, thermal expansion, vaporization, and eb mechanical pressure force.

2) Vigorous convective stirring occurs in the molten metal for each of the M553 sample materials. This fluid motion was exhibited on high-speed motion picture film taken for ground tests and low-gravity KC-135 aircraft tests.

3) Both gravity and surface tension forces control molten metal flow during M553 ground tests. These natural convection driving forces arise because of severe nonisothermality during heating.

4) Surface-tension-driven convection will occur in Skylab eb melting. In the near-absence of gravity, the surface tension forces will provide an equivalent amount of convection aboard Skylab, but the flow pattern may be different from those of operations on Earth.

5) Velocities of 20 cm/sec magnitude will be attained 0.1 sec after melting begins in the M553 nickel specimen (both for Skylab and ground tests). Fluid flow will decay 60 sec after melting begins. This means that some degree of flow will exist upon freezing, even for the free-floating M553 spheres.

6) Very small and even negative pressures can be expected for the Skylab spheres, due to outer-shell shrinkage inducing tensions on the residual interior liquid.

7) Shrinkage forces should lead to increased phase-change-induced convection in the Skylab M553 spheres.

8) Sedimentation will not be a factor in this experiment, because vigorous stirring will occur both in terrestrial and Skylab operations.

Based on the previous results and conclusions, the following predictions can be made regarding the variations expected in the specimens processed in the microgravity environment of Skylab:

1) The primary differences expected in Skylab samples will be due to containerless casting; i.e., there will be no wall effects upon nucleation and solidification. Thus, dendritic and grain structure should be finer because of the large degree of supercooling that can be obtained in homogeneous nucleation. Containerless, free suspension also will provide more perfectly spherical castings.

2) Solidification shrinkage may induce imperfections in the sphericity of the castings. Furthermore, shrinkage may

cause a number of voids or one large shrinkage cavity in the interior of each casting.

3) Finally, the residual fluid motion existing at the instant of freezing may introduce some inhomogeneity in the microstructure.

III. Summary of M551 Analyses

A summary of the most significant predicted results follows:

1) Physical forces that are operative during the cutting, joining, and dwell portions of this experiment are: gravity/acceleration, surface tension, Lorentz (beam current), electrostriction, magnetostriction, electrostatic charges, solidification shrinkage, thermal expansion, vaporization, and eb mechanical force.

2) Significant molten metal motion should be exhibited in each of the specimens in both dwell and weld (disk rotating) modes for both flight and ground tests.

3) Both gravity and surface tension forces control molten metal flow in the dwell during M551 ground tests. These natural convection driving forces arise because of severe nonisothermality during heating.

4) Surface tension still will provide an equal magnitude of convection for the dwell in zero-g, although the flow pattern may be different.

5) Spiking frequencies in the stainless steel partial penetration zones are dependent on gravity. The spiking phenomenon can be explained by oscillations of the melt caused by dynamic beam-melt interactions.

6) The mechanical pressure force associated with the impinging eb will not cause unstable splattering in the dwell mode, even in absolute zero-gravity. Thus, any splattering can be attributed to electromagnetic instabilities at the weld pool surface or to degassing.

7) Sedimentation will not be a factor in this experiment, because vigorous stirring will occur both in terrestrial and Skylab operations.

Based on the preceding results and conclusions, the following predictions were made regarding the variations expected in the disk welds processed in the microgravity conditions aboard Skylab:

1) Slightly different grain structure and/or dendrite arm spacing may result due to different melt flow patterns.

2) Lack of hydrostatic pressure and dominance of surface tension will allow dwell pool shape to be different (more spherical) and may cause shallower eb penetration.

3) Spiking frequencies in the stainless stell partial penetration welds should be increased as much as 25% or more.

The different pool shape will occur because surface tension acts to pull the melt toward cooler surfaces, which is away from the eb in this case. Assuming that the net gravitational field always is aligned with the beam in Skylab processing, the situations illustrated in Fig. 1 will result regarding bulk melt behavior of the dwell pool. As seen in Fig. 1a, surface tension dominance will pull the melt away from the beam, resulting in less resistance and deeper beam penetration than in terrestrial processing when heating from above. When heating from the side, however, terrestrial processing allows the melt to run out of the pool, which probably will lead to even less resistance and more penetration than in space processing. Shallower dwell penetrations should be expected aboard Skylab because ground samples were processed as in Fig. 1b.

IV. M553 Flight Results and Conclusions

Fluid Velocities and Flow Patterns

A compilation of fluid velocities (on the molten sphere surfaces) measured from movies taken during Skylab, KC-135 aircraft, and terrestrial processing is shown in Table 1. These velocities were measured by tracking oxide or shiny contaminant patches as they moved over the molten surfaces both before and after complete melting. Several KC-135 measurements were obtained, even after release from the ceramic pedestals. Shown in the table are the surface velocity, processing environment, gravity level, date of processing, filming information, specimen identification, and time of measurement relative to the melting sequence. Beam power data for all measurements were approximately 50 mA and 20 kV. The velocity measurements are accurate to within 20%. The variations in results probably are due to differences in material compositions and beam settings (i.e., focus, impact point, voltage, and amperage) rather than gravity effects.

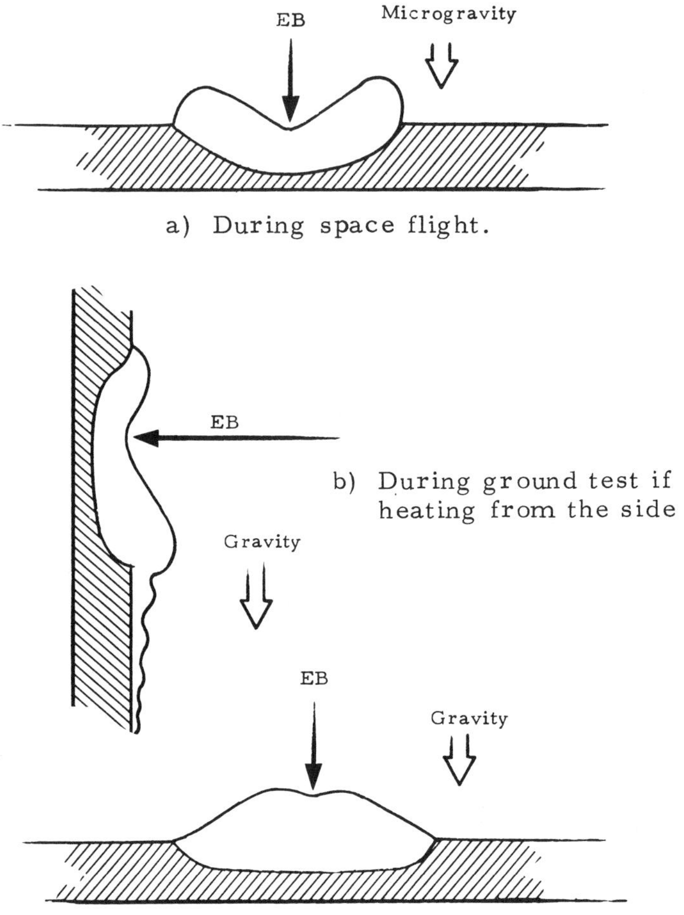

a) During space flight.

b) During ground test if heating from the side

c) During ground test if heating from above

Fig. 1 Proposed M551 dwell pool behavior.

As discussed earlier, only surface tension and gravity forces are predicted to produce these velocities. The one velocity measurement obtainable from the Skylab movie was one order of magnitude lower than that obtained from some low-gravity KC-135 aircraft and ground-based movies, but was similar to ground and KC-135 measurements also obtained long after complete melting. Thus, it can be concluded that no significant difference in magnitude of convection occurred between Skylab, KC-135, and ground processing, which reinforces the theory of surface tension as the dominating force for fluid motion.

No information could be obtained on flow pattern variations in low-g because the slow filming rate of 24 fps used aboard Skylab could not delineate the flow profiles.

Table 1 M553 surface velocity measurements

Processing environment	Gravity level[a], g	Date	Film fps[b]	Sphere material	Fluid velocity, m/sec	Time of measurement
Skylab	10^{-4}	6/15/73	Color, 24	Ni-Ag	0.02	Very long after melted
Ground	1	4/30/73	B&W, 3000	Ni-Ag	0.35 to 0.40	From early to complete melt
KC-135	$6 \cdot 10^{-3}$	7/25/72	Color, 200	Ni-Ag	0.20 0.10 0.06	Before full melt Right after full melt Long after full melt
Ground	1	10/20/72	B&W, 1000	Ni	0.15 0.20 0.33	Before complete melt
Ground	1	1972	Color, 200	Ni	0.12	Half melted

[a] $1g = 9.8\ m/sec^2$.

[b] fps = frames per sec.

Metallurgical Analysis

In addition to direct movie evidence of vigorous melt stirring, several other effects of convection were evident in metallurgical evaluations of Skylab specimens conducted by other investigators. The grain multiplication near the large shrinkage pore in the cap region of Skylab sample SL-1.6 (nickel-tin material) indicates vigorous flow probably due to solidification shrinkage.[3] Alumina was spread over the surface of SL-2.7,[4] a release-type nickel-tin specimen, which supports the existence of vigorous convective stirring to transport the alumina from the pedestal. Similar findings of alumina transport were found on SL-1.8,[5] a nickel-copper specimen. Also, most samples exhibited regions of equiaxed structure, which can be an indicator of fluid flow.

The metallurgical analyses of flight samples in general, have exhibited a greater frequency or extent of independent nucleation or growth structures than do the ground samples.[6] In addition, the structures within these isolated areas are on a significantly finer scale than in similar areas of the ground-based samples. These low-g variations agree with the predictions cited in Ref. 1.

Porosity

Several Skylab samples possessed a large spherical or oblong cavity. These large interior cavities usually were associated with a "cap region" opposite the flat, epitaxial side of the specimens. These large pores no doubt are produced by the large shrinkage forces that were predicted to exist during Skylab processing in Ref. 1. Their appearance thus was expected.

Conclusions

The primary conclusion of the preceding discussions is that significant flow and stirring in the molten spheres (during and after eb melting) occurred in both terrestrial and space processing as predicted. The magnitude of this convective fluid motion was the same in both environments. The flow patterns, however, could not be compared quantitatively because the filming rate was too slow. Also, altered microstructure, increased grain refinement, and the appearance of a single, large interior shrinkage pore have been found in the Skylab specimens as predicted in Ref. 1. These effects can be traced to a longer-duration containerless freezing than in ground and KC-135 flights; i.e., the surfaces opposite the expitaxial nucleation site were cooler than in the non-Skylab specimens (assuming release). These surfaces nucleated much sooner than their non-Skylab counterparts, thereby entrapping a larger enclosed pool of residual liquid. The solidification shrinkage forces, which cause fluid flow and tensile stresses (increased shrinkage porosity) therefore were much greater in the Skylab specimens, even though all of the samples appeared to have some degree of unplanned, heterogeneous nucleation (retainment of unmelted material or solidified prior to release).

V. M551 Flight Results and Conclusions

Dwell Shape and Penetration

As predicted in Ref. 1, the gravity sag illustrated in Fig. 1 was evident in the ground samples shown in Figs. 2a and 3a, which also lead to more extensive dwell penetration than in the flight samples.[7] No "sag" was evident in the aluminum and steel flight samples shown in Figs. 2b and 3b, as the dwell shape appeared similar to Fig. 1a.

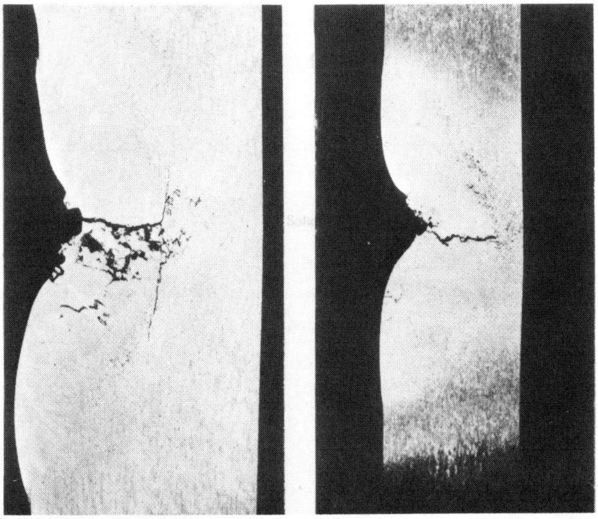

a) Ground (gravity downward) b) Flight (microgravity)

Fig. 2 Cross section of aluminum dwell region.[7]

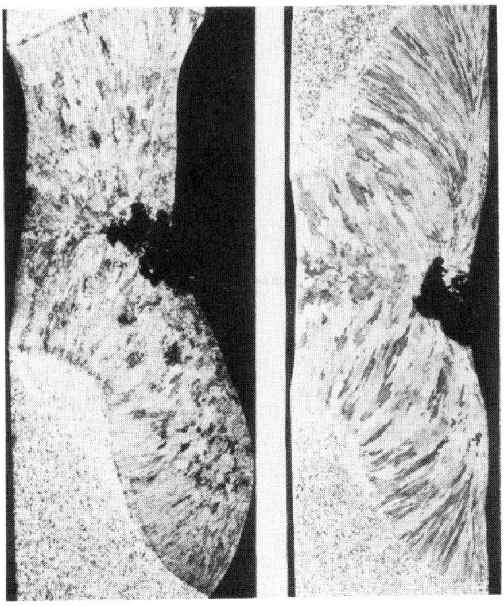

Fig. 3 Cross section of stainless steel dwell region.[7]

Convective Motion

Examination of the 24-fps flight and ground movies for all three materials indicated agreement with the analytical predictions presented earlier:

1) Significant molten metal motion was exhibited in both the dwell and continuous weld molds for both ground and flight tests.

2) Surface tension provided an equal magnitude of convection in the dwell pools in microgravity, but the filming speed was too slow to delineate flow patterns.

3) No unstable splattering was evident, even in the microgravity environment of Skylab.

Spiking Frequency

No results were reported on this characteristic of the stainless steel welds.

Beading Phenomena. Shown in Figs. 4 through 9 are photographs taken of stainless steel, aluminum, and tantalum metal disks after being subjected to eb impingement in the M551 metals melting experiment. In these photographs, Skylab flight-test specimens are compared to ground-based test specimens. The most striking phenomenon appearing in

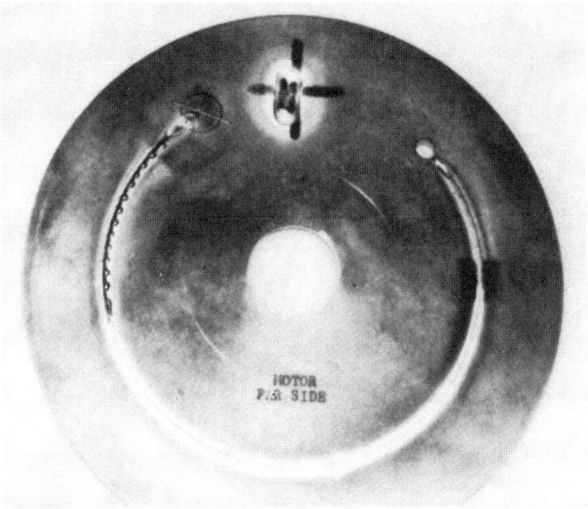

Fig.4 Stainless steel disk from M551 ground-based tests.

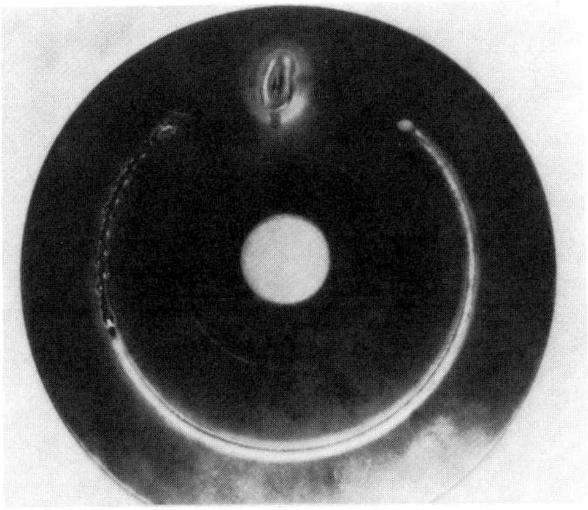

Fig. 5 Stainless steel disk from M551 flight test.

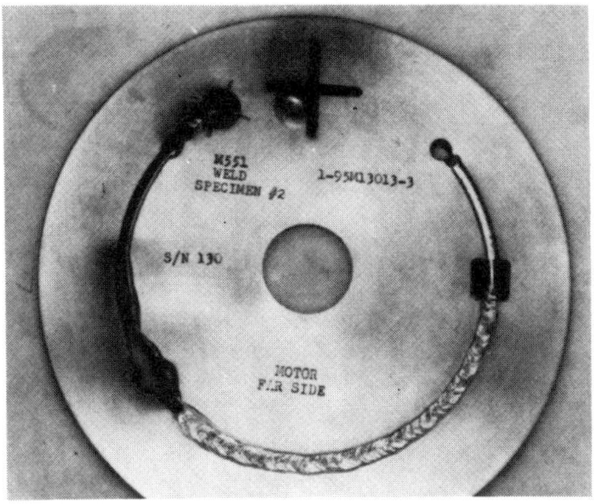

Fig.6 Aluminum disk from M551 ground-based tests.

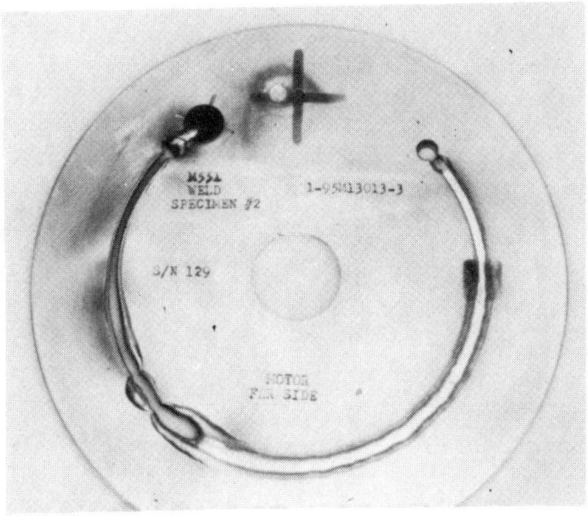

Fig. 7 Aluminum disk from M551 flight tests.

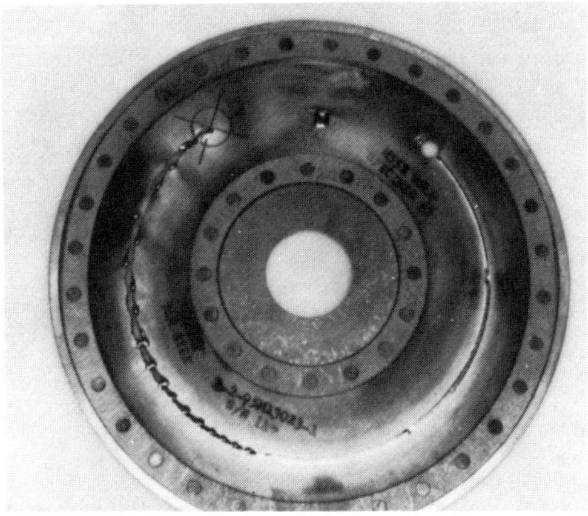

Fig. 8 Tantalum disk from M551 ground-based tests.

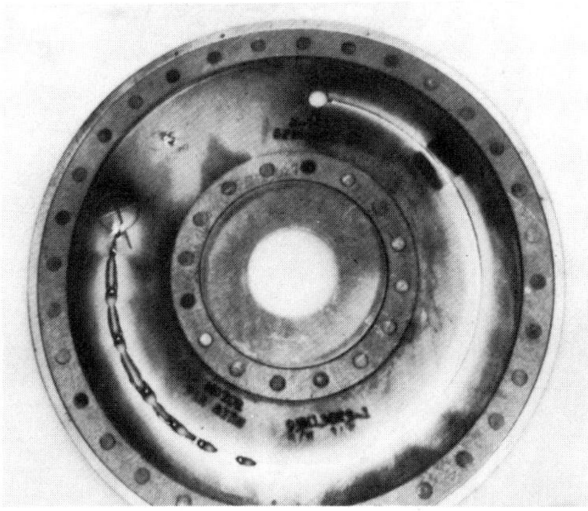

Fig. 9 Tantalum disk from M551 flight tests.

these photographs is the "beading" effect, which occurs simultaneously with total penetration in the stainless steel and tantalum specimens. It was speculated in Ref. 1 that this beading effect may be related to vortex shedding. Theoretical bead spacing along the eb track was predicted, based on calculated vortex shedding frequencies. Average bead spacing distances were estimated for both flight test and ground-based test specimens by inspection of the photographs in Figs. 4 through 9. These experimental values are compared to the predicted values in Table 2. The experimental bead spacing on the stainless steel specimens is seen to be in remarkably good agreement with the predicted value for both flight and ground-based tests. No beading is exhibited on the aluminum specimen, however, and the spacing on the tantalum specimen is considerably larger than the predicted value. Consideration was given to the possibility that the departure from vortex shedding theory might be due to "wall" effects. The presence of confining parallel has been shown[8] to modify the transverse to longitudinal stability ratio (b/a) from the well-known value of 0.281. The direction of modification is to increase the longitudinal spacing for a decreasing distance between walls.

The stainless steel ground test (Fig. 5) shows all of the beads are on the inside of the cut. This, however, is consistent with the direction of gravity, which was approximately 120° (i.e., the weld point was approximately at the 10:30 o'clock position). Note the alternating bead pattern developed for the Skylab-produced disk as shown in Fig. 4. It is felt that this resulted from the low-gravity environment and the vortex shedding mechanism.

In view of the remarkable agreement between the predicted and measured spacing for the stainless steel disks and also the alternating pattern, as verified in the low-gravity environment of Skylab, it is believed that the mechanism of vortex shedding is related to the beading pattern.

Table 2 Bead spacing

M551 materials	Bead spacing, cm Theoretical	Flight test	Ground-based test
321 stainless steel	1.0	1.1	1.1
2219 aluminum	0.8	...	...
Tantalum	0.7	3.6-3.2	2.2-1.4

Conclusions

The primary conclusion that can be reached from the results now available is that no significant practical differences exist between terrestrial and microgravity eb melting. The major difference found to date, i.e., the lack of gravity sag and shallower penetration in the aluminum and stainless steel flight-sample dwell, does not seem to have any practical benefits or detriments for conducting this operation in space. Although no results are available to date, the change in spiking frequency with gravity level and degree-of-melt superheat could lead to an increase in porosity and cold shuts in low-gravity eb welding.

It is noted that the only other known low-gravity eb welding experiments ever conducted[9] have come to similar conclusions using similar materials, beam parameters, chamber and disks, movie coverage, and low-g aircraft experimentation. Their conclusions[9] were that not much difference existed between earth and low-g specimens; aluminum rendered continuous beading, whereas stainless steel resulted in droplet beading; weld shape and penetration were the same on Earth and in low-g; and more porosity existed in one of the low-g specimens. No quantitative evaluations could be made on the magnitude and pattern of flow in the dwells because filming speed was too low. This was true for both ground and flight tests.

IV. References

[1] Bourgeois, S.V., and Brashears, M.R., "Fluid Dynamics and Kinematics of Molten Metals in the Low Gravity Environment of Skylab," AIAA Paper No. 74-205, February 1974, Washington, D.C.

[2] Brashears, M.R., Bourgeois, S.V., and Fan, C., "Analysis of Liquid Dynamics for M551 and M553 Skylab Space Processing Experiments," Proceedings of the International Colloquium on Drops and Bubbles, Vol. 1, edited by Collings, D.J., Plesset, M.S., and Saffren, M.M., California Institute of Technology and Jet Propulsion Laboratory, Pasadena, Calif., 1974, pp. 227-245.

[3] Kattamis, T.Z., "Investigation of Solidification in Zero-Gravity Environment: M553 Sphere Forming Experiment — Phase C Report," University of Connecticut, Storrs, Conn., December 4, 1973.

[4]Johnson, P.C. and Peters, E.T., "M553 Sphere Forming Experiment 90 Day Report," contract NAS8-28723, A.D. Little, Inc., Cambridge, Mass., October 1973.

[5]Brown, J. L., "Report on Preliminary Examination of Skylab Samples from the M553 Sphere Forming Experiment," contract NAS8-28735, Georgia Institute of Technology, Atlanta, September 25, 1973.

[6]"Ninety-Day Interim Report on Evaluation of M553 Sphere Forming Specimens Processed in Skylab 1/2," NASA-Marshall Space Flight Center, Huntsville, Ala., October 12, 1973.

[7]Monroe, R. E., "Characterization of Metals Melting Discs Skylab Experiment M551," Battelle Columbus Laboratories, Columbus, Ohio, December 4, 1973.

[8]Christiansen, J.P. and Zabusky, M.J., "Instability, Coalescence and Fusion of Finite-Area Vortex Structures," Journal of Fluid Mechanics, Vol. 61, Part 2, November 1973, p. 209.

[9]Paton, B.E., "Welding in Space," Welding Engineer, Vol. 57, No. 1, January 1972, pp. 25-29.

STUDIES OF ROTATING LIQUID FLOATING ZONES ON SKYLAB IV

J. R. Carruthers*
Bell Laboratories, Murray Hill, N. J.

E. G. Gibson†
NASA Johnson Spacecraft Center, Houston, Tex.

M. G. Klett‡
Lockheed Missiles & Space Company, Inc., Huntsville, Ala.

and

B. R. Facemire§
NASA George C. Marshall Space Flight Center,
Marshall Space Flight Center, Ala.

Abstract

Liquid zones of water, soap solution, and soap foam were deployed between two aligned circular disks that were free to rotate about the zone axis in the microgravity environment of Skylab IV. Such a configuration is of interest in the containerless handling of melts for possible future space processing crystal growth experiments. Three basic types of zone surface deformation and instability were observed for these

---

Presented as Paper 75-692 at the AIAA 10th Thermophysics Conference, Denver, Colo., May 27-29, 1975. We wish to thank T. C. Bannister for assistance with the configuration of the
(continued on following page)

*Head, Crystal Growth and Glass Research and Development Department, Bell Laboratories, Murray Hill, N. J.

†Member of Technical Staff, presently at The Aerospace Corp., Los Angeles, Calif.

‡Member of Technical Staff, Huntsville Research & Engineering Center, Huntsville, Ala.

§Member of Technical Staff, National Aeronautics and Space Administration, Marshall Space Flight Center, Ala.

rotational conditions: axisymmetric shape changes under single-disk rotation; nonaxisymmetric, whirling C-modes for long zones with equal rotation of both disks; and capillary wave phenomena for short zones with equal rotation of both disks. The sources of these instabilities and the conditions promoting them are analyzed in detail from videotape recordings of the Skylab experiments.

I. Introduction

One of the greatest advantages of a zero-gravity environment for the processing of materials is the elimination of containers in the handling of molten liquids. Many containers react with melts of interest during crystal growth and solidification processes so that uncontrolled contamination occurs in the crystal or ingot. One of the first successful applications was the use of floating zones to purify and grow single crystals of reactive materials such as silicon and tungsten. More recently, high-melting oxide single crystals also have been grown from floating zones. Although levitation forces may be provided by external fields to support conducting liquids away from solid surfaces, the concept of a solid in contact with its own liquid under only surface tension constraints is basically simple and central to the crystal growth process. The removal of gravitational constraints from such floating zones means that the value of the surface tension will not limit the materials that can be prepared by this technique, and that normal resistive or radiative heating of the zones can replace the more concentrated but less desirable rf heating sources currently used on Earth.

The use of a low-gravity environment removes some of the constraints imposed on the dimensions of floating zones, greatly reduces density-driven convection, and allows more extensive geometrical modifications than permitted on Earth. Studies of floating liquid zones already have been performed on Earth in a Plateau simulation system, where one transparent liquid is suspended inside another with which it is immiscible but equal in density.[1,2]

---

experimental apparatus, as well as with implementation of this work on Skylab as a science demonstration. The assistance of all flight control personnel at the NASA Johnson Space Center and J. P. Allen in coordinating the actual work is gratefully acknowledged. We also wish to thank W. Sweetland of NASA Marshall Space Flight Center for his painstaking work in the reduction of the data using the film plotter.

It was found in this simulation that static cylindrical zones of uniform radius, R, were not stable when longer than the circumference, 2πR. It was found further that rotation of the zones at a rate Ω decreased the maximum stable length, ℓ_{max}, according to

$$\ell_{max}/R = 2\pi n \quad [1 + \rho R^3\Omega^2/\sigma]^{-1/2} \qquad (1)$$

where n is the wave number, ρ is the liquid density, and σ the surface tension. The deformation of the zone from its initial cylindrical shape was axisymmetric in all cases.

These studies have provided the basis on which the present Skylab experiments were designed. However, the Plateau simulation model possesses an inherent limitation in its ability to model an actual liquid floating zone in zero-gravity because of the existence of an outer liquid surrounding the zone. This liquid influences the rotational and vibrational instability modes of the zone and also the form of the flow patterns in the zone. Consequently, important similarities as well as differences are expected between the behavior of the two systems. Such comparisons would make further Earth simulation experiments more meaningful.

Experiments with liquid floating zones on Skylab IV have indicated that nonaxisymmetric zone deformations occur in many rotational sequences.[3] Such shape perturbations, once initiated, are inherently unstable and are amplified by fluid flow in the centrifugal acceleration field. The conditions causing such instabilities are of interest, since future space experiments with molten zones, which will require rotation to provide temperature uniformity, must be designed to avoid such unstable behavior. This paper reports a detailed analysis of some experiments on Skylab IV by one of the authors (EGG).

II. Experimental Procedure

The floating zones were deployed in the arrangement shown in Fig. 1 using water and water plus dye as the liquid for most experiments.

In some sequences, a soap solution (neutrogina soap in water) and soap foam (approximately half-air,half-soap solution) were deployed to study the effects of reduced surface tension and increased viscosity respectively. The apparatus was constructed with onboard equipment and consisted of socket wrench extension rods that were mounted in four camera mounts so that they were free to rotate smoothly and could be positioned axially. The ends of the socket wrench extensions were covered with 7/8-in. diam. (2.22cm) circular aluminum

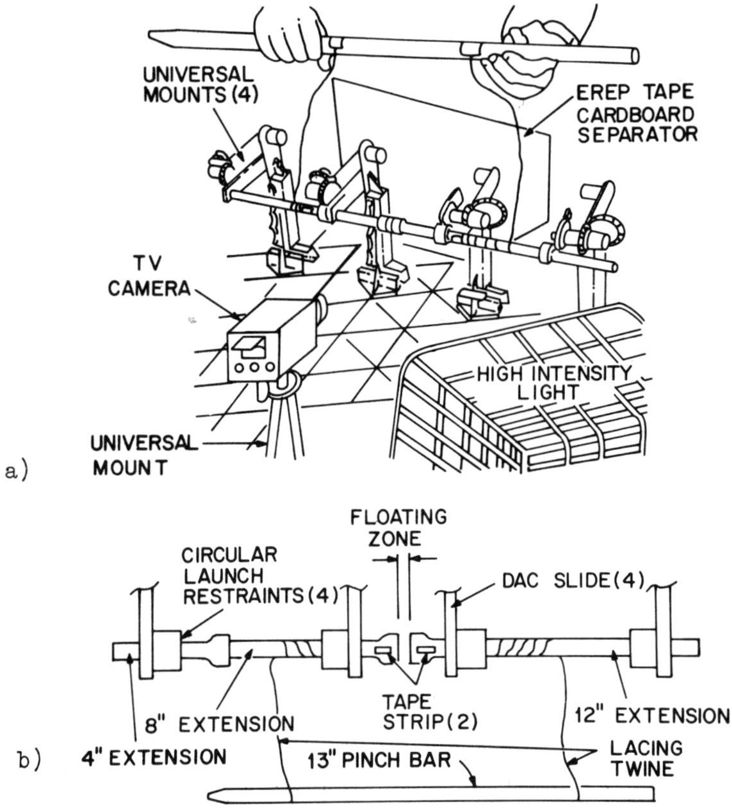

Fig. 1 Schematic of the experimental set-up for liquid floating zone studies on Skylab IV

disks. The front surfaces of the disks were coated with gray tape, which had been treated previously by immersion in acetone so as to reduce the overall contact angle with water. During the course of the experiments, the outer edges of the disks were coated with Krytox oil to prevent capillary wetting of the water in that region.

Rotation of the zones was performed manually by first winding twine around the socket wrench extensions and then withdrawing at a uniform rate. Equal isorotations and counterrotations were obtained by attaching the twine ends to a pinch bar and then withdrawing the pinch bar.

The liquid zones were deployed from calibrated syringes so that one-half of the total volume required for each zone length was placed on each disk. The zone volumes for cylindrical zones of constant circular crossection are shown in Table 1.

Table 1 Zone dimensions for a constant diam. of 7/8 in.(2.22cm)

Zone volume, cm^3	Zone length, cm
6	1.55
14	3.61
20	5.16

The zones were formed by moving the two drops together to achieve coalescence and then moving the disks apart to the specified distances. The theoretical maximum static zone length for a 7/8-in. diam. is 2-3/4 in. and nearly was achieved during a separate experiment.

The various experiments were recorded on videotape with a television camera fitted with a close-up zoom lens and a viewing monitor. Measurements subsequently were made from 16 mm films made from the videotape.

A Telereadex model 29E, manufactured by the Telecomputing Corporation, was used to read the films. Measurements were made on the projected image by positioning X and Y cross-hairs linked to magnetic reading heads. Angles are measured by a projected grid, which is rotated mechanically and digitized. The image is magnified 20 times and projected on a screen. The film is positioned and rotated on the screen by servo motors attached to the film transport. The readings are digitized by a Telecordex, which electronically is attached to the Telereadex. Punched card output was obtained from an IBM 523 summary punch. The X-Y readout has a resolution of 2000 pulses per revolution (or 7.19 cm of cross-wire travel), which is equivalent to 0.0036 cm/count (278 counts/cm). Resolution on the film is 1.8×10^{-4} cm (1.8μ). Accuracy is +0.0071 cm in X and Y. The raw data were recorded directly onto punch cards for later data retrieval and analyses. The disk diameter was used as a reference length, and tape markers on the extension rods were used as rotational timing devices.

Data are reported here for a total of 38 water, water and dye, soap solution, and soap foam zone rotation sequences. These included isorotation, counterrotation, and single rotation for the three different zone lengths. The measurements taken for each rotation sequence are illustrated in Fig. 2 and include the alignment of the rotating rods for one complete rotation sequence, the rotation rate of the rods vs. time

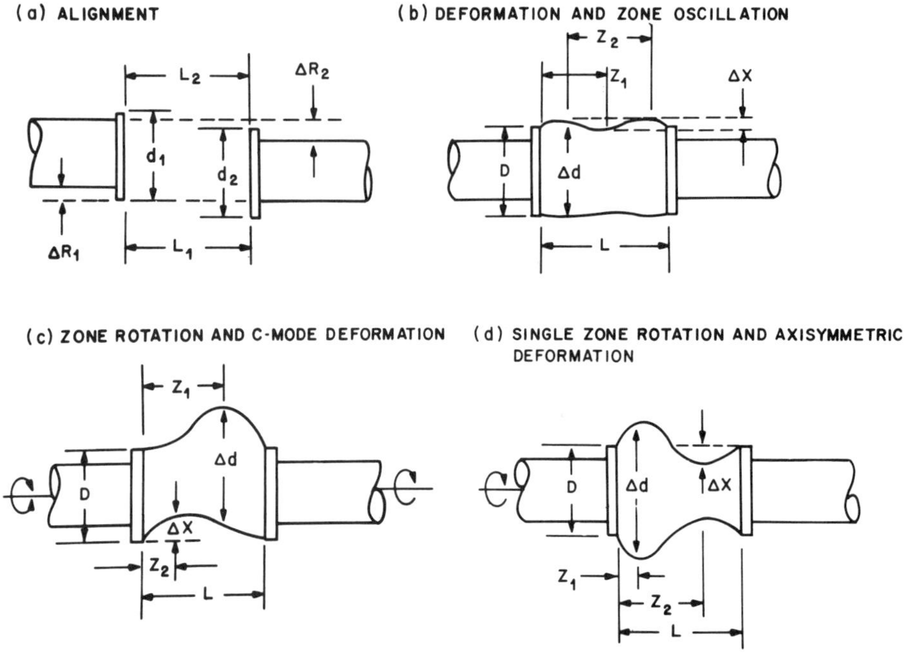

Fig. 2 Symbols used in the data reduction format of rotating liquid zone sequences

(through the end of each sequence), and the eccentric rotation rate and deformation of the liquid zones vs. time (through the end of each sequence).

It is important to distinguish between the two types of zone rotation; axisymmetric solid-body rotation, and whirling due to eccentric rotation (resembling a skipping rope). The former mode can be seen only by markers in the rotating zone, whereas the latter can be seen by the nonaxisymmetric deflection, $\Delta\chi$, as seen in Fig. 2(c).

III. Experimental Results

The transient spin-up time required for the liquid zone to reach steady-state, axisymmetric solid-body rotation after the disks have started to rotate can be estimated. Momentum is transferred to the liquid at a speed of $[\nu\Omega_D]^{1/2}$ cm/sec, where ν is the kinematic viscosity and Ω_D is the disk rotation rate. Thus for a zone length, ℓ, the spin-up time is approximately

$$\tau_s \approx \ell / \nu\Omega_D{}^{1/2} \text{sec} \qquad (2)$$

Agreement was found for water zones containing flow observation markers. The actual duration of the various rotation experiments spanned a range around τ_s values of from 3 to 25 sec. On the other hand, the nonaxisymmetric, whirling C-mode is initiated almost immediately (within a few seconds) by the eccentric nature of the rotation (measured as ΔR_1 and ΔR_2). This rotational mode is analogous to the whipping or whirling resonance found due to slight eccentricities in the axis of rotating shafts.[4] For rotating cylindrical liquid zones, the C-mode resonant frequencies, Ω_c, are

$$\Omega_c = (n\pi/\ell)^2 \, (\sigma R/\rho)^{1/2} \tag{3}$$

A second source of surface resonance is the existence of longitudinal capillary waves due to rotation at the critical rates, Ω_{cw}[5]

$$\Omega_{cw} = [2\pi(n/\ell)^3 \, (\sigma R/\rho)]^{1/2} \tag{4}$$

III.I Single Rotation Results: Axisymmetric Deformation

There were 15 sequences involving the rotation of only one disk, which in some cases, resulted in failure due to axisymmetric zone shape deformations as shown in Fig. 2(d). Since these results can be analyzed by Eq. (1), they are treated separately here. Some C-mode behavior was observed for the single rotation sequences; however, the initiation times were longer than for the other cases to be described later. The measured parameters, for a typical run (1-13) of zone length 5.08 cm, are shown in Figs. 3-5. The rod rotation and eccentric zone rotation were measured at each revolution and half-revolution respectively and are shown in Fig. 3. The theoretical spin-up time for this sequence is ∿12 sec. As noted in Fig. 3, the rotating zone became unstable at 12 sec. The positions Z1 and Z2 of the maximum and minimum diameters respectively are shown in Fig. 4. The abrupt increase in Z1 at 4 sec corresponds to the initial formation of the bottle shape indicated in Fig. 2(d). The decrease in Z2 throughout the rotational sequence indicates that the position of minimum diameter is moving (somewhat unsteadily) toward the rotating disk. The maximum diameter, Δd, increases steadily to a maximum value of 3.0 cm at 12 sec as shown in Fig. 5. The deviations of the rotation axis from the stationary position were measured as ΔR = 0.09 cm in this sequence. The resulting wobbling or whirling of the zone

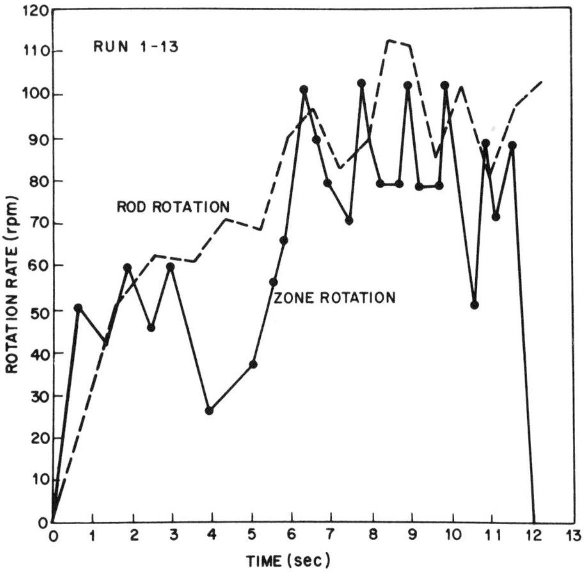

Fig. 3 Zone and rod (disk) rotation rates used for a typical single rod rotation sequence. (Water and dye zone, ℓ = 5.08 cm, τ_s = 12 sec).

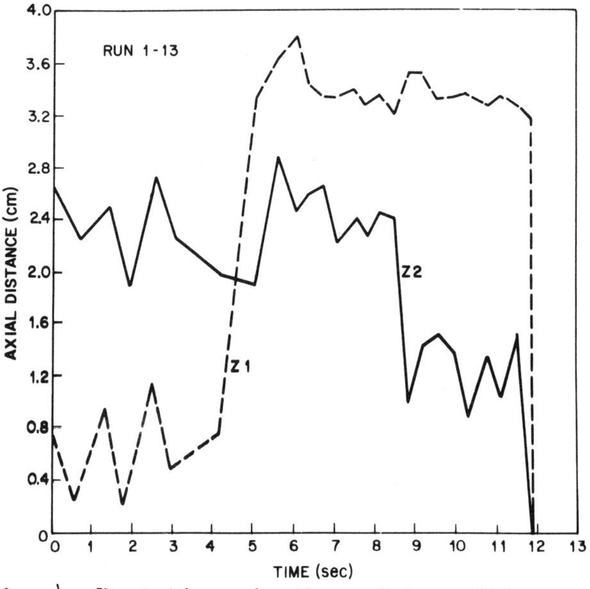

Fig. 4 Variations in the axial positions of the maximum zone diameter (at Z1) and the minimum zone diameter (at Z2) of sequence shown in Fig. 3

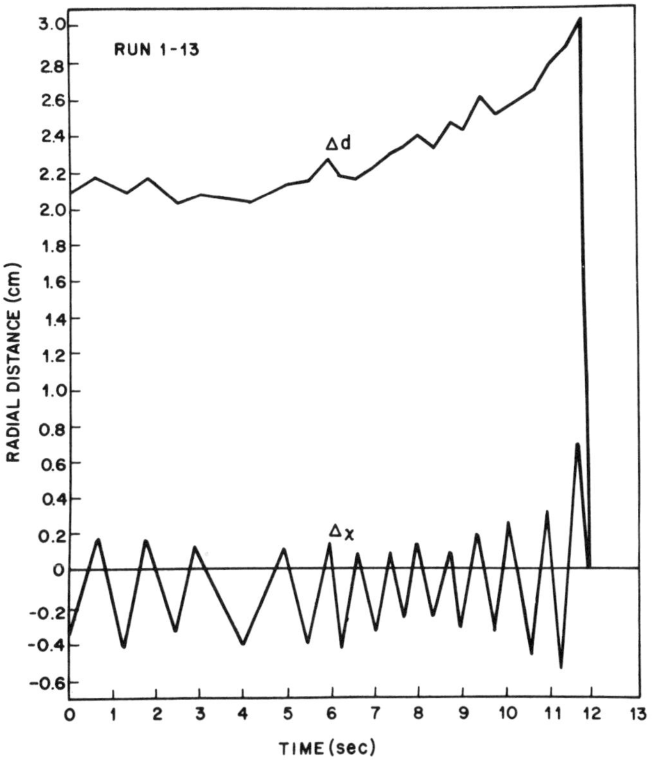

Fig. 5 Variation of the maximum diameter (Δd) and maximum surface deflection (Δχ) for the single rotation sequence shown in Fig. 3

surface is shown as Δχ in Fig. 5. This wobble occurs over Δχ values of about +0.15 to -0.35 cm from the original surface position and corresponds to a rotation axis eccentricity of e = 0.1 cm, which compares closely to the measured value of ΔR = 0.09 cm. The total range of 0.5 cm in Δχ values is small in comparison to values for C-mode instabilities to be discussed in the next section.

The rotational stability results for all single rotation sequences are shown in Fig. 6, where the estimated zone rotation rates are plotted for various zone lengths as closed symbols for stable zones and open symbols for unstable zones. The axisymmetric zone rotation rates were computed as follows.

The spin-up time, τ_s^*, for single rotation was calculated from

$$\tau_s^* = (\ell/2)\ (\nu\Omega_{avg})^{-1/2} \qquad (5)$$

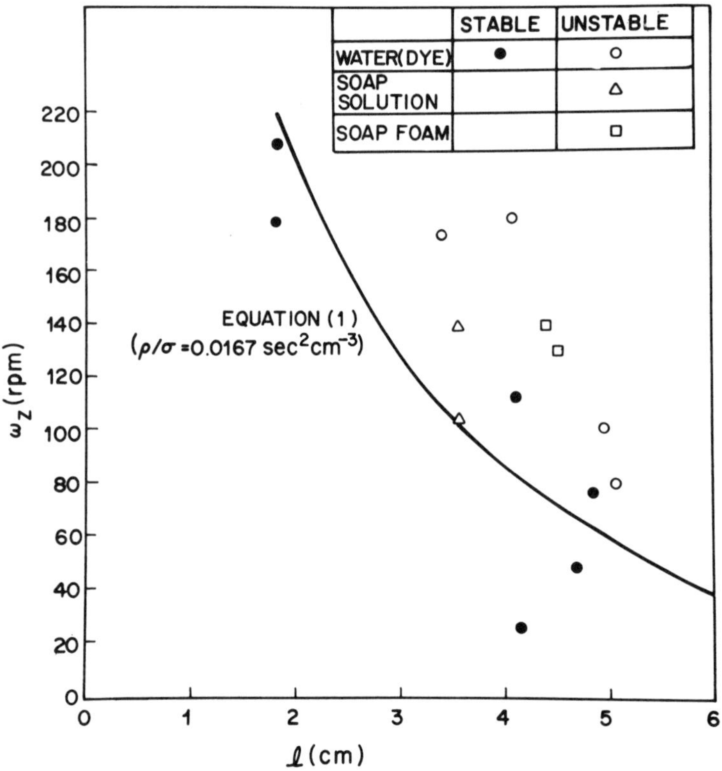

Fig. 6 Stability data for zones rotating in single rod rotation sequences at various zone lengths, ℓ. The zone rotation rates are estimated (see text).

where $\Omega_{avg} = \Omega_{max}/2$ was used because in most cases the rotation rate was increased linearly with time. The actual zone rotational rate Ω_z increases according to[6]

$$\Omega_z/\Omega_D = 1 - \exp(-2\tau/\tau_s^*) \qquad (6)$$

where Ω_D is the maximum disk rotation rate and τ is the disk rotation time. The theoretical rotation rates for unstable axisymmetric perturbations [Eq. (1)] is shown as the solid curve in Fig. 6 for a reduced surface tension of 60 dyn/cm and a liquid density of 1 g cm^{-3}. (Preliminary measurements have indicated that the addition of food coloring dyes to the water zone, as used in the Skylab work, lowered its surface tension by 10 to 15 dyn/cm[7]. The overall agreement of the experimental data with theory is very good.

The soap solution is expected to have a surface tension of 35 dyn/cm[8] and density of 1 g cm^{-3} whereas the soap foam has a comparable surface tension but a density of only 0.5 g cm^{-3}. The data of Fig. 6 do not permit a sufficiently precise comparison with Eq. (1) of the effects of changing σ and ρ.

III.II Iso- and Counter- Rotation: Nonaxisymmetric Deformation

Nonaxisymmetric zone deformations were observed for all water and soap solution zones for the isorotation and counter-rotation sequences. These resonant modes possessed several very interesting and unexpected features.

1) A resonant C-mode was initiated within a few seconds after the onset of disk rotation for the two longer-zone-length sequences.

2) The oscillation frequency, Ω_c, of the resonant non-axisymmetric C-mode was insensitive to the disk rotation rate; i.e., large variations in Ω_D produced no change in Ω_c. (In some cases, $\Omega_D < \Omega_C$).

3) The decay time of the C-mode was very long in comparison to the decay time of the superimposed axisymmetric shape perturbations. A typical decay spectrum of $\Delta\chi$ variations is shown in Fig. 7.

The initial decay of large-amplitude deflections occurs in the spindown time, $\tau_s \approx 15$ sec, and therefore must be associated with the reduction of the axisymmetric zone rotation to zero. However, the whirling C-mode continues to rotate in its non-axisymmetric fashion with very little energy dissipation. The exponential decay times are longer than the sequence times and have been estimated to be in the range of several minutes. These results indicate that such a mode would be very undesirable for space processing applications.

Further reference to Fig. 7 shows that the C-mode rotates with $\Delta\chi$ deflections between +0.25 and -0.15 cm. The measured rotation axis deflections for this sequence were $\Delta R_1 = 0.08$ cm and $\Delta R_2 = 0.13$ cm which are related to the observed zone eccentricity as follows. The theoretical maximum zone deflection at the center, y, can be related to the rotation shaft eccentricity, e, by[4]

$$y+e/e = 1/2\ [\sin(\pi/2) + \sinh(\pi/2)]. \qquad (7)$$

In the former example (Fig. 7), y = (0.25 + 0.15)/2 = 0.20 cm. The calculated value of y from Eq. (7) is 0.65 e. If it is assumed that $e = \Delta R_1 + \Delta R_2$, then y = 0.14 cm as compared to

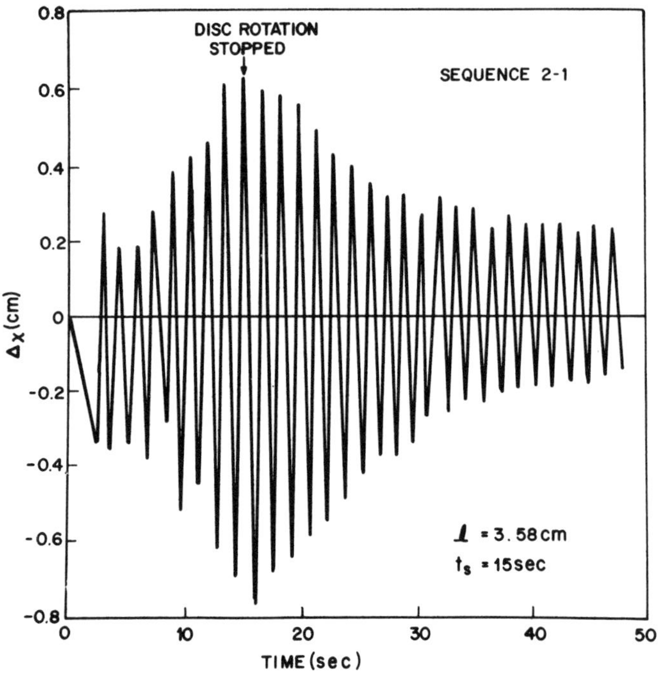

Fig. 7 Variation of the nonaxisymmetric deflection, $\Delta\chi$, of the zone surface during an isorotation sequence. The rotation of the disks (75 rpm) was stopped at the 15 sec. mark

the observed value of 0.20 cm. Consequently, the agreement of the nonaxisymmetric zone C-mode with expected theoretical behavior is reasonable.

The resonant C-mode (rotation) oscillation frequencies for all iso- and counterrotation experiments are shown in Fig. 8 for the various zone lengths.

Also plotted are the theoretical relations for C-modes [Eq. (3) with σ = 60 dyn/cm, ρ = 1 g cm^{-3}] and the resonant frequencies for longitudinal capillary waves [Eq. (4) with σ = 60 dyn/cm]. It can be seen that the longer zone lengths demonstrate the expected C-mode frequency behavior, whereas short zones exhibit only capillary waves generated by the nonparallelism of the end disks [(L_2-L_1) in Fig. 2(a)]. This was confirmed visually by the fact that the shortest zones generally did not exhibit the C-mode behavior. The intermediate zone lengths, for which the most data was collected in Figure 8, demonstrated C-mode frequencies between those of Eqs. (3) and (4). As with the single-rotation data, it was

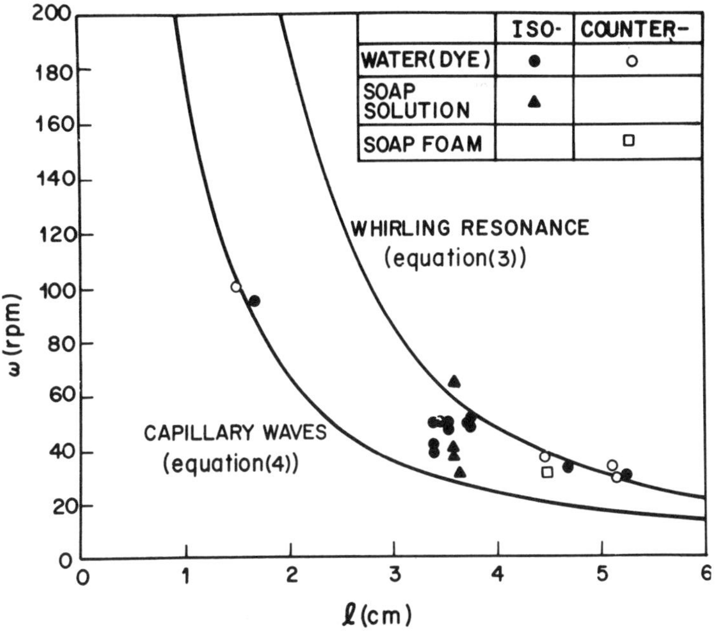

Fig. 8 Resonant oscillatory (rotation) frequencies of C-modes for zones in iso- and counter- rotation sequences at various zone lengths, ℓ.

not possible to discern easily the differences in Ω_c due to changes in σ and ρ. The soap-solution zones tended to possess a slightly lower Ω_c, as expected from the reduced surface tension of 35 dyn/cm. However, in the case of the soap-foam zones, the ratio σ/ρ remains roughly the same as that for water so that very little change in Ω_c was expected or observed.

A very important question that remains to be answered is whether a physical limit exists for the rotation axis eccentricity, e, and rotation rate below which the whirling C-mode does not occur for a cylindrical liquid zone. Such limits are important in the mechanical design of apparatus for future floating-zone space processing work. For zone lengths longer than about πR, the imposed rotation rate should be less than Ω_c [Eq. (3)] to avoid the onset of the C-mode resonance, since in principle, any finite value of e will be sufficient to cause the instability. For shorter zone lengths, where capillary wave instabilities become resonant, the imposed zone rotation rate should be less than Ω_{cw} [Eq. (4)].

IV. Summary

The rotational stability of cylindrical liquid floating zones has been studied in the reduced-gravity environment of Skylab IV. For sequences involving the single rotation of only one bounding disk, the zone assumed an axisymmetric bottle-shaped deformation possessing stability limits in general agreement with theory. For sequences involving equal rotation rates of both bounding disks, the zone becomes deformed in a nonaxisymmetric fashion resembling a turning skipping rope when the zone lengths exceed some value in the vicinity of $(2/3)\pi R$. This so-called C-mode is analogous to the whipping or whirling resonance found in eccentrically rotating shafts and, once initiated, is relatively insensitive to the axisymmetric disk rotation velocity. Such modes are self-amplifying in centrifugal acceleration fields and possess extremely long decay times upon reduction of disk rotation rates to zero. Short zone lengths generally do not develop the rotating C-mode, but do demonstrate capillary wave resonances presumably arising from nonparallel disk alignment.

All of these rotational stability features are expected to be present in molten floating zones to be used in future space processing experiments, unless proper precautions to eliminate them are taken. The most reasonable solution to eliminate nonaxisymmetric C-modes is to use end-member rotation velocities well-below the resonant Ω_c values for long zones. For short zones, the applied rotation velocities should be below the capillary wave resonance values, Ω_{cw}. For all of these cases, the rotation velocities are well-below the values for which instability by axisymmetric zone deformation will occur.

References

[1]Carruthers, J. R. and Grasso, M.,"Stabilities of Floating Liquid Zones in Simulated Zero Gravity," Journal of Crystal Growth, Vol. 13/14, June 1972, pp. 611-614.

[2]Carruthers, J. R. and Grasso, M., "Studies of Floating Liquid Zones in Simulated Zero Gravity," Journal of Applied Physics, Vol. 43, February 1972, pp. 436-445.

[3]Carruthers, J. R., "Studies of Floating Liquid Zones on Skylab IV," Proceedings of the Conference on Space Processing - Skylab Results, NASA, April 1974.

[4]Thornton, D. L., Mechanics Applied to Vibrations and Balancing, J. Wiley and Sons, N.Y., 1940, p. 404.

[5]Lamb, H., Hydrodynamics, 6th ed., Dover Publishing Co., N.Y., 1932, p. 456.

[6]Greenspan, H. P., The Theory of Rotating Fluids, Cambridge University Press, 1968, p. 171.

[7]Vaughn, O., private communication, Sept. 1974.

[8]Bourgeois, S. V., private communication, Sept. 1974.

SOLUTION CALORIMETRY IN ZERO GRAVITY

W.Hemminger*, F.Haeßner†

Institut für Werkstoffkunde und Herstellungsverfahren
der Technischen Universität Braunschweig,Germany

H.L.Lukas‡

Max-Planck-Institut für Metallforschung, Institut
für Werkstoffwissenschaften,Stuttgart,Germany

Abstract

The formation enthalpy of a metallic composite phase is measured most accurately on Earth by solution calorimetry with liquid metals as solvent. This method is not applicable for composite phases with reactive elements (Ti, V, Zr, Nb, Hf, Ta as well as the rare earth metals), since these elements react with the container material. However, in the Spacelab it is possible to position the freely suspended sample and solvent, to allow them to coalesce and then to measure the heat of solution. Supporting fields are necessary for stable positioning of the sample. There is a choice of electromagnetic and acoustic fields. For electromagnetic fields the ratio of induced heating power to supporting force is so large, that even under Spacelab conditions, it is difficult to keep the parasitic heating power low enough. Exact measurements are only possible when the supporting fields are switched off for most of the time, and are only switched on for sample transport or

---

Presented as Paper 74-666 at the AIAA/ASME 1974 Thermophysics and Heat Transfer Conference, Boston, Mass., July 15-17, 1974. Published here in a revised version. This work is part of the Space Processing Programme in Germany and was financed by the Bundesminister für Forschung und Technologie, represented by the Bereich für Projektträgerschaften in der DFVLR, Köln, Germany.

*Assistant Professor.

†Full Professor of Materials Science,
Head of the Institute.

‡Associate Professor.

correction of disturbances. The main difficulty with an acoustic supporting field is the controlled approach of sample and solvent for the purpose of mixing.

Introduction

The low accelerations which will prevail in the Spacelab permit novel types of experiment to be conducted. A particular group of these experiments are the "support-free measuring techniques", i.e. non-contact measurements on freely floating test samples. In this way chemical reactions of the test sample with the container walls and contamination of the sample by the container material can be avoided even at high temperatures. If sensors are employed which do not touch the test sample but rather react to radiation or fields, then sample characteristics may be obtained without mechanical contact of the sensor.

One might think that support free measurements could be carried out on Earth during levitation melting. However, the electromagnetic or acoustic fields required have to be of such high energy that many measurements are disturbed e.g. because of the strong and not exactly definable heating effect, or because of too intense, irregular sample movement. Calorimetry at high temperatures also belongs to this category, for instance the determination of the formation enthalpy of alloys or composite oxides by solution calorimetry in molten metals or salts respectively.

The formation enthalpy is one of the most important sources of thermodynamic data. The latter can be used to check or refine theoretical atomic bond models and also form the basis for the calculation of equilibria, such as phase diagrams.[1-3] Understanding of these diagrams for metals is one of the most important provisions for every controlled and selective development of alloys. The purely experimental determination of these phase diagrams is very painstaking compared with thermodynamic analysis, particularly for higher multi-component systems. Very sophisticated alloys, which are steadily gaining importance as engineering materials today, usually comprise four or more components. Since the corresponding phase diagrams, with a few exceptions, are only known today as far as three component systems, thermodynamic computation of the former for the improvement of alloys is of great value and so too is the determination of the formation enthalpy. Similar considerations apply in the case of the equilibrium diagrams of high melting point, non-metallic compounds such as oxides, nitrides and carbides, which have recently been in the focus of interest as high temperature raw materials. In the following, however, we shall restrict ourselves solely to the example of metals.

Solution calorimetry

The formation enthalpy of metallic phases may be measured most accurately on Earth by solution calorimetry with liquid metals as solvent [4,5]. Here the compound A_xB_y in question is dissolved in a suitable molten metal, e.g. aluminium (Fig.1). The heat of solution Q_1 of the compound A_xB_y is derived from the change in temperature of the melt. In the same manner the individual components of the compound, the elements A and B here, are dissolved in the melt in the appropriate quantities. This heat of solution too, Q_2, is measured. The formation enthalpy ΔH^F of the compound A_xB_y follows as the difference of both heats of solution. The advantage of this method, compared with other possible procedures, is that the formation enthalpy is not determined as the small difference of two large quantities, but is generally of the same order of magnitude as the measured heats of solution [4,5]. When the solvent is one of the components of the alloy the formation enthalpy versus concentration curve can be particularly accurately measured [6].

Many metallic multi-component systems (alloys) contain strongly reactive elements, which react in the liquid state (even in dilute solution) with all known crucible materials. Measurement of the heat of solution is quite impossible in this case, or only very inaccurately so, since it would be superimposed by the heat of reaction. This is true, for instance, of the elements in the IV and V sub-groups of the periodic system, namely for Ti, V, Zr, Nb, Hf and Ta and the rare earth metals (sub-group III). In these cases the heats of solution must be determined in a measuring arrangement without crucibles. At first sight, levitation-melting offers a means on ground of proceeding without crucibles. However, calorimetry cannot be carried out in this way since the temperature change of the melt can only be partly attributed to the heat of solution of the sample. In fact, under certain circumstances, a very much larger portion can be assigned to fluctuations of the power induced in the sample. On earth a strong electromagnetic field is required to hold metals in suspension. The power induced in the suspended body depends on its shape and resistivity. From the instant of coalescence of the sample and the melt, both these properties are altered in an incalculable manner. Thus, whilst the sample dissolves in the melt, the constantly present fluctuations of the induced power become extreme and can overlap the heat of solu-

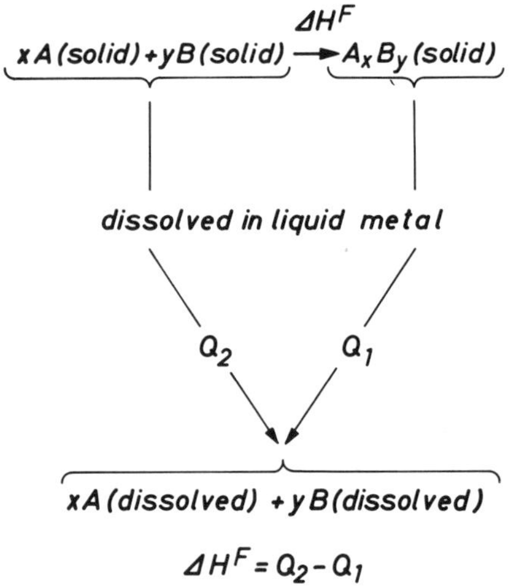

Fig. 1 The measurement of the formation enthalpy ΔH^F of a metallic composite phase A_xB_y.

tion completely. To reduce the induced power and its fluctuations it is necessary to decrease the field strength. But since the supporting force then also decreases [7] it is clear that a calorimetric arrangement with electromagnetic supporting fields can only be operated under reduced gravity.

A solution calorimeter for "zero-gravity"

Conditions in the Spacelab will offer ideal provisions for a crucible-free measuring arrangement with weak supporting fields. In the following we shall discuss how a solution calorimeter may be devised for the Spacelab, the problems which will be met in the process and which questions should be dealt with before the device is actually built.

Operating principle

The basic idea is that the solvent and the solute sample shall be inserted in a tube furnace at constant temperature (Fig.2) and freely held side by side. After the solvent metal has melted and thermal equilibrium has set in, the sample and the solvent metal are brought close to one another and allowed to mix. The heat of solution alters the temperature of the melt, this produces a change in the heat flow from the inner to the outer surface of the tube wall. The temperature difference ΔT between the inner and outer side of the tube, averaged over the surface, is proportional to the instantaneous thermal flux, i.e. $\Delta T \sim dQ/dt$. It follows that the quantity of heat transferred through the tube wall is given by

$$Q = k(T, \ldots.) \int \Delta T(t)\, dt.$$

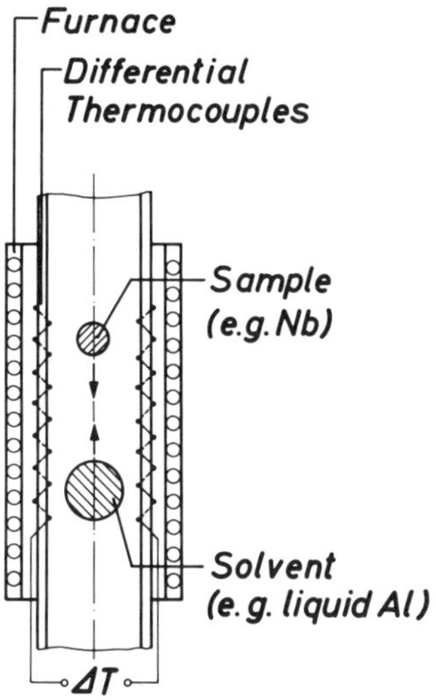

Fig. 2 Schematic representation of the solution calorimeter for freely suspended samples.

k(T, ...) is a quantity depending on the apparatus which must be determined by calibration. It is a function of the temperature, the tube dimensions and the type and arrangement of the temperature sensors. To measure the temperature difference ΔT a similar differential thermopile should be adequate as employed in heat flow calorimeters according to the principle developed by Tian and Calvet [8]. The thermopile is combined with the tube which limits the reaction zone. The measuring points of the thermoelements lie in differential connection alternately (Fig.2). In this way the temperature difference ΔT between the inside and outside of the tube, averaged over the surface, can be measured.

Experimental conditions

To measure the formation enthalpy of alloys of metals belonging to the III, IV and V sub-groups liquid aluminium or copper are considered as solvents. Since the procedure with regard to the reactants is relatively universal, a detailed account of all the systems of interest is superfluous at the present time. To guarantee a sufficiently high solution velocity and solubility of the solid samples in the melt, the operating temperature of the calorimeter should lie between 800°C and 1300°C. Densely sintered alumina can be considered as furnace material; operation is in a rare gas atmosphere. The smallest expected heats of solution are of the order of 100 J/sample. This quantity of heat should be accurately measurable to 1 %, so that differences in the formation enthalpy may be determined for those alloys which differ from one another only slightly in the concentration of one component. This condition means that undefined disturbing energies of only up to 0.1 J at the most can be tolerated during the measurement.

Positioning of the sample

Since disturbing residual accelerations are present in the Spacelab, supporting fields are necessary to hold the samples in their prescribed positions. The strength of these supporting fields is determined on the one hand by the anticipated disturbing accelerations. On the other hand, the parasitic quantity of heat produced in the sample and surrounding gas volume by the supporting field should be as small as possible, so that high accuracy of measurement may be achieved. The critical phase in the experimental run is always the time interval in which the solid sample is immersed in the liquid metal sphere and dissolves. During the solution process the shape of the suspended body changes (and that of the adjacent gas volume), as well as its chemical and physical properties. The errors which result as a consequence enter fully into the measurement.

For operation of the solution calorimeter in the Spacelab it should be observed that the supporting field used must permit automatic sequence of numerous measurements. There is only the choice of an electromagnetic or acoustic supporting field. Independent of the type of field, controlled approach of solvent and solid sample for the purpose of mixing must be ensured. Since the solid sample and the melt differ with respect to their diameters and physical properties, this requirement means that the supporting force of the field used must either be relatively independent of these parameters (acoustic field), or it must consist of individual, locally adjustable partial fields (electromagnetic fields). Both systems have advantages as well as disadvantages for the purpose in hand; these shall be briefly examined below.

A comprehensive amount of work has been done on electromagnetic positioning for reduced gravity conditions [9]. The production of suitable fields for the support and transport of samples and hence automation are possible [9,10]. Several metallic samples can be manipulated simultaneously and largely independently by locally bounded individual fields which are adapted to each respective sample. The experiments may be carried out in vacuum, or under optional protective gas atmospheres, without influencing the supporting fields. Under the heading disadvantages one may mention: the construction elements within the high-frequency coils may affect the field only slightly; the thermoelement system for measuring the temperature difference ΔT must be insensitive to the high-frequency field, e.g. by using bifilar winding. If an interference energy of only 0.1 J is tolerated during the measurement, the values of thermal power induced in the sample can easily become too high, even for weak fields. The thermal power N_1 induced in a sphere of radius R and electrical conductivity σ in a locally homogeneous alternating field of amplitude H_0, is given by (e.g. compare Eq. 14 in Ref. 7)

$$N_1 = 3\,\pi\,H_0^2\,R\,F_1/\sigma$$

F_1 is the "eddy current heating function", see Ref. 7.
An additive contribution N_2 to N_1 can be calculated [10] for the field gradient $\partial H_0/\partial z$, (z = local coordinate)

$$N_2 = 5\,\pi\,R^3\,(\partial H_0/\partial z)^2\;F_2/\sigma$$

(The function F_2 is quoted in Ref. 10).
Hence the calculation of the total power $N = N_1 + N_2$ in a sphere is possible to a second approximation. With the aid of the familiar expression for the force acting on the sphere[7], the ratio of the induced total power to the effective force may be calculated for various distances b of the center of the sphere from the field zero point. The result is

$$N/P = (5\,F_2 + 3\,b^2F_1/R^2)/2\,\sigma\,\mu\,b\,G$$

μ = permeability of the sphere material, G is the "body force function" (see Ref. 7).
This ratio is represented in Fig. 3 for a frequency of 10^5Hz as a function of the sphere radius with the resistivity as

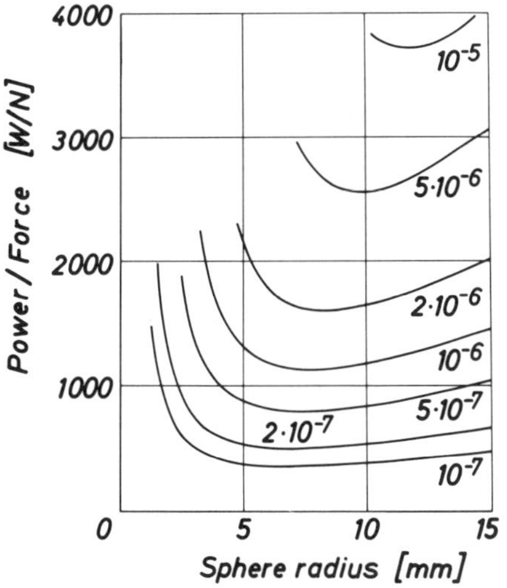

Fig. 3 Ratio of induced heating power to supporting force as a function of sphere radius. Parameter: resistivity in ohm-meters. Frequency 100 kHz; distance of sphere center from field zero point 5 mm.

parameter. The distance of the sphere center from the field zero point was assumed to be 5 mm. The following may be inferred from the calculations: a) The ratio of thermal power to force is strongly dependent on the distance between the sphere center and the field zero point. b) For calorimetry of the required accuracy working conditions should be in the region of minimum N/P.

The measuring conditions are most favourable in the Spacelab for those time intervals in which no disturbing accelerations need be compensated. The force and heating power of the field can then vanish, i.e., the coils of the positioning system can be without current. For exact measurements, therefore, the fields should only be switched on for sample transport and for monitoring disturbances. The layout of an electromagnetic positioning and transport system, with orthogonal coil pairs, which fulfills these conditions is described in Ref. 10.

Acoustic positioning has the advantage that outside the cavity no constructional restrictions exist. Compared with the electromagnetic system, here there are no restrictive conditions for the furnace material and for the system with which the temperature difference ΔT is measured. As yet, with regard to acoustic positioning, there are no such detailed investigations to hand as for electromagnetic methods. Nevertheless, on the basis of the work done to date [11,12,13,14], it is already quite clear that the main problem of the solution calorimeter project lies in mixing the sample and melt together out of adjacent suspension positions (pressure nodes). Fundamental solutions, as should be possible in an acoustic field, do exist [15]; whether these are practicable or not will have to be experimentally examined. Another problem concerns the changes in the parasitic heating power in the gas volume. Since the shape of the suspended body and so too the geometry of the gas chamber change during the dissolving process, variations could occur in the heating power of the field in the gas volume which would enter into the measurement as errors. This question too still remains to be experimentally clarified. These investigations are now in progress with the prototype of an acoustic positioning system (Fig. 4). Here multi-axial positioning is achieved by the excitation of suitable modes of the standing wave with a single transducer.

Interference effects

In all Spacelab experiments with liquids one should bear in mind that certain effects could become significant for the

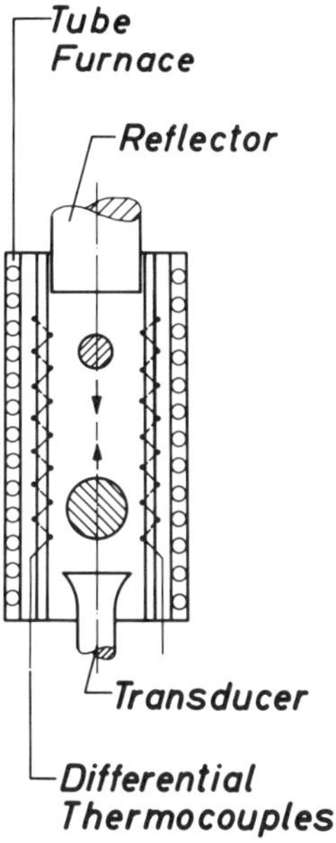

Fig. 4 Schematic representation of the solution calorimeter with acoustic positioning.

experimental sequence which are veiled by gravity on Earth [16, 17]. Most of these effects cannot be examined accurately enough on Earth and so,on the one hand, they themselves could become the testing objective in the Spacelab; on the other hand for experiments with liquids they represent disturbing factors which can hardly be assessed. For the solution calorimeter proposed here, specifically those disturbing factors are important which are caused by the coalescence and mixing of the reactants during a change in enthalpy. Oscillations can thereby be induced; temperature and concentration gradients are set up within the body and on the surface of the melt, which can give rise to strong convection currents. All these disturbing effects are only of interest here in conjunction with the following questions: Does the melt remain in cohesion or can it disperse by spattering? To which accelerations can the melt be subject as a result of these effects? These questions are still unanswered; they will have to be cleared up as far as possible by analytical evaluation and by suitable trial experiments.

The analysis so far of the proposed experiments has shown that there are no fundamental difficulties to prevent the realization of the project. A number of detailed technical questions still remain to be answered before the calorimeter is actually built. The active interest shown in the thermodynamic data measurable using the Spacelab calorimeter in our opinion justifies that this project be continued.

References

[1]Kaufman, L. and Bernstein, H., Computer Calculations of Phase Diagrams, Academic Press, New York, 1970.

[2]Hillert, M., Phase Transformations, Chapter 5, American Society for Metals, Metals Park, Ohio, 1970.

[3]Chart, T.G., Counsell, J.F., Jones, G.P., Slough, W., and Spencer, P.J., "Provision and Use of Thermodynamic Data for the Solution of High-Temperature Practical Problems," International Metallurgical Reviews, Vol. 20, March 1975, pp. 57-82.

[4]Kubaschewski, O. and Hultgren, R., Experimental Thermochemistry, Vol. 2, Chapter 16, edited by H.A. Skinner, Interscience Publishers, New York-London, 1962.

[5]Kubaschewski, O., Evans, E.Ll., and Alcock, C.B., Metallurgical Thermochemistry, Pergamon Press, Oxford, 1967.

[6]Henig, E.-Th. and Lukas, H.L., "Kalorimetrische Bestimmung der Bildungsenthalpie und die Beschreibung der Fehlordnung der geordneten β-Phase $(Ni, Cu)_{1-x}\ Al_x$," Zeitschrift für Metallkunde, Vol. 66, Feb. 1975, pp. 98-106.

[7]Fromm, E. and Jehn, H., "Electromagnetic Forces and Power Absorption in Levitation Melting," British Journal of Applied Physics, Vol. 16, May 1965, pp. 653-663.

[8]Calvet, E. and Prat, H., "Recent Progress in Microcalorimetry", Pergamon Press, 1963, pp. 12-20.

[9]Frost, R.T., Bloom, H.L., Napaluch, L.J., Stockhoff, E.H., and Wouch, G., "Electromagnetic Containerless Processing Requirements and Recommended Facility Concept and Capabilities for Space Lab," Final Report, 13 May 1974, Prepared for NASA, Contract NAS 8-29680.

[10]Haessner, F., Hemminger, W., and Lukas, H.L., "Halterungsfreie Meßtechnik, Bestimmung von Reaktionsenthalpien unter Schwerelosigkeit zwecks gezielter Verbesserung von erdgebundenen Einrichtungen," Bericht für den Bundesminister für Forschung und Technologie, vertreten durch DFVLR/BPT, Vertragsnr. RV21-B31/74-KA-50-WRT 1074, Oct. 1975.

[11]Lierke, E.G., "Study on Positioning and Stirring of Molten Material in "Zero" Gravity Environments by Ultrasonic Methods," Report for ESRO, Contract No. SC/39/40, Nov. 1974.

[12]Lierke, E.G. and Grossbach, R., "Study on Positioning of Molten Materials in "Zero" Gravity Environment by Ultrasonic Methods-Phase 2," Report for ESA, Contract SC/67/HG, Nov.1975.

[13]Whymark, R.R., "Acoustic Field Positioning for Containerless Processing," Ultrasonics, Nov. 1975, pp. 251-261.

[14]Wang, T.G., Saffren, M.M., and Elleman, D.D., "Acoustic Chamber for Weightless Positioning," AIAA Paper 74-155, Jan. 1974, New York.

[15]Lierke, E.G., private communication, Feb. 1976.

[16]Grodzka, P.G., "Types of Natural Convection in Space Manufacturing Processes," Summary Report, Prepared for NASA, Contract NAS 8-25577, Jan. 1973.

[17]Ostrach, S., "Convection at Reduced Gravity," Second European Symposium on Material Sciences in Space, Frascati (Italy), April 6-8, 1976.

JETTING ACTION DUE TO DIFFERENTIAL EVAPORATION IN SPACE PROCESSING

C.H. Li*
Grumman Aerospace Corporation, Bethpage, N.Y.

Abstract

The importance of a jetting action due to differential evaporation in space processing is first discussed. A simple jetting model is then proposed involving an ideal, differentially heated sphere under steady state conditions. Equations are derived relating the diameter and density of the sphere and the differential vapor pressures on its two sides to the acceleration of the sphere, the equivalent gravity, and time to travel known distance before impacting nearby wall or object. Typical computed results are given listing the stabilizing impurities on Ni, and the jetting actions on Ni and Fe spheres with or without surface contaminations. The resultant equivalent gravities may run as high as 10^4 or even 10^7 g that could completely mask or reverse any zero-gravity effects anticipated in space processing. Fluid disturbances due to this jetting action are next discussed with special reference to a new type of evaporative convection which is completely different in origin, characteristics, and effects from those due to surface tension and/or buoyance effects that are extensively reviewed in the literature.

I. Introduction

In any space processes, it is important not to subject the test samples to accelerations due to gravity or other forces. Furthermore, the molten samples should not touch the

---

Presented as Paper 74-667 at the AIAA/ASME 1974 Thermophysics and Heat Transfer Conference, Boston, Mass., July 15-17, 1974. This work was partially supported by NASA Contract NAS 8-27891.

*Research Scientist, Research Department.

wall of the work chamber before solidification. Different rates of evaporation at various surface regions of a freely suspended sample do, however, give rise to unbalanced forces and momenta that may produce erratic or unwanted accelerations and undesirable sample impingement onto the work chamber wall. Such differential evaporation may result from solute segregation, surface contamination, nozzle detachment, or temperature gradient. For example, one-sided heating by an electron beam introduces both severe evaporative segregation and very steep temperature gradients.[1]

When planning space manufacturing processes involving material solidification it is, therefore, desirable to have quantitative answers to the following specific questions:

1) What are the jetting forces on samples of different elemental materials under given temperature nonuniformity conditions? What chemical elements or alloys are stable (i.e., subjected to small jetting forces) at above their melting points, and what other elements or alloys are unstable?

2) What is the effect of sample size and density on the jetting forces?

3) For a given sample material, what are the critical or undesirable impurities, and what are the desirable or stabilizing impurities?

4) What are the equivalent accelerations or gravities on the samples under specified test conditions?

5) Starting from rest, how long does it take for a differentially evaporating sample to reach the wall of work chamber of a given size?

6) What is the minimum work chamber size or maximum degree of superheating for a given sample material and size?

7) How should the sample be heated and released, and with what equipment?

II. The Jetting Model

The preceding questions and others can be answered by a simple analysis of the steady-state, jetting action on an ideal, differentially heated sphere, taken as a single free body, such as is shown in Fig. 1.

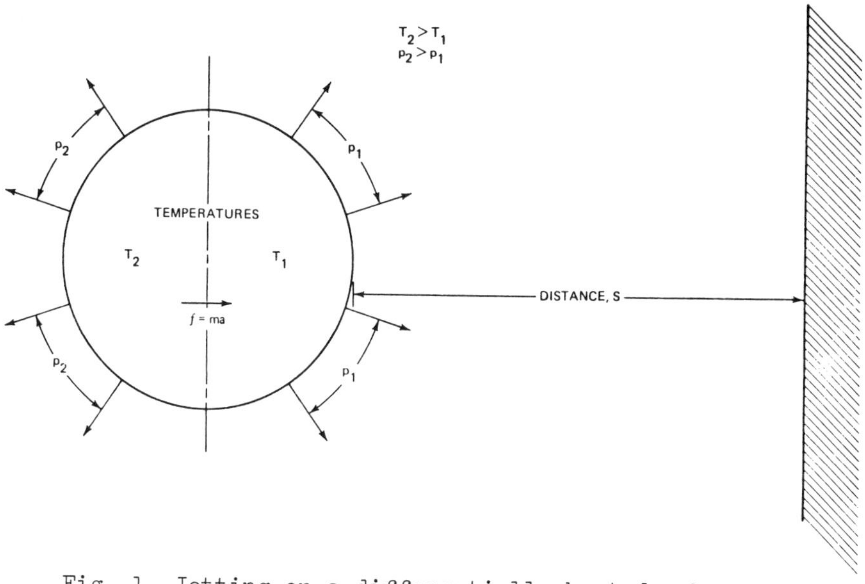

Fig. 1 Jetting on a differentially heated sphere.

In Fig. 1, the right half of the sphere is assumed to have a uniform temperature T_1, which is lower than T_2, the uniform surface temperature of the left half of the sphere. As a result of the differential heating on the sphere, the vapor pressure p_2 on the left half of the sphere is greater than that (p_1) on the right half. Hence, the non-uniform vapor pressures on the spherical surface will give rise to a larger jetting or recoil force on the left half of the sphere than on the right half. The difference between these two recoil forces, being the net and only external force associated with the spherical free body (we assume zero gravity in space), will produce an acceleration on the sphere.

This acceleration a is, of course, equal to the net jetting or recoil force f, divided by the mass of the sphere of diameter d and density ρ. Thus

$$f = [\tfrac{1}{2}(p_2 - p_1)]\ (\pi d^2/4) = [\pi d^3 \rho/6]\ a \qquad (1)$$

where $\frac{1}{2}(p_2 - p_1)$ is the unit unbalanced pressure or force and $\pi d^2/4$ the cross-sectional area of the sphere, and $\pi d^3\rho/6$ the mass of the sphere. Note in particular the numerical factor $\frac{1}{2}$ which results from the fact that the rate of momentum acquired by a liquid surface when its molecules are evaporating into a vacuum is equal to half of the saturation vapor pressure, as is shown in the Appendix due to Dr. James Yen of the Grumman Research Department.

Hence, the acceleration due to the jetting action is

$$a = (p_2-p_1)/4d\rho \qquad (2)$$

The equivalent gravity is then a divided by the gravitational constant $g = 9.81\ m/sec^2$

$$g_e = a/g = a/9.81 \qquad (3)$$

and the time t for the jetting sample to travel the distance s before impacting the nearby wall or object is

$$t = \sqrt{2s/a} = \sqrt{8ds\rho/3(p_2-p_1)} \qquad (4)$$

In the above analysis, we assume zero initial velocity and acceleration; the equations are corrected easily for non-zero initial velocity and acceleration. The times computed are, therefore, the maximum allowable for performing the experiment or processing. Note that these times are proportional to ρds raised to the one-half power. In addition, they depend even more critically on $\Delta T = T_2-T_1$ and on the evaporation behavior of the sample material, i.e., on p_2-p_1. This is because the elemental vapor pressures vary by over 22 orders of magnitude at the melting point of nickel (1726°K), and because these vapor pressure are highly temperature sensitive, as can be shown.[2]

III. Typical Computed Results

To compute the jetting action on single-component spheres, 51 metallic elements whose evaporation constants are given by Dushman[2] have been screened for potential, space-processing materials. Here, the sample diameter is fixed at 6×10^{-3} m, whereas the allowable distance of travel is constant at 0.3 m. These dimensions correspond to those used for the Skylab M512 Experiment. Furthermore, half of the spherical surface is assumed to be at T_1, the melting point of the sample material, whereas the other half is at T_2, being superheated by 5 to 100% of the absolute melting temperature. Computations show that the allowable times at 5% superheating vary widely from tens of milliseconds for K to over 10^9 yr for gallium. Table 1 summarizes the data on these highly stable sample materials, as compared to nickel. These results further stress the critical importance of surface contamination and impurity segregation due to evaporation.

Figures 2 and 3 show the jetting characteristics of nickel and iron spheres, respectively. One side of the sphere

Table 1. List of Stable Sample Materials, as Compared to Nickel

Element	Melting Point, K	Times at Degree of Superheating Indicated, sec		
		10%	20%	50%
Ga	302.9	1.68×10^{16}	3.13×10^{14}	4.88×10^{10}
Sn	505.0	1.43×10^{9}	1.09×10^{8}	3.84×10^{5}
In	429.7	6.26×10^{8}	4.96×10^{7}	1.89×10^{5}
La	1099	1.00×10^{4}	1.90×10^{3}	49.8
Bi	544	4.47×10^{3}	9.59×10^{2}	33.3
Pb	600.6	1.92×10^{2}	4.61×10^{2}	20.7
Ni	1726	2.60	0.870	8.42×10^{-2}
Fe	1812	1.09	0.399	4.78×10^{-2}

is at the absolute melting point of the pure element, whereas the other side is at a specified degree of superheat above this melting point. These figures illustrate the superheated vapor pressure, equivalent gravity, and time to travel 0.30 m, for a 6.0×10^{-3}-m molten metal sphere, heated to its melting point on one side but superheated on the other. The amount of superheating varies from 5 to 100% at 5% intervals.

The unwanted accelerations due to differential evaporation, although completely negligible in many materials, are serious factors to be considered in others, including the specified nickel samples in M512 Skylab experiments. Specifically, it takes only 10 or 20% superheating on one side of a 6×10^{-3}-m molten nickel sphere to impact the experimental chamber wall 0.3 m away within 3 or 1 sec, respectively, of its release. Complete solidification in free suspension may, therefore, be very difficult under these conditions. The movies on the M512 experiments seem to support this conclusion.

Other computations show that nonuniformly heated 6×10^{-3}-m spheres are subjected to equivalent gravities of from 2.26×10^{-39} kg for gallium to 3.25×10^{-3} kg for magnesium, if the spheres are superheated by only 5% on one side relative to the other side at its absolute melting point.

Notice that, in both nickel and iron spheres of the specified size, the computed equivalent gravity exceeds the 1-g level (i.e., orders of magnitude higher than the supposedly microgravity level of 10^{-6} g in space) if one side is super-

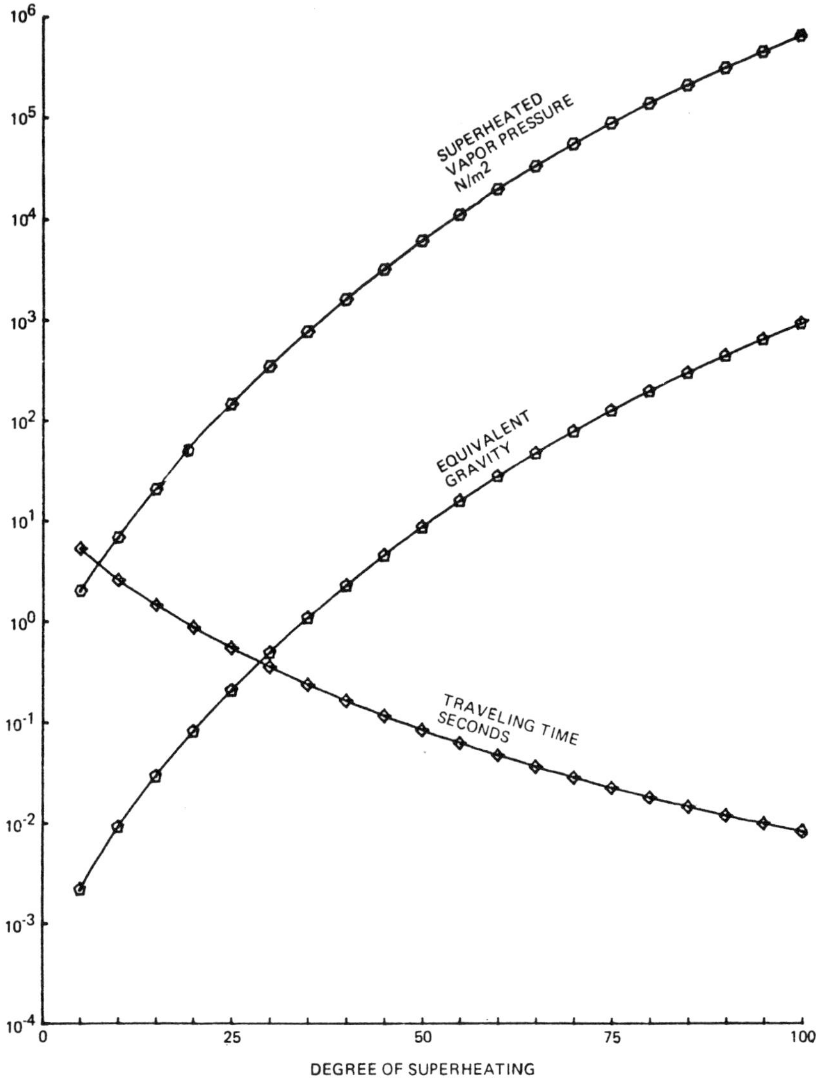

Fig. 2 Jetting action on 6×10^{-3}-m nickel sphere, one side at the absolute melting point of 1726°K and the other side at specified degree of superheating.

heated by 35 and 26%, respectively, relative to the other side at its absolute melting point. Such evaporation and jetting action is, of course, merely the familiar rocket action. In the performance of some Skylab experiments, however, such differential jetting can have important and serious implications. The 6×10^{-3}-m spheres in the M512 sphere-forming experiment, for example, are known to be heated very unevenly by

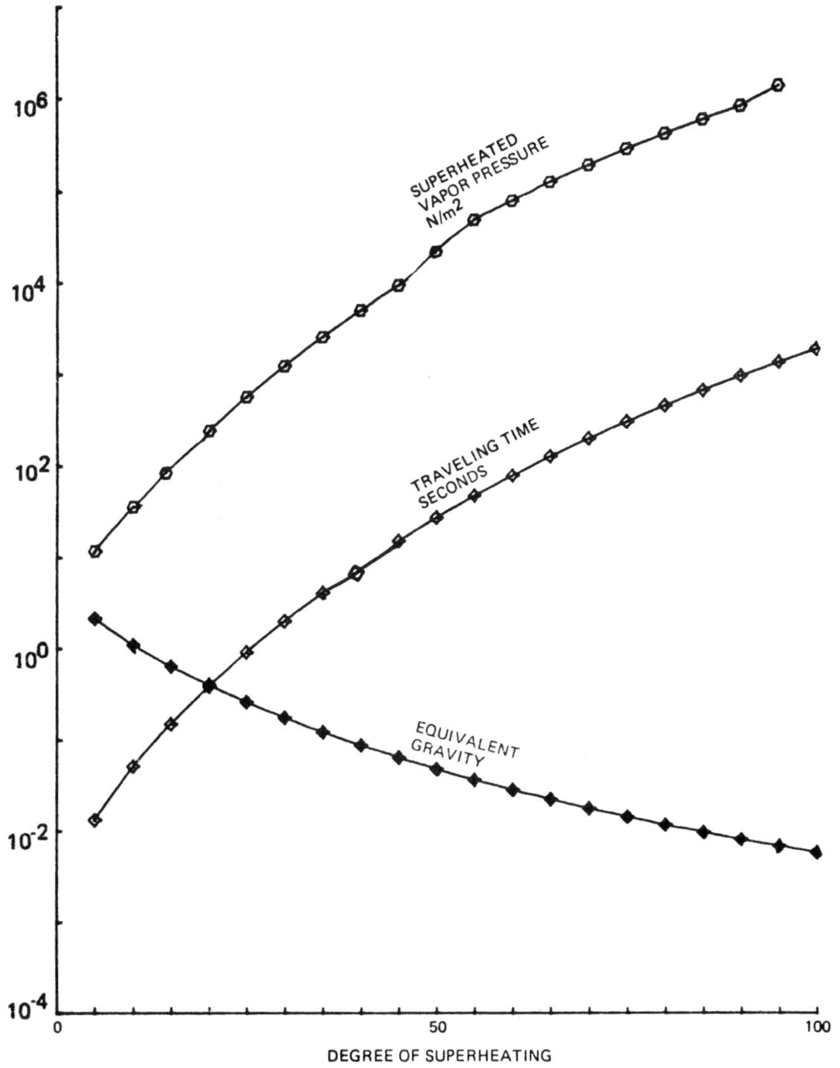

Fig. 3 Jetting action on 6×10^{-3}-m iron sphere, one side at the absolute melting point of 1812°K and the other side at specified degree of superheating.

the electron beam from one side, to the point of occasional spitting or explosion, but remain solid on the other side.[1] Such samples must have been subjected to very large, unwanted accelerations (and hence equivalent gravities) of unpredictable magnitude, direction, and duration. This condition makes it difficult to interpret many solidification results in terms of zero-gravity effects.

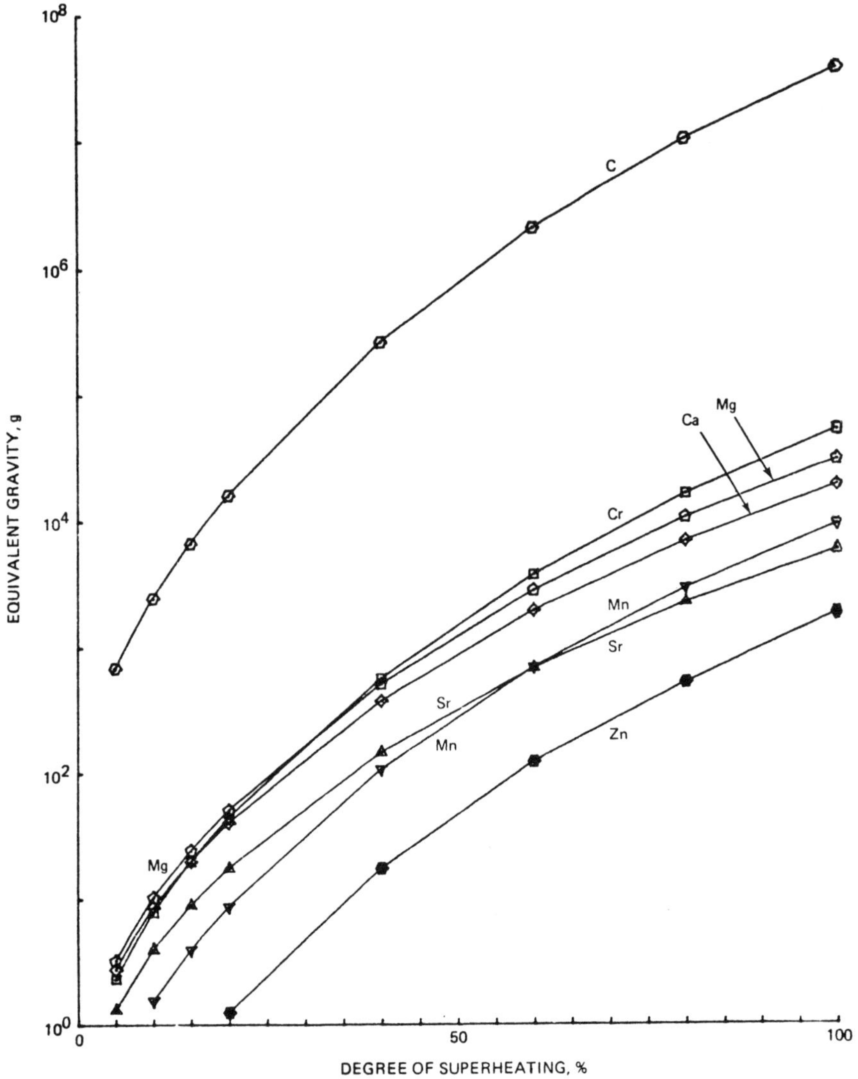

Fig. 4 Equivalent gravity on partially superheated, 6 x 10^{-3}-m sphere of highly volatile material due to differential evaporation and jetting.

Figure 4 displays the jetting characteristics on partially superheated 6 x 10^{-3}-m spheres of some highly volatile materials due to differential evaporation. This figure is for equivelant gravity and time to travel 0.3 m, for seven different volatile elements at eight different degrees of superheating from 50 to 100%.

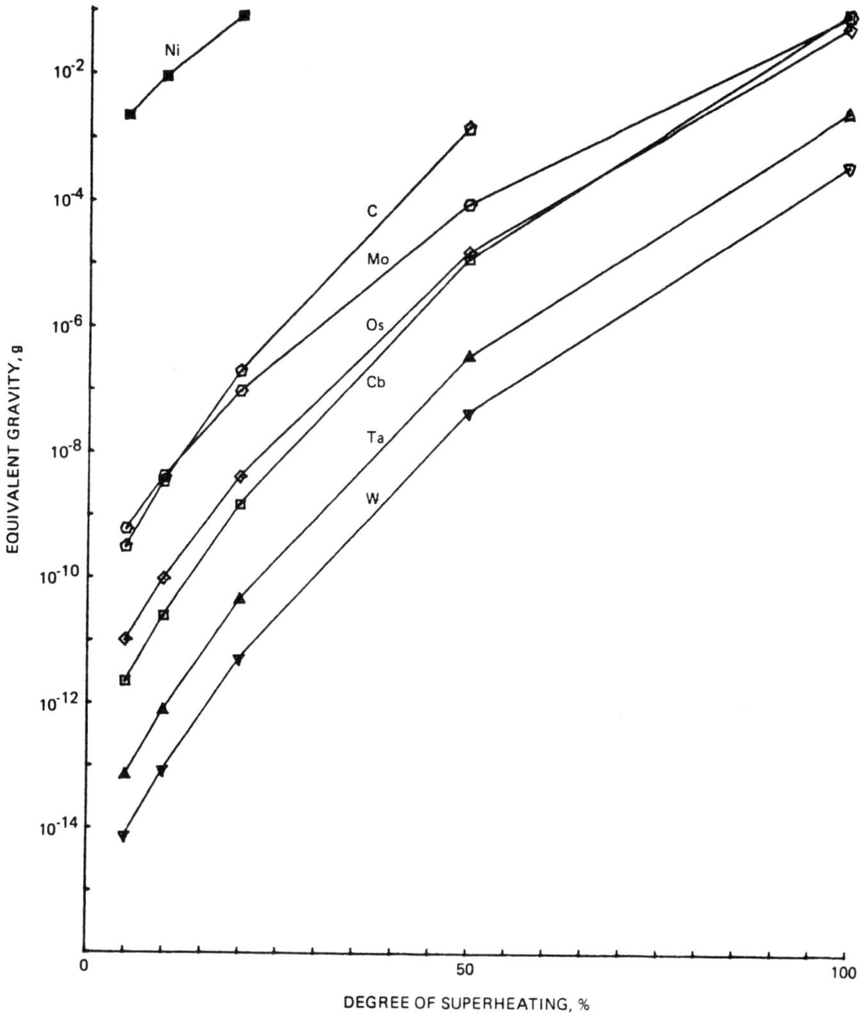

Fig. 5 Equivalent gravity due to stabilizing impurities for nickel at 1726°K, at specified degrees of superheating.

The undesirable jetting action due to certain evaporating impurities also can be replaced by the desirable stabilizing action of other impurities. Specifically, a 6.0×16^{-3}-m nickel sphere, at its melting point of 1726°K may have its normal jetting action at 5% superheating on one side reduced from 2.15×10^{-3} to 7.34×10^{-15} g by an enriched surface layer of tungsten, or to 6.75×10^{-14} g by tantalum. These data on the stabilizing impurities on nickel are illustrated in Fig. 5.

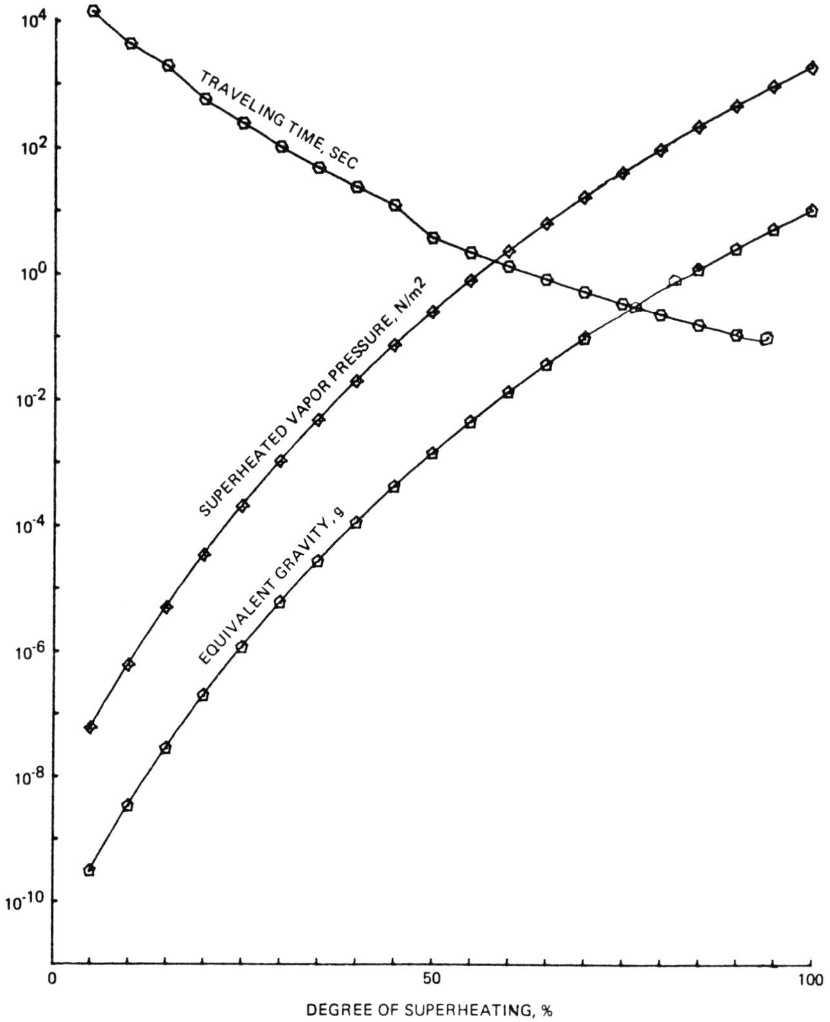

Fig. 6 Jetting action on 6×10^{-3}-m nickel sphere containing surface layer of C.

Hence, we can utilize the stabilizing actions of surface layers of some powerful stabilizers in, e.g., nickel samples. These stabilizers may be W, Ta, Cb, Os, C, and Mo. For example, Fig. 6 shows, as ordinates, the superheated vapor pressure, equivalent gravity, and time to travel 0.3 m, for a 6×10^{-3}-m molten nickel sphere. This sphere has a surface layer of the specified stabilizing element and is heated to the melting point of nickel (1726°K) on one side but superheated on the other. The amount of superheating in percentage points is plotted as the abscissa.

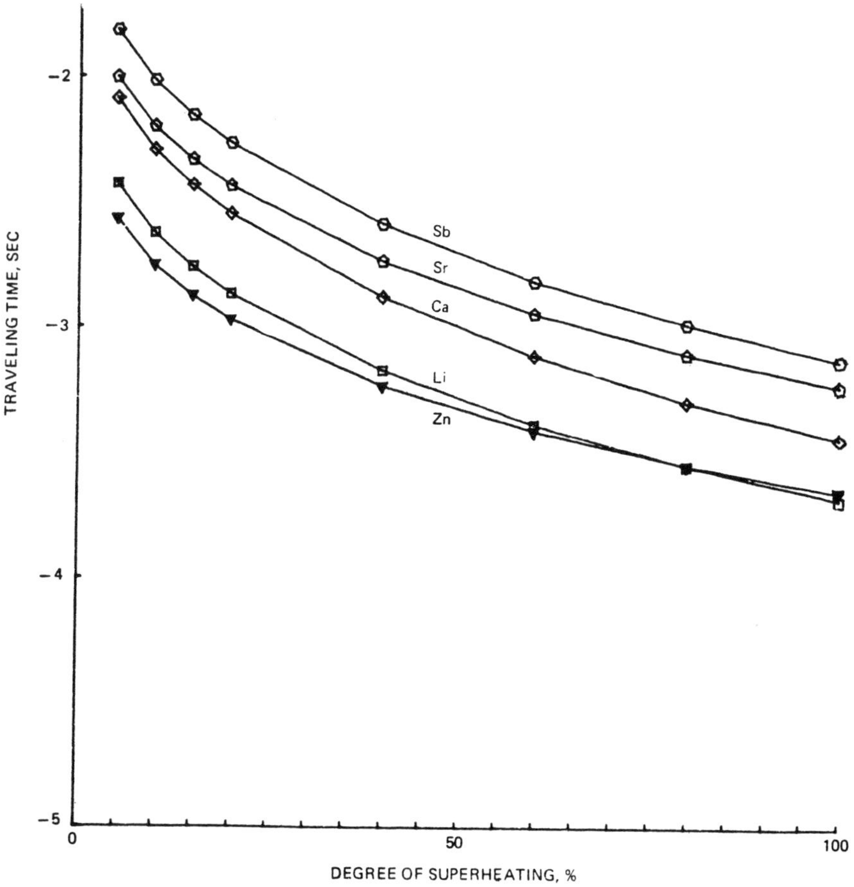

Fig. 7 Time to travel 0.3 m for 6×10^{-3}-m partially superheated nickel sphere with surface layer of highly volatile element due to differential evaporation and jetting.

Figure 7 gives the jetting characteristics on partially superheated 6×10^{-3}-m nickel spheres, surface-contaminated with powerful agitators or highly volatile elements. These figures are, respectively, for equivalent gravity and time to travel 0.3 m for several volatile elements at different degrees of superheating up to 100%.

If we compare the computed results, we see that, on a 6×10^{-3}-m nickel sphere superheated above its absolute melting point by 5% on one side, the equivalent gravity varies by 22 orders of magnitude from 4.87×10^{7} for K to 7.34×10^{-15} for W. For the same partially superheated nickel sphere, the time to travel 0.3 m varies by 10 orders of magnitude from 1.84×10^{-4} sec (i.e., 184 μsec) for K to 2.89×10^{6} sec (i.e., 0.92 yr) for W surface layer. We can readily see that the high equivalent gravities may completely mask or even reverse any possible zero-gravity effects studied in space.

IV. Fluid Disturbances Due to Jetting from Differential Evaporation

Two of the great advantages of manufacturing in space are zero-gravity conditions and the complete absence of convection currents due to the Earth's gravity. With the absence of all convection currents, localized fluid disturbances, temperature differences, concentration variations, and complex heat, mass transfer conditions do not exist. Solidification can, therefore, be controlled more easily, and, as a result, defect-free crystals are then obtained more readily.

However, even in zero gravity, localized or interfacial fluid flow, movement, instability, or other disturbance still can occur due to surface tension gradients resulting from temperature or concentration gradients. This phenomenon, generally called the Marangoni effect or instabilizy,[3-5] manifests itself in such forms as "interfacial engine," instability, twitching, cellular motion, Benard's cells, and tear drop in a wine glass.

Another type of fluid disturbance not reported previously may result from jetting or rocket action due to differential evaporation as just described. A nonuniformly heated liquid drop in space will be nonspherical because both surface tension and jetting action are strongly dependent on temperature. At equilibrium, the internal pressure of the drop is, of course, constant. The local radii of curvature must be related to the local surface tensions. However, any volume element of the sphere, no matter how large or where located, must still be acted on by perfectly balanced external forces on the element. The varying jetting pressure therefore appears as a variation in the curvature of the drop so that the algebraic sum of the jetting pressure and the internal pressure due to surface tension is constant. Since the jetting pressure and surface tension strongly vary according to entirely different functions of the surface temperature, such constancy can be maintained for only a selected point or ring on the drop surface. The overall shape of the liquid drop must, therefore, be nonspherical. In addition, surface evaporation may not be steady because of (for example) presence and periodic rupture of surface oxide films, surface oscillations may occur.

Under gravity or the equivalent, jetting action may show up as local variations in the fluid level. Figure 8 shows the heating characteristics of a liquid in a container. The instantaneous profiles for the temperature, evaporation rate, jetting pressure, surface tension, and surface curvature are shown. For a liquid being heated in a container, the sides are at higher temperatures and, hence, have higher evaporating rates and jetting pressure, but generally lower surface tension than the center region. The liquid surface must therefore convex upward if the jetting pressure is large. Large jetting pressures are often possible, as shown previously. Note that the effect of lowering surface tension with temperature partly compensates for that of the jetting action; the liquid surface is more planar than if surface tension were absent. Similarly, Fig. 8 shows the cooling characteristics of the same liquid in the same container.

V. Evaporative Convection Due to Jetting

Jetting action even may introduce a new type of powerful convection current, even with a uniformly heated liquid drop. The surface of liquid drop usually is not clean. Certain spots or regions S on the drop may be evaporating nonuniformly over its surface. Localized, differential evaporation or jetting forces then may develop to supply the necessary mechanical energy for initiating or maintaining convection currents, as shown in Fig. 9. Such convection currents have been observed on M553 test samples.[6]

Figure 9 also shows a uniformly heated liquid drop that is surface-contaminated with highly evaporative material at certain spots or regions S, resulting in higher jetting pressures p_2 at S compared to neighboring regions. Such differential jetting forces may, again, initiate powerful convection currents. It has been shown by Prof. Reid[7] that even a few atomic layers of selected contamination materials can increase the local evaporating rates by orders of magnitudes for sustained periods of time. Such selected materials may initiate the jetting type convection currents shown in Fig. 9.

Note that the convection currents resulting from differential evaporation and jetting, are completely different in origin and characteristics from, but possibly orders of magnitude stronger than (see, e.g., Fig. 4), those induced by surface tension and/or buoyancy effects and extensively reviewed, e.g., by Berg et al.[3] These "free", "natural", or "spontaneous" convection, also due to differential evaporation, arises as follows. Differential evaporation may activate the sur-

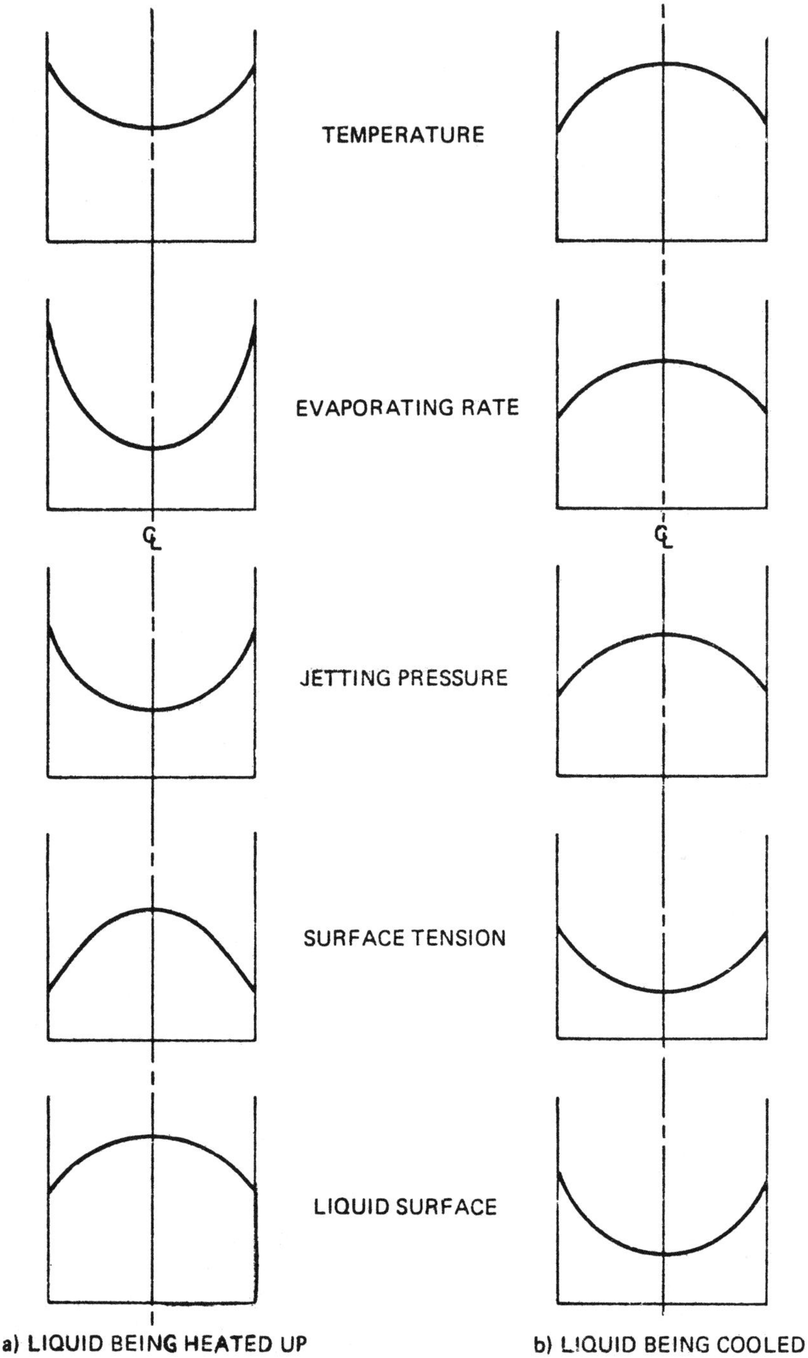

Fig. 8 Heating or cooling characteristics of liquid in a container under some true or equivalent gravity.

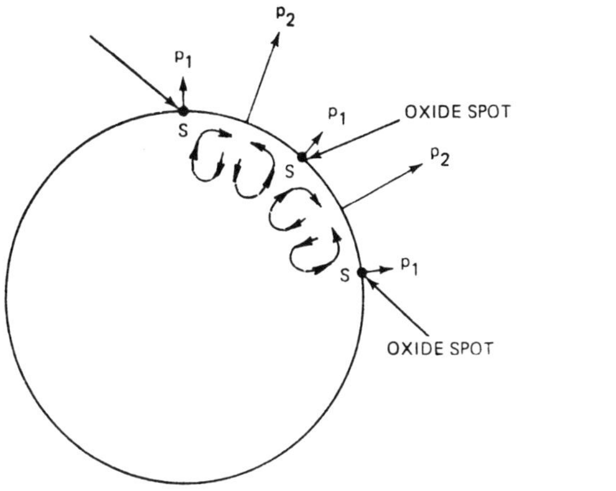

(a) LOCALIZED OXIDE CONTAMINATION

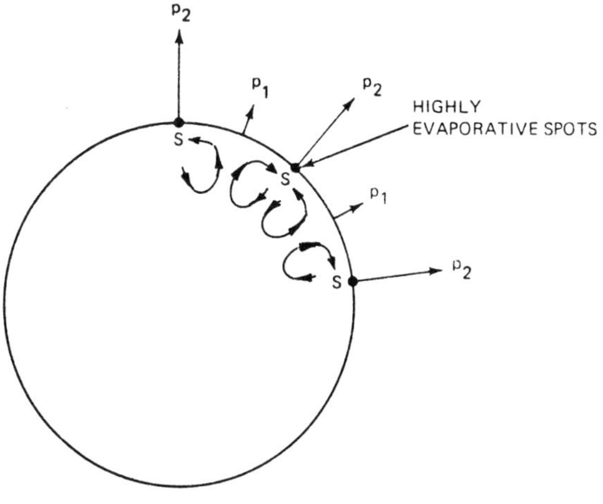

(b) LOCALIZED CONTAMINATION BY HIGHLY VOLATILE MATERIALS

Fig. 9 Convection currents induced by differential evaporation and jetting.

face tension "engine" when it causes the surface tension of the liquid right at the surface to exceed the value that would correspond to the bulk liquid beneath. This is accomplished by removal of heat from the surface region due to the latent heat of evaporation. The surface temperature is thereby reduced below that of the bulk liquid, since for practically all liquids the surface tension rises as the liquid temperature falls.[8]

According to Gibbs,[9] surface tension is defined as the surface free energy per unit area. The most stable arrangement for a liquid with a free surface would be the one in which the material of the least surface tension is on the surface layer. Since this is the opposite of the situation encountered above, the liquid is unstable with respect to surface tension and tends to exhibit surface tension driven convections to seek rearranging itself into a more stable configuration.

In addition to the surface tension effects, differential evaporation may also activate the buoyancy "engine" by causing the density of the surface liquid layer to become greater than the bulk of the liquid. This instability results from "adverse" temperature and/or concentration gradients in the surface layers due to evaporation causing instabilities.

These "free" convections have been studied both experimentally[3,4] and theoretically.[10,11]

On the other hand, the evaporative convection currents shown in Fig. 9 of this paper results not from surface tension or buoyancy effects, but from the jetting action due to differential evaporation.

The evaporative convections reported in the literature also results from the heat or mass transfer in a fluid layer and involves a liquid-liquid interface,[3] whereas the jetting type of evaporative convection results from momentum transfer in a fluid surface regions and involves a liquid-vapor interface. Both these convection currents, however, must be understood to provide the needed background for interpreting the many phenomena in space processing that involves non-uniform evaporation.

These two types of convection currents often have counteracting effects, one tending to compensate for or cancel the other. Also, they differ from gravitational convection currents. Gravitational convection currents are generally very massive, extending deep into the body of the liquid. Convection currents due to differential surface tension, on the other hand, are by nature surface-limited. The new convection currents induced by jetting due to differential evaporation extend to a degree intermediate between the other two types of convection currents. Solidification behavior predictions of a specified system based on results on one type of convection current may, therefore, not be valid when applied to other types of convection currents.

References

[1] Brashears, M.R. and Robertson, S.J., Final Report to NASA Contract NAS 8-28729 on "Research Study on Materials Processing in Space Experiment M512," Lockheed, Huntsville, Alabama, December 1973.

[2] Dushman, S., Scientific Foundations of Vacuum Techniques, Wiley, New York, 1962.

[3] Berg, J. C., Acrivos, A., and Boudart, M. "Evaporative Convection," Advances in Chemical Engineering, Vol. 6, Academic Press, New York, 1966, pp. 61-123.

[4] Bikerman, J.J., Surface Chemistry, Academic Press, New York, 1958.

[5] Scriven, L.E. and Sterling, C.V., "The Marangoni Effects," Nature, Vol. 187, p. 186, 1960.

[6] Tobin, J.M., private communication, Skylab Review Meeting, Marshall Space Flight Center, December 1973.

[7] Reid, R.C., MIT, private communications, 1972.

[8] Adamson, A.W., Physical Chemistry of Surfaces, Vol. I, Reinhold, New York, 1963.

[9] Gibbs, J.W., Scientific Papers, Vol. I, Dover, New York, 1961.

[10] Lin, C.C., The Theory of Hydrodynamic Stability, Cambridge University Press, New York, 1955.

[11] Chandrasekhar, S., Hydrodynamic and Hydromagnetic Stability, Oxford University Press, New York, 1962.

Appendix: Momentum Gain by Evaporating Surfaces

In this appendix, we evaluate the rate of momentum acquired by a liquid surface when its molecules are evaporating into a vacuum.

First, let us evaluate the evaporating rate and evaporating pressure by considering the equilibrium case. When the surface is at equilibrium with its surroundings, the rate of moleclues leaving the surface by evaporation will equilibrate the rate of condensation, resulting in zero gain or loss by the surface. These rates will be called the equilibrium rates of evaporation and condensation, and an evaluation of one will yield the value for the other. The condensing rate is readily given by

$$\tfrac{1}{4}\rho\,\bar{v} = \rho(RT/2\pi)^{\frac{1}{2}} = p/(2\pi RT)^{\frac{1}{2}}$$

At equilibrium, the rate of molecules impinging on a unit surface area is $\frac{1}{4}n\,\bar{v}$. Here, n is the number density, ρ the mass density, T the absolute temperature, and R the gas constant of the molecules in equilibrium with the liquid. The equilibrium evaporating rate is also given by the equation; this is the maximum rate at which molecules can escape from a liquid surface which is kept at a temperature T. Thus, the evaporating rate into a vacuum from this liquid surface is also given by the equation.

The pressure p in the equation is the vapor pressure at saturation. Since pressure is a scalar quantity, it represents the sum of the pressures acting on the surface by the evaporating and the condensing molecules. At equilibrium, these two contributions equilibrate with each other. Hence, the equilibrium evaporating pressure is equal to half of the saturation pressure. When the surface is surrounded by a perfect vacuum, the condensing pressure vanishes and the pressure due to the evaporating molecules is just given by the equilibrium evaporating pressure, or half of the saturation vapor pressure. Consequently, we can expect that the rate of momentum acquired by a liquid surface when its molecules are evaporating into a vacuum is equal to half of the saturation vapor pressure. This is verified analytically below.

The molecules evaporating from a liquid surface kept at temperature T have a Maxwellian distribution function $n(2\pi RT)^{-3/2}\,e^{-v^2/2RT}$. Each beam of molecules emanating with a velocity v from a unit surface area and at an angle θ inclined from the normal to the area carries a flux rate of $nv\cos\theta$ and a momentum rate of $mnv^2\cos^2\theta = \rho v^2\cos^2\theta$. Hence the total momentum rate in question is given by $\rho(2\pi RT)^{-3/2}\int\int\int v^2\cos^2\theta e^{-v^2/2RT} v^2\sin^2 dv d\theta$. Integrating v from 0 to ∞, θ from 0 to $\pi/2$, and φ from 0 to 2π readily yields $\frac{1}{2}\rho RT = \frac{1}{2}p$ and completes the verification. If the surrounding vacuum is imperfect, then the rate is given by

$$\tfrac{1}{2}\alpha\rho \text{ with } \alpha \leq 1$$

α can be determined either experimentally or from the given degree of imperfection.

Chapter II-Experimental Apparatus

SPACE PROCESSING EXPERIMENTAL APPARATUS: A SURVEY

Mathias P. Siebel*
NASA George C. Marshall Space Flight Center, Ala.

Abstract

The processing of materials in a low-g environment was started approximately 10 years ago. This article surveys the apparatus developed during that period. A low-g environment occurs naturally in a free-flying spacecraft (e.g., in manned flights such as Apollo, Skylab, and ASTP); low-g conditions also occur in other free-falling bodies such as sounding rockets and drop tower capsules. Apparatus has been developed for all these craft. Most of the apparatus described serves to melt and resolidify materials in low g; the material may be contained or, by virtue of the environment, freely floating. Other apparatus for separation of intimately mixed components or species is also described. A general conclusion is drawn that the apparatus addresses only a few of the possibilities available, is still at the experimental stage, and is of laboratory scale. It is predicted that processes showing promise will be scaled up to derive economic advantages in the Shuttle era of space flight.

Introduction

Since the inception of the Space Processing Applications Program in the mid 1960's, several generations of experimental apparatus have been used. It is the purpose of this paper to present the space processing equipment evolution to date, to discuss the factors that have influenced that evolution, and then to speculate on the probable future course of development. The existing equipment was developed and configured to take advantage of available opportunities to process materials in

---

Invited paper. Received May 17, 1976.

*Special Assistant to the Director, Space Sciences Laboratory.

low g. The experiment-carrying vehicles, or simply "carriers" used, have been drop tower (1970 - 1975); aircraft (1971); sounding rockets (1971 and 1975); Apollo 14, 16, and 17 (1971 - 1972); Skylab (1973 - 1974); and Apollo-Soyuz Test Project (ASTP) (1975). It is planned that a sounding rocket program will continue, at least until the Space Shuttle/Spacelab operational era in the early 1980's, and that then the Space Shuttle will be the carrier for space processing payloads.

The carriers have presented constraints on apparatus design; for example, there have been limitations on power, external temperature, data rates, volume, weight, and experiment time available. Safety and possible interference with other onboard equipment also have had to be considered.

As will be seen, the apparatus that has been used is small and functionally comparable to Earth-bound laboratory equipment. To achieve the ultimate goal of processing in space on a commercial scale, initially more laboratory-scale experiments will be needed; the program then will pass through a pilot plant stage to the realization of the production plant in space. The experimental equipment developed has been categorized in a number of ways; essentially, however, the processing equipment used hitherto falls into three main groups: 1) materials melting and resolidification apparatus, 2) separation apparatus, and 3) specialized apparatus for phenomenological studies.

Materials Melting and Resolidification Apparatus

The majority of low-g experiments which have been performed have involved the melting and resolidification of materials. A variety of "furnaces" have been developed and flown; studies have led to the development and testing of prototypes of other furnaces. In a very low-g environment, the option exists for the processing of liquefied materials in a containerless state as fully levitated molten drops. For the purposes of classification and description, it therefore is appropriate to distinguish between two types of melting and resolidification apparatus: that which processes materials held in a container or crucible, and that which processes materials in a freely suspended containerless manner. Clearly the energy sources, heat-transfer mechanisms, and apparatus configurations are different for the two types of process, as will be the possible manipulations of the melted material.

Apparatus for Contained Materials

Material for space processing usually has been contained in a sealed cartridge that is introduced into a furnace cavity. The use of cartridges to contain materials samples makes for a simple interface between the experiment and the furnace. All but one of the furnaces developed to date have been heated by electrical resistance element(s). The first such furnace was flown in Apollo 14 (Fig. 1). This furnace had a manual on/off switch and an isothermal cavity temperature that was controlled to 140°C by a thermostat. The cartridges used for the Apollo 14 flight were essentially plain cylindrical containers that first were heated in the furnace cavity and then, while still in the cavity, cooled by using a heat sink in contact with one end of the cartridge. Later designs of cartridges (which were not flown) used a slender specimen encased in thick-walled cartridges. The heavy walls stored heat. The heat flow path to the heat sink was designed so that during cooling the heat had to "leak" through the specimen, giving a predetermined thermal gradient and cooling rate. In this way, the directional solidification necessary for the growth of crystals and of eutectic aligned structures was obtained. This early development set the stage for the design of several subsequent furnaces in that standard cartridges were used to contain the experiment material and that the thermal design of the cartridges governed the thermal profile to which the material was exposed.

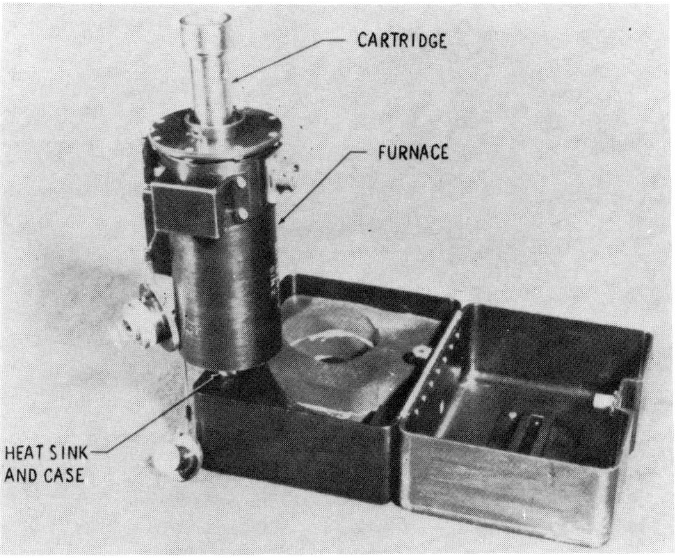

Fig. 1 Apollo 14 furnace.

Fig. 2 Sounding rocket furnace.

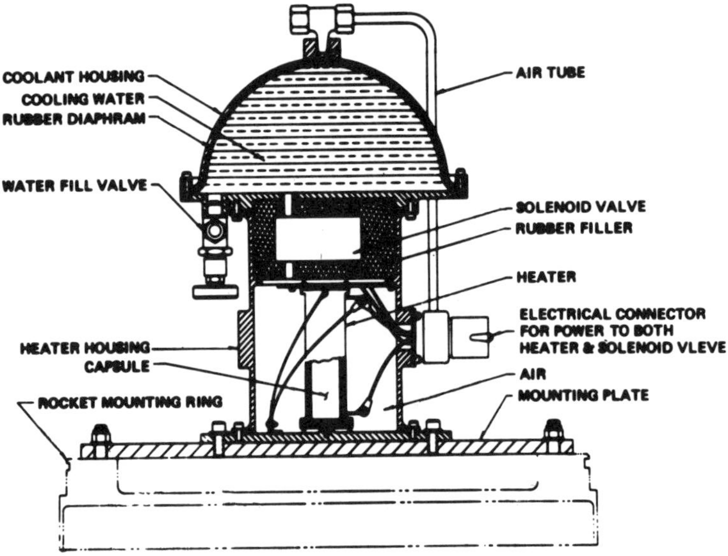

Fig. 3 Sounding rocket furnace (section).

The first sounding rocket flight experiments were flown in 1971 using the furnace shown in Figs. 2 and 3. It has a resistance-heated cavity that accepts the same cartridges as the Apollo 14 furnace. The added features of this furnace are an automatic sequencer triggered by the launch acceleration, and a water quench capability; this is necessary because

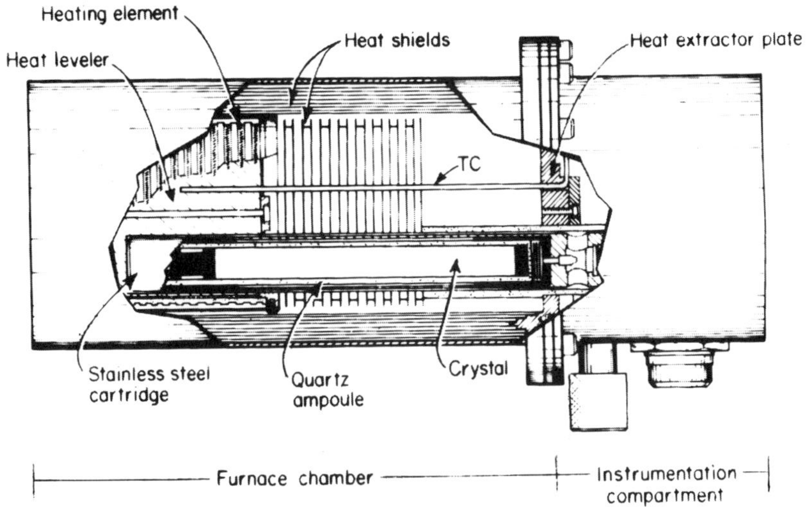

Fig. 4 Skylab multipurpose furnace.

the specimen has to be molten and resolidified within the short flight time available (5 to 6 min). The water reservoir is the hemispherical dome seen on the top of the furnace.

The next generation of flight furnaces were designed for use on Skylab and ASTP. The typical furnace construction is shown in Fig. 4. The furnace has three equally spaced experiment cavities (of which one is shown). The furnace is heated at one end by an electrical resistance element, and the heat is extracted at the other end through the heat extractor plate. Because of the thermal shielding and of the internal vacuum, the only thermal links between the heated zone and the cold plate are the cartridges inserted in the three cavities. The cartridges are used here to contain the experiment material and, by careful thermal design, to control the temperature profile to which the material is exposed throughout the experiment. The furnace is provided with controls to set any desired maximum temperature in the heated zone (up to 1200°C), to vary the soak time, and to reduce the temperature of the heated zone at one of several predetermined constant or varying rates. The ASTP furnace incorporates fast quench capability; helium gas is introduced into the furnace and acts as a conductor of heat from the hot zone to the cold plate. This was done to reduce the cooling times in order to increase the number of experiments that could be performed during the rather short ASTP mission.

Lately the furnace developments have been directed to take advantage of the Space Processing Applications Rocket

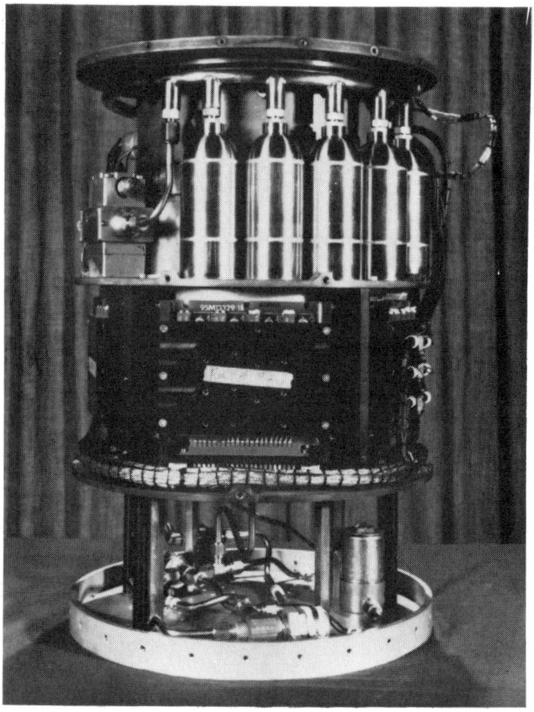

Fig. 5 Rocket multipurpose furnace.

Program, where flight times of the order of 5 to 6 min are available. One rocket furnace already has been described; another is shown in Fig. 5. The furnace conforms to the envelope of a Black Brant 5C rocket. The furnace incorporates three cavities into which cartridges may be inserted. In the present configuration, this furnace can be programmed to attain a different temperature, up to 1150°C, in each of the three isothermal cavities. The gas cylinders seen in Fig. 5 contain gases that serve to quench the specimens after melting. Future developments are directed toward modifying the furnace to incorporate cavities with thermal gradients, and a capability for unidirectional cooling.

Other electrically powered furnaces under development include a high-temperature (2200°C) furnace with a ceramic heating element in the form of a hollow cylinder. The specimen will be located within the hollow cylinder. A feature of this furnace is that an oxidizing or inert atmosphere is desirable to maintain the integrity of the heating element. This furnace therefore may be particularly well suited for the processing of glasses.

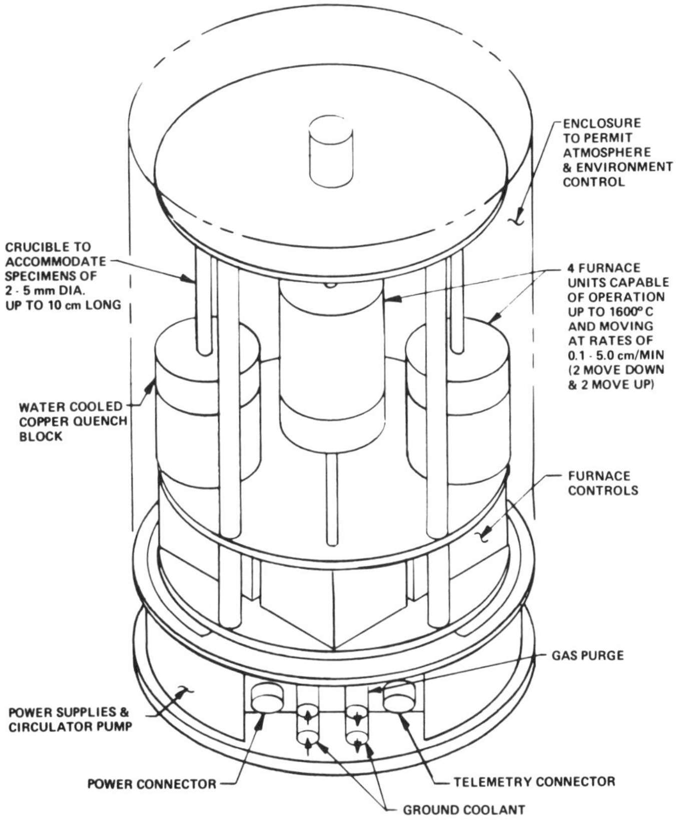

Fig. 6 Automated directional solidification system.

Finally, for use on sounding rockets and then potentially for use on the Space Shuttle, a directional solidification furnace is being developed (Fig. 6). The sample is contained in a long, slender crucible along which a furnace is traversed. As the furnace moves, the heat in its cavity melts a zone of the material contained in the crucible. Attached to the trailing end of the furnace is a chill block that insures resolidification of the experiment material at the desired rate.

The one nonelectrical furnace flown to date was used for the Skylab tube brazing experiment (M552). Here the energy was supplied by the controlled combustion of chemicals to melt the braze alloy. The general configuration of the experiment is shown in Fig. 7. The cavity temperatures and thermal profiles proved to be quite reliably reproducible. The energy

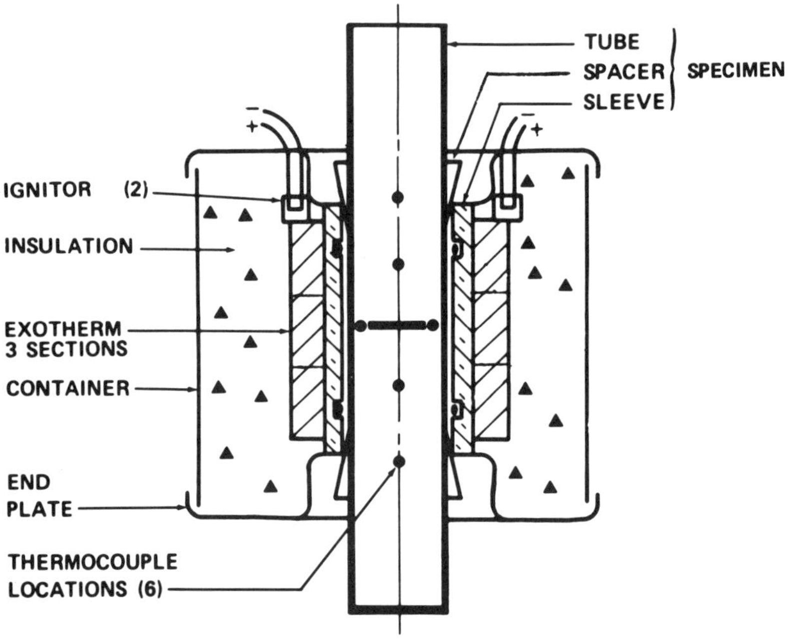

Fig. 7 Chemical furnace cross section.

of the chemical exotherm is of the order of 650 cal/g. In the configuration shown, the specimen reached a temperature of 1050° ± 40°C within 90 sec of ignition. There appears to exist no reason why chemical energy sources of this type should not be used in the future to melt suitably contained materials, providing a long soak time is not needed.

So far, various ways of providing a heated cavity for melting samples contained in crucibles or cartridges have been described. Containers permit ease in handling the material to be processed and simplicity of furnace/experiment interface. Other advantages of containing the samples are discussed briefly below. The control of temperature gradients in the sample and certain materials manipulations are possible only when a material is contained.

Temperature gradients are necessary where directional solidification is desired, as in crystal growth. A free liquid sample will tend to assume a spherical shape, and then there appears to be no way to extract heat preferentially from one point and to solidify the material directionally. Material contained in a cartridge, however, can be constrained to assume a long cylindrical shape that permits controlled direc-

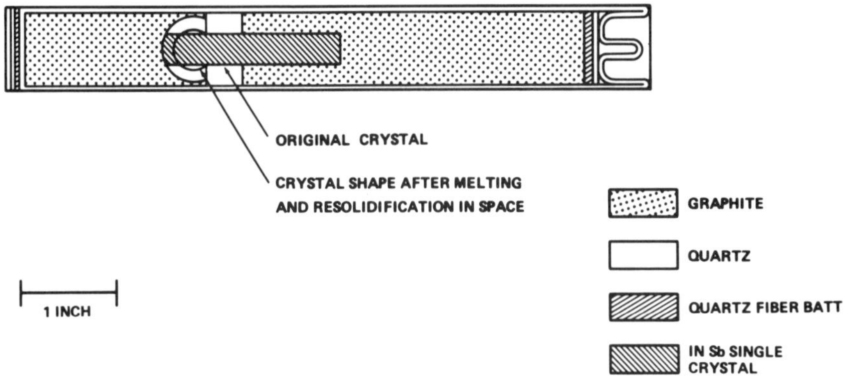

Fig. 8 Cartridge design.

tional solidification in a furnace cavity which cools while maintaining a controlled temperature gradient.

A hybrid system can be devised wherein a quasifree sample is held within a cartridge; the molten liquid then is being held in place by a nonmelting support such as a rod or a wire. This means has been used in several experiments; for example, Skylab experiment M560, where an indium-antimonide crystal was grown without wall confinement but attached to an indium-antimonide monocrystalline rod through which the heat was extracted as the sample solidified (Fig. 8).

Manipulations that can be performed best when the sample is confined include mixing and homogenization. The Apollo 14 furnace was used for the composite casting demonstrations, in which it was shown that mixtures of normally immiscible materials and mixtures of particles in a molten matrix remain stable upon solidification in the low-g environment. To mix the components, the molten mixtures were shaken manually by the astronauts. For the processing of monotectic compounds in drop tower experiments, an acoustic mixer coupled to the materials container has been used.

The uniqueness of the space environment lies in the virtual absence of relative accelerations; a condition of free fall exists. To maintain that free-fall condition, a molten sample cannot be moved in relation to the spacecraft. This means that the entire process has to take place in a cavity which heats and cools with the sample. Since the thermal capacity of the system far exceeds that of the sample, long processing times are needed. An attempt to overcome this last problem has led to the design of the zone melting furnace (Fig. 6), where the furnace moves but the specimen is fixed in relation to the spacecraft.

The use of the furnaces described above imposes limitations on the experiments that can be performed and on the materials that can be processed. These limitations arise from several facts. Since the material is contained, highly corrosive materials, materials with very high melting points, materials where no contamination from the container wall can be tolerated, or materials where other effects brought about by contact with the wall (e.g., nucleation) have to be avoided, cannot be processed. When choosing the method of processing, the first consideration is whether the sample material is to be contained or not.

Apparatus for Containerless Processing

When the material is to be processed in a containerless way, three factors have to be considered: 1) how to position the freely floating material in relation to processing apparatus, 2) how to heat and cool the material, and 3) how to manipulate the specimen, if necessary.

Slight residual accelerations in a spacecraft will cause free-floating masses to have a motion in relation to the spacecraft. The forces required to hold a material specimen in position in the process apparatus are very small; they are of the order of 10^{-4} to 10^{-6} of the terrestrial specimen weight. Several options exist. The simplest is to hold the specimen mechanically; for example, on a sting from which the specimen may or may not be released upon melting. If the specimen is small and freezes rapidly, no constraint may be needed after melting because a free specimen will drift only slowly into contact with elements of the apparatus. Larger or slow-to-freeze specimens may be levitated by electromagnetic or acoustic means.

With the specimen exposed, many means become available for supplying the energy necessary to melt it. The specimen may, of course, be held within a heated cavity; other possibilities include melting by electron beam impingement, by arc imaging, or by solar furnaces.

The first containerless solidification experiment was performed on Skylab. The samples for experiment M553 were held on a wheel (Fig. 9), each sample on a ceramic pedestal. The samples were melted by an electron beam directed normally to the plane of the wheel, as shown by the arrow in the figure. To process successive specimens, the wheel was indexed. Upon melting, each specimen separated from the wheel and then was

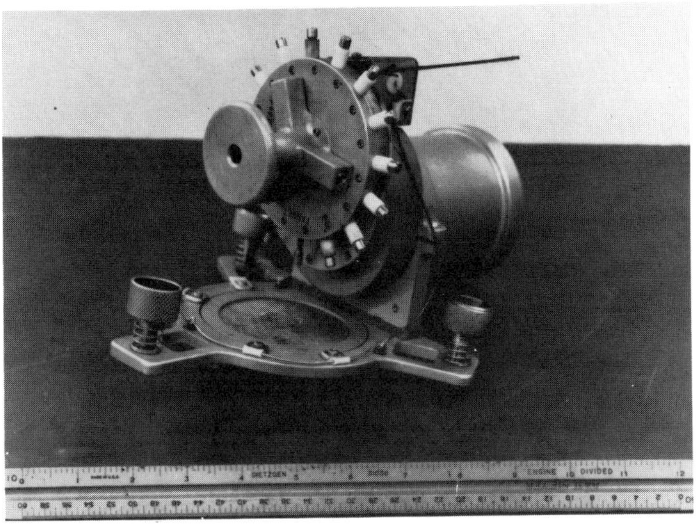

Fig. 9 Skylab experiment M553.

free to "float" within an evacuated process chamber. The specimen size had been chosen to be such that solidification would occur within 10 to 20 sec; that is, before the specimen could drift to touch the chamber wall. A few specimens were made to stay attached to their stings; one of these is seen on the lower part of the wheel. The specimen marked "target" was made of tungsten and served for adjustments to the electron beam gun before initiation of the experiment sequence.

The results of experiment M553 led to a drop tower experiment, where material was melted and allowed to freeze in a vacuum chamber during the free-fall period of 3.5 sec. The material was supplied in the form of wire (Fig. 10) held on busses and melted by a current pulse much like a fuse wire. Very little relative motion occurred between the apparatus and the molten free-floating globules; hence contact between the molten material and the chamber wall was avoided during the free-fall time without an elaborate positioning device.

No low-g containerless melting experiments other than the preceding two have been performed, but several techniques are under development. On a sounding rocket flight in 1976, glass is to be melted in the heated cavity of the high-temperature furnace. The glass will be positioned on a sting. Precursor experiments have been performed on the ground; a typical sample obtained is shown in Fig. 11. To fuse the sample shown, a laser beam was used, and the molten material was prevented from dripping from the sting by a vertical stream of

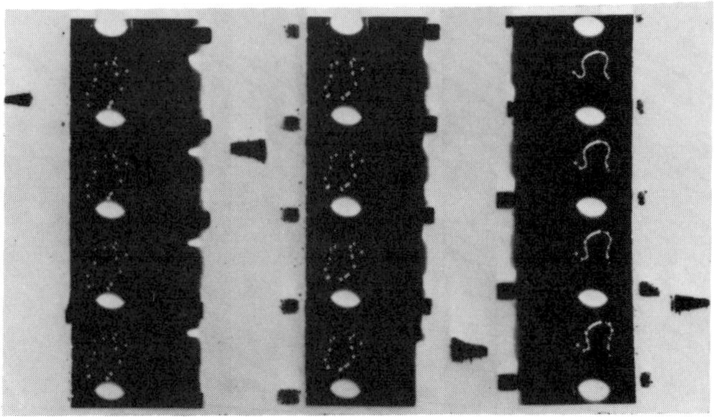

Fig. 10 Containerless melting and solidification.

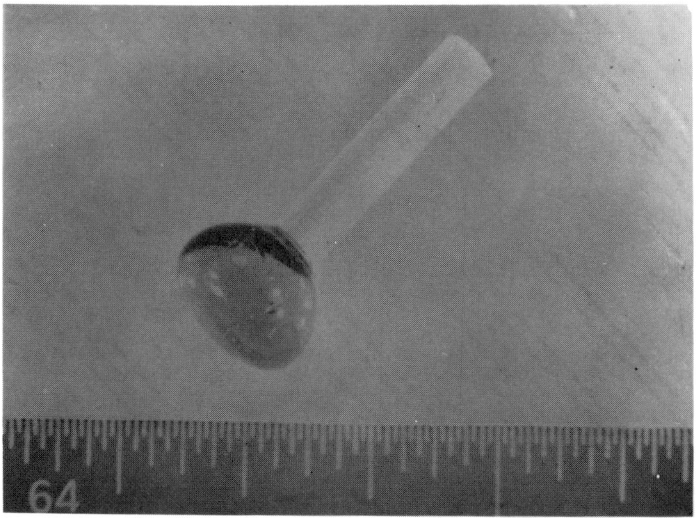

Fig. 11 Glass sample.

air (Fig. 12). When a gas is present, acoustic positioning can be used. A standing wave pattern is established, and the particles (solid or molten) are drawn to and held in the areas of minimum sound pressure.

One method of creating a standing wave pattern is to use a simple plane sound source radiating sound toward a parallel reflecting surface (Fig. 13). Specimens then may be levitated in one or more planes. The forces generated are adequate for

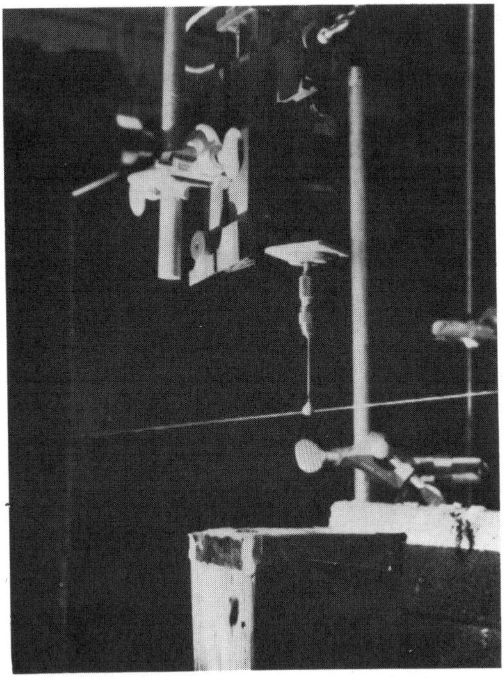

Fig. 12 Setup for melting glasses.

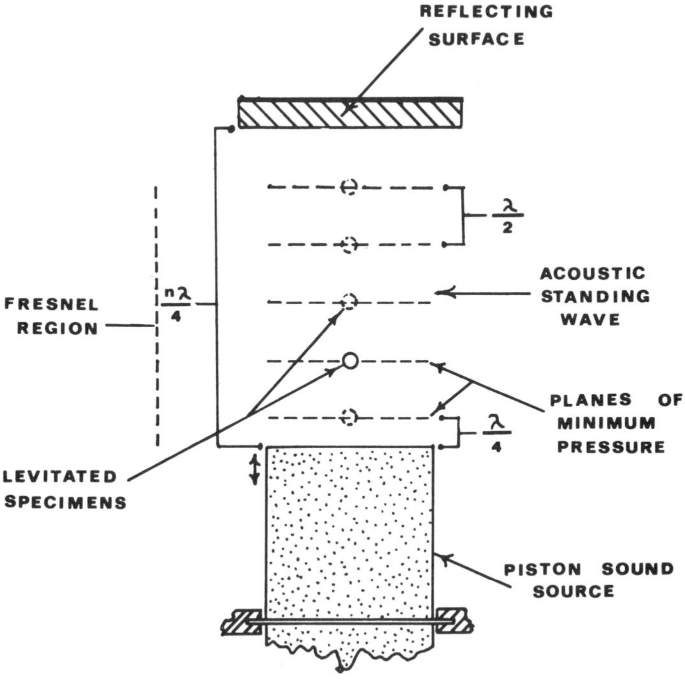

Fig. 13 Acoustic levitator.

Fig. 14 Specimen levitated within furnace for containerless melting.

levitating on the ground masses exceeding 1 g in weight. In space, of course, much more massive specimens can be handled, providing they do not overlap adjacent standing wave planes. The effects upon liquid circulations and other phenomena in the specimen appear to be negligible on the ground and may be reduced even further in space. Because of the essentially linear configuration of this levitation device, the specimen may be levitated within a cylindrical furnace cavity as shown in Fig. 14.

Another acoustic levitator that has been developed is shown in Fig. 15, where, for demonstration purposes, a styrofoam ball is shown levitated within the positioning chamber. In this device, three mutually orthogonal sound sources are used. A standing wave pattern results, with the positioning effect again due to the low pressure present at the antinode. No heating/cooling apparatus yet has been integrated with this latter device.

A great deal of effort has been applied to the development of inductive levitation devices; with sufficient power input, such devices also can serve to heat and melt the specimen. A variety of induction coil configurations have been

Fig. 15 Triaxial acoustic positioning chamber.

studied and tried in 1 g and in the drop tower. Examples of coil configurations are shown in Fig. 16. The presently available apparatus for use in sounding rockets is shown in Fig. 17.

For electromagnetic levitation/heating devices, an electrically conductive specimen is required. The range of conductivities, however, may range over six decades below that of a good conductor. Frequency adjustments have to be made for best performance.

Where electrical coupling between the coil and the specimen is inadequate for the heating requirements (e.g., for very high-temperature materials), heating power additional to that applied indirectly may be supplied (for example, by an electron beam gun or a solar device). When levitation with precise positioning is required, a position-sensing servoloop may be used to hold and damp the motion of the specimen; varying the frequency or power in one part of the levitation system shifts the area of lowest intensity of the magnetic field effects and, with it, the specimen. Electromagnetic positioning devices do not require the presence of a gas for

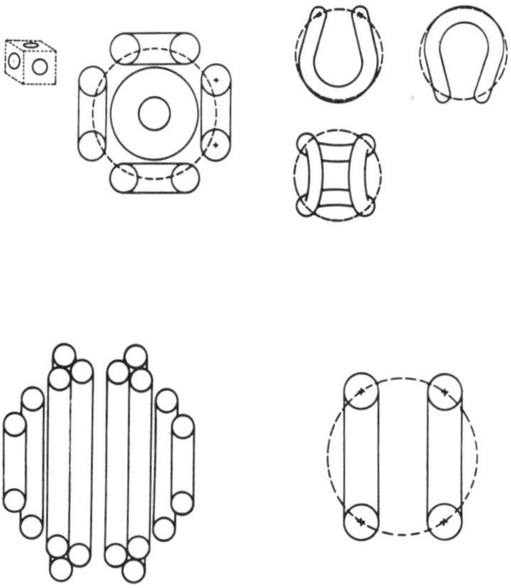

Fig. 16 Levitation coils.

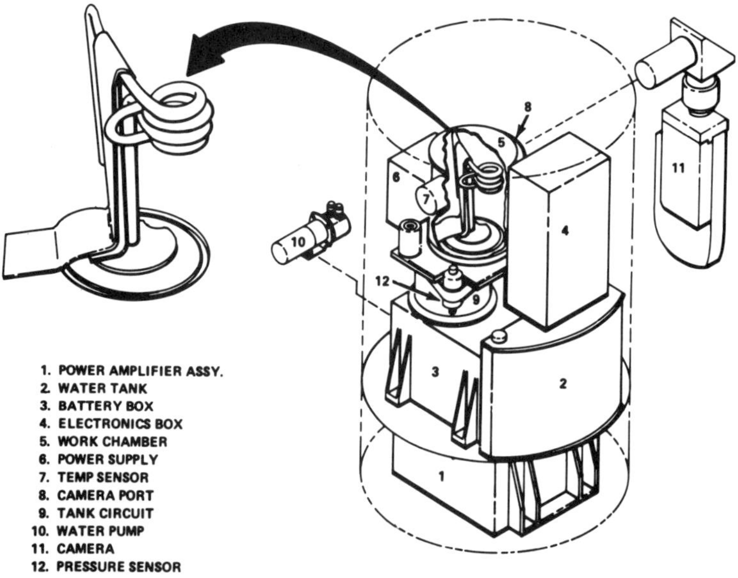

Fig. 17 Electromagnetic levitation furnace.

their operation and hence may be used for a wide variety of materials that have to be processed in a vacuum.

As has been mentioned, when a quantity of material is t be melted in a free containerless manner, new energy sources may be used. As an example of one such heating system, a concept for a solar furnace to melt silicon is shown in Fig. 18. The furnace shown incorporates a forming device. When the molten material is not constrained by a container, it may be shaped either as a whole into, say, a disk, or continually, as shown conceptually here, into a continuous ribbon (Fig. 19).

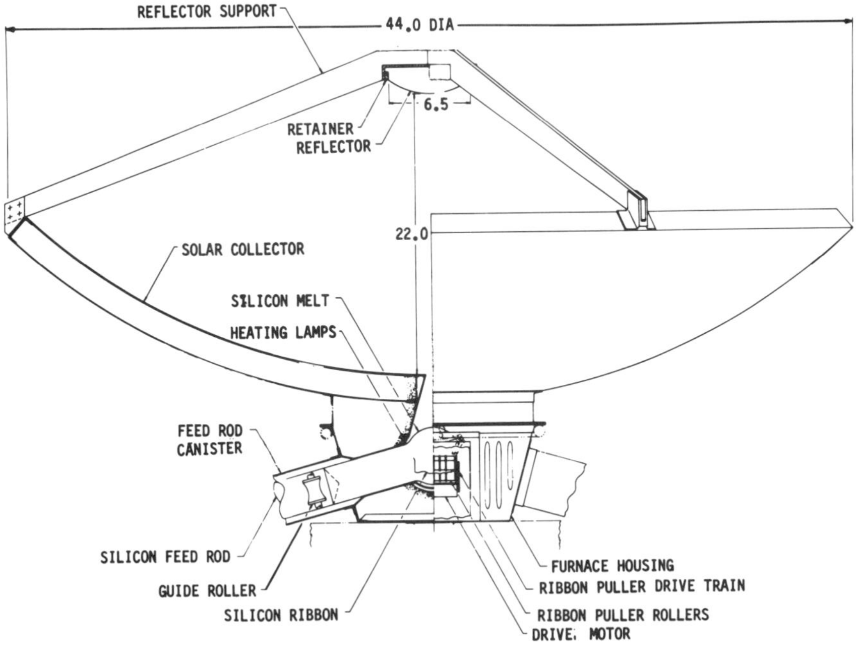

Fig. 18 Solar furnace.

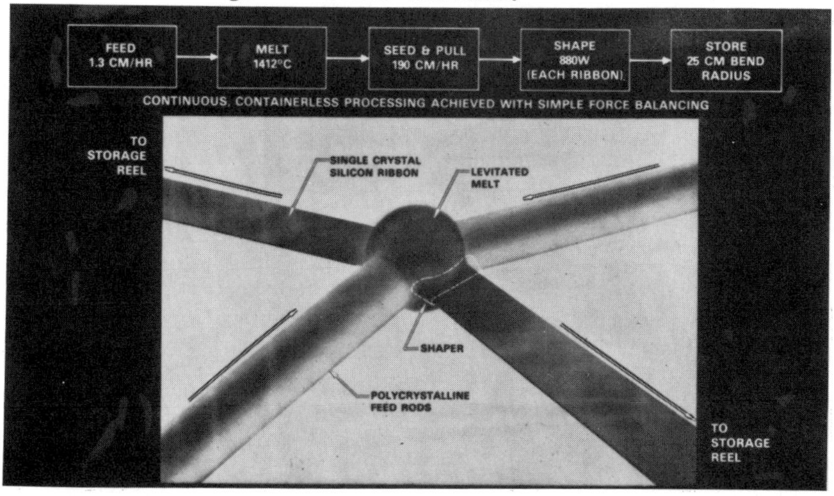

Fig. 19 Ribbon from melt growth in space.

Processing Systems

So far, typical individual items of processing equipment have been described. It is implicit that they can function meaningfully only when provided with a number of services. For example, all equipment requires a means of attachment to the spacecraft: typically a mounting surface; electrical furnaces require electrical power; they also require a heat sink to dissipate the power; certain items of equipment require special atmospheres or a vacuum. Most experiments require data acquisition systems for control and experiment evaluation; e.g., thermocouples and pressure gages with their associated readout systems, cameras, operator voice recorders, and others.

To date, two systems have been constructed and flown. Both accommodate several experiments. In the Skylab M512 facility, experiments were performed sequentially by astronauts. In the sounding rocket system, experiments are performed simultaneously and automatically. The Skylab M512 facility is shown in Fig. 20. It provided the capability of performing experiments by the use of individual experiment modules using the same general ancillary equipment. The M512 facility was mounted on a panel which, in turn, was attached to the Skylab structure by shock mounts. The panel also served as a radiator of heat. The facility was made up of the following main parts: a spherical work chamber, a control

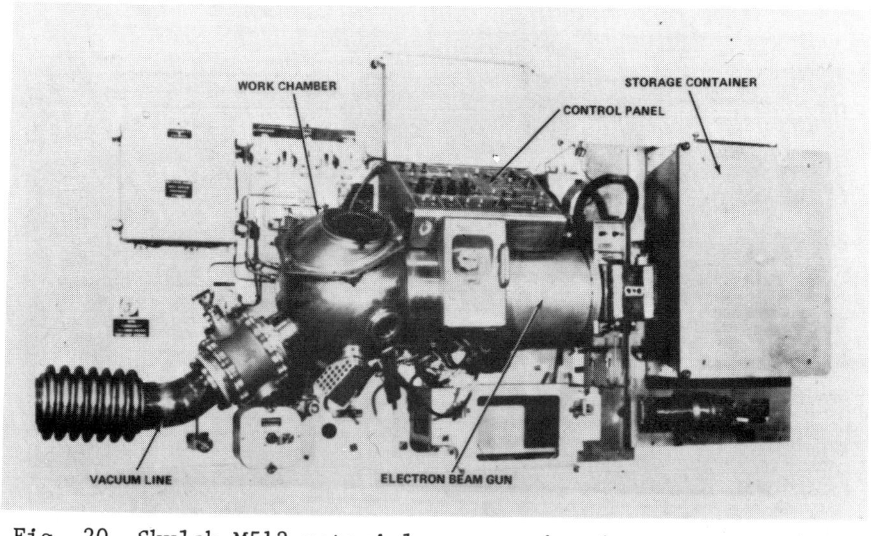

Fig. 20 Skylab M512 materials processing in space experiment facility.

panel, an electron beam gun and batteries (cylindrical portion of apparatus below control panel), and storage containers for experiment modules and ancillary equipment. The work chamber incorporated a mount to accommodate each experiment module in turn. The mount also served as a heat sink with a predetermined and calibrated thermal impedance. Near the mount and inside the chamber was located an electrical connector through which power and signals were provided to the experiment modules.

The work chamber could be vented to space and thus provide an evacuated environment for the experiments when desired. Windows and illumination within the work chamber permitted viewing of the experiments in progress and also photography by a fixed camera (not shown). Gages on the control panel were used to monitor the pressure in the chamber, certain temperatures, and the beam current and voltage of the electron beam gun. In addition, switches and potentiometers served to operate and control the individual experiments.

For illustration, two experiments, metals melting (M551) and sphere forming (M553), are shown mounted in the chamber (Fig. 21). Both used the electron beam gun to melt the specimens. Most of the experiment modules and their accessories were stored in the storage container seen toward the right in Fig. 20. To perform an experiment, the appropriate module with its accessories was mounted in the chamber.

Fig. 21 M551 metals melting experiment (left) and M553 sphere forming experiment (right).

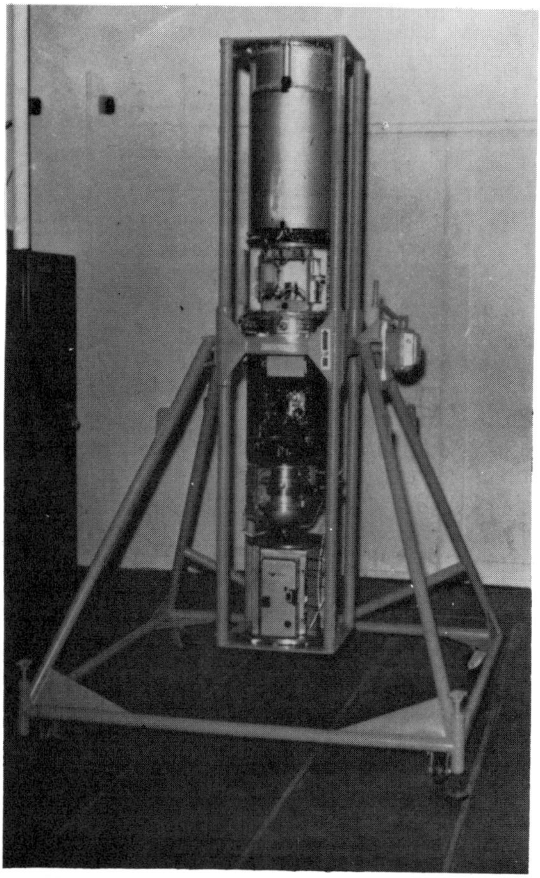

Fig. 22 Sounding rocket payload.

A typical rocket payload is shown in Fig. 22. The experiments make use wherever possible of common vehicle resources provided by two standard modules: a measurement module and a general-purpose support module. The measurement module provides information about the flight environment. It incorporates highly sensitive accelerometers and sensors for the measurement of ambient temperature, pressure, shock, and acoustic and structural vibration. The general-purpose support module provides and controls the electrical power for each of the experiments. The module also incorporates a 20-channel FM-FM telemetry system to transmit experiment data to a ground station.

Separation Apparatus

The only separation technique that has been used in space is electrophoresis. Electrophoresis is defined as the separation of charged components of a solution in an electric field due to their different electric mobilities. In practice, the separation is performed in either a batch or a continuous mode.

Batch processing is performed in liquid- (or gel-) filled columns. An electric gradient is established along the column. When the specimen, consisting of a mixture of particles, is introduced at one end of the column, the electric field in the tube will cause these particles to migrate toward the other end of the tube at rates depending on the species. Since each species has specific electric mobility, bands of different species appear along the tube. Under conditions of gravity on the ground, several factors detract from the ideal behavior described; for example, heavy particles will sediment in the separation columns, and the electric current passing through

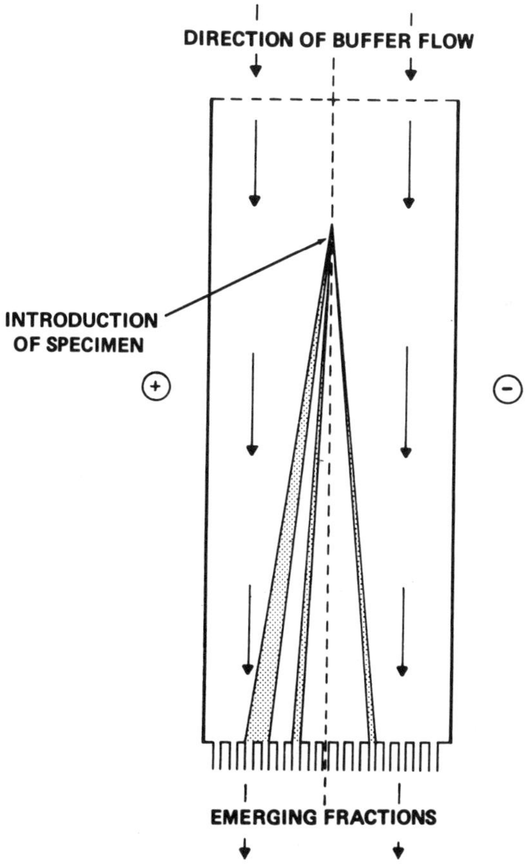

Fig. 23 Continuous flow electrophoresis.

the column will heat the medium and cause thermal convection to occur. Such convection currents will tend to remix the separated particles.

In the continuous flow mode, the particles to be separated are introduced into a rectangular prism-shaped cavity through which the liquid medium flows. The electrical potential is established across two opposing faces of the prism (Fig. 23). The particles migrate under the action of the electrical field to fan out as shown. Undesirable gravity effects again may include heating, causing secondary flow, sedimentation, and buoyancy. All of these effects become particularly evident when the chamber dimensions are increased for greater throughput and when large particles are separated.

The electrophoresis of living cells in a life-sustaining medium is of particular interest. Batch processing electrophoretic apparatus has been developed for such cells and has been flown on Apollo 14 and 16 and on ASTP. The apparatus flown on the Apollo flights is shown in Fig. 24. The three separation columns may be seen clearly. The separation technique used is that of the batch processing described previously. The first experiments showed that, in the low-g environment of gas, bubbles formed in the columns and secondary flows occurred near the column walls. Although these phenomena had been evident on the ground, they became primary problems in space. They were resolved by using a recirculating buffer in the electrode chambers at the ends of the separation columns and by developing suitable coatings for the inner surfaces of the columns. The data were recorded by camera, and no actual samples were returned to the ground for analysis.

The ASTP apparatus is shown in Fig. 25. Here only one column at a time is in use in the apparatus. Several columns were used sequentially. In order to return the samples to the ground for analysis after the separation was complete, the column contents were frozen in place by a thermoelectric device located behind the column. All switches and controls as well as the recirculating pumps are contained in the main housing. The continuous flow electrophoretic separation flown on ASTP was a German experiment performing on the principles shown in Fig. 23 and with an optical detector placed near the emerging ports. The optical detector was used to characterize the separations obtained. For rocket flight applications, another continuous flow separator is under development again, with, at this stage, only optical means of acquiring separation data. Although to date only electrophoretic separation techniques have been tried, many others may be possible in space.

Fig. 24 Apollo flight apparatus for electrophoresis.

Light, magnetic, thermal, and many other effects could be used to separate particles or molecules freely floating in a gas or a liquid. In the absence of gravity-driven sedimenta-

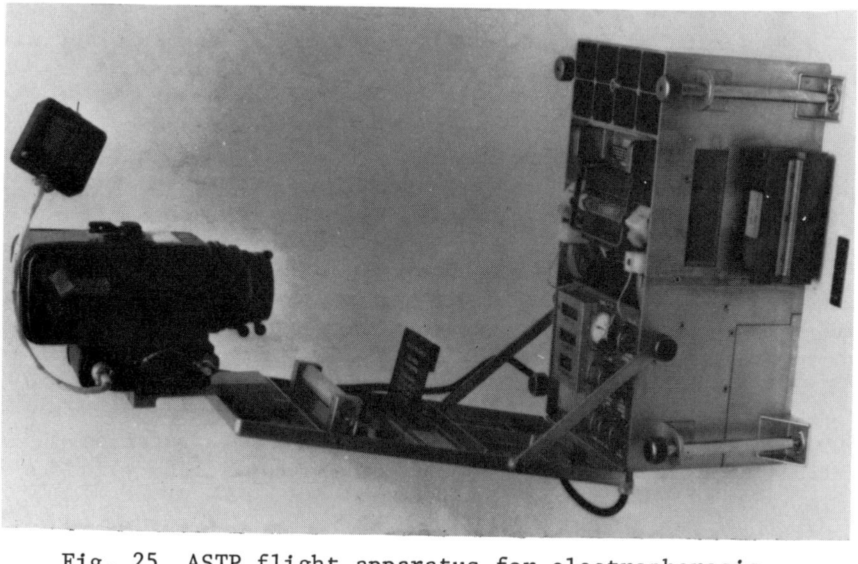

Fig. 25 ASTP flight apparatus for electrophoresis.

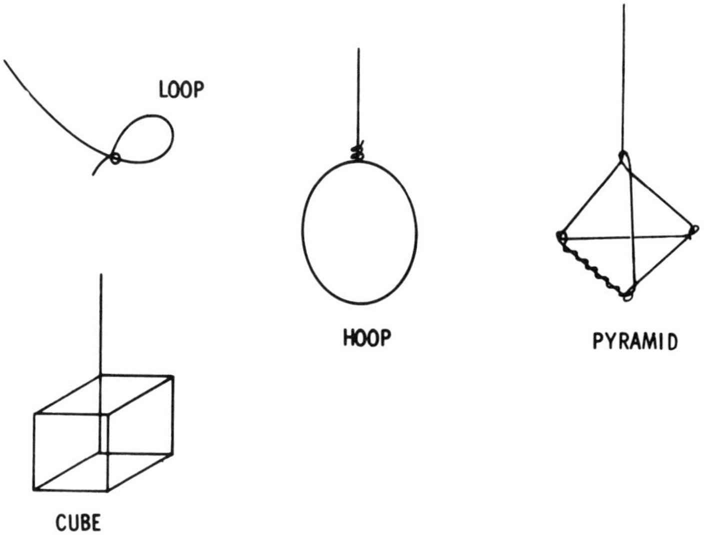

Fig. 26 Skylab science demonstration, liquid films.

tion and fluid circulations, very minute force differences on particles may be exploited for effective separations.

Specialized Apparatus for Phenomenological Studies

Meaningful scientific demonstrations can be performed with quite simple equipment, such as the following:

1) The behavior of liquid films was studied (Skylab IV) by dipping two- and three-dimensional wire frames into water. The surface tension was varied by adding soap to the water. Typical wire frames are shown in Fig. 26.

2) Even simpler demonstrations were carried out when the coalescence of two free-floating spheres of water was studied, one sphere being colored orange (using orange juice) and the other purple (using grape juice).

3) The rotational stability of a freely suspended drop of water was studied, as was the stability of a rotating cylindrical liquid zone confined between two solid cylinders (Fig. 27).

4) The stability of dispersions of immiscible liquids was demonstrated using the apparatus shown in Fig. 28.

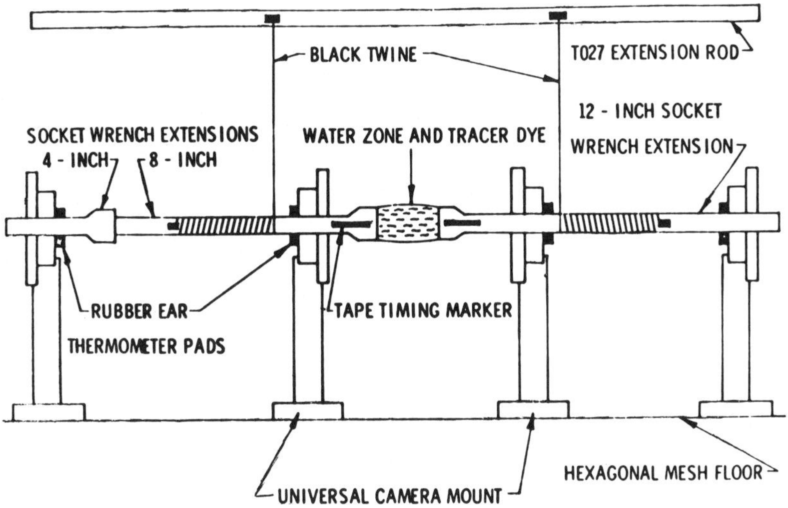

Fig. 27 Schematic of Skylab science demonstration, liquid floating zone.

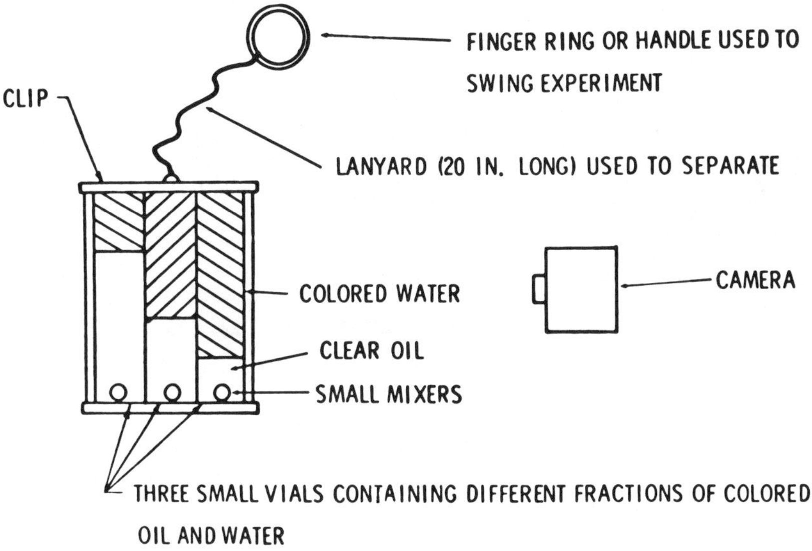

Fig. 28 Skylab science demonstration, immiscible liquids.

The preceding are typical examples of experiments that demonstrate very clearly the rather startling changes in behavior of liquids when these are manipulated in effectively

Fig. 29 Apollo 17 heat flow and convection demonstration (recording camera omitted).

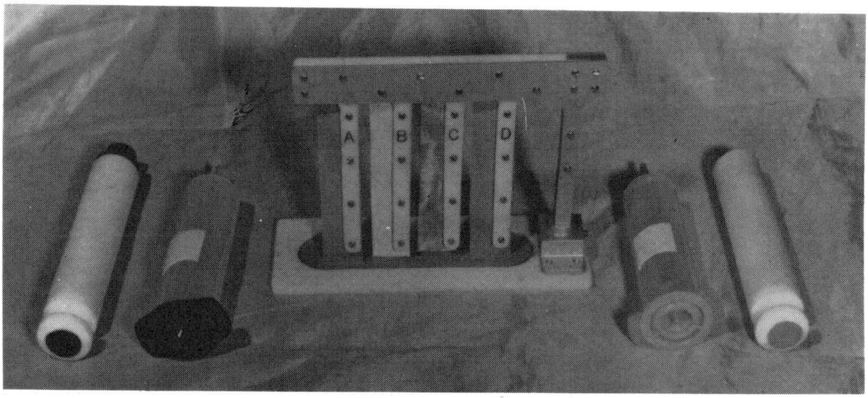

Fig. 30 ASTP wicking demonstration.

zero-g conditions. Somewhat more complicated and well-instrumented demonstrations, for example, in heat flow and convection, were performed on Apollo 14 and 17 using the apparatus shown (less camera) in Fig. 29. A paper is given on the results of these studies elsewhere in this volume.

On ASTP, a number of simple experiments relying on photographic data were performed. One of these, the "wicking demonstration," is shown in Fig. 30. Four different wicks are dipped into a pool of colored liquid (not shown), and the flow of the liquid into the wicks is recorded by a movie camera. Low-g and ground data then are compared.

Conclusions

As may be seen, a wide variety of apparatus has been developed to date. Some has been designed quite specifically for a single experiment. Other apparatus has been multipurpose in nature. The common characteristics of the apparatus have been that 1) all apparatus has been of laboratory scale; 2) the apparatus has been derived from known ground-based apparatus; 3) the apparatus has been adapted to meet the requirements of the carrier, e.g., weight, power consumption, electrical characteristics, external temperature, etc.; and 4) the processes carried out in the apparatus usually have been derivations of commonly used ground-based processes.

As space processing technology progresses, the apparatus increasingly will depart from using adaptations of ground-based processing methods, and a specific space technology will evolve using not only the low-g feature of space flight but also the vacuum, the immense volume, the intense heat and cold, the magnetic fields, and the high spacecraft velocity, among others. As the utility of the space environment is recognized, space processes will be developed which can be performed only in space (as indicated previously, for example, in the section on "Separation Apparatus"). With the use of desired combinations of the features offered by space flight, the present laboratory-scale multipurpose apparatus will evolve to a much larger-scale apparatus which will be designed for a single purpose.

Progress has been made in the first 10 years' development of the new space processing technology, but many more scientifically interesting and commercially attractive ventures lie ahead.

Bibliography

Aubin, W. M., Larson, Dave, Jr., and Geschwind, Gary I., "Research of Metal Solidification in Zero-g State, Test Apparatus and Instrumentation," Final Rept., Contract NAS8-28604, Sept. 1973, Grumman Aerospace Corp.

"Automatic Directional Solidification System for Space Processing," Contract NAS8-31536, General Electric Co. (in progress).

Bannister, T. C., Grodzka, P. G., Spradley, L. W., Bourgeois, S. V., Hedden, R. O. and Facemire, B. R., "Final Results, Apollo 17 Heat Flow and Convection Experiment," TM X-64772, July 1973, NASA.

Bier, M., "Role of Gravity in Preparative Electrophoresis," Contract NAS8-29566, University of Arizona (in progress).

Bier, M. and Snyder, R. S., "Electrophoresis in Space at Zero Gravity," AIAA Paper 74-210, Feb. 1974, Washington, D. C.

Carruthers, J. R., "Studies of Liquid Drops in Simulated Zero Gravity," AIAA Paper 74-158, Feb. 1974, Washington, D. C.

Carruthers, J. R., Gibson, E. G., Klett, M. G. and Facemire, B. R., "Studies of Rotating Liquid Floating Zones on Skylab IV," AIAA Paper 75-692, May 1975, Denver, Colo.; also, published elsewhere in this volume.

Darbro, W., "Liquid Film Demonstration Experiment Skylab SL-4," TM X-64911, Jan. 1975, NASA.

Duncan, C. S., Mazelsky, R. and Rubenstein, M., "Zero Gravity Crystal Growth," Final Rept., Contract NAS8-24509, April 1970, Westinghouse Research Lab.

Eiss, A., Dussan, B., Schadis, W. and Frank, L., "High Temperature Radiation Furnace," Final Rept., Contract NAS8-28059, April 1973, Weiner Associates.

"Feasibility Study of Commercial Space Manufacturing," Final Rept., Contract NAS8-31353, November 1975, McDonnell Douglas Corp.

Feret, J. M. and Mazelsky, R., "Skylab Furnace System Provides Precise Thermal Environment for Materials Experiments," Westinghouse Engineer, Vol. 33, Nov. 1973.

Frost, R. T., "Electromagnetic Containerless Processing Requirements and Recommended Facility Concept and Capabilities," Final Rept., Contract NAS8-29680, May 1974, General Electric Co.

Frost, R. T., Buerger, E. H., Lambert, R. H., O'Connor, M. F., O'Dell, E. L. G., Nataluch, L. J., Stockhoff, E. H. and Wouch, G., "Electromagnetic Free Suspension System for Space Manufacturing," Final Rept., Contract NAS8-27228, Dec. 1972, General Electric Co.

Halbach, C. R., Page, R. J., Russell, J. and Arthur, Paul D., "2200°C Oxidizing Atmosphere Furnace for Space Manufacturing," AIAA Paper 74-154, Feb. 1974, Washington, D. C.

Happe, R. A. and Topol, L. E., "Experiments Leading to Production of New Glasses in Space," AIAA Paper 74-159, Feb. 1974, Washington, D. C.; also, published elsewhere in this volume.

Lacy, L. L. and Otto, G. H., "The Stability of Liquid Dispersions in Space," AIAA Paper 74-1242, Oct. 1974, Huntsville, Ala.

"Manufacturing Technology Unique to Zero Gravity Environment," Presentations at Marshall Space Flight Center, Nov. 1968.

McDermit, J. H., "Solar Energy Concentrator System for Crystal Growth and Zone Refining in Space," Final Rept., Contract NAS8-30268, Feb. 1975, Lockheed Missiles & Space Co.

McKannan, E. C., Krupnick, A. C., Griffin, R. N. and McCreight, L. R., "Electrophoresis Separation in Space — Apollo 14," TM X-64611, Aug. 1971, NASA.

"MSFC Skylab Corollary Experiment Systems — Mission Evaluation," TM X-64820, Secs. V and VII, Sept. 1974, NASA.

"NASA Announcement of Opportunity (AO No. OA-76-02)," Space Processing Rocket Experiment Project, Feb. 6, 1976.

Parks, P. G., "Skylab Materials Processing Facility Experiment — Developer's Report," TM X-64977, July 1975, NASA.

Proceedings: Third Space Processing Symposium — Skylab Results, Rept. 74-5, June 1974, NASA.

Reger, J. L., "Experimental Development of Processes to Produce Homogenized Alloys of Immiscible Metals," Final Rept., Contract NAS8-27805, Phase III, Dec. 1972, TRW.

Reger, J. L., "Study on Processing Immiscible Materials in Zero Gravity," Final Rept., Contract NAS8-28267, June 1975, TRW.

Snyder, R. S., "Electrophoresis Separation in Space — Apollo 16," TM X-64724, Nov. 1972, NASA.

"Space Processing and Manufacturing Symposium," Presentations at Marshall Space Flight Center, Oct. 1969.

Steurer, W. H. and Gorham, D. J., "Processes for Space Manufacturing — Definition of Criteria for Process Feasibility and Effectiveness," Final Rept., Contract NAS8-24979, June 1970, General Dynamics/Convair.

Vaughan, O. H. and Hill, C. K., "Drop Coalescence in Zero Gravity Environment of Skylab IV," Bulletin of the American Meteorological Society, Vol. 55, Sept. 1974, p. 1127.

Wang, T. G., Saffren, M. M. and Elleman, D. D., "Acoustic Chamber for Weightless Positioning," AIAA Paper 74-155, Jan. 1974, Washington, D. C.; also, published elsewhere in this volume.

Whymark, R. R., "Acoustic Field Positioning for Containerless Processing," Nov. 1975, Ultrasonics.

Whymark, R. R., "Acoustic Processing Methods for Space Processing," Final Rept., Contract NAS8-29030, June 1973, Interand Corp.

Wouch, G. and Frost, R. T., "Development of Containerless Process for Preparation of Tungsten with Improved Service Characteristics," Final Rept., Contract NAS8-29879, Nov. 1975, General Electric Co.

Wuenscher, H. F., "Low and Zero-g Manufacturing in Orbit," AIAA Paper 67-842, Oct. 1967, Anaheim, Calif.

Yates, I. C., "Apollo 14 Composite Casting Demonstration, Final Report," TM X-64641, Oct. 1971, NASA.

Yates, I. C. and Yost, V. H., "Research Rocket Tests RR 1 & 2," TM X-64665, April 1972, NASA.

THERMAL DESIGN AND ANALYSES OF SKYLAB MULTIPURPOSE FURNACE AND EXPERIMENTS

J. W. H. Chi,* R. G. Seidensticker,+ and C. S. Duncan≠

Westinghouse Electric Corporation, Pittsburgh, Pa.

Abstract

The Skylab multipurpose electric furnace was designed to accommodate 11 different materials processing experiments, with their respective thermal requirements and constraints. Extensive prototype and ground-based tests were carried out, and detailed thermal analyses were performed to insure that these requirements and constraints were met. The basic features of the multipurpose electric furnace and the 11 experimental cartridges are described. The design and development problems encountered and the solutions to these problems are discussed. The analytical techniques used for thermal design and analyses are described.

Introduction

Skylab is an orbiting laboratory designed to house equipment, instruments, and personnel so that long-term experiments in a number of scientific areas can be carried out. Among these are a series of 11 materials processing experiments to be carried out in the M-512 Materials Processing Facility. The major purpose of these experiments is to study the effect

---

Presented as Paper No. 74-650 at the AIAA/ASME Thermophysics and Heat Transfer Conference, Boston, Mass., July 15-17, 1974. Westinghouse Electric Corporation, under NASA Contract NAS-8-28271, administered by George C. Marshall Space Flight Center, designed, developed and fabricated the multipurpose electric furnace and the experimental cartridges for the program.

*Fellow Engineer, Astronuclear Laboratory.
+Fellow Scientist, Central Research Laboratory.
≠Manager, Crystal Technology, Central Research Laboratory.

of the absence of gravity-induced density effects on the formation and on the physical properties of materials produced in space. Scientists have speculated that processing of materials in orbital flight may yield important results that include improved material properties (physical and mechanical) and the possibility of growing significantly larger single crystals.

NASA selected 11 out of a number of proposed materials processing experiments for study in Skylab. The key to this study program is the development of the M-518 multipurpose electric furnace. This special furnace was designed to accommodate the 11 experiments with their different requirements on temperatures, temperature gradients, and rates of resolidification. These requirements imposed stringent constraints and goals on the design of the multipurpose furnace. One constraint is that only a limited number of thermocouples can be accommodated in the furnace. Consequently, in order to obtain meaningful flight test data, extensive prototype and ground-based tests were carried out to determine the thermal characteristics of the furnace and of each experiment. Detailed thermal analyses were carried out to supplement the experimental measurements and to obtain information that was not or could not be measured experimentally.

This paper describes the basic features of the multipurpose furnace and experimental cartridges. The problems encountered, the design solutions, and changes obtained are discussed.

Description of Furnace and Experimental Cartridges

Basic Thermal Environments

The general thermal environments required by the experiments can be seen in Fig. 1 and the three typical axial temperature distributions shown. These consist of a relatively isothermal heated section, a temperature gradient section, and a heat-sink section. During testing of each experiment, it was desired to maintain the hot end of a given test sample at a specified temperature for a fixed length of time ("soak" period). Simultaneously, a

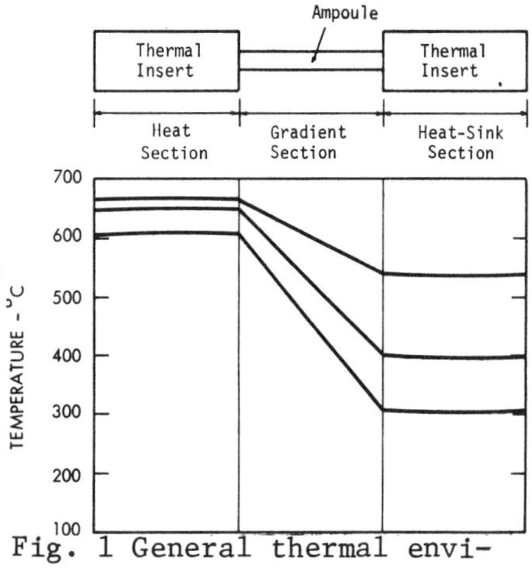

Fig. 1 General thermal environment for experimental cartridges.

prescribed axial temperature gradient must be maintained in the gradient region. Following the soak period, the sample must be cooled down at a controlled rate to provide a desired rate of sample resolidification. The M-518 multipurpose electric furnace was designed to supply this necessary thermal environment.

Experimental Cartridges

To achieve the desired thermal environment for each experiment, separate experimental cartridges were designed. The experimental cartridge accommodates the test specimen, generally held within quartz tube ampoules. Several typical cartridge designs are illustrated in Fig. 2. Each experimental

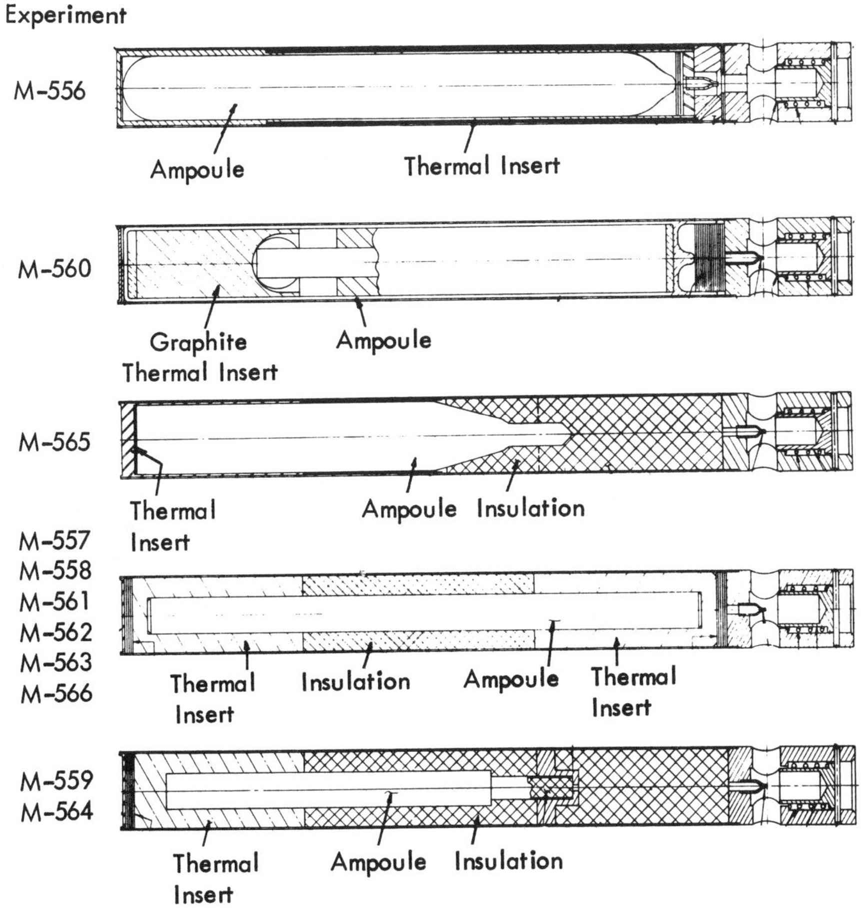

Fig. 2 Typical types of cartridge-ampoule designs

cartridge is designed to provide the desired axial temperature distribution. For this purpose, the cartridges have three distinct sections characterized as the hot end, the gradient section, and the cold end. Since the furnace temperature profile must be limited so that all 11 different experiments can be accommodated, the specific temperature distributions of the experiments (established by the principal investigators) were obtained by controlling heat flow through the cartridges and ampoules by thermal design. This consisted of judicious use of insulators, conductors, and surface coatings to achieve the desired thermal performance.

The Furnace

The furnace consists of three major components: the furnace, a control package, and the experimental cartridges. The basic function of the furnace is to provide a controlled thermal environment for the experiments. A schematic diagram (see Fig. 3) shows that the furnace consists of two main sections: the furnace chamber and the instrumentation compartment. The furnace accepts three experimental cartridges, spaced 120° apart. Access to the furnace chamber is from the instrumentation compartment through three access ports. Major operating requirements of the furnace included capability to perform experiments at temperatures up to 1000°C at the hot end and a

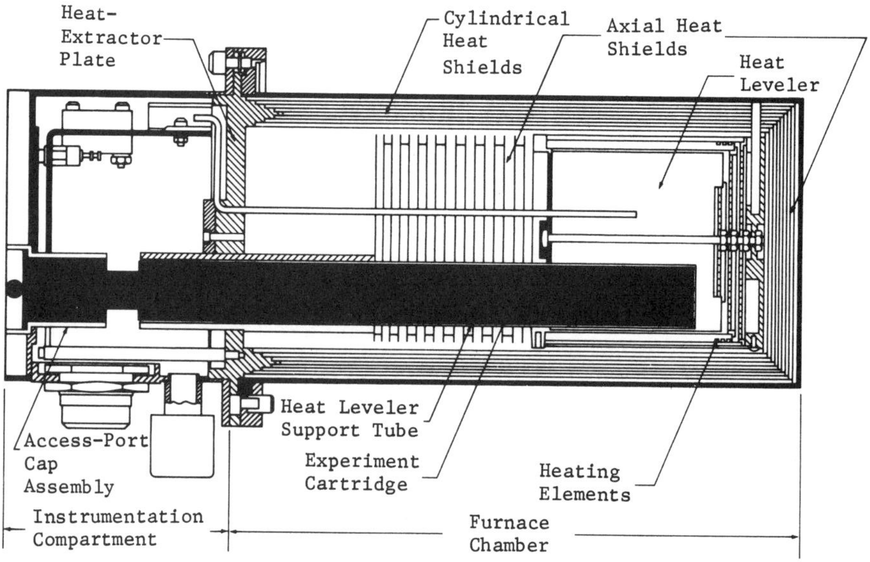

Fig. 3 Schematic of multipurpose furnace and components

total power consumption less than 144 w. [This is based on the maximum allowable temperature (at the cold end) that can be tolerated by the thermocouple reference junction, since the bulk of the total power must pass through the heat extractor plate. It is also the minimum power available to the multipurpose furnace.] Because of the latter constraint, a major furnace design goal was to minimize furnace and cartridge heat losses. This was accomplished through the use of multiple thermal radiation shields in a vacuum environment. The insulation system consists of eight concentric cylindrical shells of side shields made of molybdenum, eight layers of molybdenum hot-end shields, and 16 layers of molybdenum cold-end shields.

To provide the general temperature profile needed for all experiments, the hot ends of the experimental cartridges were inserted into a graphite block called the "heat leveler." The heater assembly consists of two resistance heating elements wound on an alumina sleeve that fits around the heat leveler. The heat leveler provides an essentially isothermal hot-end environment. It is supported by three stainless steel tubes that connect to three copper heat-transfer tubes attached to the copper heat-extractor plate. The experimental cartridges are held within the tubes through latching mechanisms at the access port end. The transitions from the low to high thermal conductivities of the tube materials (stainless steel to copper) provides a thermal gradient region for the cartridges.

Most of the heat generated in the heaters is transferred to the heat leveler by thermal radiation; the remainder is lost through the heat shields. Heat transferred to the heat leveler is either lost by axial conduction through the stainless steel support tubes or transferred to the experimental cartridges by thermal radiation; all of it is ultimately conducted through the copper heat extractor plate to the heat sink of the Materials Processing Facility.

Temperatures at three furnace locations are monitored: the periphery of the heat leveler next to the heater form (for power control purposes), the center of the heat leveler, and the heat extractor plate (for furnace performance evaluations). A back-up thermocouple was provided in each location.

Control Package

The furnace temperature is controlled automatically in response to a preset time-temperature program. Means are provided for manual setting of soak temperature, soak period, and cooldown rate. The control accuracy is approximately $\pm$ 1°C. Soak periods of 1 - 64 hr and cooldown rates of 0.6 - 2.4°C/min can be selected, as well as a "passive" cooldown. The controlled cooldown rates were all higher than the passive cooldown rates, so that heat addition was necessary to provide the controlled rates of cooldown.

Cartridge Design and Development

Experimental Requirements

The 11 materials processing experiments were submitted by principal investigators from various institutions, as shown in Table 1. The experiment titles, descriptions, thermal requirements of each experiment, the hot-end temperatures, temperature gradients, and the desired rates of solidifications are given in the table.

The total power required by the furnace for a given experiment consists of "intrinsic" furnace heat losses (heat that does not pass through the experimental cartridges) and the cartridge heat losses. The intrinsic furnace heat loss is related directly to the hot end and the heat leveler temperature. It is necessary to know the intrinsic furnace heat losses so that the amount of power allowed for the experimental cartridges can be determined, given the total power constraint of 144 w. It was recognized that, for the majority of the experiments, 144 w of total power would not present any serious problems because the maximum temperature requirements were fairly low. However, for some of the experiments, in which the desired hot end temperatures were in excess of 950°C, judicious designs of the experimental cartridges must be made in order to stay within the design power limit. Experimental determination of the intrinsic furnace heat loss was carried out by calibrating the furnace with three "low-heat-loss cartridges." These consisted of shorter cartridges packed with fiberfrax insulation. The input power and the corresponding heat leveler temperature were measured over a range of power levels. The heat losses through the low-heat-loss cartridges were estimated by assuming conduction loss down the cartridge walls only. With these estimates, the net furnace intrinsic heat losses were calculated. With these data, preliminary cartridge designs and total power requirements for all of the experiments could be predicted.

Test Program

The furnace cartridge developmental program consisted of five phases: 1) design, construction, and test of a prototype

Table 1 Description of materials experiments and thermal requirements

Experiment	Institution	Experiment title and description	Maximum temperature in isothermal region, °C	Temperature gradient in gradient region, °C/cm	Length of meltback, cm	Cooldown °C/cm
M-556	Rensselaer Polytechnic Institute	Vapor growth of IV-VI compounds: to determine the degree of improvement which can be obtained in the perfection and chemical homogeneity of crystals grown by chemical vapor transport under weightless conditions.	520 ± 20	135°C total ΔT	...	...
M-557	TRW Systems Group	Immiscible alloy compositions: to determine the effect of near-zero gravity on the processing of material compositions that normally segregate on Earth.	700-730	<0.5 in isothermal region	...	...
M-558	NASA Marshall Space Flight Center	Radioactive tracer diffusion: to measure self-diffusion and impurity diffusion effects in liquid metal in space flight and to characterize the disturbing effects, if any, due to spaceflight acceleration.	775	>20	...	...
M-559	Texas Instruments Corporation	Microsegregation in germanium: to determine the degree of microsegregation of doping impurities in germanium caused by convectionless directional solidification under conditions of weightlessness.	>938	>15	>3	0.6
M-560	University of Alabama at Huntsville	Growth of spherical crystals: to grow indium antimonide crystals of high chemical homogeneity and structural perfection and study their resulting physical properties in comparison with theoretical values for ideal crystals.	>520	>15	0.13 ± 0.03	2.4
M-561	National Research Institute for Metals, Tokyo, Japan	Whisker-reinforced composites: to produce void-free samples of silver reinforced with oriented silicon-carbide whiskers.	>960	...	...	...
M-562	Massachusetts Institute of Technology	Indium-antimonide crystals: to produce doped semiconductor crystals of high chemical homogeneity and structural perfection and to evaluate the influence of weightlessness in attaining those properties.	>520	>20	3-5	0.6
M-563	University of Southern California, Los Angeles	Mixed III-V crystal growth: to determine how weightlessness affects directional solidification of binary semiconductor alloys and, if single crystals are obtained, to determine how their semiconducting properties depend on alloy composition.	950	>60	>2	...
M-564	University of California at Los Angeles	Halide eutectics: to produce highly continuous controlled structures in samples of fiber-like sodium fluouride/sodium chloride and to measure physical properties.	900	30-50	>5	...
M-565	Catholic University, Belgium	Silver grids melted in space: to determine how the configurations of perforated silver foils and a porous block of fine silver wires change when melted and resolidified in space.	>960	Minimize	3 out of 9 specimens	Maximize
M-566	NASA Marshall Space Flight Center	Copper-aluminum eutectic: to determine the effect of weightlessness on formation of lamellar structure in eutectic alloys when directionally solidified.	855	~50	>5	1.2

unit; 2) redesign of the prototype system for reproducible construction, using standardized materials, components, processes, etc.; 3) acceptance testing of the first production system to demonstrate that it retained the characteristics of the prototype unit; 4) qualification testing of the first production system to demonstrate that it retained the characteristics of the prototype system; and 5) acceptance testing of follow-on production systems (for flight and backup) to demonstrate that they had the same initial characteristics as the system subjected to qualification testing.

For the experimental cartridges, prototype units were tested in a simulated ("SIM") furnace designed to test a single cartridge at a time. The first seven production units were acceptance tested in a prototype furnace, using three identical cartridges at a time, unless different materials were to be processed in a single test, i.e., Exp. M-556.

Thermal Analyses

During these various stages of design and testing, preliminary and detailed thermal analyses were carried out to provide thermal designs and information for design iterations. Preliminary cartridge designs were carried out using one-dimensional conduction analyses. Detailed thermal analyses were carried out using two-dimensional (r,z) TAP-A models of the furnace, of the cartridges alone, and of integrated furnace and prototype cartridges. (TAP-A is a computer code for three-dimensional, arbitrary geometry heat-transfer analyses.[1])

A TAP-A model of the furnace was used to verify the furnace intrinsic heat losses and to study the paths of the heat losses so that potential improvements of the furnace design can be identified. TAP-A models of the cartridges alone were developed to provide information for cartridge redesign and to analyze the SIM furnace test results. Integrated furnace-cartridge thermal models were used for the following purposes: 1) to verify the redesigned prototype cartridges in conjunction with the acceptance tests in the prototype furnace; 2) to predict flight test conditions that included hot-end temperature, total power requirement, and rates of resolidification; and 3) to determine the "time line" for each experiment from sample heatup through testing and furnace cooldown to the "touch" temperature of 40°C (at the hot end of the cartridge).

Results of Analyses and Tests

Furnace Thermal Analysis

The multipurpose furnace contains a number of heat leak paths. This includes the following (listed in the order of descending heat loss contributions): 1) heat loss through hot-end and side radiation shields; 2) axial loss along side shields by radiation to stainless steel support tubes and copper heat-transfer tubes; 3) axial along three spacer tubes; 4) heat loss through three cartridges; 5) heat loss through six heater support tubes; 6) axial along side shields to the shield support tree; 7) heat loss through the axial baffles; and 8) heat loss along heater wire sleeve.

Because of the different modes of heat transfer involved and the existence of several unknown heat-transfer properties, accurate prediction of the furnace heat loss characteristics was extremely difficult. In particular, the actual emissivities of various surfaces had not been measures, i.e., gold plating on the radiation shields, stainless steel 310, emmisivity coatings and the contact resistances between the side shields and the support tree, the heater support tubes, and the furnace outer can were unknown. Empirical adjustments to the analytical model were necessary to arrive at a good correlation of predicted furnace characteristics with experimental measurements. The latter consisted of total input power, heat leveler and heat sink plate temperatures, and cartridge temperatures in the gradient region.

A detailed thermal model of the furnace and the low-heat-loss cartridge was developed[2] to simulate the thermal characteristics of the furnace. A schematic diagram of this model (not to scale) is shown in Fig. 4. The figure illustrates the nodal network used in the model and the various heat-transfer mechanisms involved. The model is two-dimensional (r,z). This is satisfactory, since the only region of θ-asymmetry is the three cartridge bores within the heat leveler, which is made of high-conductivity graphite. Consequently, the bore surfaces have relatively uniform surface temperatures. Moreover, the total circumference of the three bores was less than the outer circumference of the heat leveler. These facts permitted the simulation of the furnace cartridge by a two-dimensional model, provided that all dimensions critical to heat transfer were reproduced in the model.

The low-heat-loss cartridge simply consisted of the cartridge filled with fiberfrax thermal insulation. The portion of the integrated model occupied by the low-heat-loss

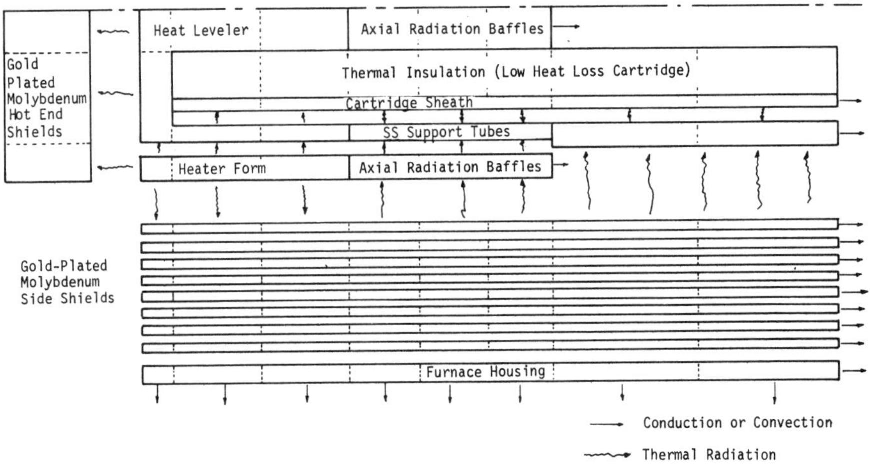

Fig. 4 Schematic of TAP-A furnace thermal model.

cartridge was replaced readily by a model of any experimental cartridge to be analyzed.

A comparison of the predicted (based on the furnace model evolved) and measured (in the prototype furnace) total furnace heat loss characteristics is shown in Fig. 5. It is evident that there is an excellent correlation. It must be pointed out that a correlation of the total heat loss characteristics alone is inadequate. A complete correlation of all heat fluxes and furnace temperatures is necessary to provide proper boundary conditions to the cartridge. At 1000°C, the predicted heat loss through the low-heat-loss cartridges (with bare stainless steel surfaces), based on the integrated furnace-cartridge model evolved, is 8.73 w. This may be compared with 8.7 w measured in the prototype furnace. The excellent agreement between measured and calculated temperatures and heat fluxes provides a high degree of confidence in the furnace model for subsequent integrated furnace-cartridge thermal analyses.

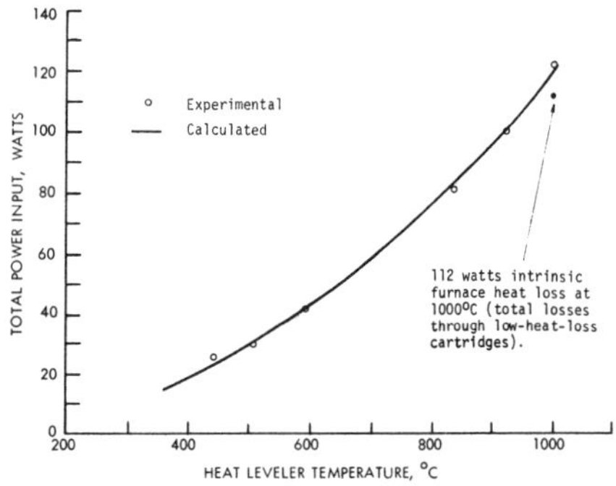

Fig. 5 Observed and predicted furnace heat loss characteristics with low-heat-loss cartridge.

Cartridge Thermal Analyses

Detailed thermal analyses of each experimental cartridge design were performed in two steps: 1) TAP-A model of the cartridge only, and 2) an integrated furnace-cartridge model, by integrating the separate furnace and cartridge TAP-A models. Steady-state and transient analyses were performed for each experiment. The latter was carried out to determine the rates of sample resolidification and the total length of time for each experiment. A typical experimental cartridge TAP-A model and the results of steady-state and transient analyses are shown in Fig. 6 for experiment M-557. The cartridge design and the nodal structure of the thermal model are shown at the bottom of the figure. The steady-state and transient temperature distributions are given in the figure. Other temperatures at various locations of the furnace and cartridge are shown in Fig. 7. These figures show clearly that extensive thermal information can be obtained by supplementing experimental measurements with detailed thermal analyses. However, a high degree of confidence can be placed in the calculated data only if there are good correlations between calculated and measured temperatures. A high degree

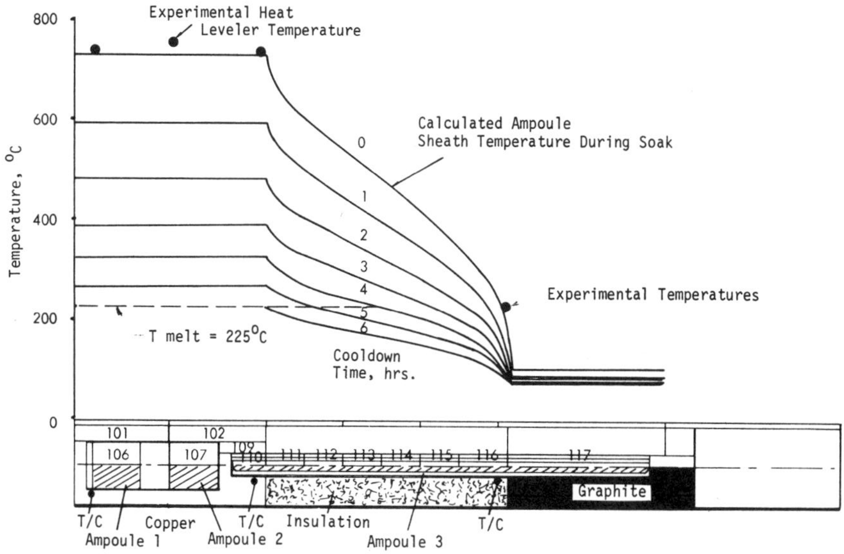

Fig. 6 Comparison of experimental and calculated temperatures during steady-state soak and cooldown (experiment M-557; temperatures, °C).

of correlation was assured by the following: 1) detailed simulation of the furnace, and 2) specification of measured boundary temperatures and total input power.

The degree of correlation achieved in the analyses is illustrated further in Table 2, in which the more important experimental and predicted thermal data are compared for a typical experiment, M-557.

For experiments with controlled rates of cooldown, the rate of resolidification was calculated from the rate of cooldown divided by the temperature gradient at the melt front

$$dx/dt = (dT/dt)/(dT/dx)$$

For experiments using passive cooldown, the rates of resolidification were estimated by either numerical differentiation of the melt position with respect to time (at any given time during cooldown, the melt front was determined from the axial temperature distribution) or by the preceding equation. The latter was used when the cooldown period of interest was relatively short or where the passive rates of cooldown were relatively constant in the cooldown period of interest.

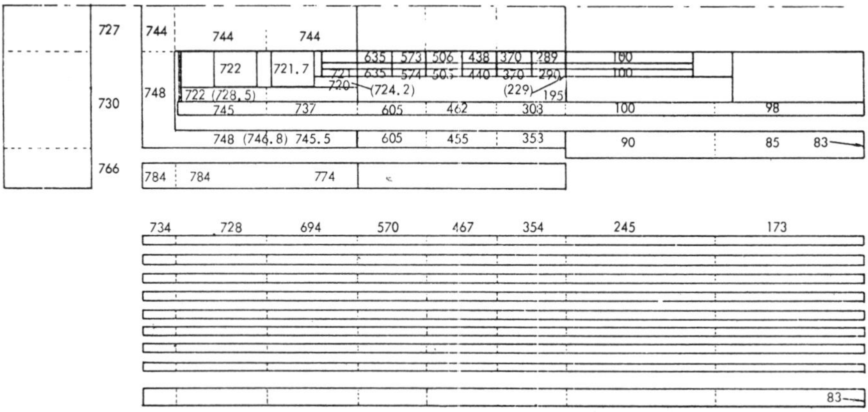

Fig. 7 Comparison of experimental (in parentheses) and calculated furnace-cartridge temperatures during steady-state soak prototype furnace testing (experiment M-557; temperatures, °C).

Table 2 Comparison of experimental and calculated thermal characteristics of furnace-cartridge experiment M-557

	Experimental	Calculated
Heat leveler control temperature, °C	758.8	...
Heat leveler temperature, °C	746.8	746
Ampoule temperatures, °C		
Hot end of isothermal region	728.5	722
Cold end of isothermal region	724.2	720
Cold end of gradient region	229.0	195
Heat extractor temperature, °C	83.8	83.8[a]
Ambient temperature, °C	...	21[a]
Controlled cooldown rate, °C/min	Passive cooldown	Passive cooldown
Time to completely resolidify sample, hr	5.4	6.5
Time for cartridge hot end to reach touch temperature (40°C), hr	15[b]	17
Time for heat leveler to reach 40°C, hr	15[b]	17
Heat loss per cartridge, w	6.8[c]	6.1
Heat loss for three cartridges, w	20.4	18.4
Furnace intrinsic heat loss, w[d]	61.5	61.5
Total power to furnace, w, intrinsic furnace loss plus cartridge losses	81.9	79.9
Total power to furnace, w[e]	76.2	76.2[a]
Difference in total power, w	5.7	3.7

[a]These are input data to the thermal model.

[b]Extrapolated.

[c]Based on SIM furnace data, corrected to prototype test conditions.

[d]Based on prototype furnace heat loss calibrations.

[e]Based on calibration of heat extractor temperature.

Cartridge Development Problems

It was recognized in the design phase of the program that several cartridges would present design difficulties. These were identified to be experiments M-556, M-559, M-560, M-561, and M-565. With the exception of M-556, the other experiments had the same general problem: the maximum hot-end temperature requirement resulted in excessive total power (greater than 144 w). Experiment M-560 originally stipulated the use of germanium samples (melting point = 938°C). Following a number of design iterations, it was finally concluded that the thermal requirements and total power constraint of this experiment could not be met. The test sample was subsequently changed to indium antimonide.

Experiment M-556 had a unique problem. This was in the extremely shallow temperature gradient desired, which is directly opposite to those generally required by the other experiments and to the steep gradients for which the multipurpose furnace was designed. Following a number of design and test iterations, all of these problems were resolved by controlling thermal parameters through materials selection to effect the following: 1) cartridge surface emissivities desired to control temperature drops and heat losses; 2) thermal conductivities of thermal inserts at the hot end, cold end, and along the ampoule to control axial temperature distribution; and 3) radial heat transfer from the ampoule to the cartridge sheath to control heat flow through the ampoule/cartridge.

The surface emissivity of the stainless steel cartridge sheath is on the order of 0.2 - 0.3, depending on the temperature level. The surface emissivity was changed by the following: 1) gold plating the cartridge sheath; 2) oxidizing the surface; and 3) painting the surface with a high-emissivity paint of Aquadag (a graphite slurry).

Gold plating was used primarily at the cold end, although it was used in the gradient region for experiment M-559. This had the effect of raising the cold-end temperature and reducing heat flow through the cartridge. Both oxidized and Aquadag-coated surfaces were used for the hot end. These had the effect of reducing the temperature drop between the heat leveler and the cartridge.

The temperature distribution along the ampoule was controlled by selecting the proper thermal insert material. For the hot and cold ends, this was either copper or graphite. To control the temperature gradient in the gradient region, copper or stainless steel sheaths were used around the ampoules. A combination of the thermal conductivity of the sheath material and the sheath thickness provided the desired temperature gradients. (For details on the cartridge designs, see Ref. 3.)

A major problem encountered in the development of the cartridge designs was the lack of experimental data on the following: 1) surface emissivities of gold plating, oxide, and Aquadag coatings as functions of temperature; 2) thermal conductivities of test samples as functions of temperature; 3) specific heat of test samples; 4) the latent heats of fusion of test samples; and 5) contact resistances among various components.

For this reason, trial and error and iterations were used to determine the properties indirectly by correlation of the measured temperatures with those calculated by the TAP-A models. It becomes evident that, in order to predict meaningful temperatures and temperature distributions, the TAP-A models must carefully reproduce the cartridge dimensions and thermal environments. The final thermal conditions attained are summarized in Table 3. Preliminary results from the flight experiments have been reported in Ref. 4 and 5. Detailed results are given in Ref. 6.

Table 3 Summary of furnace power requirements for various experiments

Experiment number	Principal investigator	Ampoule hot-end temperature goal °C	Prototype furnace heat leveler temperature °C	Furnace intrinsic heat loss w	Total cartridge heat loss w	Maximum total power requirement w
M-556	Wiedemeier	520 ± 20	594	40	16	56
M-557	Reger	700 ± 10	747	62	18	80
M-558	Ukanwa	700 > T > 630	804	72	44	116
M-559	Padovani	980 ± 10	998	115	32	147[a]
M-560	Walter	> 520	613	42	39	81
M-561	Kawada	970 ± 10	990	116	24	140
M-562	Gatos-Witt	700	804	71	44	115
M-563	Wilcox	~900	958	107	29	136
M-564	Yue	~900	952	102	30	132
M-565	Deruyttere	965 ± 10	1002	120	24	144
M-566	Hasemeyer-Aldrich	800	868	82	40	122

[a] This is slightly in excess of nominal maximum available power of 144 w.

Potential Furnace Improvements

Thermal analysis of the furnace was carried out to study potential redesigns to lower the furnace heat losses. The results showed that the surface temperature of the innermost radiation shield is relatively high along the entire axial length. Since this surface views directly the stainless steel support tubes and copper heat-transfer tubes, approximately 20 w were lost by radiation to these tubes. In addition, axial conduction through the side shields to the cold end and radiation to the copper support tree constitute another 20 w heat loss. These facts suggested a number of potential modifications of the furnace to reduce overall heat loss. Three of the most promising ones were as follows: 1) terminate the side shields and tie them to the baffles to provide isothermal cans (with mitered corners similar to those at the hot end); 2) provide radiation shields between the existing shields and the stainless steel support tubes and copper heat-transfer tubes; and 3) provide additional radiation shields between existing ones.

The first represents a major furnace modification, which can yield the greatest reduction in heat loss. With this modification, the two major heat loss components just discussed would be eliminated. However, the shield temperatures and heat loss through the shields at the hot end would increase. Consequently, a combination of modifications 1 and 3 was considered for a "major mod" analysis. Modification 2 represents a relatively simple fix to the furnace; however, it is expected to yield a relatively small reduction in heat loss, and it was defined as the "simple mod" for analyses.

To analyze these furnace modifications, the reference furnace thermal model with the low-heat-loss cartridge was modified accordingly. The results of the analyses are compared in Fig. 8. It can be seen from this figure that the reduction in heat loss for the simple modifications is 8 w at 1000°C (112-104 w). For the case with major furnace modifications, the reduction in heat loss is 67 w (112-45 w). A summary of these results is presented in Table 4.

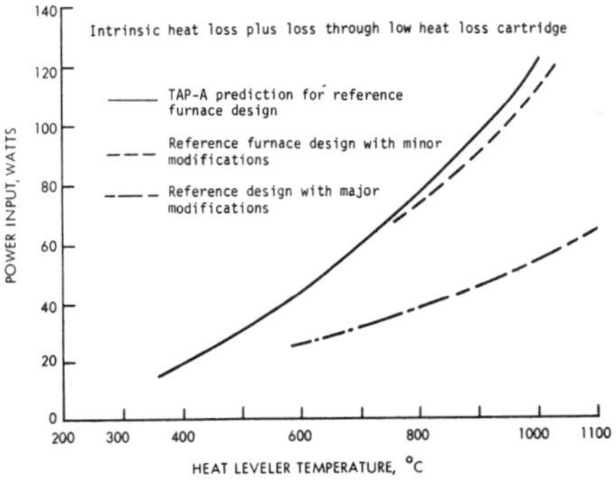

Fig. 8 Comparison of furnace heat losses for three furnace configurations.

Table 4 Summary of furnace heat-loss characteristics

	Reference design	With simple modifications	With major modifications
Characteristics	Quartz wool in end and side shields	Triple end and side shields; 20 layers of 0.5-mil Moly shields around copper tubes; 3 layers of 0.5-mil Moly shields around baffles	Termination of side shields at baffles; triple end and side shields by adding Moly shields
Total heat loss, w	122	114	55
Heat loss through three cartridges, w	10	10	10
Intrinsic furnace heat loss	112	104	45
Intrinsic loss plus loss through experimental 560 cartridges (1000°C)	137	129	70

It must be pointed out that although a reduction in furnace losses provides margin, the furnace cooldown time would be increased. A reduction in furnace heat losses reflects on improvement in the insulation of the furnace; consequently, cooldown would be more difficult. Passive cooldown of the reference furnace design has been measured. From the data, the cooldown time required for any reduction in furnace heat loss can be estimated. If cooldown time is defined to be the time required to reach 105°F "touch temperature", then calculations showed that a 10% reduction in heat loss would increase the cooldown time by approximately 11%. A 20% reduction in furnace heat loss would increase it by 25%, whereas a 50% reduction would increase it by 100%.

For some of the experiments, a programmed cooldown was required. The rate of cooldown in these instances was slower than the rate of passive cooldown so that heat addition would be required to maintain the desired cooldown rate. If, by reducing the furnace heat loss, the rate of cooldown is reduced excessively, forced cooling may be necessary to achieve the desired cooldown rate.

Conclusions

The good agreement between the prototype furnace and ground-based tests and the predicted performance from detailed thermal analyses demonstrated that successful thermal modeling of the furnace, cartridge, and integrated systems was accomplished. Excessive heat loss mechanisms were identified, and useful modifications have been suggested. This work has shown that detailed thermal analysis serves not only as a design aid, but also as a tool for the prediction and interpretation of materials-processing parameters.

References

[1]Pierce, B.L., TAP-A, "A Program for Computing Transient or Steady State Temperature Distributions," WANL-TME-1872, Dec. 1969, Westinghouse Astronuclear Lab., Pittsburgh, Pa.

[2]"Thermal Analysis Report - Multipurpose Electric Furnace System, M-518," WANL-TME-2829, July 1972, Westinghouse Astronuclear Lab., Pittsburgh, Pa.

[3]"Data Package for Cartridges for the Multipurpose Electric Furnace System, M-518," WANL-TME-2831, Vols. I and II, Nov. 1972, Westinghouse Astronuclear Lab., Pittsburgh, PA.

[4]Yaffee, M.L., "Skylab Science Data Found Promising," Aviation Week, Vol. 100, No. 7, Feb. 18, 1974, pp. 54-56.

[5]Yaffee, M.L.,"Skylab Space Processing Results Studied," Aviation Week, Vol. 100, No. 8, Feb. 25, 1974, pp. 40-43.

[6]Proceedings of the Third Space Processing Symposium: Skylab Results, NASA Report M-74-5, Sept. 1974.

FREE SUSPENSION PROCESSING: SELECTED USER INTERESTS AND REQUIREMENTS

G. Wouch* and H. L. Bloom+
General Electric Company, Valley Forge, Pa.

Abstract

This paper addresses specific processing needs of 18 representative materials/combinations likely to be processed advantageously in weightlessness of space flight using electromagnetic positioning and heating. Requirements are documented for preheating, specimen insertion and recovery, heating and cooling profiles, processing environment, and power. Processing wastes and potential safety hazards also are listed. Conclusions are that electromagnetic positioning and heating are adequate for 75% of identified materials; supplementary electron beam heating is adequate for the remainder; many development experiments are compatible with sounding rocket capabilities; and production-level processing aboard the Space Shuttle will require large amounts of power and thermal dissipation, as well as protection against several types of unique potential hazards.

I. Introduction

Within the next decade, the Space Shuttle will provide scientific and applications users with direct, frequent, long-duration, economical access to the unique environment of orbital flight. Materials processing is one area of science and applications which is expected to derive major benefits from the utilization of this space transportation system. In particular, shuttle flights to orbit with free suspension processing payloads will be used to eliminate, or at least minimize, a number of process-inhibiting physical effects inherent in the 1-G field of Earth-bound facilities. Typically, free suspension melting and solidification in the weightlessness of orbital flight

---

Presented as Paper 74-649 at the AIAA/ASME 1974 Thermophysics and Heat Transfer Conference, Boston, Mass., July 15-17, 1974.

*Physicist, Space Division.
+Senior Systems Engineer, Space Division.

should eliminate crucible walls and other melt/solid interfaces, significantly reduce segregation of melt components with different specific gravities, and minimize convective flows in the melt. The impacts of these benefits on materials being processed may range from decreased contamination of the melt and solidification in new, more regular monolithic structures to more uniform dispersions and composite structures.

In an effort to initiate the establishment of a uniform set of processing requirements for materials of interest to the potential user community, General Electric's Space Sciences Laboratory has conducted the initial tasks of a NASA[1] Marshall Space Flight Center sponsored study. This paper is essentially a summary of those tasks.

Previous investigations have indicated the necessity of providing position control for materials undergoing free suspension processing, and have found that such positioning may be provided advantageously by electromagnetic forces. Hence, this initial effort did not consider other positioning forces such as acoustic, electrostatic, and gas stream. As a preliminary guideline, therefore, the spectrum of materials considered was limited to those on which electromagnetic forces likely could produce useful positioning effects. During the study, this spectrum was shown to include a large variety of materials.

The previous investigations have indicated definite advantages of electromagnetic positioning over other techniques, where it can be applied. These include 1) the capability of working either in a high vacuum or an inert gas environment as required; and 2) the ability to use either electron beam heating or induction heating to heat the work piece. (Electron beam heating requires vacuum less than a few torr, an environment in which positioning techniques that require a gaseous medium cannot function).

II. Survey of Users

The identification of users and ascertainment of their interests has been carried out by both direct dialogs with potential users and review of documented past, relevant studies. Dialogs were held with key individuals from a number of industrial companies. In addition, information obtained from dialogs with other organizations during the work of Ref. 2 was reviewed.

The bulk of data, however, was extracted from publications and reports documenting space-processing concepts, experiments, and tests recommended by various individuals and groups involved in materials research. Major contributions to this data bank were provided from such sources as Ref. 3 through 11.

As a result of the aforementioned dialogs and literature reviews, a tabulation was compiled of 18 user interests (Table 1) which ran the gamut from such specific commercial applications as tungsten with improved grain structure for X-ray targets to such potential applications and research areas as more uniform dispersions of eutectic and monotectic alloys (e.g., tungsten-copper for potential electric power control components). In all, the tabulated user areas of interest are representative of approximately 400 different materials and material combinations.

Although several of the examples cited have been drawn from commercial applications identified by industrial users who supported the study of Ref. 2, the documented requirements are not limited to commercial user interests. Account also has been taken of materials and combinations that have been identified by previous studies as having both potential applications and research value.

III. Identification of Materials and Processes; Problems and Benefits of Space Processing

For each of the identified materials or material combinations exemplifying an area of user interest, initial effort was directed at establishing the sequence of transformations through which materials passed in progressing from raw materials, through preprocessing on the ground, space processing, and final ground processing (Table 2). Raw materials, in most cases, have been identified as commercial-grade stock, powders, or pellets. Ground preprocessing has called for such activities as sintering, pressing, cutting to size, etc. Free suspension space processing has been aimed at producing boules, spheroids, ingots, and rods. Final ground processing has been identified as producing such diverse products as X-ray targets, petroleum pump seats and valves, electronic substrates, lenses, etc.

Where users were willing to identify specific commercial applications, the study tabulated quantities of space-processed product required per year (which range from 300 to 160,000 (kg) and value of product per year (which range from \$3,000,000 to \$170,000,000)

Table 1. Application Areas, Potential Users

Application Area	User or Uses
Tungsten	GE Medical Systems
Transparent Metal Oxide Glasses	Corning
High temp Eutectics	GE Aircraft Eng.
Tungsten Carbide	Omniferous Eng'g.
Beryllia Dispersion in Beryllium	Kawecki-Berylco
Refractory Metals, Alloys (20)** Molybdenum	Aircraft Engine Manufacturers
Tantalum-Niobium-Based Alloys (10)** NbN	Electronics Industries
Chalcogenide Glasses (30)** GeTe	Electronics & Laser Industries
Monotectic Alloys (100's)** Tungsten-Copper	Power Distribution Industry
Superalloys with Dispersed Rare Earth Oxides (15-20)** Titanium-Lanthanum Oxide	Gas Turbine Components, Nuclear Reactor Control Rods
Uniform Dispersions of Semi-conductive/Photoconductive Particles in Glass (20-40)** Silver Chloride in High Silicate Glass	Striking Glass
Magnetoresistive and Infrared Eutectics (4)** Iron Antimonide-Indium Antimonide	Infrared Polarization Lenses, Electronic Components
Superconducting Monotectics (5)** Niobium Tin-Tin	Electrical Equipment
Rare Earth Borides (5)** Lanthanum Boride	High Power Cathodes
Refractory Silicides (10)** Molybdenum Disilicide	High-temp Corrosion Resist., Electronic Substrates
Uniform Dispersion of Photochromic Particles in Glass (20)** SiO_2 Glass with Europium and/or Cerium	Phototropic Windows
Amorphous Metallic Conductors (10)** Palladium Silicon	Electronic Substrates
Ferromagnetic Eutectics (10)** Iron-Iron Sulphide	Magnetic Applications

**Estimated Number of Applications, Representative Example is Shown.

Table 2A. Product Steps - Raw Materials to Consumer Product

Application Area	Raw Material(s)	Ground Preprocessed Product(s)	Space Processed Product(s)	Final Ground Processed Product(s)
Tungsten	Commercial Grade Tungsten	Pressed, Sintered Bar Stock Slugs	Fine Grained Spheroids	3-5 in. Frustrum X-Ray Targets
Transparent Metal Oxide Glasses	ZrO_2, CeO_2, ThO_2, Y_2O_3	Pressed, Sintered High Purity Boule	Glass Boules	Lenses, Windows
High Temp Eutectics	Tungsten, Ni (Typical)	Composite Ingot	Eutectic Boule	Turbine Blades
Tungsten Carbide	Tungsten Carbide	Pressed, Sintered Ingot	Polycrystalline Boule	Ball & Seat Valves
Beryllia Dispersion in Beryllium	Beryllium & Beryllia	Pressed, Sintered Composite Ingot	Uniformly Dispersed Ingot	Nuclear Reactor Reflectors
Refractory Metals, Alloys (20)** Molybdenum	Commercial Grade Molybdenum	Pressed, Sintered Bar Stock Slugs	Fine Grained Spheroid	Turbine Blades
Tantalum-Niobium-Based Alloys (10)** NbN	Commercial Grade NbN	Pressed, Sintered Bar Stock Slugs	Fine Grained Spheroid or Single Crystal	Wire or Wafers
Chalcogenide Glasses (30)** GeTe	Crystalline GeTe	Rod Slugs	Glass Boules	Wafers, Windows
Monotectic Alloys (100's)** Tungsten-Copper	Commercial Tungsten Copper	Liquid Sintered Slugs	Uniformly Dispersed Spheroid	Power Equipment Contacts

**Estimated Number of Applications, Representative Example is Shown.

Table 2B. Product Steps - Raw Materials to Consumer Product

Application Area	Raw Material(s)	Ground Preprocessed Product(s)	Space Processed Product(s)	Final Ground Processed Product(s)
Superalloys With Dispersed Rare Earth Oxides (15-20)** Titanium-Lanthanum Oxide	Titanium, Lanthanum Oxide	Pressed, Sintered Ingot	Uniform Dispersion Ingot	Gas Turbine Components
Uniform Dispersions of Semiconductive/Photoconductive Particles in Glass (20-40)** Silver Chloride in High Silicate Glass	High Silicates & Silver Chloride	Tablet of Commercial Silicate Glass Powder, Silver Chloride Powder	Uniform Dispersion Boule	Light Filters
Magnetoresistive and Infrared Eutectics (4)** Iron Antimonide Indium Antimonide	Iron Antimonide & Indium Antimonide	Billet	Eutectic Boule	Polarization Lenses
Superconducting Monotectics (5)** Niobium Tin-Tin	Niobium & Tin	Sintered Composite Ingot	Monotectic Boule	Electrical Components
Rare Earth Borides (5)** Lanthanum Boride	Lanthanum Hexaboride	Pressed, Sintered Ingot	Polycrystalline Boule	Cathodes
Refractory Silicides (10)** Molybdenum Disilicide	$MoSi_2$	Pressed, Sintered Ingot	Polycrystalline Boule	Electrical Components
Uniform Dispersion of Photochromic Particles in Glass (20)** SiO_2 Glass with Europium and/or Cerium	Silicate Glass and Europium and/or Cerium	Tablets of Glass Powder and Eu or Ce	Amorphous Boule	Phototropic Windows
Amorphous Metallic Conductors (10)** Palladium Silicon	Crystalline Palladium Silicon	Polycrystalline Ingot	Amorphous Boule	Electronic Components
Ferromagnetic Eutectics (10)** Iron-Iron Sulphide	Iron-Iron Sulphide Composite	Composite Ingot	Lamelar Ingot	Magnetic Components

**Estimated Number of Applications, Representative Example is Shown.

(Table 3). In addition, estimates were provided for the size of the batch of each space-produced product that would be commensurate with the size of final ground-processed product. The sizes for identified commercial applications ranged from 0.025-to 0.23-mradius spheres, and from 0.7 to 100 kg. Since early development of space processing for any of the identified areas initially will entail considerable experimental work, the study also tabulated batch sizes for meaningful experimental quantities. Such sizes cover a range from 0.005-to 0.04mradius spheres, and 0.0025 to 1.5 kg.

The key to user interests, whether identified commercial applications, potential applications, or research, is the identification of problems encountered in ground processing which might be overcome by space processing (Table 4). In that light, an important step in this study has been the tabulation of such problems for each example material or combination. Typically, where applicable, problems that have been noted include contamination from crucible walls, nucleation from crucible walls, convection in the melt, buoyancy or sedimentation in melts of multiple materials, limited rates and uniformity of supercooling, etc.

IV. Space-Processing Requirements

The requirements for processing the aforementioned materials have been determined and are summarized in Table 5. Specific requirements for each such product include the following:

1) There is a necessity, where required, for preheating the material before insertion into the free suspension processing facility. Many materials, such as zirconia, have high electrical resistivities at room temperature, which precludes electromagnetic position control at room temperatures. Preheating zirconia above 2000°C, however, decreases the electrical resistivity to 10^{-2} Ω-m and so may enable preheated specimens to be positioned by electromagnetic forces in the free suspension processing facility.

2) The method of sample insertion into the free suspension processing facility is important. The methods considered were mechanical and electromagnetic.

3) The heating profile, including heating dwells, is required. A process to produce tungsten with enhanced service pro-

Table 3A. Space Processed Product

Application Area	Material(s)	Quantity Required Per Year (kg)	Estimated Product Value Per Year to User(s)*	Batch or Unit Size (Meters)	Batch or Unit Weight (kg)
Tungsten	Fine Grained High Purity Tungsten	(3, 000)	[$5, 000, 000]	.005 [.025] Radius Sphere	.01 [1.25]
Transparent Metal Oxide Glasses	Transparent ZrO_2, CeO_2, ThO_2, Y_2O_3	?	[$10, 000, 000]	.005 [.04] Radius Sphere	.003 - .006 [1-3]
High temp Eutectics	Eutectic W, Ni	[80, 000 - 160, 000]	[$70, 000, 000 - $140, 000, 000]	.005 [~.04] Radius Sphere	.006 [2-5]
Tungsten Carbide	Fine Grained Polycrystalline Tungsten Carbide	[155, 000] (Total)	[$136, 000, 000 - $170, 000, 000]	.005 [~.03 & ~.05] Radius Sphere	.009 [.7 - 1.5]
Beryllia Dispersion in Beryllium	Ingot of Uniformly Dispersed Beryllia in Beryllium	[4, 000] (Minimum)	[$3, 000, 000]	.01 [~.23] Radius Sphere	.09 [100]
Refractory Metals, Alloys (20)** Molybdenum	Fine Grained Molybdenum Dispersion	(80, 000 - 160, 000]	[$70, 000, 000 - $140, 000, 000]	.005 [~.04] Radius Sphere	.006 [2-3)
Tantalum-Niobium-Based Alloys (10)** NbN	Fine Grained NbN or NbN Crystals	Experimental	Experimental	.005 Boule	.0045
Chalcogenide Glasses (30)** GeTe	Amorphous Boule of GeTe	Experimental	Experimental	.01 Radius	.0025
Monotectic Alloys (100's)** Tungsten-Copper	Ingot of Dispersed Copper in Tungsten Matrix	Experimental	Experimantal	.005 Radius	.006

**Estimated Number of Applications, Representative Example is Shown.
[ ] Indicates Data for a Production Quantity of Materials; Unbracketed Data is for Experimental Quantity.

Table 3B. Space Processed Product

Application Area	Material(s)	Quantity Required Per Year (kg)	Estimated Product Value Per Year to User(s)	Batch or Unit Size (Meters)	Batch or Unit Weight (kg)
Superalloys With Dispersed Rare Earth Oxides (15-20)** Titanium-Lanthanum Oxide	Ingot of Uniformly Dispersed Lanthanum Oxide in Titanium	[80,000-160,000]	[$70,000,000-$140,000,000]	.005 [.04] Radius Sphere	.003 [1.3]
Uniform Dispersions of Semiconductive/Photoconductive Particles in Glass (20-40)** Silver Chloride in High Silicate Glass	Boule of Finely Dispersed Silver Chloride in Silicate Glass	Experimental	Experimental	.04 Radius Sphere	1.3
Magnetoresistive and Infrared Eutectics (4)** Iron Antimonide-Indium Antimonide	Boule of Lamelar in Sb-FeSb	Experimental	Experimental	.04 Radius Sphere	1.5
Superconducting Monotectics (5)** Niobium Tin-Tin	Boule of Lamelar NbSn-Sn	Experimental	Experimental	.02 Radius Sphere	.03
Rare Earth Borides (5)** Lanthanum Boride	Boule of Poly-crystalline LaB_6	Experimental	Experimental	.02 Radius Boule	.16
Refractory Silicides (10)** Molybdenum Disilicide	Boule of Poly-crystalline $MoSi_2$	Experimental	Experimental	0.02 Radius Boule	0.32
Uniform Dispersion of Photochromic Particles in Glass (20)** SiO_2 Glass With Europium and/or Cerium	Boule of Amorphous SiO_2 Glass with Dispersed Europium and Cerium	Experimental	Experimental	0.02 Radius Sphere	0.1-0.4
Amorphous Metallic Conductors (10)** Palladium Silicon	Boule of Amphous Palladium Silicon	Experimental	Experimental	0.02 Radius Sphere	0.32
Ferromagnetic Eutectics (10)** Iron-Iron Sulphide	Ingot of Lamelar Fe-FeS	Experimental	Experimental	0.02 Radius Boule	.31

**Estimated Number of Applications, Representative Example is Shown.
[ ] Indicates Data for a Production Quantity of Materials; Unbracketed Data is for Experimental Quantity.

Table 4A. Present Processing Problems

Application Area	Contamination From Crucible	Nucleation From Crucible Walls	Convection in Melt	Buoyancy or Sedimentation	Fast or Uniform Cooling	Fast or Uniform Supercooling	Other
Tungsten	-	-	-	-	-	-	Undesirable Grain Structure & Purity
Transparent Metal Oxide Glasses	Yes	Yes	Yes	No	Yes	Yes	-
High Temp Eutectics	-	Yes	Yes	Yes	Uniform	Uniform	-
Tungsten Carbide	-	-	-	-	-	-	Undesirable Grain Structure & Purity
Beryllia Dispersion in Beryllium	Yes	Yes	Yes	Yes	Yes	Yes	Undesirable Grain Structure, Nonuniform Dispersion
Refractory Metals Alloys (20)** Molybdenum	Yes	Yes	Yes	-	Yes	Yes	-
Tantalum Niobium-Based Alloys (10)** NbN	Yes (Very Reacting)	-	-	-	-	-	Undesirable Purity Grain Structure
Chalcogenide Glasses (30)** GeTe	-	Yes	Yes	-	Yes	Yes	No, Generally, (Selenium Sensitive to Light)
Monotectic Alloys (100's)** Tungsten-Copper	-	-	-	-	-	-	Non-Uniform Dispersion

**Estimated Number of Applications, Representative Example is Shown.

Table 4B. Present Processing Problems

Application Area	Contamination From Crucible	Nucleation From Crucible Walls	Convection in Melt	Buoyancy or Sedimentation	Fast or Uniform Cooling	Fast or Uniform Supercooling	Other
Superalloys with Dispersed Rare Earth Oxides (15-20)** Titanium-Lanthanum Oxide	-	-	-	Yes	-	-	Non-Uniform Dispersion
Uniform Dispersion of Semiconductive/ Photoconductive Particles in Glass (20-40)** Silver Chloride in High Silicate Glass	Yes	Yes	Yes	Yes	-	Yes	Non-Uniform Dispersion
Magnetoresistive and Infrared Eutectics (4)** Iron Antimonide-Indium Antimonide	-	Yes	Yes	Yes	Uniform	-	-
Superconducting Monotectics (5)** Niobium Tin-Tin	-	Yes	Yes	Yes	Uniform	-	-
Rare Earth Borides (5)** Lanthanum Boride	-	-	-	Yes	-	-	Undesirable Grain Structure & Purity
Refractory Silicides (10)** Molybdenum Disilicide	-	-	-	Yes	-	-	Undesirable Grain Structure & Purity
Uniform Dispersion of Photochromic Particles in Glass (20)** SiO_2 Glass with Europium and/ or Cerium	Yes	Yes	Yes	Yes	Yes	Yes	Uniform Dispersion
Amorphous Metallic Conductors (10)** Palladium Silicon	No	Yes	Yes	No	Uniform	Uniform	-
Ferromagnetic Eutectics (10)** Iron-Iron Sulphide	No	No	Yes	Yes	Yes	-	-

**Estimated Number of Applications, Representative Example is Shown.

Table 5A. Space Processing Requirements

Application Area	Preheating (Temp) °C	Insertion (Mechanical or Electromagnetic)	Heating Rate - °C/sec		Heating Dwells (Temp °C)		Other Functions During Heating		
			High	Low	First Dwell	Second Dwell	Vacuum-N/M^2	Gas Type-N/M^2	Stirring
Tungsten	-	Either	10-100	5-10	[2400-3200]	3420	$< 10^{-3}$, or	/Inert, 10^5/	Yes
Transparent Metal Oxide Glasses	2000	Mechanical	10-100	5-10	-	2000-3000	-	Inert, 10^5, O_2	Yes
High Temp Eutectics	-	Either	10-100	5-10	-	1560	$< 10^{-3}$	-	No
Tungsten Carbide	-	Either	10-100	1-10	[2200-2750]	2900	$< 10^{-3}$, or	/Inert, 10^5/	Yes
Beryllia Dispersion in Beryllium	-	Either	10-100	5-10	[1000]	1300	$< 10^{-3}$, or	Inert, 10^5	Yes

Application Area	Maximum Temp °C	Cooling Rate °C/sec			Cooling Method Radiation	Gas (Type) Temp °C	Liquid (Type)/ Temp °C
		High	Medium	Low			
Tungsten	3420	/1000 (Quench)/	~ 100 (No Quench)	10 (Controlled)	Yes	Inert, 25, or	H_2O, 25
Transparent Metal Oxide Glasses	2000-3000	-	~100	0.1-10 (Controlled)	Yes	-	-
High Temp Eutectics	1560	-	-	.02-.05 (Controlled)	Yes	-	-
Tungsten Carbide	2900	/1000 (Quench)/	~100 (No Quench)	10 (Controlled)	Yes	Inert, 25 or	H_2O, 25
Beryllia Dispersion in Beryllium	1300	/1000 (Quench)/	~50 (No Quench)	5-10 (Controlled)	Yes	Inert, 25 or	H_2O, 25

Application Area	Cryo (Type)	Heating Power (Watts)	Product Recovery Mechanical			
			Retrieval	Free Suspension Controls	Other (Type)	Quench (Type)
Tungsten	Liquid N_2	3000-5000 [$4.5x10^4$ - $5x10^4$]	Yes, or	Yes	-	H_2O
Transparent Metal Oxide Glasses	-	1000-2000 [$5x10^4$ - $6x10^4$]	Yes	-	-	-
High Temp Eutectics	-	1000-2000 [10^4 - $2x10^4$]	-	Yes	-	-
Tungsten Carbide	Liquid N_2 (Controlled)	2000-5000 [10^5 - $2.5x10^5$]	Yes, or	Yes	-	Inert Gas (Controlled)
Beryllia Dispersion in Beryllium	Liquid N_2	4000-5000 [$2x10^5$ - $4x10^5$]	Yes, or	Yes	-	-

[ ] Indicates Data for a Production Quantity of Materials; Unbracketed Data is for Experimental Quantity.
/ / Indicates Unresolved Option.

Table 5B. Space Processing Requirements

Application Area	Preheating (Temp) °C	Insertion (Mechanical or (Electromagnetic)	Heating Rate - °C/Sec		Heating Dwells (Temp) °C		Other Functions During Heating		
			High	Low	First Dwell	Second Dwell	Vacuum-N/M^2	Gas, Type N/M^2	Stirring
Refractory Metals Alloys (20)** Molybdenum	-	Either	10-100	5-10	2400-2550	2700	<10^{-3}, Or	/Inert, 10^5/	Yes
Tantalum Niobium-Based Alloys (10)** NbN	-	Either	10-100	5-10	-	2300	<10^{-3}, Or	/Inert, 10^5/	Yes
Chalcogenide Glasses (30)** GeTe	600	Either	10-100	5-10	-	800	<10^{-3}, Or	/Inert, 10^5/	Yes
Monotectic Alloys (100's)** Tungsten-Copper	-	Either	10-100	5-10	-	1100	<10^{-3}, Or	/Inert, 10^5/	Yes

Application Area	Maximum Temp °C	Cooling Rate °C/sec			Cooling Method			
		High	Medium	Low	Radiation	Gas (Type)/ Temp °C	Liquid (Type)/ Temp °C	Cryo (Temp)
Refractory Metals Alloys (20)** Molybdenum	2700	/1000 (Quench)/	~100 (No Quench)	5-10 (Controlled)	Yes	Inert, 25	H_2O, 25	-
Tantalum Niobium-Based Alloys (10)** NbN	2300	/100 (Quench)/	~100 (No Quench)	5-10 (Controlled)	Yes	(Boule Only) Inert, 25	-	/Liquid He (Controlled)/
Chalcogenide Glasses (30)** GeTe	800	-	-	10	Yes	-	-	-
Monotectic Alloys (100's)** Tungsten-Copper	1100	/1000 (Quench)/	~100 (No Quench)	/5-10 (Controlled)/	Yes	Inert, 25	H_2O, 25	-

Application Area	Heating Power (Watts)	Product Recovery Mechanical			
		Retrieval	Free Suspension	Other (Type)	Quench (Type)
Refractory Metals Alloys (20)** Molybdenum	2×10^3-3×10^3 [4.5×10^4-5×10^4]	Yes, or	Yes	-	H_2O
Tantalum Niobium-Based Alloys (10)** NbN	10^3-2×10^3	Yes, or	Yes	-	Inert Gas (Controlled)
Chalcogenide Glasses (30)** GeTe	10^3-2×10^3	Yes	-	-	-
Monotectic Alloys (100's)** Tungsten-Copper	10^3-2×10^3	Yes, or	Yes	-	H_2O

** Estimated Number of Applications, Representative Example is Shown.
[ ] Indicates Data for a Production Quantity of Materials; Unbracketed Data is for Experimental Quantity.
/ / Indicates Unresolved Option.

Table 5C. Space Processing Requirements'

Application Area	Preheating (Temp) °C	Insertion - Mechanical or Electromagnetic	Heating Rate - °C/sec		Heating Dwells (Temp) °C		Other Functions During Heating			Maximum Temp °C	Cooling Rate °C/sec		
			High	Low	First Dwell	Second Dwell	Vacuum - N/M^2	Gas, Type - N/M^2	Stirring		High	Medium	Low
Superalloys With Dispersed Rare Earth Oxides (15-20)** Titanium-Lanthanum Oxide	-	Either	10 - 100	5 - 10	1700	2000	$<10^{-3}$, or	/ Inert, 10^5/	Yes	2000	/1000 (Quench)/	~50 (No Quench)	5 - 10 (Controlled)
Uniform Dispersions of Semiconductive/ Photoconductive Particles in Glass (20-40)** Silver Chloride in High Silicate Glass	1300	Either	10 - 100	5 - 10	-	1500	$<10^{-3}$, or	Inert, 10^5, O_2	Yes	1500	-	25 - 50	1 - 10 (Controlled)
Magnetoresistive and Infrared Eutectics (4)** Iron Antimonide-Indium Antimonide	-	Either	10 - 100	5 - 10	-	~1200	$<10^{-3}$, or	/Inert, 10^5/	Yes	1200	-	~20	2 - 5 (Controlled)
Superconducting Monotectics (5)** Niobium Tin-Tin	-	Either	10 - 100	5 - 10	-	900	$<10^{-3}$, or	/Inert, 10^5/	Yes	900	-	~ 20	2 - 5 (Controlled)
Rare Earth Borides (5)** Lanthanum Boride	-	Either	10 - 100	5 - 10	-	2300	$<10^{-3}$, or	/Inert, 10^5/	Yes	2300	-	~ 50	1 - 10 (Controlled)

** Estimated Number of Applications, Representative Example is Shown.
[ ] Indicates Data for a Production Quanity of Materials; Unbracketed Data is for Experimental Quantity.
/ / Indicates Unresolved Option.

Table 5C. Space Processing Requirements (Continued)

Application Area	Cooling Method				Heating Power (Watts)	Product Recovery			
	Radiation	Gas (Type) Temp °C	Liquid (Type) Temp °C	Cryo (Type)		Mechanical Retreival	Free Suspension Control	Other (Type)	Quench (Type)
Superalloys With Dispersed Rare Earth Oxides (15-20)** Titanium-Lanthanum Oxide	Yes	Inert, 25, or	H_2O, 25	-	2000 - 3000 [$5x10^4$]	Yes, or	Yes	-	Inert Gas
Uniform Dispersions of Semiconductive/ Photoconductive Particles in Glass (20-40)** Silver Chloride in High Silicate Glass	Yes	-	-	-	10^4 - $2x10^4$	Yes	-	-	-
Magnetoresistive and Infrared Eutectics (4)** Iron Antimonide-Indium Antimonide	Yes	-	-	-	10^4 - $2x10^4$	Yes, or	Yes	-	-
Superconducting Monotectics (5)** Niobium Tin-Tin	Yes	-	-	-	10^3 - $5x10^3$	Yes, or	Yes	-	-
Rare Earth Borides (5)** Lanthanum Boride	Yes	Inert, 25	-	-	$5x10^3$ - 10^4	Yes, or	Yes	-	-

** Estimated Number of Applications, Representative Example is Shown.
[ ] Indicates Data for a Production Quanity of Materials; Unbracketed Data is for Experimental Quantity.
// Indicates Unresolved Option.

Table 5D. Space Processing Requirements

Application Area	Preheating (Temp) °C	Insertion (Mechanical or Electromagnetic)	Heating Rate - °C/sec		Heating Dwells, Temp °C		Other Functions During Heating			Maximum Temp °C
			High	Low	First Dwell	Second Dwell	Vacuum - N/M^2	Gas Type - N/M^2	Stirring	
Refractory Silicides (10)** Molybdenum Disilicide	-	Either	10 - 100	5 - 10	-	2200	$<10^{-3}$, or	/Inert, 10^5/	Yes	2200
Uniform Dispersion of Photochromic Particles in Glass (20)** SiO_2 Glass with Europium and/or Cerium	1300	Either	10 - 100	5 - 10	-	1500	-	Inert, 10^5, O_2	Yes	1500
Amorphous Metallic Conductors (10)** Palladium Silicon	-	Either	10 - 100	5 - 10	-	960	$<10^{-3}$, or	/Inert, 10^5/	Yes	960
Ferromagnetic Eutectics (10)** Iron-Iron Sulphide	-	Either	10 - 100	5 - 10	-	988	$<10^{-3}$, or	/Inert, 10^5/	No	988

Application Area	Cooling Rate °C/sec			Cooling Method				Heating Power (Watts)	Product Recovery			
	High	Medium	Low	Radiation	Gas (Type) Temp °C	Liquid (Type) Temp °C	Cryo (Type)		Mechanical Retreival	Free Suspension Control	Other (Type)	Quench (Type)
Refractory Silicides (10)** Molybdenum Disilicide	-	~50	1 - 10 (Controlled)	Yes	Inert, 25	-	-	$5x10^3 - 10^4$	Yes, or	Yes	-	-
Uniform Dispersion of Photochromic Particles in Glass (20)** SiO_2 Glass with Europium and/or Cerium	-	~25	1 - 10 (Controlled)	Yes	-	-	-	$2x10^3 - 5x10^3$	Yes, or	Yes	-	-
Amorphous Metallic Conductors (10)** Palladium Silicon	-	~20	1 - 10 (Controlled	Yes	Inert, 25	-	-	$10^3 - 5x10^3$	Yes, or	Yes	-	-
Ferromagnetic Eutectics (10)** Iron-Iron Sulphide	-	-	0.01 - 0.03 (Controlled)	Yes	-	-	-	$10^3 - 5x10^3$	Yes, or	Yes	-	-

** Estimated Number of Applications, Representative Example is Shown.
[ ] Indicates Data for a Production Quantity of Materials; Unbracketed Data is for Experimental Quantity.
/ / Indicates Unresolved Option.

perties for medical X-ray targets, for example, requires at least two dwells for vacuum purification. These are a dwell in the temperature range of 2400° to 3200°C lasting from 10 to 20 minutes and a dwell in the molten state in the temperature range 3410° to 3420°C from 1 to 5 minutes. Between the heating dwells, the temperature may be raised as rapidly as the available power permits. The heat radiated per second by a spherical specimen is given by $P = 4\pi R^2 \epsilon \sigma (T^4 - T_S^4)$, where P is the power in watts or heat radiated in joules per second; R is the radius of the specimen in meters; ϵ the emissivity; σ Stephan's constant; T the absolute temperature in degrees Kelvin; and T_S the starting temperature in degrees Kelvin. A 5 cm radius sphere of tungsten at its melting point (3410°C) would radiate about 100,000 W, whereas a 0.5-cm-radius sphere would radiate about 1000 W using an emissivity of 0.4.

4) The processing environment, which might be vacuum or inert gas, and the processing facility are important. For tungsten X-ray targets, a vacuum level of 10^{-3} N/m^2 or less is required or a high-purity inert gas at 10^5 N/m^2.

5) It is necessary to stir the melt during processing.

6) The maximum temperature to be obtained must be known. Tungsten, for example, would require a temperature of 3410°C, whereas beryllium would require only 1300°C.

7) The cooling rates required also must be known. These are established either for free radiation cooling or for a quench. Typically cooling rates of 1000 deg/sec might be obtained with a quench for high-temperature materials such as tungsten, whereas 100°C/sec might be obtained by free radiation cooling. For controlled cooling, where the power is reduced slowly, rates of less than 10°C/sec are required. The types of quench considered were gas quench at 70°F, liquid at 70°F, or a cryogenic quench at much lower temperatures. The use of a quench will depend upon whether or not the desired grain structure can be achieved by supercooling and solidification, allowing the release of latent heat to be dissipated through free radiative cooling. If this cannot be achieved, then quenching in the structure initiated

by nucleation must be considered. There is no clean answer to this problem yet, and the necessity of a quench must be determined experimentally.

8) The heating power required, which could range from 1000 W for small specimens to as much as 200, 000 W which was required for a large piece of beryllium with a beryllia dispersion, must be known.

9) The method of product recovery must be known which would be mechanical for semiconductors or glasses, and electromagnetic for relatively good conductors such as the metals.

10) The process duration (Table 6) must be known. This includes time to melt, time spent in dwells, time molten, and cooling time. (When considering initial experimental work, processing time has been reduced through use of high-purity materials, which require a shorter purification cycle than the commercial-grade materials used in production).

11) The wastes produced are important (Table 7), including gaseous products, liquid products, solid products, and heat.

12) The process safety requirements are given in Table 8. Since it is anticipated that the processes treated in this study will be carried out aboard the Spacelab, consideration must be given to those aspects of the process steps, product state, and process by-products which could represent potential hazards to the crew and the facility. Safety considerations, for example, considered the hot product, which, for tungsten, reaches 3410°C; the presence of reactive product gases, liquids, or solids; the presence of particulate radiation such as secondary electrons from electron beam heating; and specular reflection from a laser beam (if used), or electromagnetic radiation, which could be optical or RF. Tungsten, for example, at 3410°C could not be observed directly without risk of damage to the eye.

In those cases for which users identified commercial applications, the determination of space-processing requirements considered two objectives. First, the requirements were established for manufac-

Table 6A. Process Duration

Application Area	Time to Dwell	Time at Dwell (Solid)	Time to Melt, Superheat	Time at Dwell (Molten)	Time to Cool to Recovery Temp	Total Time
Tungsten						
Product	[1-10 min]	10-20 min	[2-5 min]	[1-5 min]	[0.1-10 min]	[~15-50 min]
Experiment	1-2 min	0	0	2-4 min	2-4 min	5-10 min
Transparent Metal Oxide Glasses						
Product	[1-10 min]	0	0	[1-5 min]	[10-100 min]	[12-115 min]
Experiment	1-2 min	0	0	2-4 min	2-4 min	5-10 min
High Temp Eutectics						
Product	[0.05-5 min]	0	0	[1-5 min]	[60-360 min]	[62-370 min]
Experiment	0.05-5 min	0	0	1-5 min	60-360 min	62-370 min
Tungsten Carbide						
Product	[1-10 min]	[10-20 min]	[2-5 min]	[1-5 min]	[1-5 min]	[15-50 min]
Experiment	1-2 min	0	0	2-4 min	2-4 min	5-10 min
Beryllia Dispersion in Beryllium						
Product	[0.2-5 min]	[1-3 min]	[1-3 min]	[1-5 min]	[1-10 min]	[14-43 min]
Experiment	0.2-2 min	0	0	2-4 min	2-4 min	5-10 min
Refractory Metals Alloys (20)** Molybdenum						
Product	[1-10 min]	[10-20 min]	[2-5 min]	[1-5 min]	[0.1-10 min]	[15-50 min]
Experiment	1-2 min	0	0	2-4 min	2-4 min	5-10 min
Tantalum-Niobium-Based Alloys (10)** NbN						
Product	-	-	-	-	-	-
Experiment	1-2 min	0	0	2-4 min	2-4 min	5-10 min
Chalcogenide Glasses (30)** GeTe						
Product	-	-	-	-	-	-
Experiment	0.1-1 min	0	0	2-4 min	1-4 min	4-9 min
Monotectic Alloys (100's)** Tungsten-Copper						
Product	-	-	-	-	-	-
Experiment	1-2 min	0	0	2-4 min	2-4 min	5-10 min

**Estimated Number of Applications, Representative Example is Shown.
[ ] Indicates Data for a Production Quantity of Materials; Unbracketed Data is for Experimental Quantity.

turing the product, and second, the requirements were established to perform an experiment that would produce a small quantity of the material for investigation and evaluation. In this way, a range of requirements was determined which reflects both small quantities of materials and relatively low power requirements suitable to such test facilities as sounding rockets and the large magnitudes representative of production.

Table 6B. Process Duration

Application Area	Time to Dwell	Time at Dwell (Solid)	Time to Melt, Superheat	Time at Dwell (Molten)	Time to Cool to Recovery Temp	Total Time
Superalloys With Dispersed Rare Earth Oxides (15-20)** Titanium-Lanthanium Oxide						
Product	[0.2-4 Min]	] 10-20 Min]	[2-4 Min]	[1-5 Min]	[0.1-5 Min]	[14-38 Min]
Experiment	0.2-2 Min	0	0	2-4 Min	2-4 Min	5-10 Min
Uniform Dispersion of Semiconductive/Photoconductive Particles in Glass (20-40)** Silver Chloride in High Silicate Glass						
Product	-	-	-	-	-	-
Experiment	2-5 Min	0	0	1-5 Min	2-5 Min	5-15 Min
Magnetoresistive and Infrared Eutectics (4)** Iron Antimonide-Indium Antimonide						
Product	-	-	-	-	-	-
Experiment	2-5 Min	0	0	1-5 Min	2-5 Min	5-15 Min
Superconducting Monotectics (5)** Niobium Tin-Tin						
Product	-	-	-	-	-	-
Experiment	2-5 Min	0	0	1-5 Min	2-5 Min	5-15 Min
Rare Earth Borides (5)** Lanthanum Boride						
Product	-	-	-	-	-	-
Experiment	0.2-2 Min	0	0	2-4 Min	2-4 Min	5-10 Min
Refractory Silicides (10)** Molybdenum Disilicide						
Product	-	-	-	-	-	-
Experiment	0.2-2 Min	0	0	2-4 Min	2-4 Min	5-10 Min
Uniform Dispersion of Photochromic Particles in Glass (20)** SiO_2 Glass With Europium and/or Cerium						
Product	-	-	-	-	-	-
Experiment	2-5 Min	0	0	1-5 Min	2-5 Min	5-15 Min
Amorphous Metallic Conductors (10)** Palladium Silicon						
Product	-	-	-	-	-	-
Experiment	0.1-5 Min	0	0	1-5 Min	2-5 Min	3-15 Min
Ferromagnetic Eutectics (10)** Iron-Iron Sulphide						
Product	-	-	-	-	-	-
Experiment	0.1-3 Min	0	0	1-5 Min	1-3 Hrs	121-188 Min

** Estimated Number of Applications, Representative Example is Shown.
[] Indicates Data for a Production Quantity of Materials; Unbracketed Data is for Experimental Quantity.

V. Key Material Properties

Certain key material properties determine what type of free suspension processing facility should be considered to obtain the desired product. The electrical resistivity and its variation with tem-

Table 7A. Space Process Waster

Application Area	Gas (Type)	Liquid (Type)	Solid (Type)	Heat (Joules)
Tungsten	Inert, CO, CO_2, O_2, N_2, Steam	H_2O	Tungsten, WO_2	10^6 - $3x10^6$ [$6x10^7$ - $2x10^8$]
Transparent Metal Oxide Glasses	Inert, O_2	-	Oxides	$3x10^5$ - $3x10^6$ [10^8 - $3x10^8$]
High Temp Eutectics	-	-	-	$4x10^6$ - $5x10^7$ [10^7 - 10^8]
Tungsten Carbide	Inert, CO, CO_2, O_2, N_2, Steam	H_2O	WO_2, WC	10^6 - $2x10^7$ [10^8 - $3x10^8$]
Beryllia Dispersion in Beryllium	Inert, CO, CO_2, O_2, N_2, Steam	H_2O	-	10^6 - $3x10^6$ [$5x10^7$ - 10^8]
Refractory Metals Alloys (20)** Molybdenum	Inert, CO, CO_2, O_2, N_2, Steam	H_2O	Molybdenum, MoO_2	$6x10^5$ - $2x10^6$ [$6x10^7$ - $2x10^8$]
Tantalum-Niobioum-Based Alloys (10)** NbN	Inert, CO, CO_2, O_2, N_2, H_2	-	Nitrides	$3x10^5$ - 10^6
Chalcogenide Glasses (30)** GeTe	-	-	-	$3x10^5$ - 10^6
Monotectic Alloys (100's)** Tungsten-Copper	Inert, CO, CO_2, O_2, N_2, Steam	H_2O	Tungsten, WO_2, Cu	$3x10^6$ - $6x10^6$

**Estimated Number of Applications, Representative Example is Shown.
[ ] Indicates Data for a Production Quantity of Materials; Unbracketed Data is for Experimental Quality.

perature determine the applicability of electromagnetic position control, electromagnetic spinning for simple shaping of the specimen, induction heating, and electromagnetic stirring. The coefficient of secondary electron emission as a function of primary electron energy determines the feasibility of heating the free suspended material via electron beam without providing for grounding the piece. The maximum temperature to which the material must be heated and its total emissivity determine the minimum required heating power, whereas its specific heat and latent heat of fusion are required to estimate the heating time.

The advantages of using electron beam heating are independent control of temperature and positioning force, as well as the ability to heat initially high-resistivity materials such as zirconia to temperatures where the resistivity is sufficient for electromagnetic posi-

Table 7B. Space Process Wastes

Application Area	Gas (Type)	Liquid (Type)	Solid (Type)	Heat (Joules)
Superalloys With Dispersed Rare Earth Oxides (15-20)** Titanium-Lanthanum Oxide	Inert, CO, CO_2, H_2, Steam	H_2O	Ti, TiO_2, LaO_2	$6 \times 10^5 - 2 \times 10^6$ ($6 \times 10^7 - 10^8$)
Uniform Dispersions of Semiconductive/Photoconductive Particles in Glass (20-40) Silver Chloride in High Silicate Glass	Inert, O_2, SiO_2, Si Suboxides	-	Oxides	$3 \times 10^6 - 2 \times 10^7$
Magnetoresistive and Infrared Eutectics (4)** Iron Antimonide-Indium Antimonide	Inert	-	Sn, Fe, In	$3 \times 10^6 - 2 \times 10^7$
Superconducting Monotectics (5)** Niobium Tin-Tin	Inert	-	Sb, Sn	$3 \times 10^5 - 5 \times 10^6$
Rare Earth Borides (5)** Lanthanum Boride	Inert, CO, CO_2, O_2, N_2, H_2	-	Borides, Subborides	$2 \times 10^6 - 10^7$
Refractory Silicides (10)** Molybdenum Disilicide	Inert, CO, CO_2, O_2, N_2, H_2	-	$MoSi_2$, Other Silicides of Mo	$2 \times 10^6 - 8 \times 10^6$
Uniform Dispersion of Photochromic Particles in Glass (20)** SiO_2 Glass With Europium and/or Cerium	Inert, O_2, SiO_2, Si, Suboxides CeO_2, EuO	-	Oxides, Ce, Eu	$8 \times 10^5 - 8 \times 10^6$
Amorphous Metallic Conductors (10)** Palladium Silicon	Inert	-	PdSi	$2 \times 10^5 - 5 \times 10^6$
Ferromagnetic Eutectics (10)** Iron-Iron Sulphide	-	-	Fe, S, FeS	$8 \times 10^6 - 6 \times 10^7$

**Estimated Number of Applications, Representative Example is Shown.
[ ] Indicates Data for a Production Quantity of Materials; Unbracketed Data is for Experimental Quantity.

tion control. Electron beam heating and electromagnetic heating are complimentary, since, for the examples chosen in this paper, where electromagnetic heating alone cannot achieve the desired result, the use of the electron beam as a supplement, can.

The important material parameters for the specific example of each area of interest were compiled. Subsequently, graphs of the number of examples vs resistivity (in the range of 10^{-8} to 10^{-2} Ω-m (Fig. 1) and also the number of examples vs second crossover points for secondary electron emission (in the range of 0.5 to 20 kev) (Fig. 2) were prepared. Materials falling within these ranges include examples of carbides, borides, nitrides, silicides, beryllides, sulfides, and oxides of metals (when preheated), chalcogenide glasses (when preheated), pure metals, alloys of metals, and semiconductors (when preheated). The overwhelming number of cases of these materials fall into the range of resistivity of metallic conductors between 10^{-8} and 2×10^{-6} Ω-m and thus are suitable for electromagnetic free

Table 8A. Space Process Safety Considerations

Application Area	Hot Product (Temp) °C	Reactive Gas	Product Liquid	By-Product Solid	Partic. Radiation	Laser Beam	Electromagnetic Radiation	Other
Tungsten	3400	-	-	-	/Electrons (Low)/	-	Yes (Include Optical)	-
Transparent Metal Oxide Glasses	2000-3000	-	-	-	/Electrons (Low)/	/Specular Reflection/	Yes (Include Optical)	-
High Temp Eutectics	1560	-	-	-	-	-	Yes (Include Optical)	-
Tungsten Carbide	2900	-	-	-	-	-	Yes (Include Optical)	-
Beryllia Dispersion in Beryllium	1300	-	-	-	-	-	Yes	Toxic Beryllium Vapor
							Electromagnetic	
Refractory Metals Alloys (20)** Molybdenum	2700	-	-	-	/Electrons (Low)/	-	Yes	-
Tantalum-Niobium-Based Alloys (10)** NbN	2300	-	-	-	-	-	Yes	-
Chalcogenide Glasses (30)** GeTe	800	-	-	-	/Electrons (Low)/	-	Yes	-
Monotectic Alloys (100's)** Tungsten-Copper	1100	-	-	-	/Electrons (Low)/	-	Yes	-

**Estimated Number of Applications, Representative Example is Shown.
//Indicates Unresolved Option.

Table 8B. Space Process Safety Considerations

Application Area	Hot Product (Temp) °C	Reactive Gas	Product Liquid	By-Product Solid	Partic. Radiation	Laser Beam	Electromagnetic Radiation	Other
Superalloys with Dispersed Rare Earth Oxides (15-20)** Titanium-Lanthanum Oxide	2000	-	-	-	-	-	Yes (Include Optical)	-
Uniform Dispersion of Semiconductive/ Photoconductive Particles in Glass (20-40)**Silver Chloride in High Silicate Glass	1500	-	-	-	/Electrons (Low)/	/Specular Reflection/	Yes	-
Magnetoresistive and Infrared Eutectics (4)** Iron Antimonide-Indium Antimonide	1200	-	-	-	-	-	Yes	-
Superconducting Monotectics (5)** Niobium Tin-Tin	900	-	-	-	/Electrons (Low)/	-	Yes	-
Rare Earth Borides (5)** Lanthanum Boride	2300	-	-	-	-	-	Yes (Include Optical)	Toxic Boride Vapors
Refractory Silicides (10)** Molybdenum Disilicide	2200	-	-	-	/Electrons (Low)/	-	Yes (Include Optical)	-
Uniform Dispersion of Photochromic Particles in Glass (20)** SiO_2 Glass with Europium and/or Cerium	1500	-	-	-	Electrons (Low)	Specular Reflection	Yes (Include Optical)	-
Amorphous Metallic Conductors (10)** Palladium Silicon	960	-	-	-	-	-	Yes	-
Ferromagnetic Eutectics (10)** Iron-Iron Sulphide	988	-	-	-	-	-	Yes	-

**Estimated Number of Applications, Representative Example is Shown.
//Indicates Unresolved Option.

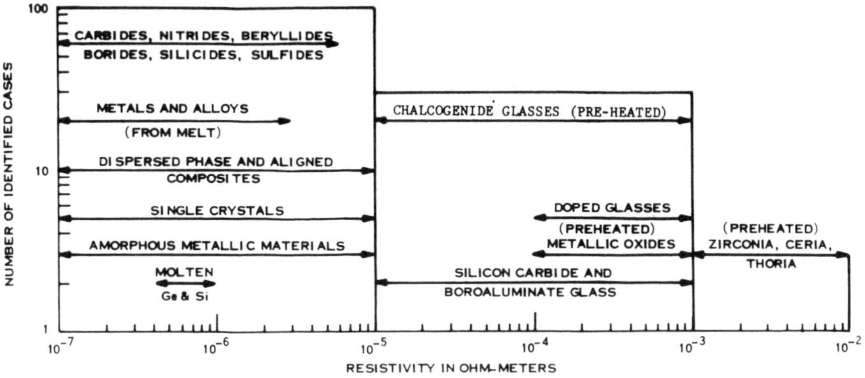

Fig. 1. Numbers of identified candidate materials with various ranges of electrical resistivity.

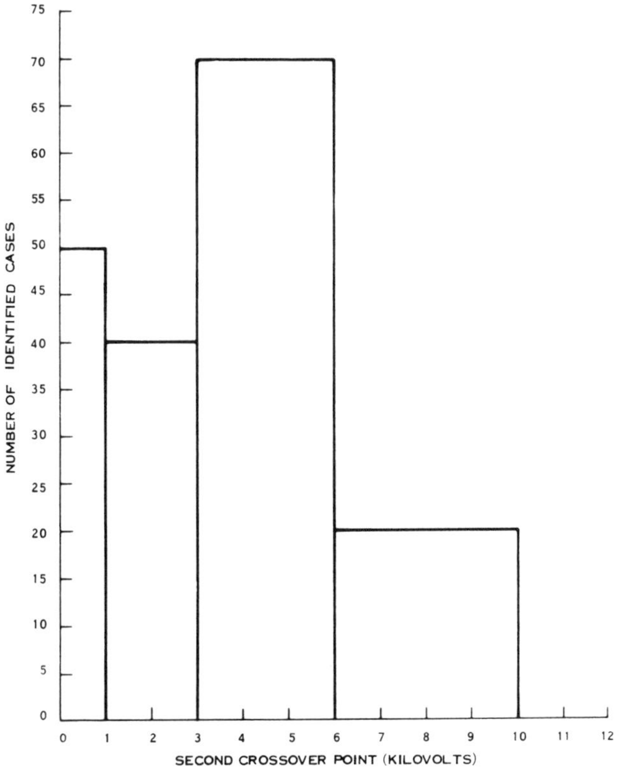

Fig. 2. Numbers of candidate materials arranged according to second crossover point in electron emission.

suspension processing. At the same time, a large number of cases have second crossover points that make electron beam heating suitable.

VI. Conclusions

As a result of this early effort, some preliminary key conclusions can be drawn:

1) In addition to providing position control, electromagnetic is capable of providing the heating requirements for 75% of the analyzed materials and material combinations. With supplemental heating via electron beam, this applicability increases to 100%.

2) Heating durations and power requirements for experiment size batches appear amenable to sounding rockets for early developmental steps on such portions of the total process as, for example, melting and supercooling experiments.

3) Commercial free suspension space-processing payloads may require significantly large power input and thermal dissipation.

4) A number of potential hazards result from several of the processes under study. Specific design and operating precautions must be imposed on processing equipment and procedures involved in carrying out these processes.

References

[1]Frost, R. T., Bloom, H. L., Napaluch, L. J., Stockhoff, E. H., Wouch, G.; "Electromagnetic Containerless Processing Requirements and Recommended Facility Concept and Capabilities for Spacelab," NASA, Final Rept., Contract NAS8-29680, May 13, 1974.

[2]"Study for Identification of Beneficial Uses of Space, Phase I," Final Rept., General Electric Doc. DIN73SD4259, Dec. 1972 and April 1973.

[3]Wuenscher, H. F., "Manufacturing in Space," Astronautics and Aeronautics, 10, p. 42, September 1972.

[4]McCreight, L. R., "Use of Shuttle for Manufacturing and Materials Process Experiments in Low G". American Astronautical Society, Space Shuttle Payloads Session, Vol. 30, Science and Technology, 1973.

[5]Ulrich, D. R., Chung, A. M., Yan, C. S. and McCreight, L. R.: "Economic Analysis of Crystal Growth in Space." Final Report on NASA Contract No. NAS 8-27942, General Electric Company Space Sciences Laboratory, July 1972.

[6]Steurer, W. H., Kaye, S., Gorham, D. J., "Space Processes for Extended Low-G Testing", Convair Report CASD-STT-73-005, June 15, 1973.

[7]Wechsler, A. E., "Spherical Forming and Composite Casting in Zero-G," Space Processing and Manufacturing, NASA Pub. ME-69-1, 1969.

[8]"Space Processing and Manufacturing," Report No. MS-69-1, NASA-George C. Marshall Space Flight Center, Oct. 21, 1968.

[9]Bredt, J. H., "New Space Processing Experiments for the Skylab Mission." Paper presented at the 23rd International Astronautical Congress, Vienna, Austria, Oct. 8-15, 1972.

[10]"Requirements and Concepts for Materials Science and Manufacturing in Space Payload Equipment Study" TRW Report DCN No. 1-2-21-00172, July 1973.

[11]Gonser, B. W., "Modern Materials" Volume 6, 1968, Academic Press, 1968, New York.

Chapter III-Applications

NASA ACTIVITIES IN MATERIALS SCIENCES IN SPACE

James H. Bredt*

NASA Office of Applications, Washington, D.C.

Abstract

In the year since the 18th Plenary Meeting of COSPAR, NASA has conducted eight materials processing experiments on the Apollo-Soyuz mission and 17 on two rocket flights. In addition, these three missions have implemented one Soviet and three German experiments. The Apollo-Soyuz results have confirmed and extended the findings of the Skylab experiments on solidification and crystal growth effects and also have established capabilities for separating living cells by electrophoresis and returning them still living to earth. The rocket missions provide repetitive flight opportunities much as the Space Shuttle will do, and they are being used to develop research approaches in which investigators will undertake projects calling for multiple space experiments rather than proposing experiments individually. During the year, NASA also has completed definition work on the major payload facilities planned for its initial materials processing experiment program on the Space Shuttle and Spacelab missions of 1980-1981.

1. Introduction

The 12 months between the 18th and 19th Plenary Meetings of COSPAR have been a very active period for materials research in space. During this time, the Apollo-Soyuz Test Project (ASTP) mission has carried 10 experiments on processes in materials, as well as three related "science demonstrations," which is a term applied to ad hoc activities developed late in the program to make use of residual resources. In addition, the NASA Space Processing Program has sponsored two rocket flights that carried 9 and 10 experiments, respectively, in the Space Processing Applications Rocket (SPAR) project. These activities have brought the total number of space experiments and demonstrations to 60, distributed among flight missions as shown in Table 1. It is noteworthy that about half of all of

---

Presented as Paper D.1.1. at the COSPAR Symposium on Materials Sciences in Space, Philadelphia, PA, June 9-10, 1976.

*Manager, Space Processing Applications.

Table 1 Distribution of space processing experiments and science demonstrations among missions flown through June 1975

Mission	Experiments	Science Demonstrations
Apollo 14	...	3
Apollo 16	...	1
Apollo 17	...	1
Skylab	14	9
ASTP (July 1975)	10	3
SPAR I rocket (Dec. 11, 1975)	9	...
SPAR II rocket (May 17, 1976)	10	...
Totals	43	17

the space experiments performed on processes in materials have been done during the past year.

This level of activity was actually larger than that achieved during the year of the Skylab missions. It is even more striking, however, to compare the year under review here with the year preceding the 18th COSPAR Plenary Session, when active preparations were being made for the ASTP mission but no materials experiments at all were performed in space. As far as we can foresee, that was the last year that will pass with no materials experiments in space, because the SPAR project has initiated a series of regularly scheduled materials experiment flights that will be continued into the indefinite future by the Space Shuttle and Spacelab missions.

Clearly, then, the past year must be regarded as a milestone signifying the beginning of a new phase in the NASA program and probably in the overall development of space activity in the materials sciences. Its significance is underlined by a further statistic on the year's activity: among the investigators who participated in the ASTP and rocket missions, there were several who performed their second space experiments on these missions. Thus, at least provisionally, materials science has begun to emerge as an area of continuous activity in space research.

On the scientific side of the program, this was also a transitional year, and its results cannot be summed up in a few compact conclusions. For example, although the Apollo-Soyuz mission was the last manned flight of its kind, its space processing experiment program was characterized more by new lines of investigation that were initiated than by things that were concluded. A list of the experiments is given in Table 2. Detailed reports on most of them are included in this volume, but it will be appropriate to comment briefly on the eight U.S. experiments in order to draw out some conclusions on how materials science in space is developing as a discipline.

2. ASTP Experiments

In the first place, four of the ASTP experiments sponsored by NASA comprised continuations of work that had been initiated on previous missions. These four experiments are fairly typical of the most highly developed methods that have been used for materials science experiments in space so far, and their results illustrate how much remains to be done as well as how much has been achieved.

Experiment MA-011, Electrophoresis Technology, was the third flight of apparatus developed by NASA to separate materials of biological origin by zone electrophoresis in a quiescent fluid medium. The two preceding experiments with this technique had been "science demonstrations" performed on the Apollo 14 and 16 lunar missions. Each had accomplished necessary steps in technology development and partially successful separations of model materials, but neither had provided a clear demonstration of the potentialities of space electrophoresis.

In the ASTP experiment, the technology developed for the Apollo demonstrations was extended and combined with newly developed sample handling techniques to attempt separations of living human cells as well as fixed red blood cells that were used as model materials. Photography of one successful red blood cell separation and postflight analysis of one separation run performed with cortical kidney cells clearly showed that the apparatus had electrophoretically transported the cell samples over distances of the order of 10 cm without significant disturbance due to fluid flows. This is a capability possessed by no earth-based apparatus; in addition, the kidney cell run achieved a substantial concentration of urokinase activity in a single fraction of cells that remained viable after separation, which no earth-based method of any kind has accomplished. Thus, the ASTP experiment

Table 2 Space processing experiments in the Apollo-Soyuz Test Project

A) Electrophoresis experiments	
MA-014:	Electrophoresis (EPE) K. Hannig, Max-Planck-Institut fuer Biochemie
MA-011:	Electrophoresis Technology R.E. Allen, NASA Marshall Space Flight Center P.E. Bigazzi, State University of New York, Buffalo, N.Y. G.A. Barlow, Abbott Laboratories M. Bier, Veterans Administration Hospital, Tuscon, Ariz.
B) Experiments using the MA-010 multipurpose furnace system	
MA-041:	Surface-Tension-Induced Convection R.E. Reed, Oak Ridge National Laboratory
MA-044:	Monotectic and Syntectic Alloys C.Y. Ang, Universities Space Research Administration
MA-060:	Interface Marking in Crystals H.C. Gatos and A.F. Witt, Massachusetts Institute of Technology
MA-070:	Zero-G Processing of Magnets D.J. Larson, Grumman Aerospace Corporation
MA-085:	Crystal Growth from the Vapor Phase H. Wiedemeier, Rensselaer Polytechnic Institute
MA-131:	Sodium Chloride-Lithium Fluoride Eutectic A.S. Yue, University of California, Los Angeles, California
MA-150:	Multiple Material Melting Soviet Academy of Sciences
C) Experiments on crystal growth in aqueous solution	
MA-028:	Crystal Growth in Space M.D. Lind, Rockwell International, Inc.

afforded a fairly convincing preliminary demonstration that electrophoretic separation methods designed for use in space can provide capabilities that are not available with earth-based techniques. On the other hand, various engineering and operational problems compromised six of the eight separation runs that were attempted, so that it is fair to say that work remains to be done to reduce space electrophoresis to consistent practice.

In experiment MA-060, Interface Marking in Crystals, H. C. Gatos and A. F. Witt of the Massachusetts Institute of Technology continued the investigation of impurity distribution in directionally solidified semi-conductors which they had pioneered on the Skylab mission. Whereas their Skylab work had been done with indium antimonide and the precision of the results was limited by the precision with which measurements could be made on that material, the improved performance of the electric furnace carried on the ASTP mission made it possible for them to use germanium as their sample material and take advantage of high-precision spreading resistance measurement techniques to characterize the impurity distributions. In addition, means were provided to pass pulses of electric current through the samples at precisely timed intervals during solidification, thus providing a series of artificial growth bands that could be used to determine the instantaneous rate of solidification and the shape of the solid-liquid interface at all stages of solidification.

The results of the experiment were complicated, but when fully analyzed they confirmed the finding of the Skylab experiment that the impurity distributions obtained in Bridgman growth of doped semiconductors were determined fully by diffusion effects in the melt at the acceleration levels experienced in manned spacecraft. On the other hand, the more accurate measurement methods employed in the ASTP experiment also revealed a variety of kinetic effects that seemed almost paradoxical at first sight but were found to be caused by the combined influences of the starting transient in the growth rate and changes in the shape of the solid-liquid interface. The analysis of these effects has shown that rather precise three dimensional control over impurity distributions in semiconductor crystals should be achievable by manipulating thermal conditions during solidification, but it also has shown that some substantial extensions of the existing theoretical treatments will be needed to make quantitative predictions of the results of such experiments.

Somewhat similar conclusions can be drawn from experiment MA-131, in which A.S. Yue of UCLA grew oriented samples of the rodlike NaCL-LiF eutectic composition. Here the effects of the thermal conditions could be seen in the changing orientation of the eutectic structure, and it was clear that the dependence of the latter on the former was very sensitive under weightless conditions. It would appear possible to exercise very detailed control over the texture of a solidifying sample of such a material system by controlling the thermal conditions, and the characteristic optical properties of the material even should be capable of furnishing a basis for feedback control of the process of solidification. On the other hand, a good deal of theoretical development obviously is needed to accomplish quantitative design calculations for such processes.

In the last of the four experiments that had predecessors on the Skylab missions, experiment MA-085, H. Wiedemeier completed an elegant survey of the effects that occur in crystal growth by chemical vapor transport under weightless conditions. This work comprised a comparison of the results obtained when identical methods were used to grow crystals on the ground and in space with a variety of transport systems, crystal materials, temperatures, and gas pressures. One of the most striking results was that the crystals grown in space were highly perfect in absolute terms and much better than those obtained under even the best conditions on the ground. This high perfection seems to indicate that the crystals grew under conditions of quasiequilibrium between the vapor and the growing surfaces and tends to confirm the evidence from other experiments that fluid phases are effectively quiescent under real spacecraft conditions.

The other principal result of Wiedemeier's work was to show that the rates of material transport to the growing crystal surfaces were much higher in the space experiments than one would calculate on the basis of ground data taken under supposedly comparable conditions. Since this effect appeared consistently through all variations of materials and growth conditions, it is almost certainly intrinsic to the growth process itself. At this time, the preferred explanation is that, at relatively high pressures where the effect is most pronounced, the growth rates are controlled by thermochemical effects that occur in the neighborhood of the crystal surface, rather than by mass transport effects in the bulk of the vapor. If this is the case, the same effects must be influential on the ground under conditions that previously were thought to be controlled by convection effects in the vapor. Further work on the ground can be expected to resolve the latter question, and detailed theoretical analysis will be needed to exploit the new effects uncovered by this work. In view of the high perfection obtained in the crystals grown on the Skylab and ASTP missions, however, it certainly seems that the exploitation of this kind of process can prove rewarding.

It seems to be appropriate to sum up the results of the last three experiments just discussed by observing that in each case enough work now has been done to point out interesting prospects for further development and that the logical next steps in these areas should be to work out designs for experiments in which the effects in question will be brought under detailed control. In the case of the electrophoresis experiment, the ASTP mission clearly has demonstrated that the necessary technology now is available to perform systematic research on the separation of biological materials, but confirming evidence is needed to verify the promise held out by the single apparently successful kidney cell separation.

Each of the four NASA experiments that broke new ground on the ASTP mission also will require further refinement or confirmation before many firm conclusions can be drawn. Experiment MA-041 was an attempt to measure the diffusion coefficient of gold in molten lead by the methods used to observe self-diffusion in molten zinc on Skylab. However, the experiment produced segregation effects that do not seem amenable to detailed analysis, and further work along these lines probably will call for apparatus in which segregation can be confined to quantitatively predictable behavior by detailed control over the thermal conditions. Experiment MA-044 sought to produce a homogeneous sample of aluminum antimonide by melting aluminum and antimony together and also to make a dispersion of lead in zinc by heating an appropriate alloy composition above its consolute temperature and then cooling it through the two-melt temperature range and freezing it. The AlSb sample proved to be highly homogeneous with only very small inclusions of minor phases, but the Pb-Zn alloy exhibited gross segregation of the two elements instead of the fine dispersion that was expected. Together with parallel results obtained with the aluminum-indium system on the second SPAR mission, this has prompted a reassessment of the fluid effects that take place in contained two phase melts.

Experiment MA-070 provided similarly mixed results. It succeeded introducing samples of the MnBi-Bi eutectic in which the instrinsic coercive force of the MnBi phase was very high, but an attempt to produce oriented cobalt/rare-earth alloy samples in the same experiment was frustrated by an unexpected chemical reaction between the sample and the container. Obviously both types of materials will need to be pursued in further space experiments, and it would appear desirable to plan these experiments to process only one material at a time. As a general rule, all of the Skylab and ASTP experiments that sought to maximize their data output by processing more than one material at once in the same container have suffered in some substantial way from their complex designs.

Finally, experiment MA-028 provided encouraging preliminary results with a method for crystal growth from aqueous solution which will be practical for experiments of a few days' duration. In this technique, two soluble reactants are allowed to diffuse into a water filled vessel, where they combine to form a relatively insoluble product. Well-formed small crystals of calcite, zinc sulfide, and calcium tartrate were obtained on the ASTP mission despite operational limitations on the experiment's duration and temperature variations of the order of several degrees. When performed under more controlled conditions, this type of experiment may be capable of producing results as interesting as those of the chemical vapor transport experiments.

3. SPAR Experiments

At the time of the Annual Review presented at the 18th COSPAR Plenary Meeting, the Space Processing Applications Rocket (SPAR) project had just completed the process of selecting 19 proposals for flight from among 63 submitted in response to its first solicitation. During the ensuing year, the project has conducted the two flights indicated in Table 1 and thus has reached full operational status; it also has published its second call for experiment proposals and received another 51 responses.

The assignments of selected experiments among scheduled SPAR flights are listed in Table 3, where the numbers in the columns corresponding to the flights are the numbers of samples processed for each investigator on the flight in question. As the table indicates, investigations performed in the SPAR project ordinarily include experiments performed on at least two flights. By making multiple flight experiments available, we hope to make it possible for investigators to employ step-by-step research approaches analogous to those that commonly are used on the ground. In this way, we also expect to learn some of the basic management techniques that will be needed to integrate continuing scientific investigations with the flight schedule of the Space Shuttle and Spacelab, since the SPAR project involves very similar planning and scheduling problems. Although the research strategies that investigators can use on the SPAR missions are beginning to resemble those that they would plan to use in their own laboratories, the experimental techniques that they must use on these flights are essentially new because all of the effects that they wish to study must be produced, and in some cases measured, during the rocket's 5-minute period of weightless flight. Therefore, the project has had to begin with quite simple experiments and will work up to sophisticated methods such as levitation melting and electrophoresis, only rather gradually over the next year or two.

Only one set of SPAR flight experiments has been analyzed fully so far, and none of the investigators involved in the project has completed his whole program of research. Therefore, it would be premature to express any but a few tentative and preliminary observations about where these investigations seem to be taking the discipline of materials science in space. One general conclusion that does seem justified is that the rockets themselves provide a suitable environment for the kinds of experiments that are being attempted: measurements indicate that the acceleration levels on the first two flights were of the order of 10^{-5} g, which is rather better than the conditions that prevailed on the Skylab and ASTP missions. On the other hand, the behavior of the material systems studied in the experiments was generally more complex than had been expected. In the present preliminary stage of rocket experimentation, three apparent developments seem to stand out.

In the first place, the Dendrite Remelting and Macrosegregation experiment of M.H. Johnston and C.S. Griner on the SPAR I mission appears to have shown that dendritic solidification evolves quite differently in weightless melts as compared to ground experiments. The

Table 3 Investigations selected for the NASA Space Processing Applications Rocket (SPAR) project

Investigations		Experiments assigned to SPAR flights SPAR I	SPAR II	SPAR III
A) High-temperature melting and freezing experiments				
74-5:	Lead-Antimony Eutectic R.B. Pond et al., Marvalaud, Inc.	1	2	...
74-10:	Foams from Sputter-Deposited Metals J.W. Patten, Battelle-Northwest Laboratories	1	2	...
74-30:	Agglomeration in Immiscible Liquids S.H. Gelles and A. Markworth, Battelle Columbus Laboratories	...	1	...
74-34:	Thoria Dispersed Magnesium L. Raymond and C.Y. Ang, The Aerospace Corporation	1	2	...
74-62:	Aluminum-Indium Alloys H. Ahlborn, University of Hamburg and K. Lohberg, Technical University of Berlin	...	1	...
74-63:	Dispersion-Strengthened Pb-Ag Alloys W. Heye, Technische Universitaet Clausthal	...	1	...
B) Low-temperature melting and freezing experiments				
74-15:	Particle-Interface Interactions D.R. Uhlmann, Massachusetts Institute of Technology	1	...	...
74-18:	Liquid Mixing C.F. Schafer, Space Sciences Laboratory, Marshall Space Flight Center	1	...	...

Table 3 (continued)

74-21:	Dendrite Remelting and Macrosegregation M.H. Johnston and C.S. Griner, Materials Laboratory, Marshall Space Flight Center	1	2	...
74-36:	Bubble Behavior in Melts J.M. Papazian, Grumman Aerospace Corporation	1	...	1
74-37:	Contained Polycrystalline Solidification T.Z. Kattamis, University of Connecticut, and J.M. Papazian	1	...	...
C) Experiments with special apparatus needs				
74-42:	Gallia, Lanthana, and Alumina Glasses R.A. Happe, Rockwell International, Inc.	...	...	...
74-45:	Gallium Arsenide and Garnet Epitaxy M.D. Lind, Rockwell International, Inc.	...	...	1
74-48:	Beryllium Grain Refinement G.J. London, Kawecki Berylco Industries, Inc.	...	...	1
74-49:	Amorphous Ferromagnets A.E. Lord, Drexel University and G. Wouch, General Electric Company	...	...	...
74-53:	Viscous Coalescence R.W. Hopper and D.R. Uhlmann, Massachusetts Institute of Technology	...	...	1

differences seem to occur because the undercooling and/or supersaturation that drive the solidification process are controlled by diffusion and heat conduction in space, and the effects observed by

Johnston and Griner may lead to some quite sophisticated means of controlling solidification in the future.

Secondly, the experiments of Papazian and Uhlmann appear to show that the interactions of freezing interfaces with foreign particles and voids are more complex than expected. And finally, the preliminary results of Ahlborn and Gelles on the SPAR II flight have revealed some wholly unexpected gross segregation effects in twophase melts of monotectic alloys and are motivating reassessments of previous experiments performed with such alloys in drop tower work and on the Skylab and ASTP missions.

4. Conclusions

In reviewing the experiment results just summarized, I think it is possible to distinguish a series of definite phases that characterize every space investigation. The first phase, broadly speaking, consists of acquiring the technical means to perform experiments of the types required for the investigation. This is always a complex and time-consuming process for space investigations, because the necessary means include space vehicles and the large supporting facilities and organizations required to operate them. In addition, at this stage in the development of materials science in space, it happens fairly frequently that a new type of experiment requires new technology to be developed before it can be performed. Several examples of this can be found in the history of the discipline, the most striking being that of the NASA electrophoresis investigation in which two preliminary flight "demonstrations" were needed to make the necessary technology ready for the ASTP experiment.

The second characteristic phase that can be found in all of the investigations conducted up to now comprises the performance of space experiments that establish the nature of the phenomena to be observed. In some cases, only one experiment is necessary: for example, Wiedemeier was able to determine that the mass transport rates were unexpectedly large in the first run of his Skylab experiment. At the other extreme, however, a whole series of experiments may be needed to complete this phase. A current instance can be seen in the status of research on montectic alloys, where a set of very complex results obtained in the drop tower and on the Apollo, Skylab, ASTP, and SPAR Missions only now seems to be yielding workable hypotheses about what happens when weightless melts of theses alloys freeze.

The most satisfying feature of the flight projects that have been conducted so far is that it has been possible for the participating scientists to bring so many lines of investigation to some degree of maturity using only a few pieces of space flight equipment. We may expect that similar achievements will be registered in other fields of study as they pass through the two initial phases that I have discussed. On the other hand, we also should expect that investigations in the established fields of study will call for increasingly sophisticated and specialized apparatus as they pass into the third phase, which will be one of detailed investigation and exploitation of the effects of weightlessness. Very few investigations have reached this phase as yet, but one can see a small-scale instance of the special requirements of advanced experiments in the circuitry that had to be provided to pass pulses of electric current through the samples in the ASTP experiment of Gatos and Witt.

In addition to the experiment activities of the past year, NASA has conducted a detailed analysis of equipment requirements and designs for materials science investigations on the future missions of the Space Shuttle and Spacelab. The latter effort included consideration of issues arising from each of the characteristics phases of space research activity. A careful assessment of the fields of investigation likely to be represented on the early Shuttle/Spacelab missions has led us to conclude that there are no substantial technology barriers to the development of apparatus which will satisfy the foreseeable needs of investigators. Nevertheless, some considerable technical and administrative questions are involved in the problem of realizing the Shuttle/Spacelab system's potential for providing routine access to space at low costs. These questions are especially important for materials science in space, because materials research typically requires many individual experiments to establish results in any area, and because the numbers of investigators who can participate in space research will depend on the costs of their investigations. During the next few years, therefore, the NASA program will include significant amounts of effort devoted to establishing the most convenient and economical methods for integration and operation of materials science payloads on Shuttle/Spacelab missions.

In the development of experimental apparatus, the main problem that we foresee is to provide equipment that can support research that has entered the third investigative phase just discussed as well as the second, exploratory, phase. To accomplish this, it will be necessary to have the closest possible participation of active scientists in the design and development of the equipment. Accordingly, NASA's first step toward developing its materials science payloads for the early Shuttle/Spacelab missions will be to solicit and select proposals for a group of key experiments whose requirements will be controlling on the design of the equipment. The investigators for these experiments will be selected in the first half of 1977, and they will be required to assume the obligation of guiding the apparatus design work and participating in all design reviews. Our experience in past flight experiment projects leads us to expect that the apparatus designed in this way will be useful for many investigations besides those of the original group of experimenters, and in 1978 and succeeding years NASA also plans to solicit experiment proposals from scientists who may wish to use the equipment but do not need to participate in its design.

By following these procedures, we expect to be able to begin an enterprising program of materials research on the missions assigned to the NASA space processing program in the early 1980's. Judging by past experience, we may expect the Shuttle/Spacelab experiment program to be productive of interesting results from its beginning and to lead to the progressive introduction of space techniques into the materials sciences as a new and valuable experimental resource with a broad field of application.

SURVEY OF THE MICROGRAVITY PROGRAM IN THE FEDERAL REPUBLIC OF GERMANY

A. Bewersdorff

Deutsche Forschungs- und Versuchsanstalt
für Luft- und Raumfahrt e.V., Köln-Porz,
Federal Republic of Germany

Abstract

The prospect of experiments under microgravity has stimulated considerable interest in the FRG. Presently 150 experiments have been proposed. Most of them are aimed at gaining new insight into material processes such as nucleation or solidification, or at obtaining improved data of material properties. The program includes experiments in the fields of metallurgy, crystal growth, chemistry, physical chemistry, fluid dynamics, and it relates even to biology and biophysics. Experiments have been conducted aboard Apollo-Soyus and NASA rockets. More rocket flights are planned over the next years.

History and Status

The origin of the German program dates back as far as 1971, when the question of participating in the post-Apollo program came up. In the beginning, of course, we went to NASA to learn about the prospects offered by microgravity. The first groups of interested people in Germany then began to meet regularly in 1972/1973, and first studies were initiated already in 1973. It also was felt that it would be highly desirable to have a pilot experiment as soon as possible, since with microgravity we were moving into an entirely new field. This chance was offered by the flight of Apollo-Soyus, for

---

Presented as Paper D.1.2 at the COSPAR Symposium on Materials Sciences in Space, Philadelphia, Pa., June 9-10, 1976.

which NASA accepted a German experiment on electrophoresis, a rather ambitious kind of experiment. Development started in 1973, and the experiment was flown successfully in 1975.

The second phase of our program began in 1974 at about the time when th e final decision to build Spacelab was made by the European Space Agency. A call for ideas was issued by the German Ministry for Research and Technology, which, together with an active search for ideas, has yielded so far 140 proposals from the material sciences. Table 1 gives the distribution of the proposal according to discipline, and Table 2 shows the institutions from which the experiments come. A conclusion that can be drawn from these statistics is that the aspects of science and applications are of about equal importance in the German microgravity program.

The scope of the program is outlined by Table 3. Starting from six studies in 1973, the number of studies and hardware

Table 1 Proposals

Metallurgy	65	Process technology	7
Crystals	17	Fluid dynamics	10
Glasses	5	Physical chemistry	23
Ceramics	4	Biology	1
Chemistry	7		

Table 2 User interest

	Proposals
24 University labs	36
8 Research institutes	44
22 Industrial companies	60

Table 3 German program 1976 (45 projects)

Basic research (material sciences, fluid physics)
Experiment definition studies
Implementation of pilot experiments (rockets)
Development of standard equipment
Conception of material sciences laboratory
Planning of Spacelab missions

projects has been boosted to 45 projects in 1976. Studies presently are devoted to basic research on experiment ideas in the material sciences and in fluid physics, and to experiment definition. Besides the electrophoresis experiment in Apollo-Soyus, two metallurgical experiments have been performed aboard NASA rockets and are now under evaluation. Another one will be executed in August 1976. For practical reasons, it has been found desirable to launch rockets with microgravity experiments also in Europe, and scientists from other European countries also will participate. Presently 30 proposals are under consideration for these flights, with most of them in the field of metallurgy. The first launch is anticipated for the end of 1977, and two flights then are planned for each year. Of course, the program really is aimed at the utilization of Spacelab, and here standard equipment will be of great importance. Consequently, the development of equipment has been initiated, as is illustrated by Table 4. We expect that the same equipment will be flown many times and assume that Spacelab will be used for the purpose of material sciences about twice per year.

Some words must be said about the organization of the German program. It is funded by the Federal Ministry for Research and Technology; it is directed and promoted by five planning groups (glasses and ceramics, metallurgy, crystals, transport phenomena, chemistry); and it is managed on behalf of the Ministry by the German space agency DFVLR, which also provides technical support.

Scientific Objectives

Tables 4 and 5 outline the contents of the German program and show its broad scope. As this paper will focus on the scientific aspects of microgravity, experiments are grouped after the phenomenon or physical process that is to be studied

Table 4 Equipment under development (1976)

Electromagnetic positioning
Electrostatic positioning
Support-free measuring technique for determination of reaction enthalpies
Acoustic and aerodynamic positioning
Multizone furnaces (isothermal, gradient)
Modular process chamber
Mixing and stirring devices
Image furnace with drawing and turning device

Table 5 Experiment groups

Phenomenon or process	Proposals
Solidification of melts	10
Casting of composite materials	18
Directional solidification of eutectics	6
Growth of single crystals	17
Ultrapure materials	8
Nucleation	5
Undercooling of liquids	3
Chemical reactions	8
Electrophoresis	1
Vapor deposition	3
Electrolysis	3
Transport phenomena	13
Fluid dynamics	10
Fluid physics	7
Critical point phenomena	4
Sedimentation of particles	4
Forming	11

under zero g or to be used. The number of proposals that have been received also is indicated in order to give an idea of the relative importance of each group. Quite naturally, the program that will be executed in the 1980's could have different priorities.

In the first place, we have the large number of experiments that deal with the solidification of multicrystalline matter. This category includes also those experiments that probably come closest to applications.

In the group "solidification of metallic melts" the objectives are the study of dendritic growth and of segregation processes of immiscible alloys or of alloys with heterogenous nucleation. The solidification of alloys with an immiscibility gap in the liquid state is expected to yield materials with thus far impossible combinations of properties. The fine dispersion that can be obtained only in space also modifies many physical properties such as electrical resistance, magnetic susceptibility, and mechanical strength, and this dependency also will be investigated. New combinations of physical properties are also the aim of the class "composite materials". It seems important to note that under the absence of buoyancy the wetting behavior will be crucial, and this presently is being investigated. Space experiments also will give new insight into the question of how particles are incorporated into a matrix on freezing. The growth of "aligned eutectics" under the absence of gravity-induced thermal convection has drawn considerable interest and is given a high priority. The generation of possible microconvections near the phase boundary and their influence on the microstructure will be studied, as well as the effects of supercooling.

The feeling among German scientists is that production in space of crystals for commercial purposes is certainly not imminent, but the phenomenon of "crystal growth" can be studied more in depth under the absence of thermal convection. German crystal growers have become more aware of the importance of fluid mechanics, and more consideration is given now to the processes in the melt or solution, and it is strongly felt that space experiments will make a valuable contribution to understanding.

"Purification of materials" concerns metals, glasses, and ceramics and will be done either by zone melting (glasses) or by deposition from the vapor phase in an acoustic field. In spite of the number of proposals, this group has not been given a high priority.

"Nucleation" experiments in the next place aim at studying the generation of a new phase (solid, liquid, or vapor) in a liquid or gas. Under microgravity, longer times will be available for observations, and the lack of gravity-induced convection will allow control of temperature with more ease. On the other hand, under zero g it also may be possible to eliminate heterogenous nucleation altogether by avoiding contact with a solid. This will make it easier to "undercool melts", and it then may be possible to obtain certain materials in a vitreous state.

The next group, "chemical reactions", is rather heterogeneous. It includes investigations of diffusion-controlled exothermic reactions, as well as an experiment in which reaction energies are measured with higher accuracy than on Earth. The basic idea is that reaction partners will be floating freely, and any disturbance by contact with a crucible can be avoided in space. Other fields of interest are the study of the role of segregation in chemical reactions and of polymerization of reaction partners that tend to separate under gravity.

One proposal deals with "electrophoresis". "Chemical vapor depostion" which also is of considerable technical interest, is the subject of three proposals. Another three proposals deal with "electrolysis". Here the galvanic deposition of suspended particles will be investigated, and other interest concerns the generation of hydrogen bubbles at the cathode.

The group "transport phenomenon" comprises precision measurements of diffusion coefficients in various systems of thermal conductivity and heat transfer, of thermodiffusion, and of other coefficients of irreversible thermodynamics. For these experiments, the absence of thermal convection offers a high degree of freedom and allows higher temperature gradients or new geometric configurations.

"Fluid dynamics" in the next group is, of course, of basic importance to the entire program. Microgravity means essentially that novel ways of manipulating fluids become available. The new ways have to be studied, elaborated, and implemented. This justifies also experiments in their own right, because there also is new territory here for fluid mechanics. Some of the topics are behavior of emulsions, cellular convection in a rotating system, visualization of flow patterns in zone melting, and drop dynamics. It also seems useful to study the various effects of electric fields on the mechanics of liquids, because this may lead to additional means of control.

"Fluid physics" is another class of basic importance. Under the absence of gravity, the role of interfacial tension is enhanced. It turns out that the material coefficients of interfacial tension and their dependence on temperature often are not well known or even cannot be measured with good accuracy. Here again, space offers a new access by measurements on free-floating drops. Another experiment is directed at investigating the structure of molten salts and at measuring the volume viscosity without disturbance by thermal convection. Furthermore, we have four proposals dealing with the gas-liquid "critical point". Under normal conditions on Earth, critical conditions can be maintained only in a small volume, because of the extreme dependency of density on height. Gravity-driven separation of phases is another cause of disturbances. Experiments thus are facilitated vastly by zero g, and measurements of heat capacity and thermal conductivity are under study. The experiments in the last two groups "sedimentation of particles" and "forming" are more of technical and not scientific interest and are listed here only for the sake of completeness.

General Character of the Microgravity Program

The microgravity program as it has emerged in Germany over the past two years can be characterized by the following four points:

1) Zero g is a physical condition that can be used for applications, as well as in experiments with purely scientific objectives. We did not try to separate proposals into two categories. Three good reasons may be quoted here: a) In the material sciences, it often seems difficult to draw a line between fundamental research and applications because there is a continuous transition between the two. It may also be risky: what is considered pure science now may lead to applications a few years later. b) This holds particularly in a program dealing with an entirely new condition, as is the case here. At this time, a separation would appear to be at least premature. c) A third reason for a broad program has been of a more historical nature. When in Germany we started to think of zero g, a number of experiments already had been identified by American scientists which clearly were directed toward applications. It would make little sense just to copy these ideas, and therefore we had to look also into other fields.

2) The program is very heterogeneous, as experiments can come from all disciplines dealing with fluid matter, and scientific objectives in these disciplines are very different. However, there is one element in common, and this is, of course, fluid dynamics and fluid physics. Nearly all experiments start from novel ways of manipulating fluids, and this means that convection theory, interfacial phenomena, and thermodynamics of fluids must have an important role in the program and also find new fields for themselves. Zero g then leads to a close cooperation between fluid physics and other disciplines where the objectives come from the material sciences, whereas the tools largely are supplied by fluid physics. This is considered an important feature of the program, and we have formed an interdisciplinary group in our space agency DFVLR in order to promote this idea. This group will support experiments and will try to stimulate new ideas.

3) Space experiments must be connected closely with ground-based research: the individual experiment must be preceded by extensive research on Earth because any trial-and-error approach would be too costly, and of course evaluation of experiments will be done on the ground. Furthermore, experiments come from disciplines in which the overwhelming part of research will continue in laboratories on Earth. Space experiments then will serve objectives that are established and pursued in larger programs.

4) Microgravity experiments can have three different objectives: enlarge understanding of a phenomenon; yield improved data of material properties; and yield a new material or a unique structure. Presently, our program is directed largely at the first two possibilities.

Outlook

If present trends continue, experiments will tend to become more sophisticated. For example, an experiment will consist of not just melting a sample and solidifying, but it may include, for example, optical observations and active control of residual flows. Also, experiments will be discussed thoroughly with experts of fluid mechanics.

Furthermore, the program will continue to expand. Zero g is essentially a new tool that has been made available, and we probably do not conceive yet of all of the different purposes for which it can be used. For example, it seems that the possibilities in chemistry, physical chemistry, and biology or biophysics have not yet been explored fully. High-precision measurements in physical chemistry and manipulating of living cells in suspension could become important branches of the zero g program. In any case, new proposals now are coming in Germany at a rate faster than experiments probably could be performed if Spacelab already were available. And this makes us confident that microgravity will be a lasting and important part of future space programs.

SOME RESULTS OF STUDIES IN SPACE TECHNOLOGY IN THE USSR

A. S. Okhotin, V. F. Laptchinsky, and G. S. Shonin

Space Research Institute, Academy of Sciences,
Moscow, USSR

Abstract

This paper concerns the results of studies in space technology in the USSR. Main trends in this area and experimental results of welding in weightlessness, development of welded spacecraft equipment, studies of the spacecraft (micro)atmosphere and of its impact of technological extravehicular processes, as well as the impact of controlled external disturbances of the crystallization of multiphase media and eutectic alloys under various gravitational conditions are discussed. Prospects are outlined for scientific studies in space technology.

Space exploration gave a powerful impetus to various branches of science and technology, including processing technology and fabrication of various materials. There is no doubt that very soon not only will it be necessary to carry out various processing operations, involving, for instance heating and melting, but the prospects of applying some technological processes to manufacture materials and units with radically new physical and chemical properties also seem to be very promising. Such specific space conditions as zero gravity, high vacuum, and idiosyncrasies of thermal processes may affect technological processes positively or negatively. Hence, specialists should study the behavior of materials and the way in which various technological operations are to be carried out in space. Substantial fundamental studies are required to analyze the behavior of melted materials in these conditions and to

---

Presented as Paper D.1.3 at the COSPAR Symposium on Materials Sciences in Space, Philadelphia, Pa., June 9-10, 1976.

determine the major procedures of their processing in space. The most probable trends of these studies are as follows:

1) The behavior of one- and multiphase liquid and gaseous materials in space should be studied thoroughly. It requires that main principles of melts cooling and crystallization be studied in space both in free state and in the case of forced heat removal. Basic principles of phase separation, the way they can be controlled, the effect of surface tension forces, and adhesion and wettability for various combinations of phases and materials also should be studied, as well as diffusion and heat-transfer processes, in particular, natural convection on the free surface and in the finite region, etc.

2) Materials and units should be identified which are worthwhile and feasible to be fabricated in space. Here priority should be given to various composite materials, i.e., metal-to-metal and metal-to-oxide compounds, ceramic and organic materials immiscible on the Earth, light alloys reinforced by high-strength threads, and so on. The possibility of obtaining uniform gas-metal mixtures gives every reason to believe that high-strength, heat-resistant foamy metals with low specific gravity can be manufactured in space. Of great interest is a possibility of fabricating optically transparent materials (glasses or single crystals) in space with minimum possible impurity content or with their prescribed distribution. It is extremely essential to grow in space highly pure semiconductor single crystals that are perfect in structure. It also is important to carry out some chemical and biological processes in space, such as electrophoresis or the growth of bacterial cultures of high purity.

3) Emphasis should be given to the development of procedures and means for maintenance, repair, and assembly operations in space. Here, cutting of the structure into separate units to be connected later by welding, soldering, or gluing may be important. One of the most essential problems here lies in studying ergonomic and physiological capabilities of a spaceman-operator, in designing all possible auxiliary instruments and parts in facilitating operations, and making them safer.

4) With all of this progress, one of the top-priority problems should be the design and testing of the equipment and setups that are required to carry out research and development programs for studying the behavior of materials and technological operations in space. At present, regular and systematic studies along all of these lines are underway in the Soviet Union. This review deals only with those aspects

of the problem about which rather interesting results have been obtained recently.

The joint Soviet-American project "Apollo-Soyuz" included an experiment called "Universal Furnace," during which possibilities were studied of fabricating composite and semiconductor materials in weightlessness. Preliminary results of these studies have shown several interesting anomalies that now have been analyzed thoroughly. The "Universal Furnace" experiment data also have been studied thoroughly; final results will be reported after the completion of the scientific EPAS project.

Technological investigations in space should take into account the effect of the spacecraft atmosphere, which forms due to outgassing and sublimation of structural materials, gas leakages from pressurized bays, exhaust products of jet engines, etc. In these cases, part of the molecules and atoms of the atmosphere are ionized, whereas others are charged.

A typical feature of technological operations in space is almost zero gravity. On the Earth, gravitational energy of 1 mole of liquid is of the same order or higher than the specific energy of a mole in biological reactions and in the reactions of crystal growth and bubbles and drops' formation. The same is true about the moistening in the case of surface tension in bubbles and drops and about catalysis. Therefore, zero gravity should affect the preceding reactions and hence the behavior of liquids. Thus, technological processes related to the reprocessing of materials in liquid state in space will have some characteristic features as compared with similar processes on the Earth. In the absence of external forces, mechanical properties of a liquid are determined only by the interaction of surface tension forces with intermolecular adhesion (viscosity) forces; hence any liquid, in free bulk, tends to become spherical in shape if there are no disturbances. It is these very forces that essentially are sensitive to the presence of low impurity concentration. Impurities can fall onto the free surface of the liquid from the spacecraft atmosphere, which is highly inhomogeneous in space and time (a local source of the spacecraft atmosphere proper). Therefore, impurity concentration in the surface layer of the melt and hence the local surface tension value may change, which affects many properties of liquid alloys. For instance, it is expected for iron that drops of the liquid metal contract with high surface velocity (370 m/sec) from an arbitrary shape into an ideal sphere, since iron is characterized by strong surface tension (1500 dyn/cm) and relatively low viscosity (0.04 n). It also is expected that spheres could be fabricated with an accuracy of the order of 1 Å because of molecular forces in zero-gravity conditions. Obviously this will be possible if surface tension of a liquid metal drop remains the same over the whole sphere. When a considerably greater amount of impurities from the spacecraft (natural) atmosphere (e.g., glycerine or paraffin with low surface tension of about 20 dyn-cm^{-1}) falls onto the right hemisphere of liquid metal as compared with the left, the right hemisphere swells; that is, the sphere will not be that ideal, and a liquid metal drop will bounce off to the right as a mercury ball. So, in the case of steady inhomogeneous flow of free molecules of carbonaceous impurities, a drop of melted metal will not take the shape of a perfect sphere; besides, the resultant surface tension arises opposite to the main direction of the carbonaceous impurity flow from the spacecraft atmosphere. Moreover, if that flow of carbonaceous impurities falling onto a melted metal drop will change its direction in time, then the melted metal drop will move chaotically in free space, with no external forces, like a Brown particulate (a large Brown particle). Along with this, inhomogeneous impurity concentration in the surface layer will change the value of local surface tension, thus bringing about the motion of bubbles in the heated liquid and, therefore, dynamic convection of the liquid. This makes it difficult to get castings with required characteristics, so that they have no internal defects, i.e., without crystal lattice defects (dislocations and twinning) or internal tensions.

Certain substances present in the spacecraft atmosphere (in particular, metal oxides, i.e., of Fe, Mo, Pt, etc.) may act as catalysts in some endothermal reactions, thus breaking the chosen catalytic reactions (e.g., enzymatic reaction). When superpure materials are produced in space, the impurities from the spacecraft atmosphere can reduce space technology advantages sharply because of the high degree of vacuum.

One of the major conditions of growing high-quality crystals from the melt is the reduction of turbulent convection in the melt. The convection flow in melted materials is known to be caused mainly by gravity. Warmer regions of the melt are less dense than colder; they become buoyant in the gravitational field and bring about upward convection. Experiments show that these somewhat chaotic flows of warm convection contribute much to the formation of defects (e.g., furrows formation) in single crystals observed but not desired there. It is quite natural that warmer parts of the melt are no more buoyant in zero-conditions; hence one of the main restrictions in the growth of perfect crystals is removed.

However, the spacecraft atmosphere again hinders the growth of perfect crystals in space. As already mentioned, inhomogeneity of the spacecraft atmosphere causes dynamic convection in the liquid, thus preventing the growth of perfect crystals, and so inhomogeneity of flow directions in the spacecraft atmosphere can remove many advantages of space technology.

A wide range of experiments was carried out in the Soviet Union to study welding processes in the conditions of zero gravity and the problems of developing equipment needed for this purpose. When welding equipment is developed, a number of requirements toward its structure and operation, imposed by space conditions, should be taken into account. Safe operation of equipment onboard the spacecraft is provided by taking into account the following factors: 1) heating as a potential source of failure; 2) the presence of metal bath and melted metal sparks; 3) too high power supply voltage; and 4) byproduct effects such as thermal or x-ray radiation, and so on. To give an example, the accelerating voltage of the "Vulkan" (the setup for electron beam welding) was chosen to be less than 15 V, since this ruled out possible x-ray bremsstrahlung. The appropriate choice of arc-welding regime made it possible to prevent metal spark formation. The problem of localization of potentially dangerous sources in the same setup was solved by putting high-voltage elements and circuits in one and the same block and potting it with epoxy. Metal dust and thermal and light radiation in the "Vulkan" are localized in a special protective cover. A system of electric and mechanical protection is required to observe operation (regime) parameters and not to exceed them. With all of this taken into account, the analysis of various welding techniques proves that relative simplicity of electron-beam welding operation, high efficiency of the process, and the possibility of its application for all metals make this particular technique very promising. It should be taken into account, however, that almost all of the spacecraft maintenance operations, if neither the area where they are to be carried out nor the parameters of the details or assemblies to be involved are known, will be either fully manual or partially mechanized. A setup for arc electron-beam welding has been developed for this purpose. It is based on the commercial-diode electron-beam welding with indirect heat of 1.5 kW and operating beam current of 100 μA. The optics insures stable beam focusing at distances of some dozens or even hundreds of millimeters from an electron gun. A high-voltage power supply is an integrated epoxy unit like the one that operated in the welding setup "Vulkan." The unit, together with a high-voltage cable, was enclosed in a metal screen, the latter connected to the common ground circuit of electron-beam setup. For safety purposes, its accelerating voltage does not exceed 15 V. When the setup was developed and tested, stainless steel, aluminum, and titanium melts 1.5 to 3 mm thick were welded at distances 200 to 220 mm from the beam. The welding rate was kept within 7 to 10 m/H for the beam current 55 to 75 mm. Changes in gun-to-sample distance within ± 20 mm did not change the melting depth and the weld width. Experiments confirmed that the setup can provide a high quality of welding split and butt joints with and without flanging.

The welding "Vulkan" setup was used to carry out experiments and assess whether aluminum melts can be welded by an electron beam in zero-gravity conditions. The setup consumes 1.5 kW, and the welding rate was 28 to 36 $m\text{-}hr^{-1}$. The analysis of the results obtained showed that weightlessness did not influence the process weld seam formation and the depth of melting strongly. The material of weld seams is characterized by substantially greater porosity as compared with samples welded on the Earth. Maximum porosity could be up to 40 times higher, this being the result of lowering the rate of gaseous and liquid phase separation in weightless conditions; pores formed because of the presence of vapors of highly volatile elements. It also was shown that, if there were large gaps in joints and if components rose above the edge, in case of zero gravity, a single bath of liquid metal formed; the latter did not leak into the gaps. Comparative analysis of the percentage of alloying elements in the basic metal and in the metal of weld seams showed that the loss of alloying elements via evaporation is almost gravity-independent.

The number of pores in a weld seam can be reduced by subjecting the process to various vibrational effects. Nonlinear vibration constitutes one of the most promising methods of affecting welding and other technological processes from the outside. They may be of help in outgassing materials and in shaping surfaces of ingots and crystals, particularly so if they are being grown in the conditions of free crucibleless melting, etc.

Processes of consumable-electrode welding were carried out mainly to study melting and transfer of electrode metal in weightlessness. Argon-arc welding processes were studied with electrodes of stainless steel, Ti and Al melts, their diameter being 1 mm. Basic metal had the same composition as that of the electrode. The main outcome of those experiments is the fact that they have shown the change in the relationship of forces acting on a drop of melted electrode in case of weightlessness. If the value of the welding current is small (about 40 to 50 α), then in a weightless environment drops of electrode metal become larger and their flow into the welding bath irregular, which violates the process of weld seam formation. Deviations in welding process due to weightlessness can be ruled out by making an arc gap smaller or by applying current pulses through the gap.

There are reasons to assume that weightlessness can affect the crystallization of metal alloys strongly, and therefore their structure, particularly the structure of alloys of eutectic systems. The studies of such systems allowed a conclusion to be made that weightlessness affected the structure formation through changing the melt dispersion during its crystallization from the liquid melt. Here eutectic melts comprising two components, different in their composition and properties, with infinite mutual solubility in liquid state and only slightly soluble in each other in solid state, are most sensitive to weightlessness effect.

Studies of the possible influence of controlled external disturbances also have started, in particular, that of ultrasonic vibrations on the crystallization of multiphase media. There are two main trends in theoretical and experimental studies: 1) to provide forms of motion in liquids and impurities which insure dynamic stability of mixtures in order to remove the effect of external disturbances on crystallization, and 2) to provide degassing and cleaning techniques for liquids or melts in weightlessness. First results of these studies showed that some effects can be used effectively in space technology, i.e., resonance mixing of liquid media immiscible on the Earth, formation of stable periodic structures, steady unidirectional motion of liquid metal drops and gaseous bubbles and localization and controlled transport of gaseous bubbles.

Thus, a conclusion can be made that space exploration gave a new impetus to technological and materiological studies in metallurgy, welding, and fabrication of new materials. This made designers and specialists turn to the development of new high-efficiency processes and reliable miniature equipment, the first tests of which have been carried out successfully both in the USSR and the U.S. Apparently, new experiments in space technology are expected in the near future which will be of practical value for both the fabrication of new materials and space flights.

Bibliography

Belyakov, I. T. and Borisov, U. D., "Technology and Cosmos," Maminostrenie, Moscow, USSR, 1974, p. 290.

Ganiev, R. F., Laptchinsky, V. F., and Okhotin, A. S., "Possible Application of Controlled Processes in Space Technology," published elsewhere in this volume.

Okhotin, A. S., Livanov, L. K., Tzviling, M. Ya., and Cheshlya, Yu. V., "Influence of the Force Field on Eutectic Structure of Alloys," published elsewhere in this volume.

LOW-GRAVITY SYNTHESIS OF POLYMERS WITH CONTROLLED MOLECULAR CONFIGURATION

A. H. Heimbuch* and J. A. Parker*
NASA, Ames Research Center, Moffett Field, Calif.

and

A. Schindler† and H. G. Olf‡
Research Triangle Institute, Research Triangle Park, N. C.

Abstract

Heterogeneous chemical systems have been studied for the synthesis of isotactic polypropylene to establish baseline parameters for the reaction process and to develop sensitive and accurate methods of analysis. These parameters and analytical methods may be used to make a comparison between the polypropylene obtained at 1-g (gravity) with that of 0-g. Baseline reaction parameters have been established for the slurry (liquid monomer in heptane/solid catalyst) polymerization of propylene to yield high-purity, 98% isotactic polypropylene. Kinetic data for the slurry reaction showed that a sufficient quantity of polymer for complete characterization can be produced in a reaction time of 5 min; this time is compatible with that available on a sounding rocket for a 0-g simulation experiment. The polymer preparations from the slurry reactions had melting points of 162° to 167° C as measured by differential scanning calorimetry. The polymers have been characterized further by ^{13}C NMR and wide-angle x-ray diffraction. The samples obtained were highly crystalline. Initial experiments have been performed to determine possible effects of convection, by controlled stirring, upon the stereoregularity of the polymer.

Presented as Paper 75-697 at the AIAA 10th Thermophysics Conference, Denver, Colo., May 27-29, 1975.

*Research Scientist.
†Senior Polymer Chemist.
‡Senior Physicist.

Introduction

Chemical reaction processes of heterogeneous material systems are being studied as possible applications where a near-0-g environment might be useful. Zero-g could prove beneficial in reaction processes that present difficulties with respect to sedimentation (where vigorous stirring is needed) and thermal-convection-sensitivity. Polymers with specific stereogeometry (molecular configuration) require heterogeneous reaction systems for synthesis. It is expected that such polymers synthesized in a 0-g environment might have improved physical properties resulting from a more uniform catalyst dispersion in the absence of shear forces.

The synthesis of isotactic polypropylene (PP) is being investigated as a model reaction, since its preparation requires a heterogeneous reaction system. Although 0-g will not have observable effects on the reacting molecules, it does have an effect on sedimentation and agglomeration rates of particulate matter, such as the solid catalysts used in polymerization systems. Since PP "grows" from the crystal catalyst surface, local heat buildup could occur in the agglomerate, which could affect the propagation and termination steps as well as the initiation mechanism. Such effects should be reflected in changes of the polymer's physical properties.

The immediate objectives of this study have been 1) to establish the baseline reaction parameters for the preparation of isotactic polypropylene at 1-g, and 2) to develop analytical procedures required to characterize the resulting polymer.

To develop an experimental package for simulated 0-g testing, two modes of synthesis have been studied: 1) a solid catalyst suspended in a liquid reactant phase (slurry reaction), and 2) a solid catalyst suspended ("fluidized") in a gas phase. Analytical procedures that have been developed to characterize the polymer include differential scanning calorimetry, carbon-13 NMR, and x-ray diffraction.

Experimental

Polymer Preparation

The catalyst components, reaction solvent, and monomer were obtained from the following sources:

1) Propylene, polymerization grade, supplied by Phillips Co.

2) n-Heptane, pure grade, supplied by Phillips Co.

3) Titanium trichloride ($TiCl_3$) AA, aluminum reduced activated, supplied by Stauffer Chemical Co.

4) Diethylaluminum chloride (Et_2AlCl), 24.8 wt% (based on aluminum) in n-heptane, supplied by Texas Alkyls.

Slurry Polymerization. Slurry polymerization was performed in a three-neck round-bottom flask with water jacket. The flask was connected with a mercury manometer and the propylene tank. For purification purposes, the propylene was fed through a column of alumina granules coated with metallic sodium.

At the beginning of an experiment, the flask was flushed with helium, and a small amount of a dilute solution of Et_2AlCl in heptane was introduced. The solution was splashed over the inside walls of the flask by rapid stirring and then discarded. Purified heptane then was introduced under helium followed by a dilute solution of Et_2AlCl in heptane. After the helium was displaced by purging with propylene, the contents were brought to polymerization temperature. The propylene pressure then was adjusted to the desired initial value, and a slurry of a weighed amount of $TiCl_3$ in heptane was introduced by means of a syringe. At the end of the polymerization interval, the catalyst was deactivated by introducing isopropanol containing some hydrochloric acid. The white polymer then was filtered, washed with methanol, and dried in vacuo at 40°-50° C.

Kinetics for the Slurry Polymerization. Large slurry volumes were necessary for providing a sufficient amount of polymer for further evaluations. Although detailed kinetic studies were not performed, a few kinetic data were necessary for testing the proper performance of the polymerization equipment and for supplying baseline data for future space shuttle experiments.

All polymerizations were carried out at constant volume; therefore, kinetic data are derived from the decrease in the partial pressure of propylene, p, with reaction time. Since the polymerization takes place at the interface between solid catalyst and solvent, the rate of polymerization, R_p, in moles/min, should be given by the first-order law

$$R_p = kAc \tag{1}$$

where A is the active surface area of the catalyst and c is the concentration in moles/liter of propylene in heptane, the latter value being given by Henry's law

$$c = \alpha p \tag{2}$$

provided equilibrium between gas phase and solution is maintained throughout the polymerization.

On the other hand, the rate of polymerization equals the sum of the rates of disappearance of propylene from both the liquid (') and the gas (") phases

$$R_p = R_p{}' + R_p{}'' \tag{3}$$

By use of the gas laws it can be shown that

$$R_p = kAc = -B(dp/dt) = kA\alpha p \tag{4}$$

where B represents an experimental factor depending on the reaction temperature and on the volumes of both the solvent and the gas phases.

Integration of Eq. (4) yields

$$p = p_o \exp - (kA\alpha/B)t \tag{5}$$

where p_o is the initial propylene partial pressure at $t = 0$, and α is the coefficient in Henry's law relating propylene concentration, c, in heptane with its partial pressure. Consequently a plot of ln p vs time should yield a straight line, the slope of which allows the calculation of kA and thus the comparison of the activities of catalyst systems under different experimental conditions.

Gas Phase Polymerization. In fluidized bed techniques, a fluid (liquid or gas) is passed upward through a bed of fine particles. As fluid velocity increases, the pressure drop across the solid bed increases, until a point is reached at which particles just are suspended, and the frictional force between a particle and the fluid equals the weight of the particle. Beginning about 1956, gas phase polymerization of olefins in fluidized bed reactors with metal-containing catalysts was being patented.[1,2]

Because there was very little detailed information on fluidized bed polymerization of propylene, a brief investigation of the relationship of reactor geometry and experimental variables to polymerization efficiency was undertaken. The reactor design found to be most suitable for our purpose consisted of borosilicate glass tubes sealed to fritted glass disks of appropriate area (1 cm^2 or less) and fastened in a vertical position (see Fig. 1). The required pressure drop in the reactor was obtained by a combination of needle valves.

The polymerization procedure consisted of the following steps. The assembled fluidization system was disconnected at joint 6, Fig. 1, and the diethylaluminum chloride bubbler was

FLUIDIZATION SYSTEM FOR GAS PHASE REACTION

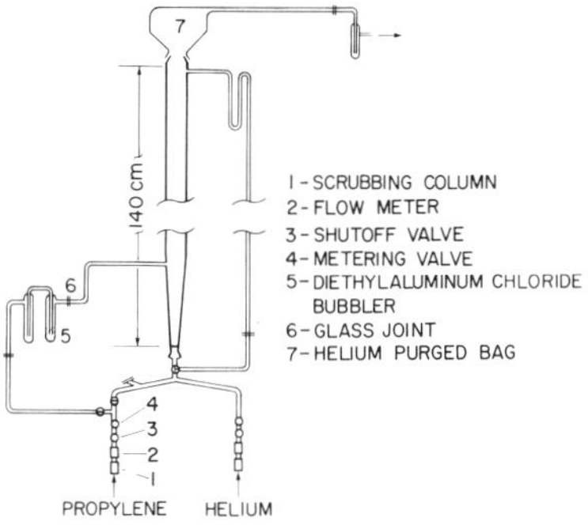

Fig. 1 Fluidization system for gas phase reaction.

connected to a cold finger placed in an ice-water bath. The other opening, leading to the reactor, was closed with a glass plug. A syringe, equipped with a three-way polypropylene valve, was used to transfer the 25%-heptane solution of diethylaluminum chloride to the helium-purged bubbler. A fast helium stream at room temperature was used to strip the heptane. Next, the top of the reactor was fitted with a plastic bag, and the reactor, as well as the bag, were purged with helium. The diethylaluminum chloride bubbler then was reconnected to the reactor. Next, $TiCl_3$(AA) (2.0 g) was weighed out, bottled under helium, and transferred to the bag enveloping the top of the reactor. Following this, the helium purge was discontinued, a propylene flow was initiated, and the $TiCl_3$ was poured into the reactor. The propylene flow then was stopped, fluidization of the $TiCl_3$ was started with helium, and propylene then was readmitted. Experimental conditions for the gas phase polymerizations are given in Table 1.

Polymer Characterization

Differential Scanning Calorimetry. In principle, differential scanning calorimetry (DSC) allows one to record the specific heat of a sample as a function of temperature. The Perkin-Elmer DSC-1 instrument used for these measurements permits a temperature range from -100° C to well above the melting point of the polymer ($T_m \simeq$ 160° to 165° C) to be covered.

The melting point is taken either as the maximum of the melting peak or as the temperature at which the last traces of crystalline material have disappeared; the latter temperature can be defined as the intersection of the straight-line extension of the sharply falling trailing edge of the melting peak, with the linear specific heat curve in the melt.

Table 1 Gas phase polymerization of propylene

Sample	$TiCl_3$(AA), g	Temp., °C	Flow rate, ml/min		Catalyst[a]	Duration, hr	Polymer, g	
			He	Propylene[b]			Powder	Skin
PP-101	2.0	25	158	138	i.s.	8	0.74	0.25
PP-102	2.0	25	158	93	i.s.	9	0.58	0.10
PP-103	<2	25	133	121	pre.	9.5	0.66	...
PP-104	<2	70	133	121	pre.	1	...	...
	...	...	146	146	...	7	1.5	...

[a]i.s. = catalyst formed in situ; pre. = catalyst was preformed.
[b]Propylene partial pressure 300-400 torr.

Wide-Angle X-Ray Diffraction. Measurements by wide-angle x-ray diffraction were made to determine the apparent crystallite sizes of both the slurry and gas phase polymerized polymers. The x-ray method used is essentially that described by Weidinger and Hermans.[3] In this method, isotropic samples were used, and x-ray diffraction patterns between 10° and 30° (2θ) were divided into amorphous and crystalline segments. The areas under the crystalline and amorphous portions of the diffraction pattern were obtained for several samples, preferably of widely different crystallinity, and were adjusted so as to correspond to constant experimental conditions.

NMR Spectroscopy. The spectra were obtained on a pulsed multinuclear spectrometer equipped with an on-line Nicolet computer for data accumulation and fast Fourier transformation.

Spectra were obtained on 10% (0.2 g PP in 2 cm^3 solvent) solutions of PP in 1,2,4-trichlorobenzene at 150° C. This non-symmetrically substituted benzene has the advantages that its ^{13}C resonances appear at low fields, far removed from the PP spectrum, and that each carbon has its separate line; this is beneficial, since the solvent lines remain small and do not lead to early saturation of the computer memory during accumulation of the free induction decays.

Discussion

Polymer Preparations

Slurry Polymerization. Experimental conditions and results of slurry polymerizations performed in n-heptane are summarized in Table 2. Most of the polymerizations were carried out with 400 ml heptane in order to obtain sufficient amounts of polymer for characterizations, but still providing proper equilibration between gas and liquid for meaningful interpretations of propylene partial pressure changes.

The changes of propylene partial pressure with polymerization time are shown graphically in Fig. 2 for an in situ-catalyst reaction (PP-24) and a preformed-catalyst reaction (PP-26). One clearly can see the induction time in the first 5 min of the curve for the in situ catalyst (PP-24). In Figs. 3 and 4, logarithmic plots of propylene partial pressure vs polymerization time are presented. With two exceptions, straight lines were obtained for all slurry reactions, confirming first-order kinetics for the polymerization rate with respect to propylene partial pressure. As outlined in the pre-

Table 2 Experimental conditions for slurry polymerization of propylene in n-heptane

Sample	Heptane, ml	Temp., °C	$TiCl_3$(AA), mmoles	Et_2AlCl, mmoles	Cat. prep.[a]	P_o, torr	Duration, min	Polymer,[b] g	$kA \times 10^3$
PP-10	800	65	1.0	2.0	i.s.	886	5	0.10	...
PP-11	200	60	1.0	2.0	i.s.	913	187	4.09	...
PP-12	200	70	1.0	2.0	pre.	807	291	4.24	...
PP-14	200	60	1.0	2.0	i.s.	895	35	10.84	...
						868	30	...	...
						868	33	...	...
						875	197	...	...
PP-15	1000	61	1.0	2.0	i.s.	780	19	0.50	...
PP-16	900	62	1.0	2.0	pre.	859	8	0.60	...
PP-17	200	62	1.0	4.0	i.s.	878	121	3.40	...
PP-18	900	62	1.0	4.0	pre.	837	6	0.61	...
PP-19	900	62	1.0	2.0	pre.	841	9	0.53	...
PP-20	900	61	1.0	1.0	pre.	861	11	0.26	...
PP-21	900	50	1.0	2.0	pre.	...	14	0.58	...
PP-22	400	60	1.0	2.0	pre.	848	148	5.56	4.71
PP-23	400	62	1.0	4.0	pre.	871	165	5.21	6.98
PP-24	400	62	1.0	2.0	i.s.	864	274	5.76	5.01
PP-25	400	62	1.0	2.0	pre.	873	133	9.06	5.58
						813	110	...	4.77
PP-26	400	62	1.0	2.0	pre.	813	129	11.12	6.89
						806	79	...	6.55
PP-27	400	62	1.0	2.0	i.s.	859	182	8.76	4.50
						796	132	...	3.96

[a]Catalyst preparation: i.s. = in situ, pre. = preformed.
[b]Values refer to total amount of polymer formed.

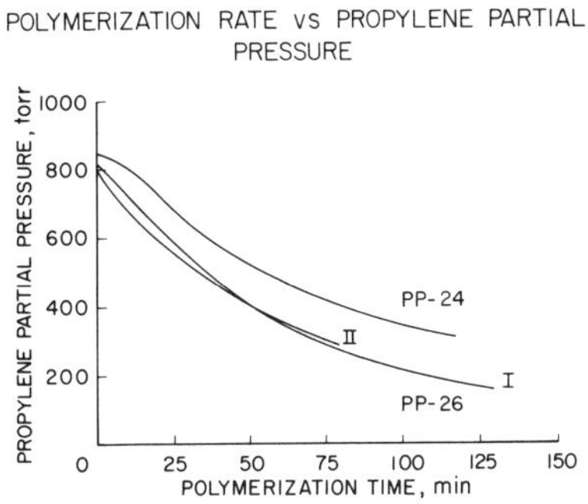

Fig. 2 Time dependence of polymerization rate on propylene partial pressure.

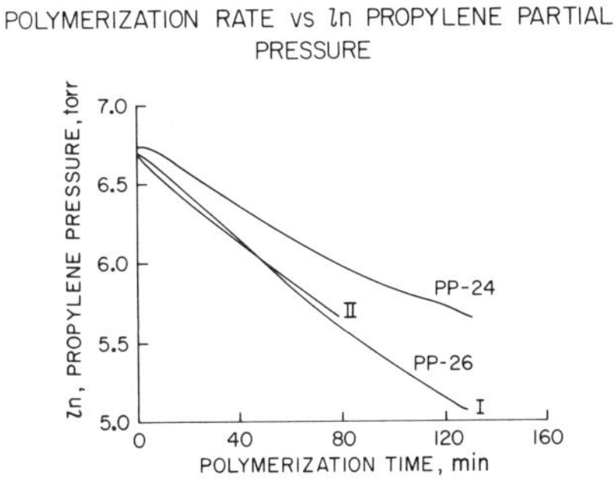

Fig. 3 Time dependence of polymerization rate on ln propylene partial pressure according to Eq. (5).

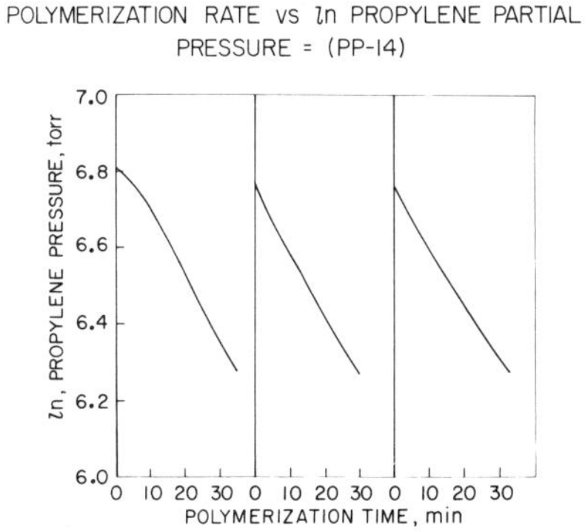

Fig. 4 Time dependence of polymerization rate on ln propylene partial pressure according to Eq. (5). [Reaction system (PP-14) repressured twice.]

ceding section, under this condition the time dependence of the propylene partial pressure is given by Eq. (5). From the slopes of the ln p vs t plots, values of kA were calculated and are included in Table 2. Considering that these numbers are quite small, the activities (kA) for both the in situ and preformed catalysts are reasonably close and consistent.

Gas Phase Polymerization. The first gas phase polymerizations were performed with the catalyst formed in situ, whereby

$TiCl_3$ was activated inside the fluidization column by entrainment of Et_2AlCl vapor with the propylene feed. The main disadvantage of the method is that the activation conditions are undefined. Therefore, an experimental method was developed and tested for the preparation of small quantities of preformed catalyst for gas phase polymerization. It was found that preformed catalyst could be handled easily, without apparent loss in activity.

Table 1 shows the experimental conditions for the gas phase reactions. It may be noted that it took several hours to get sufficient polymer for analysis. By raising the reaction temperature from 25° to 70° C, the polymer yield doubled for the same reaction time. It is expected that if one were to double or triple the propylene partial pressure, the polymer yield would increase proportionately. The polymerization rate observed with the preformed catalyst was 1.92×10^{-4} g hr^{-1} $torr^{-1}$.

Polymer Characterization

Isotacticity Index. There are a number of factors that have been determined to affect the tacticity or stereogeometry of polypropylene (during its synthesis), as indicated by the isotacticity index measurement. This index is given as the weight percent of the polymer residue that remains after extraction with boiling heptane, and it indicates only the apparent atactic portion, since some low molecular weight *isotactic* polymer is soluble in this solvent. The following factors have been observed to decrease the isotacticity index (or increase the apparent atactic fraction):

1) Unstirred (nonagitated) reactions.
2) A decrease in the monomer partial pressure.
3) An increase in the polymerization temperature.
4) An increase in the ratio of grams of polymer produced per gram of catalyst ($TiCl_3$).

Preliminary experiments have been performed to determine the effect(s) of convection (stirring) upon the stereogeometry of polypropylene (PP) during the heterogeneous synthesis of this polymer. Because the analyses of the polymers resulting from unstirred and very slightly stirred reactions have not been completed, one cannot make definite statements about convection effects upon tacticity. The unstirred reactions give a significantly greater percent of heptane soluble polymer than the highly agitated reaction. However, this "atactic" fraction may be more apparent than real, since the heptane solubles may also contain low molecular weight *isotactic* PP. Indeed, on one sample of the heptane soluble fraction, from an unstirred reaction, a wide angle x-ray measurement showed a large amount of crystalline material, thus indicating low molecular weight isotactic PP. A C-13 NMR spectrum of this fraction has not yet been taken. The isotacticity of the baseline polymer has been 96-99% so that the amount of geometric impurities is too low to readily determine in the presence of the large quantity of isotactic polymer. The heptane-soluble fraction was not large enough for NMR analysis; however, larger runs will be made so that this can be done.

The unstirred reaction does not really simulate the space environment, because the solid catalyst settles to the bottom of the reaction flask, and the propylene monomer in the gas phase is not in equilibrium with the solution phase. This results in a catalyst-solvent interface which is "starved" for monomer. In the case of polyethylene, it was shown by Schindler[4] that there was a decrease in molecular weight with a decrease in partial pressure of the monomer; the same can be anticipated for polypropylene.

The work on the gas phase polymerization of propylene likewise has shown that 0-g is not too well simulated by the "fluidized bed" reactor. A uniform suspension of the catalyst particles was not obtained; a significant fraction of the catalyst adhered to the surface of the glass reaction vessel. However, a gas phase polymerization of propylene is being studied in which there is no agitation of the catalyst or the gas phase (in the absence of any solvent). The catalyst crystals will be spread out uniformly on the lower one third of the glass reaction vessel. The rate of polymerization, isotacticity index, and morphology of the resulting polymer will be compared with those of polymers prepared by the slurry technique.

The fact that an increase in the reaction temperature causes a decrease in the isotacticity index is not surprising, since reactions competing with the propagation step would be expected to have different energies of activation. However, the temperature factor will have to be borne in mind in the designing of a space experiment. Likewise, the increase in the ratio of polymer produced per amount of catalyst used would also be a consideration in the design of an experiment.

An unexpected observation was made while studying the effects of convection upon tacticity. Upon measuring the viscosity molecular weights of the polymers, after heptane extraction, it was found that nonstirred reactions yielded polymers with 30% higher molecular weights than those of polymers resulting from stirred reactions. This would allow for the possibility that shear forces, due to stirring, might have an effect upon the molecular weight of the polymer when the growing chain reaches a certain degree of polymerization, e.g., 4500, or a molecular weight of 190,000. More experiments are needed for statistical verification.

Melting Point as Determined by DSC. The melting points of both slurry and gas phase polymerized PP samples are reported in Table 3. Melting points, defined by the peak maxima of the DSC scans, were found to be 164° C for most of the polymers with a range from 162° to 167° C. With respect to melting points, there were no apparent differences between polymers synthesized by in situ and preformed catalysts; nor did the reaction times show any effect on the melting point.

After complete melting of the as-polymerized sample, the melt was allowed to crystallize in the DSC dish, and a second melting cycle was scanned. Generally, the melting points of the melt-crystallized samples were about 2°-3° C lower than those found for their as-polymerized state (see Fig. 5). Tentative estimates of the heats of fusion indicated about 30%-higher values for the melt-crystallized samples as compared with the as-polymerized ones.

X-ray Diffraction. Wide-angle x-ray diffraction studies, performed to determine the degrees of crystallinity, showed

Table 3 Melting points (temperature at the maximum of the specific heat vs temperature curve) of polypropylene samples

Sample	Reaction system[a]	Catalyst[b]	Reaction time, min	Melting point, °C
PP-11	S	i.s.	187	164
PP-12	S	pre.	291	165
PP-14	S	i.s.	197	164
PP-15	S	i.s.	19	162
PP-16	S	pre.	8	164
PP-17	S	i.s.	121	164
PP-18	S	pre.	6	164
PP-19	S	pre.	9	164
PP-20	S	pre.	11	164
PP-21	S	pre.	14	164
PP-22	S	pre.	148	164
PP-23	S	pre.	165	167
PP-24	S	i.s.	274	164
PP-26	S	pre.	129	163
PP-27	S	i.s.	182	163
PP-101, powder	G	i.s.	480	163
PP-101, skin	G	i.s.	480	167
PP-104, powder	G	pre.	480	162

[a]S = slurry, G = gas.
[b]i.s. = in situ, pre. = preformed.

excellent reproducibility. The polypropylene samples obtained by slurry polymerization were highly crystalline (53 to 61%). Figure 6 shows an example of a highly crystalline polymer (PP-16) obtained by the slurry reaction. Line widths indicated rather small crystallite sizes on as-polymerized samples.

Apparent crystallite sizes perpendicular to the polypropylene helix axis were obtained for most of the polymers. Table 4 lists all values obtained of apparent crystallite sizes D_{040} app and D_{110} app, as determined by the reflections from the 040 and 110 crystal planes. The slurry polymerized samples are listed according to increasing values of D_{110} app. It is apparent that D_{110} app decreases as the yield of slurry-polymerized polymer increases. This is consistent with the model in which the as-polymerized polymer grows from the catalyst site and is subjected to ever-increasing stress, as it is forced to lie on the surface of an ever-expanding sphere. This stress results in strain on the crystallites and their fracture as the polymerization continues. The values of D_{040} app are not correlated so closely to polymer yield, but the extremes

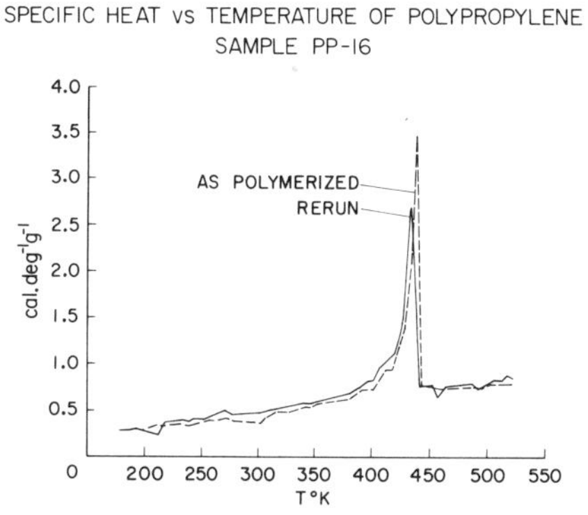

Fig. 5 Specific heat vs temperature curves of polypropylene sample PP-16.

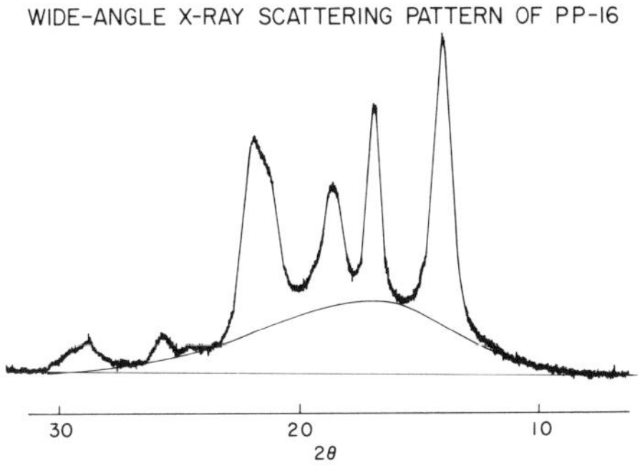

Fig. 6 Intensity profile obtained from wide-angle x-ray scattering pattern of PP-16, showing division into crystalline and amorphous scattering.

Table 4 Apparent crystallite sizes and polymerization conditions for slurry and gas phase polymerized polypropylene samples

Sample	Heptane, ml	Temp., °C	Molar ratio $\frac{Et_2AlCl}{TiCl_3(AA)}$	Catalyst preparation	Polymer yield, g	D_{040}app, Å	D_{110}app, Å
PP-26	400	62	2	pre.	11.12	135	99
PP-22	400	60	2	pre.	5.56	155	100
PP-22[a]	...	...	...	...	...	140	114
PP-24	400	62	2	i.s.	5.76	142	104
PP-23	400	62	4	pre.	5.21	150	110
PP-17	200	62	4	i.s.	3.40	139	111
PP-19	900	62	2	pre.	0.53	142	116
PP-16	900	62	2	pre.	0.60	160	120
PP-101	...	...	...	i.s.	0.74	115	115
PP-101F[b]	...	...	...	i.s.	0.25	151	153
PP-102	...	...	...	i.s.	0.58	115	110
PP-103	...	...	...	pre.	0.66	105	105
PP-104	...	...	...	pre.	1.5	115	100

[a]Extracted with hot heptane.
[b]Polymer skin.

are associated with extremes in polymer yield. Comparison of the breadths of the (110) and (220) reflections revealed that there was a large contribution to broadening from microstrain or paracrystalline disordering of the crystal lattice for all samples.

Determination of Stereoregularity in Polypropylene by Carbon-13 NMR. Since polypropylene (PP) can be synthesized highly isotactic (98%) at 1-g, one needs a sensitive and accurate analytical method to determine low levels of stereoisomeric impurities and structural defects of the order of 1% or less, so that subtle differences in polymers prepared at 1-g vs 0-g can be detected. For this reason, the stereoregularity of the PP samples was determined by ^{13}C rather than proton NMR. The resolution of lines in the spectra of polymers, and particularly in PP, is superior in ^{13}C to that in proton NMR, because the chemical shifts are so much greater in ^{13}C NMR.

In a recent paper by J. C. Randall[5] the distribution of monomer configurations in polypropylene was presented as determined by ^{13}C NMR. All of the ten possible methyl resonances resulting from monomer pentads were observed and assigned. (A methyl pentad is any segment of the polymer molecule containing five consecutive methyl groups.) The intensity distribution of the observed methyl resonances agreed with second-order Markov statistics. Since it was shown experimentally that an equal nuclear Overhauser effect exists for each of the methyl resonances, the structure of differently prepared polypropylene samples can be elucidated with confidence. For any two monomer units joined together (a dyad) in which the stereogeometry of the two monomer units is the same, the dyad is referred to as the meso (m) form; when the two monomer units are of opposite geometry, the dyad is said to be of the racemic (r) form. In pure isotactic PP, all the dyads are of the m form; in atactic PP, the dyads occur randomly in both the m and r forms.

Johnson, Heatley, and Bovey[6] were the first to report ^{13}C NMR spectra of PP. Their spectra of isotactic and atactic PP show three major peaks or groups that have been assigned to the methylene carbon (at low field), the methyl carbon (at high field), and the methine carbon (at intermediate field). These assignments are unequivocal. Figure 7 shows a ^{13}C NMR spectrum of PP-16 that agrees very well with that of the isotactic polymer reported. Whereas these lines are structureless singlets in isotactic PP, they show splitting in atactic PP, due to the presence of different stereochemical sequences. The CH_3-carbon shows the most pronounced splitting; under the relatively low resolution a multiplet, seemingly consisting of three peaks, was visible. As was shown by Randall,[5] up to ten methyl-carbon

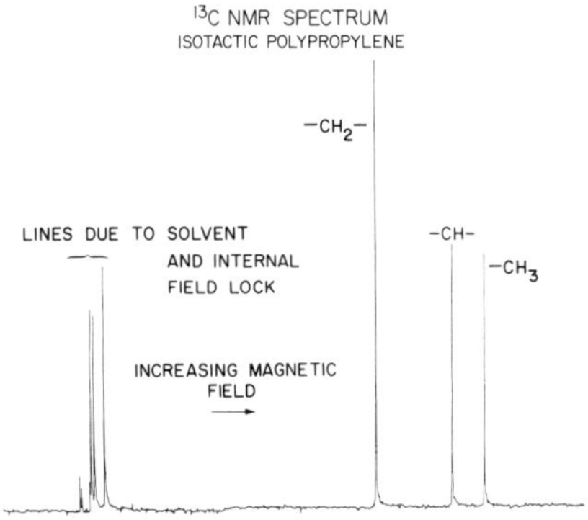

Fig. 7 ^{13}C NMR spectrum of PP-16.

resonances can be observed under conditions of higher resolution.

The importance of obtaining spectra of better signal-to-noise ratio than in spectra published to date became apparent when it became necessary to demonstrate slight differences in steric purity between variously polymerized, highly isotactic PP samples. The main obstacle to obtaining better signal-to-noise ratios has been limited by computer memory. This limitation was overcome by means of a technique called "block averaging."

This method has helped to overcome the experimental difficulties involved in detecting the extremely weak methyl resonances that arise from pentads having syndiotactic impurities; these weak lines must be detected in the presence of several very strong lines, of which an example is shown in Fig. 7. The CH_3-carbon line at the far right of the spectrum is due to the all-isotactic pentad (also called mmmm in the nomenclature introduced by Frisch et al.[7]). The pentads involving steric impurities give rise to lines to the right of the all-isotactic CH_3-carbon peak. Under the conditions chosen for recording this spectrum, these impurity pentads do not begin even to be observable.

A ^{13}C spectrum of sample PP-16 (8-min slurry reaction) is shown in Fig. 8, which was obtained by block averaging the sum of 25 spectra that contained a total of 12,800 free induction decays. The isotactic peaks have gone off-scale and doubled back. An estimate of the impurity was made based on the assumption of Zambelli et al.[8] that the steric impurity in the highly isotactic PP consists of single, isolated r dyads with random distribution. The signal-to-noise ratio is roughly 120, and since no pentad lines due to steric impurities are distinguishable on the high-field side (on the right) of the CH_3-line, one may conclude that if these lines are present at all, their

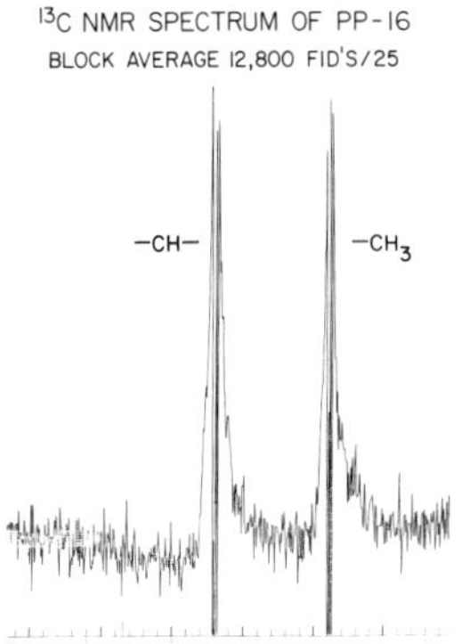

Fig. 8 ^{13}C NMR block average of 25 spectra (containing 12,800 free induction decays) of PP-16.

signal-to-noise ratio must be smaller than 1, and that less than 1% steric impurities are present in the sample.

One sample polymerized in the gas phase, PP-104, has been studied extensively by ^{13}C NMR. Block averaging of 114 spectra, with a total of about 60,000 free induction decays, has resulted in a spectrum in which all possible ten pentad lines are visible. This is rather unusual for a highly isotactic PP, which usually shows only two or three of the pentad lines because of the isolated occurrence of r dyad impurity. The spectrum of this PP not only indicates a predominance of isotactic pentads, but it also shows that most of the r dyads do not occur randomly. One may reconcile the apparent contradiction by concluding that PP-104 consists predominantly of isotactic PP, with a small admixture of atactic PP. An estimate of [r] from the pentad concentrations, according to a relationship first derived by Frisch et al.,[7] is that sample PP-104 contains 14% racemic dyads.

Summary and Conclusions

The parameters for the preparation of isotactic polypropylene by the slurry reaction have been established so that a sufficient quantity of polymer can be produced for analysis in about a 5-min reaction time. Thus, an experimental package can be developed for the sounding rocket. The induction period for the reaction, as occurs in normal preparations, has been eliminated by the use of preformed (activated) catalysts.

Analytical techniques have been developed to characterize the polymers with respect to stereoregularity (tacticity) by ^{13}C NMR, crystallinity by x-ray diffraction, and melting point by differential scanning calorimetry. Crystallinity and melting point were determined on the as-polymerized polymer, rather than on polymer crystallized from solvent, in order to assess better the morphology of the variously synthesized polymers.

No methyl pentad resonances due to steric impurity have been detected in the slurry-polymerized samples. It is estimated that these samples contain less than 1%-syndiotactic dyad impurities. In the gas phase-polymerized sample, however, impurity pentads definitely have been observed. The concentration of syndiotactic dyads has been derived from the pentad concentrations and is estimated to be 14%.

The gas phase reaction parameters have not been developed sufficiently for 0-g simulation experiments; higher temperature and pressures are indicated. It appears that a "space-lab" environment would be the preferred way in which to carry out a gas fluidized bed reaction, since the suspension of a solid is not dependent upon gas flow (velocity).

References

[1]Phillips Petroleum Co., Belgium Patent 551,826, Oct. 16, 1956.

[2]Wisseroth, K., Herbeck, R., School, R., and Trischmann, H. G., German Patent. 1,905,835, March 9, 1970, to Badische Anilin and Soda Fabrik A. G.

[3]Weidinger, A. and Hermans, P. H., "On the Determination of the Crystalline Fraction of Isotactic Polypropylene from X-Ray Diffraction," Makromolekulare Chemie, Vol. 50, 1961, pp. 98-115.

[4]Schindler, A., "Kinetic Studies in Ethylene Polymerization with Ziegler Type Catalysts: II The Catalyst System Diethylaluminum Chloride - Titanium Tetrachloride in the Presence of Nitrogen and Hydrogen," Makromolekulare Chemie, Vol. 70, 1964, pp. 94-111.

[5]Randall, J. C., "Distribution of Monomer Configurations in Polypropylene as Determined with ^{13}C NMR," Journal of Polymer Science, Polymer Physics Edition, Vol. 12, April 1974, pp. 703-712.

[6]Johnson, L. F., Heatly, F., and Bovey, F. A., "Polymer Nuclear Magnetic Resonance Spectroscopy. XIX. Carbon-13 resonance observations of stereochemical configuration," Macromolecules, Vol. 3, March-April 1970, pp. 175-177.

[7]Frisch, H. L., Mallows, C. L., and Bovey, F. A., "On the Stereoregularity of Vinyl Polymer Chains," Journal of Chemical Physics, Vol. 45, September 1966, pp. 1565-1577.

[8]Zambelli, A., Dorman, D. E., Brewster, A. I. R., and Bovey, F. A., "Carbon-13 Observations of the Stereochemical Configuration of Polypropylene," Macromolecules, Vol. 6, Nov.-Dec. 1973, pp. 925-926.

Chapter IV–Flight Results and Studies

RESULTS FROM METALLURGICAL FLIGHT EXPERIMENTS

Eugene McKannan*

NASA Marshall Space Flight Center, Huntsville, Ala.

Abstract

Research in metallurgical processing to study the effects of reduced gravity started with Apollo 14 and was continued with Skylab, Apollo-Soyuz and the Space Processing Applications Rockets. Flight experiments provided specimens for analysis and comparison with ground-based experiments which were solidified while constrained and while free. Some contained normally immiscible materials, some showed the ordered growth of dendrites and of the second phases in eutectics, some showed that diffusion controls mass transfer in the absence of convection. It is obvious that sedimentation and bouyancy effects along with thermal convection are absent for practical purposes in the low gravity environment. There may be more subtle metallurgical effects such as the tendency to shift from dendritic growth to cellular growth due to enhanced constitutional supercooling in the quiescent conditions available only in space. Based on these preliminary explorations, the future is bright for both the broader understanding of materials science and for the production of special, highly-valued materials in space.

Introduction

Over 48 materials science experiments have been made in the low-gravity ($\sim 10^{-5}$ g) environment of space flight including 18 in metallurgy. The question is this: "Has each experiment been unique, or has there been a general relationship among them involving common scientific principles?" What use-

---

Presented at the COSPAR Symposium on Materials Sciences in Space, Philadelphia, June 9, 1976; based on AIAA paper 74-1239, presented at AIAA/AGU Conference, Huntsville, AL October 1974.

*Manager, Space Processing Applications Task Team.

ful results and conclusions can be drawn? What have we learned about the solidification of metals, alloys, single crystals, and model materials in the low-gravity environment? It is the purpose of this paper to examine the answers to these questions.

Basic fluid flow, convection, and solidification demonstrations were made on Apollo flights. There was a series of more sophisticated experiments on Skylab in 1973 involving liquid diffusion of zinc, directional solidification of the copper-aluminum eutectic alloy, microsegregation, homogeneity of normally immiscible compounds, electron-beam melting of aluminum, exothermic brazing of nickel capillary passages, and free surface solidification, in addition to several methods of single-crystal growth. The highly successful crystal growth experiments have been reported in detail elsewhere, so they will not be discussed herein. The Apollo-Soyuz Test Project (ASTP) in 1975 carried experiments on surface tension induced convection in lead; miscibility of the syntectic semiconductor, aluminum antimonide; homogeneous solidification of manganese bismuth, a high-strength permanent magnet materials; and, again, the growth of single crystals.

During the hiatus between Apollo and Shuttle flights, there have been Black Brant sounding rocket flights providing about 5 min of low gravity during coasting. Some of the early rocket experiments involved lead antimonide eutectic; forced migration of bubbles and particles by solidification in carbon tetrabromide; casting of dispersion-strengthened alloy, thoria in magnesium; and dendrite remelting of the model ammonium chloride solution. The theory of all of these experiments was reported by Miller,[1] Yue,[2] and others.[3] However, the basic premise is that in low gravity the density-driven thermal and mass convection and sedimentation are reduced greatly compared to 1g. Also, the lack of convection allows liquid diffusion to be the prime mechanism of growth. Density-driven sedimentation of heavy particles and bouyancy of lighter particles is reduced, allowing many compounds to form from phases with widely separated densities. In this paper, we shall discuss some of the experiments that have not been reported elsewhere.

Casting and Remelting of Dendrite Models

Johnston's[4] experiment 74-21 on Space Processing Applications Rocket (SPAR) flight 1 in December 1975 employed the freezing of a clear aqueous solution of ammonium chloride to simulate quenching of a metal casting. Previous ground studies

Fig. 1 Dendrites which solidified on the sides of the crucible are detached and transported to the core by convection currents on Earth.

along this line were done by Fleming[5] at Massachusetts Institute of Technology. With back lighting, it is possible to take pictures through the transparent crucible to observe the formation of dendrites, grains, and/or crystals as they freeze. The pictures taken on the ground (Fig. 1) show the stirring due to convection currents and, consequently, the random packing of dendrites. The pictures taken in space (Fig. 2), by comparison, show the quiescent conditions and the aligned, predictable freezing front, even at this rapid solidification rate. These pictures provide dramatic evidence of the quiescent conditions in space compared to ground solidification. Secondary measurements also indicated that in space there was regular arm spacing of dendrites (all of which were attached to the solidification front) and no remelt of crystals. On the ground, there was a large variation in dendrite arm spacing, remelting, "necking" of dendrites and microsegregation. The conclusion is that precisely controlled solidification of castings and crystal growth can be accomplished in space much more readily than on the ground.

Fig. 2 Dendrites solidify on the sides of the crucible remain attached due to the quiescent conditions in low gravity.

Electron Beam Melting

The metals melting experiment of Poorman,[6] Skylab M551, used an electron beam to produce a melt in a rotating disk for the study of solidification and cast microstructures in space. Disks of varying thicknesses were rotated in the electron beam. Each disk of 2219-T87 aluminum was placed in the vacuum chamber, which was vented overboard to space. The electron beam was initiated with a sharp focus on a target area. The disk then was rotated so that the beam traversed around a circle through different thicknesses of material, providing a range of penetrations from partial to complete cut through. Finally, a large molten pool was formed when the rotation was stopped, as the beam was defocused and allowed to dwell on the one spot (see Fig. 3).

Previously it was reported that the ground specimens contained large elongated grains and a wide chill zone and that the Skylab specimen contained more equiaxed fine grains and a more symmetrical pattern of grain structure. The finer grain

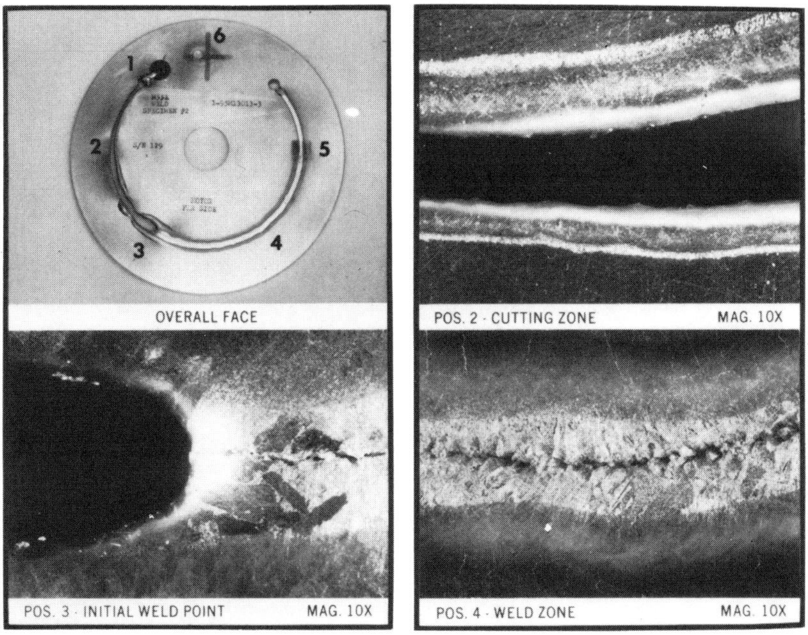

Fig. 3 Aluminum 2219-T87 Electron-beam melted flight specimen.

structure observed in the space specimen was attributed to constitutional supercooling, which results when a solid freezes with a composition slightly different from that of the liquid from which it forms (see Fig. 4). Additional studies of other cross sections of the molten zone indicate that the differences in microstructure are not nearly so pronounced in the partial penetration zones as they were in full penetration. Also, it has been recognized that there was an increase in heat input in the Skylab specimens as compared to the ground specimens. Therefore, interpretation of the microstructure presents a complex, challenging problem.

Li[7] interpreted the difference between Skylab and ground specimens on the basis of the reduced diffusion coefficient in space. The initial solidification layer or chill zone at the melt interface was similar in both specimens. They had similar texture and grain sizes dominated by the nucleation process. In the ground specimen, however, convection currents produced a large effective liquid diffusion coefficient so that the solute segregation extended over long distances in the melt, providing liquid for growth of dendrites. Constitutional

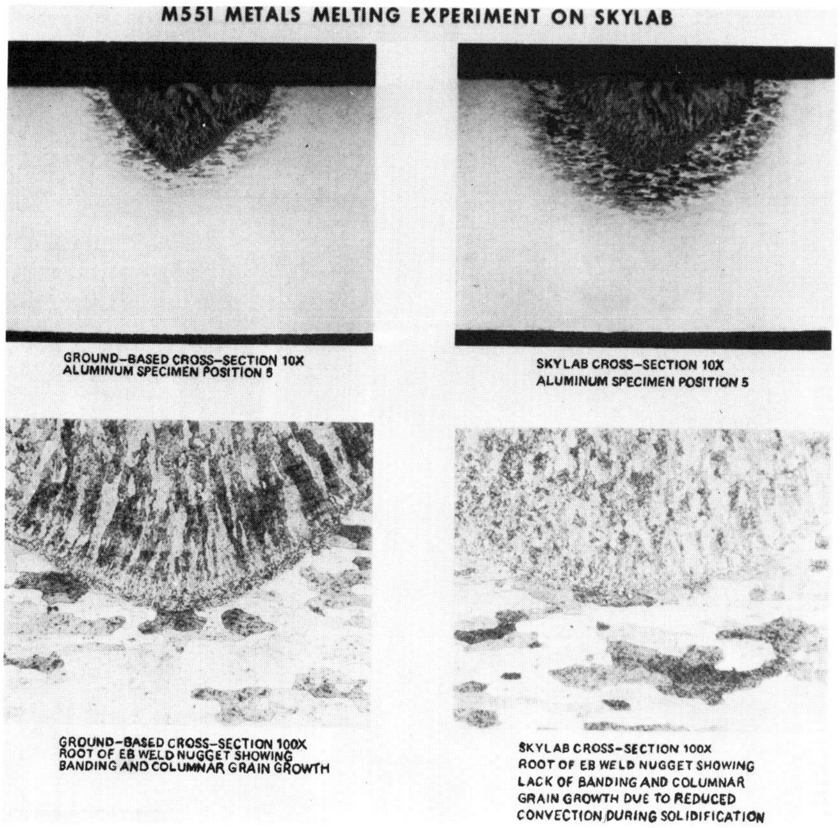

Fig. 4 Comparison of microstructure in Aluminum 2219-T87 ground-based and flight specimens.

supercooling, related to the reciprocal of diffusion coefficient, was unimportant in the ground specimen, and the nucleated grains grew uninterrupted as well-oriented dendrites deep into the melt. In the space samples, the grain growth encountered significant constitutional supercooling, which prevented continued epitaxial growth. It also allowed repeated within-melt nucleation at locations away from the existing solid-liquid interface, resulting in multiple interfaces and a finer texture. Some of this within-melt nucleation occurred under considerable undercooling, resulting in a radiating growth pattern causing the symmetrical rosettes observed in Skylab specimens.

Therefore, Li has explained the solidification observed in the Skylab specimens based on the predominance of constitutional supercooling as opposed to dendritic growth. The apparent reduction in mass transfer observed in this and other experiments provides for a greater solute concentration gradient, so that growing grains are retarded, and new grains are nucleated within the melt at locations ahead of the main solid-liquid interface. In the ground specimens, the dendrites can grow in a more normal, uninterrupted pattern deeper into the melt because the circulation replenishes the solute at the dendrite tip.

The foregoing experiments, SPAR 74-21 and Skylab M551, represent rapid cooling and high solidification rates. At the slow end of the spectrum of solidification rates are the diffusion and microsegregation experiments, Skylab M559 and ASTP MA041.

Microsegregation

An experiment to measure the influence of low-gravity solidification on the microsegregation of gallium-doped germanium crystals was made by Yue and Voltmer.[8] Solute microsegregation, which limits the use of semiconductors, is defined as microinhomogeneities of solutes which occur during solidification and which lead to resistivity variations in semiconductors, with adverse effects on device performance. The germanium crystal was doped with gallium to a concentration of 8×10^{16} atoms/cm^3. Portions of the crystals were remelted and resolidified at 5 μm/sec under controlled conditions on Earth and in space using the gradient freeze technique. This process was chosen for its simplicity; that is, no movement of the melt was required during growth, and a constant rate of solidification was maintained. The solute segregation was measured by the spreading resistance technique. Space-grown crystals were compared with identical crystals resolidified on Earth. Microsegregation in space was measured to be one-half to one-fifth that on Earth in the bulk material, which implies a reduced diffusion or mass transport of the solute in the host material during solidification. The conclusion is that liquid diffusion theory alone in the absence of convective mixing can explain the improved homogeneity and reduced solute segregation of the melt. This is consistent with the observations of Gatos and Witt on crystal growth in ASTP MA060.[9]

Liquid Diffusion

The MA041 liquid diffusion experiment on ASTP by Reed[10] employed a cylinder of lead and a thin disk on the end of the

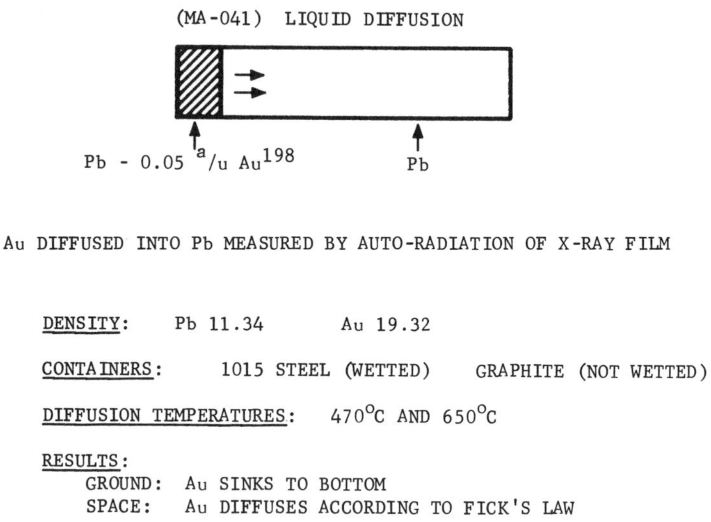

(MA-041) LIQUID DIFFUSION
Pb - 0.05 a/u Au198
Pb
Au DIFFUSED INTO Pb MEASURED BY AUTO-RADIATION OF X-RAY FILM
DENSITY: Pb 11.34 Au 19.32
CONTAINERS: 1015 STEEL (WETTED) GRAPHITE (NOT WETTED)
DIFFUSION TEMPERATURES: 470°C AND 650°C
RESULTS:
GROUND: Au SINKS TO BOTTOM
SPACE: Au DIFFUSES ACCORDING TO FICK'S LAW

Fig. 5 Diagram of Lead cylinder with a disk of Lead-0.05 atomic % Gold. The Gold diffused into the pure Lead in space but sank to the bottom on Earth.

cylinder of lead with 0.05 at. % gold to obtain a liquid-diffusion couple (see Fig. 5). When melted on Earth, the gold sinks rapidly to the bottom of the cylinder. In space, the gold mass transfer can be calculated precisely based on Fick's law of diffusion. The experiment measured any possible subtle effects due to surface tension convection, because one cylinder was contained in a steel crucible that would wet the lead surface, and another cylinder contained in a graphite nonwetting crucible. The condition of wetting and nonwetting made no difference in the diffusion of gold into the lead in space. The gold was measured by autoradiographs. The specimens were irradiated in a reactor for 4 hr at 2 MW to obtain the isotope gold 198, which is a beta emitter. This is a good way to obtain ultrafine-grain x-ray film images. The cooling rates of the lead-gold cylinders were about 4°C/min, and the solidification rate was about 2 cm/min. The flight samples showed a sharp diffusion interface of the gold into the lead and a diffusion distance of about 1.2 cm. The ground-based specimens showed gold activity only at the bottom of the cylinder. The conclusion from this experiment is that there was no extensive stirring in the space flight experiment either from density-driven convection or surface-tension convection. Instead, all of the mass transfer of gold into the lead can be explained by a typical liquid-diffusion profile. This experiment proves independently that convection is reduced in the quiescent condition of space flight for all practical purposes.

Eutectics

There is great interest in eutectic compounds and alloys in space, particularly directionally solidified eutectics with rodlike phases. Theory indicates that the rodlike phase can be cast continuously in space instead of discontinuously as generally obtained on Earth because of the large amount of convective stirring causing many terminations and faults. First let us discuss eutectics. A binary eutectic is an alloy or compound in which a single liquid phase freezes to form two solid phases simultaneously, and this occurs at only one compositional ratio of the two phases. Therefore, a eutectic reaction in a binary system takes place at a constant temperature that is the minimum freezing temperature of either of the two phases (see Fig. 6). Eutectic structures commonly will have one phase that is continuous called the matrix and another phase that has harder particles dispersed throughout the matrix. The particles may be shaped like spheroids, dendrites, "Chinese script," lamellae, or rods with high aspect ratio, depending on the thermodynamic requirements for minimum surface energy as the two phases are formed. We are concerned most with the rodlike second phase because it acts like a fiber-composite-strengthened structure. When the eutectic is cast on Earth, the rods are short because of the many terminations caused by convective stirring. When the eutectic is cast in low-gravity conditions, the rods can grow to be continuous throughout the structure, which is analogous to a continuous fiber-reinforced composite. The long fibers

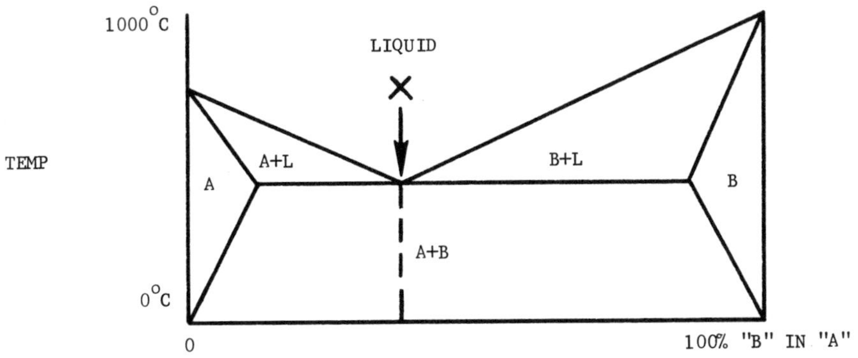

Fig. 6 Eutectic phase diagram. A single liquid freezes to form two solid phases.

may provide reinforcement and mechanical strength as in structural alloys, or may produce optical fibers to form light guides for laser communications, or may form continuous superconducting paths in normally conducting matrices.

Among the several directionally solidified eutectic flight experiments, two were flown on Skylab 4. The first was a copper-aluminum structure of Hasemeyer[11] which reached a peak temperature of 790°C in the specimen for 1 hr and then solidified at a rate of 2.4°C/min in an average thermal gradient of 45°C/cm. The eutectic compound is 67% aluminum and 33% copper and is used as a model system because of extensive background information on this particular alloy. Because of the lamellar microstructure, continuous platelets were not achieved. However, the number of terminations and defects was reduced more than 20% in the flight specimens (see Fig. 7). This was the first indication that the expectations for reduced terminations in the quiescent conditions of space actually could be achieved.

The second eutectic experiment on Skylab, M564 by Yue,[12] was performed not on a metallic alloy but on a salt mixture, sodium chloride/sodium flouride for optical applications. The sodium flouride forms fibers in the matrix of sodium chloride

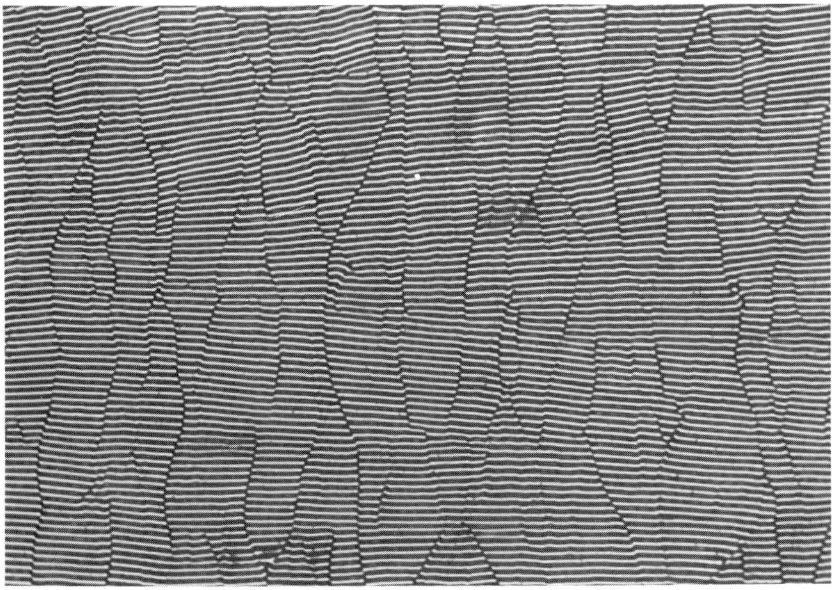

Fig. 7 Microstructure of Aluminum-Copper lamellar Eutectic magnified 545 x, courtesy of Georgia Institute of Technology.

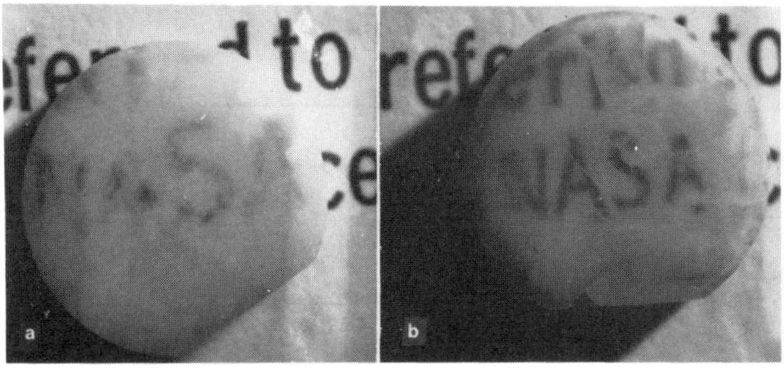

Fig. 8 Macrophotograph of Sodium Chloride - Sodium Fluoride Eutectic magnified 8 x. a) Solidified on Earth, b) Solidified in low gravity.

which are discontinuous and short when frozen on Earth and, therefore, are not useful for optical transmission purposes. The ingots of the sodium chloride/sodium flouride eutectic were 0.75 cm dia and 6.5 cm long.

First, it was most interesting to note that the surfaces of the stainless-steel crucible were in perfect condition when they were returned from flight, indicating that there was no reaction between the specimens and crucibles. Although the direction of the heat extraction was both normal and parallel to the growth direction, the sodium flouride fibers were aligned with the long axis of the ingot. The fibers were spaced regularly and parallel in the space-grown ingot as compared to those that were imbedded randomly in the Earth-grown ingot. A single grain was not obtained, and low-angle grain boundaries and subgrains were present throughout the ingot; however, the fibers still were aligned within $\pm 2^{o}$ and regularly spaced. The true test of the difference between space- and Earth-grown salt ingots was in the optical transmission tests. The Earth-grown ingot does not transmit an image but disperses the light, whereas the space-grown ingot transmits an image (see Fig. 8). Additionally, infrared transmission plots were made of the two ingots for comparison, and the space-grown ingot is shown to have both a much higher transmittance and much wider spectrum than the Earth-grown crystal (see Fig. 9). The transmittance of the Earth-grown ingot was about 10% over a narrow range or spectrum. The transmittance of the space-grown ingot was about 64% over the much wider spectrum. This was attributed to the continuous sodium flouride fibers imbedded in the sodium chloride matrix, so that losses due to reflection and refraction of light were reduced greatly. This subject is discussed in detail by Yue[12] in his report on Skylab results.

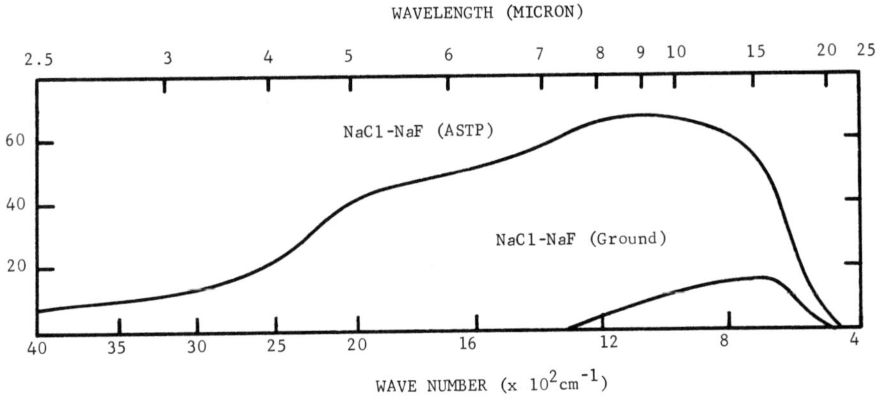

Fig. 9 Infrared transmission spectrum for Sodium x Chloride - Sodium Fluoride Eutectic grown on Earth and in low gravity. (Specimen thickness 0.107 in).

The experiment was repeated on Apollo Soyuz in the summer of 1975; however, the rodlike structure was changed to lithium flouride in the matrix of sodium chloride. Much the same results were obtained; however, the final report of the data has not been completed. The conclusion from these experiments is that continuous fibers, regularly spaced and aligned with the growth direction, can be produced in the space environment because of the quiescent conditions. Optical light guides may be produced which provide much greater infrared transmittance over a wider spectrum with a better image transmission than anything obtained from ingots grown on the ground. These results and conclusions prove that the theory of continuous rodlike eutectic growth is correct, and they give promise for the future of eutectics of well-defined structures grown in space.

Permanent Magnet Alloy

ASTP experiment MA070 by Larson[13] was aimed at solidification of a high-coercive-strength magnetic material, manganese bismuth, with a eutectic microstructure. The low-gravity specimen had higher intrisic coercive strength (230 kG) than any manganese bismuth previously reported (113 kG). The former was "as-received" from flight or essentially annealed, whereas the latter was heat-treated to the optimum structure. The microstructure was directional (anisotropic), more homogeneous, and the lamellar spacing was smaller than the randomly oriented ground specimen. Magnetic and metallurgical analyses are still in process, but there does appear to be an important correlation in these properties.

Superplastic Materials

Since lead-tin structure is known to be superplastic, it is expected that lead-antimony should be superplastic also, if only the eutectic phases were dispersed finely. However, in practice, ground specimens are not dispersed finely and will mix on cooling only if stirred violently, to keep the antimony-rich crystals from floating. Therefore, in SPAR experiment 74-5 by Pond,[14] a specimen was dispersed carefully in the solid state by casting, rolling, cutting the foil, and extruding to obtain a well-dispersed specimen that could be remelted in space. The sample of 88.8% lead 11.2% antimony was prepared in a composition that was believed to be the eutectic; however, there is some question that the exact eutectic has not been achieved on Earth. Subsequent specimens will be made from off-eutectic compositions to delineate more precisely the phase diagram. The flight specimen was heated to 400°C and cooled to below 200°C at a solidification rate of 1/2°C/sec, providing a dendritic structure of lead with the crystallization product of an antimony-rich matrix. This work is still in progress. Lead-antimony indeed may show a binary eutectic structure with the proper dispersion to provide a superplastic material that has many practical applications.

Another experiment, ASTP MA044 by Lacy,[15] is related to the homogeneity problem of lead-antimonide. It involves the syntectic alloy, aluminum antimony, which is a III-V semiconductor, if properly mixed. This experiment is explained in detail elsewhere, and so it will be mentioned only as reference here. It is another excellent example of the achievement of a homogenious mixture in space of two elements that differ greatly in density and, therefore, segregate so strongly on Earth that a homogenious mixture is not possible. However, when solidified in space, aluminum-antimonide is miscible and very homogenious because of the lack of density segregation in low gravity.

Two very practical lessons were learned in the segregation, diffusion, and other solidification experiments performed in metal, ceramic, or graphite cylindrical crucibles. In every case in which the specimens of ground-based experiments stuck to the walls of the crucible/container, the comparable low-gravity experiments did not. This is not well understood but may be related to a redirection in wetting characteristics in low gravity. It also may be related to the observation that any gas in the closed container migrated to the outer surface of the specimens in space whereas gas migrated to internal bubbles on the ground. This opposing migration can be attributed to the natural drive to minimize surface energy and area of the molten specimen in space which is overcome by gravity on the ground.

Summary and Conclusions

In summary, a number of metals-processing experiments show consistent results, pointing to reduced turbulence and liquid mass transfer in the low gravity of space. This is observed in terms of reduced diffusion; a shift from dendritic to cellular growth due to constitutional supercooling which requires a concentration gradient in the melt ahead of the solid-liquid interface; a tendency for the eutectic second-phase particles of high aspect ratio in directional solidification to grow continuously or at least longer; and for phases with wide density differences to disperse uniformily and homogeneously. There is beginning to emerge a central relationship among the several different experiments in solidification. It is that, at low-gravity conditions in space, the reduced convective stirring and mass transfer affects the microstructure in much the same manner as a reduction in the growth rate on the ground. This statement implies that regular, aligned, and predictable solidification can be achieved at faster growth rates in space compared to that experienced on the ground. Therefore, the future holds great expectations, based on the results and conclusions just listed, for both the broader understanding of materials science and the production of highly valued products in space.

References

[1]Miller, R., "Undercooling of Materials During Solidification in Space," Rept. 4, Contract NAS8-31238, Oct. 1975, Boeing Aerospace Corp.

[2]Yue, A. S., "Directional Solidification of Eutectic Composites in Space," Final Rept., Contract NAS8-26402, Dec. 1972, Univ. of California at Los Angeles.

[3]Johnston, M. H. and Baldwin, D. H., "The Influence of Acceleration Forces on Nucleation, Solidification, and Deformation Processes in Tin Single Crystals," Metallurgical Transactions, Vol. 5 (1974) p. 2399.

[4]Johnston, M. H. and Griner, C. S., "Dendrite Remelting and Macrosegregation: The Direct Observation of Solidification as A Function of Gravity Levels," Rept. on SPAR Experiment 74-21, May 1976, NASA Marshall Space Flight Center.

[5]Fleming, M., Solidification Processes, 1968, ISI Publication p. 110.

[6]McKannan, E. C. and Poorman, R. M., "Skylab M551 Metals Melting Experiment," Proceedings, Third Space Symposium, Skylab Results, Vol. I, April 30, 1976, NASA Marshall Space Flight Center, pp. 85-93.

[7]Li, C. H., "Segregation Effects During Solidification in Weightless Melts," Rept. 10, Contract NAS8-29166, May 1974, Grumman Aerospace Corp., Bethpage, NY.

[8]Yue, J. T. and Voltmer, F. W., "Influence of Gravity-Free Solidification on Microsegregation," Proceedings, Third Space Symposium, Skylab Results, Vol. I, April 30, 1974, NASA Marshall Space Flight Center, pp. 375-424.

[9]Gatos, H. C. and Witt, A. F., "Interface Markings in Crystals: Experiment MA-060," Apollo-Soyuz Test Project, Preliminary Science Report, TMX-58173, Sec. 25, Feb. 1976, NASA Johnson Space Center.

[10]Reed, R. E., "Surface-Tension, Induced Convection: Experiment MA-041," Apollo-Soyuz Test Project, Preliminary Science Report, TMX-58173, Sec. 23, Feb. 1976, NASA Johnson Space Center.

[11]Hasemeyer, E. A., Lovoy, C. V., and Lacy, L. L., "Skylab Experiment M566 Copper-Aluminum Eutectic," Proceedings, Third Space Symposium Skylab Results, Vol. I, April 30, 1974, NASA Marshall Space Flight Center, pp. 457-468.

[12]Yue, A. S., "Zero Gravity Growth of Na F-Na Cl Eutectics in Skylab," Final Rept., Contract NAS8-28310, Jan. 1976.

[13]Larson, D., Jr., "Zero-G Processing of Magnets: Experiment MA-070," Apollo-Soyuz Test Project, Preliminary Science Report, TMX-58173, Sec. 26, Feb. 1976, NASA Johnson Space Center.

[14]Pond, R. B., Sr., Winter, J. M., Jr., Van Doren, S. L., and Shifler, D. A., "Postflight Technical Report for SPAR Experiment 74-5: Space Solidification of Pb-Sb Eutectic," First Phase Rept., Contract NAS8-31534, Mar. 1, 1976, Marvalaud, Inc., Westminister, MD.

[15]Ang, C. Y. and Lacy, L. L., "Monotectic and Syntectic Alloys: Experiment MA-044," Apollo-Soyuz Test Project, Preliminary Science Report, TMX-58173, Sec. 24, Feb. 1976, NASA Johnson Space Center.

STATIC FREE-FLUID ELECTROPHORESIS IN SPACE

R. S. Snyder* and R. E. Allen+

NASA Marshall Space Flight Center, Huntsville, Ala

Abstract

The weightless environment onboard spacecraft in drifting flight has provided a unique opportunity to do experiments that cannot be done on the ground. High resolution free-fluid electrophoresis of particles proposed in the late 1960's to take advantage of reduced gravity began with brief experiments done during two Apollo flights. The recent Apollo Soyuz Test Project mission had two major experiments that accomplished the separation of viable biological cells. The space and ground experiments completed over the past several years clearly have shown the advantages of weightlessness for this process. Experiments now are being planned for the Space Shuttle which will attempt to achieve high resolution of the separated species by using zone electrophoresis. These experiments will return a quantity sufficient for laboratory testing and establish the potential of fractionation and purification of biological materials in space.

Introduction

The disturbing influence of the Earth's gravity field on processes involving fluids of different density or a solid phase in the fluid has been either minimized by ingenuous techniques or used to advantage by the orientation of the apparatus. The best methods have been adopted universally and accepted as a condition of the experiment. The process of electrophoresis is conceptually simple but often complex in

---

‡Invited paper.

*Chief, Physical Sciences Branch, Materials and Processes Laboratory.

+Chief, Biotechnology Branch, Materials and Processes Laboratory.

practice because of the influence of gravity. In addition to the sedimentation of the heavier soluble macromolecules or solid particles, the electric current in the electrophoresis apparatus produces heat and thus thermal convection at the location of different phases or species. The sedimentation of the heavy phase plus the buoyancy of the hotter and, therefore, less dense, liquid phase produces motion just at the location where a precise separation according to electrical properties is taking place.

For some materials, gravity effects can be circumvented by immobilizing the liquid medium in the pores of a supporting material, such as filter paper, gel, or starch, where porosity is fine enough to hinder bulk fluid flow effectively. These methods have been highly successful for samples composed of molecules small enough enough to pass easily through the porous supporting materials and have become widely used for clinical and research analysis of proteins, blood serum, etc. On the other hand, methods involving supporting media are not useful for large molecules, and the net amounts of material that can be processed by these methods are very small. Another method to avoid convection is to establish a stable density gradient in the electrophoresis buffer which is steeper than any density gradient caused by the electrophoresis process itself. A solute, such as sucrose, must be selected which has no electrical charge, and it must be layered carefully into the column. Stabilizing media also introduce disadvantages of increased viscosity and unwanted interactions with the media.

It now has been shown that electrophoresis can be done without any disturbances in the fluid phase by going into a reduced gravity environment. The space experiments have demonstrated the capability of electrophoresis to purify materials to an extent not previously possible. In addition, a new generation of experiments based upon variations of electrophoresis, such as isotachophoresis and isoelectric focusing, will be done in the future on the Space Shuttle.

Electrophoresis on Apollo

After the concept of electrophoresis in a weightless liquid medium was proposed, an early flight opportunity was sought. On Jan. 31, 1971, an electrophoresis demonstration was placed aboard the Apollo 14 spacecraft and done on the return trip from the moon.[1] The objective was to replace all supporting structure, density gradients, and other anticonvective media necessary on Earth with a cylindrical column of electrolyte in space.

Three transparent columns, 6 mm i.d., were used to conduct a sequence of experiments which would give significantly more information collectively than could be obtained from a single column. The separation columns, 10 cm long, were filled with a dilute borate solution with a pH value of 9.0. The platinum electrodes were isolated from the fluid in the columns by semi-permeable membranes. A pump and tubing system was provided to circulate the buffer solution around the electrodes and through a phase separator to remove gases produced by electrolysis. Electrolyte from both electrodes was exchanged by the same circulation system to minimize pH changes at the electrodes.

The sample materials used in the three columns were 1) a mixture of red and blue dyes; 2) hemoglobin; and 3) deoxyribonucleic acid (DNA) from salmon sperm tagged with a fluorescent marker. Prior to operation of the apparatus, the sample materials were isolated in small cavities in a plastic slide arranged to run in a slot intersecting the separating columns. To initiate the separation run, the operating astronaut turned a screw to move the plastic slide so that the sample cavities coincided with the separation columns. An electric field then was established in each column by applying 270 V across the electrodes. Data on the separations attempted in the demonstration all were obtained by photography, and no attempt was made to collect separated fractions of the samples. The quality of the photographic data obtained on the flight was somewhat impaired by poor lighting and camera positioning problems. The photographs showed, however, only the separation of red and blue dye, and it had been injected next to the tube wall by misalignment of the insertion slide. Densitometer measurements made on the photographs showed that the sharpness of separation between the dyes was at least as good as that obtained in a liquid column under the best conditions on Earth.

The pH of the solutions in the separation columns had fallen to values between 7.5 and 7,8, and no identifiable trace of any of the other sample materials was found in the apparatus. This was attributed to bacterial growth in the system, in spite of the fact that cleanliness had been enforced during assembly and prior storage over the period between loading and operation of the apparatus. There is no evidence of gas in the fluid system and no indication that any fluid had leaked out of it.

Since remedies were available for the problems that compromised the separation results, and additional ground research indicated that the idea of fluid electrophoresis in space was worth pursuing further, plans were made and apparatus was developed for a second demonstration on the Apollo 16 launched on April 16, 1972. The Apollo 16 electrophoresis apparatus was similar in size and shape, but several modifications were made based upon the Apollo 14 results.[2] An automatically actuated camera was mounted rigidly on the unit by an adapter, which included a lens extension tube so that the image of the window substantially filled each frame of film. The window also was enlarged, so that the electrode region, as well as the separations

the separation columns, could be seen. Figure 1 shows the 10-x13-x18-cm unit with Hasselblad camera attached. Photographs were taken automatically every 20 sec during the separation run.

The Apollo 16 apparatus also contained three separation columns, but only a single sample material was used. One column contained a mixture of monodispersed polystyrene latex particles of 0.2 and 0.8 μm diam; in the other two columns, particles of these diameters were run separately to provide comparative data. Polystyrene latex was used because it is a model material whose electrophoretic mobility is well known, and it is substantially immune to bacterial degradation. The sample injection system also was redesigned to provide for smoother and more reliable release of the samples in the columns.

Approximately 25 hr into the flight of Apollo 16, the electrophoresis apparatus was set up and photography was initiated. The sample was released into the columns by pulling a strip of plastic film that isolated the sample. This exposed the latex particles to the cell buffer and the electric field. Although the sample was injected as a cylindrical disk, the electro-osmotic flow pattern of the buffer in the electrophor-

Fig. 1 Apollo 16 electrophoresis unit with camera.

esis tubes quickly modified the shape of the particle bands into parabolas. By the time the latex particles were visible in the photographs, less than 0.5 cm from the sample input, the front of each group of particles was already parabolic. The strong influence of electro-osmosis was confirmed by comparing the flow patterns in the cells with theoretically calculated patterns. The separation of the two sizes of latex particles in the single tube did occur as planned, but very sensitive photographic techniques were required to resolve the separation. No convection occurred in the columns, since the pattern of polystyrene latex particles trailing the major bands did not change during the migration down the column. Figure 2 shows photographs taken 1 min apart.

Electrophoresis Technology Experiment on ASTP

The Apollo-Soyuz Test Project (ASTP) continued the development of static free-fluid electrophoresis by eliminating the problems of the previous flight experiments (bacterial degradation of biological samples on Apollo 14 and electro-osmosis on Apollo 16) and separating viable biological cells in space

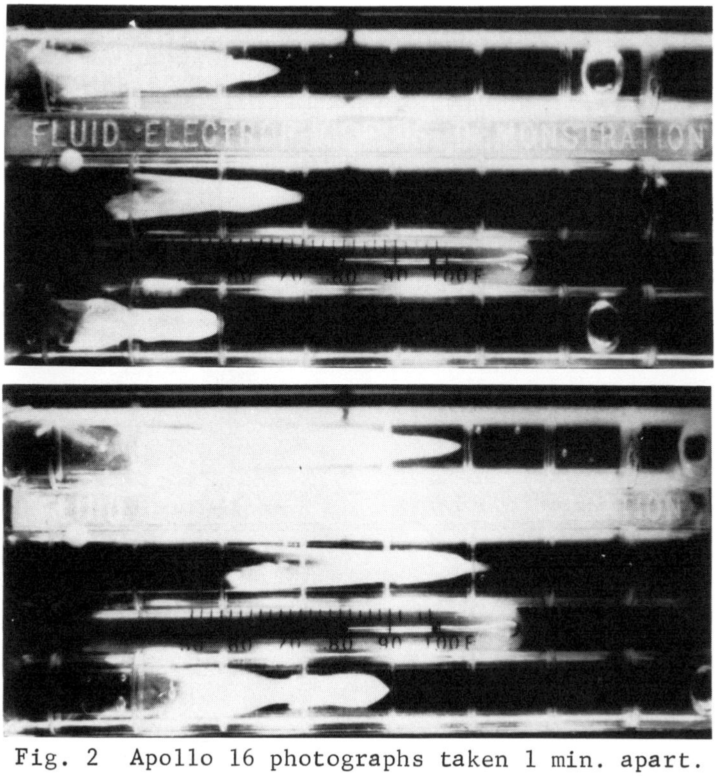

Fig. 2 Apollo 16 photographs taken 1 min. apart.

for analysis on Earth.[3] The objectives of the experiment were to 1) demonstrate free zone electrophoresis in space undisturbed by fluid phenomena such as electro-osmosis and convection; 2) verify that a biological sample can be applied to an electrophoresis column in a precise manner without affecting the subsequent electrophoresis; 3) separate and return viable lymphocyte and kidney cell fractions; 4) preserve the isolation and viability of the separated biological samples after electrophoresis; 5) evaluate and analyze the resolution and sharpness of the bands formed by free zone electrophoresis in space; and 6) demonstrate the isotachophoresis of cells.

The experiment equipment consisted of 1) an electrophoresis unit with Hasselblad camera (Fig. 3); 2) a cryogenic freezer (Fig 4); 3) eight experiment columns (six electrophoresis, two isotachophoresis) (Fig. 5); and 4) eight sample insertion slides (Fig. 6). The following biological materials were contained in duplicate sample slides; 1) a mixture of aldehyde-fixed red blood cells from human, rabbit, and horse; 2) human peripheral blood lymphocytes; 3) human kidney cells; and 4) rabbit and human red blood cells for isotachophoresis. (One

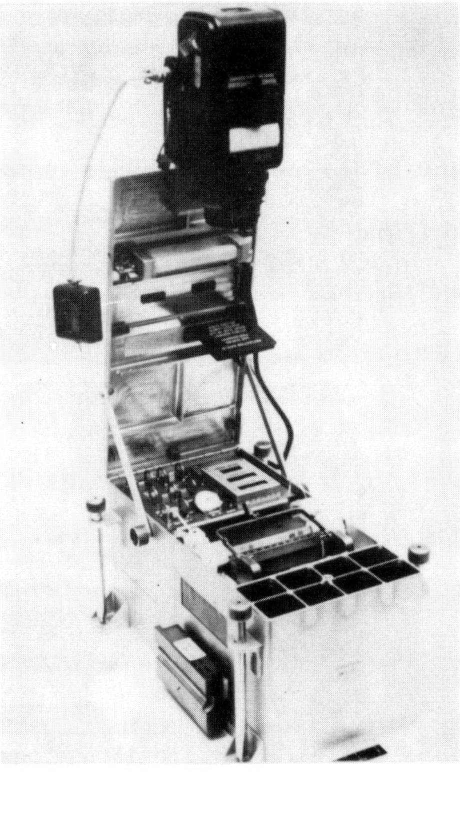

Fig. 3 ASTP electrophoresis unit with camera.

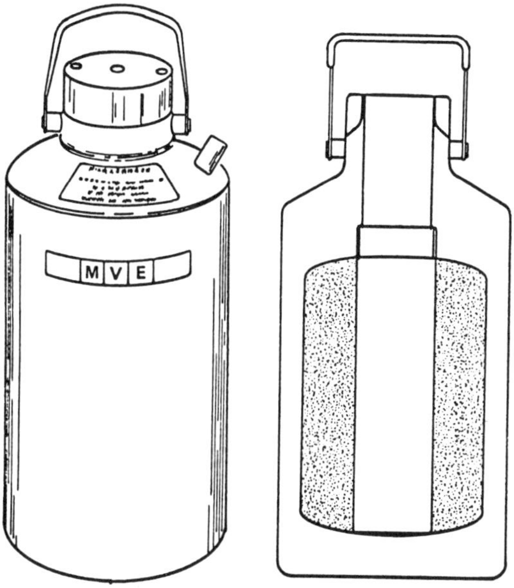

Fig. 4 Cryogenic freezer.

slide contained fresh cells, and the other slide contained fixed cells.)

In order to conduct the experiment in space, the astronaut removed an electrophoresis or isotachophoresis column from its storage location and installed it in the electrophoresis unit. Fluid couplings were attached to each electrode chamber of the electrophoresis columns only. Next, the slide containing the frozen biological sample was removed from the cryogenic freezer and inserted into the column. The camera mounted on the unit cover photographed critical settings of the equipment controls and digital readouts during each column run. At the end of each electrophoresis separation, the column was frozen by the thermoelectric module part of the electrophoresis unit. The crewman then quickly removed each electrode chamber from

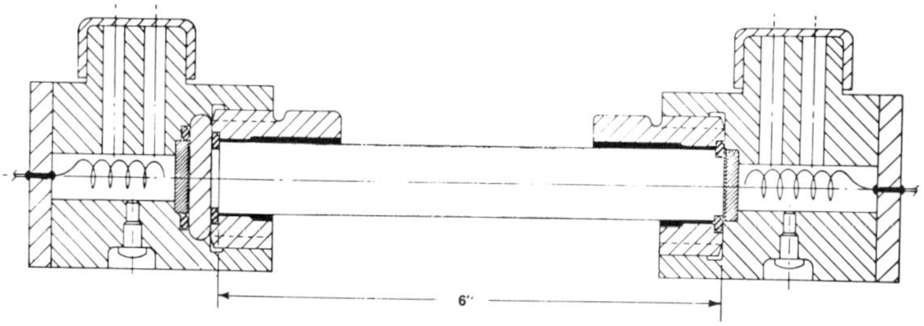

Fig. 5 Electrophoresis column detail.

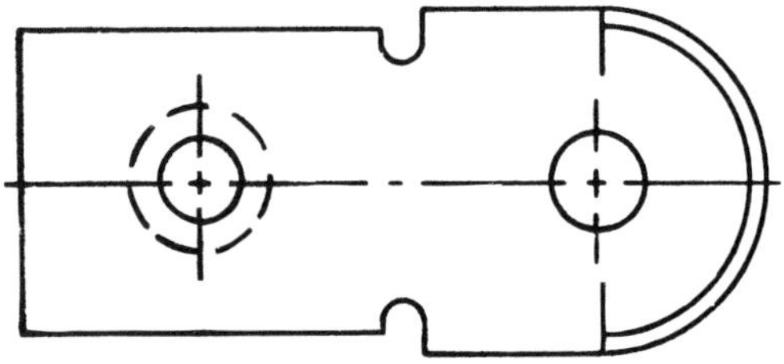

Fig. 6 Sample insertian slide.

the frozen column and placed the column in the freezer for return to Earth. The isotachophoresis columns only were photographed in orbit during their operation and not returned to Earth.

The electrophoresis unit and the data collection assembly operated successfully, but the fluid connect lines (located in the electrode housings) of some of the columns were clogged during manufacture. Without circulation of the electrolyte in the electrode housing, chemical and gas products of electrolysis accumulated in the electrode region, triggering changes in the buffer which caused column voltage fluctuations and pH changes in the column fluid. The photography was also poor, and it was not possible to discern the characteristics of the bands. In the laboratory, the frozen buffer containing the processed samples was separated from the glass electrophoresis columns. These frozen ice columns were sliced into sections (5 mm in width) for analysis of separation quality. The results of the analyses available to date are presented in the following sections.

The fixed red blood cells of rabbit, human, and horse were selected as a standard, or control, because their electrophoretic mobilities are well known.[4] The photographic record clearly demonstrates separation of the sharp bands of cells in one of the columns. The sharp particle band boundaries and location of the bands relative to their expected migration in the columns clearly showed that electro-osmosis was eliminated. The inside surfaces of the cleaned glass columns were precoated with Z-6040 (γ -glycidoxypropyltrimethoxysilane, Dow Corning) and then coated with methylcellulose to yield a stable, biocompatible surface with close to zero wall charge. The coated columns were used for all experiments.

To identify specific cells, mobility data were collected using micro electrophoresis techniques. The highest mobility was shown by horse cells, the next highest by human cells, and the lowest by rabbit cells, as expected. One column had a pH range from 6.0 to 9.2 instead of the expected 7.2. This condition, in addition to an unexplained shift in position of the bands from one photograph to the next one, caused indistinct bands. Mobility data indicate the occurrence of cellular separation, but not to the concentration necessary to show cohesive bands in the photographs. The pH problems were induced by the fluid line blockage already discussed. Two specific instances of sudden disruption of boundaries can be seen in the flight photographs. The disruptions probably were caused by movement of the apparatus or perhaps of the spacecraft.

Migration of the human lymphocyte cells during electrophoresis was not detected in either column. In one column, current was established for less than 3 min because of the fluid line blockage. Gas bubbles blocked current and prevented operation of the experiment. In addition, the cell viability was only 6%. In the other column, current existed for approximately 30 min. In this case, the electrode housings were returned, and a failure analysis confirmed that the right electrode chamber fluid lines were restricted. This condition resulted in an acid pH throughout the column which killed the cells.

Only one column of human kidney cells was done in space, and the electrophoretic pattern of viable cells (Fig. 7) shows a separation into several subpopulations. The postflight pro-

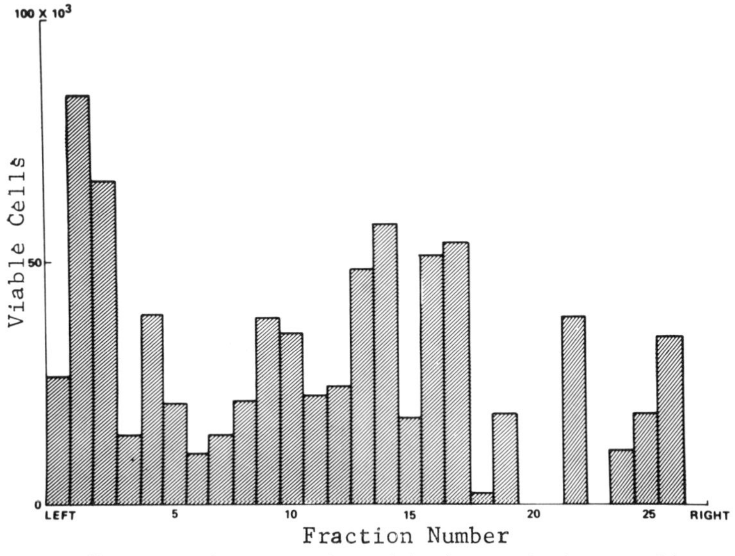

Fig. 7 Distribution of viable human kidney cells in flight column after electrophoresis.

cedure for analyzing the kidney cells was as follows. The frozen slices were thawed rapidly at 37°C, centrifuged, and resuspended in growth media. These fractions were weighed, tared, and the pH determined. An aliquot was taken for viable cell count, and, based on this information, the cells were cultured. After 28 days, only fractions 11 to 19 had reached confluency. The other fractions were removed from the culture plates and tested for urokinase activity by fibrin plate method and showed no fibrinolytic activity[5]. Those cells that were put on production media were tested for urokinase activity at various times. The cells that were subcultured were removed from the dishes with EDTA and then recultured.

The results of the urokinase production obtained with the primary and first subculture cells after 35 days on production showed an obvious enrichment of urokinase activity in fraction 15 of 2.0 urokinase (UK) units per 100 cells. An increased production also was tested for the presence of human granulocyte conditioning factor, and the highest concentrations of these producing cells were in a separate band (fraction 17). These results show that cells can be separated under sterile conditions and returned from orbit in such a manner that they retain their ability to grow in culture. The electrophoresis in space showed good separation of the kidney cells into subpopulations. The results indicated that there were at least three and maybe four subpopulations. These results are in agreement with the best data obtained using the endless belt electrophoresis. Although subpopulations have been observed using the endless belt apparatus, sterile collection of these bands has proved to be impossible. Even though each fraction from the ASTP flight showed viable cells by the strain technique and they all attached to the glass surface, only the few fractions, between 11 and 20, multiplied. The reason for this is not known. The only possible explanation is that the "nongrowers" were more sensitive to unfavorable conditions and, therefore, could not recover to grow in culture.

The isotachophoresis experiments were partially successful, and full expectations were not realized.[6] There is evidence only of frontal boundaries in the photographs, but not of any separation or details of the rear boundaries. In retrospect, the duration of the run, 45 min, was insufficient to bring the isotachophoretic bands into full view. The 45-min duration was based on the calculated and experimentally observed temperature rise in groundbased experiments. A better photographic record might have provided some indications of possible emergence of the rear boundary or the expected intercompartmental boundaries in the fresh cell sample. The predicted overall migration rate was 1 mm/min for both samples. The last four frames of the fixed cells have confirmed this migration rate, but the overall migration rate appears to be substantially lower than expected (0.68 mm/min). With the fresh cells, the migration rate was still lower, ranging from 0.55 to 0.64 mm/min. Interpretation of these mobility differences is made difficult by several possible contributing factors, such as possible variation in time, power, and starting position.

Conclusions

The basic objectives of the ASTP Electrophoresis Technology Experiment were to conduct engineering and operational tests of a space-rated static electrophoresis separation apparatus and to further current research efforts through separation of viable cellular species. A method that would allow for the precise application of a biological sample without affecting the subsequent electrophoresis was accomplished by inserting the sample as a frozen disk. Attempts were made to separate and return viable lymphocytes and kidney cells. This goal was accomplished with the kidney cells but not with the lymphocytes. A technique needed to assure viable candidate preservation after separation was accomplished for the first time in space by using a thermoelectric module to freeze the sample at a prescribed rate after separation was completed. A coating was developed which eliminated electro-osmosis in the columns. The experiment allowed, therefore, the testing and evaluation of many important aspects related to spaceflight electrophoresis, and, in most cases, the concepts developed were proven operationally or shown to offer significant improvements over past efforts.

References

[1]McKannan, E. C., Krupnick, A. C., Griffin, R. N., and McCreight, L. R., "Electrophoresis Separation in Space - Apollo 14," NASA TM X-64611, August 21, 1971.

[2]Snyder, R. S., Bier, M., Griffin, R. N., Johnson, A. J., Leidheiser, H., Furtunato, J. M. Vanderhoff, J. W., Sydney, R., van Oss, C. J., "Free Fluid Particle Electrophoresis on Apollo 16," Separation and Purification Methods, Vol. 2, September 1973, pp. 259-282.

[3]Allen, R. E., Barlow, G. H., Bier, M., Bigazzi, P. E., Knox, R. J., Micale, F. J., Seaman, G. V. F., Vanderhoff, J. W., van Oss, C. J. Patterson, W. J., Scott, F. E., Rhodes, P. H., Nerren, B. H., and Harwell, R. J.,"Electrophoresis Technology MA-011", Apollo Soyuz Test Project Preliminary Science Project Preliminary Science Report, NASA TM X-58173, February 1976.

[4]Vassar, P. S., Hards, J. M., Brooks, D. E., Hagenberger, B., Seaman, G. V. F., "Physicochemical Effects of Aldehydes on the Human Erythrocyte," Journal of Cell Biology, Vol. 53, June 1972, pp. 808-818.

[5]Bernik, M. B., and Kwaan, H. C. "Plasminogen Activator Activity in Cultures from Human Tissues. An Immunological and Histo-Chemical Study," Journal of Clinical Investigation, Vol. 48, September 1969, pp. 1740-1753.

[6]Bier, M., Hinckley, J. O. N., and Smolka, A. J. K., "Potential Use of Isotachophoresis in Space," <u>Protides of the Biological Fluids, 22nd Colloquium</u>, edited by H. Peeters, Pergamon Press, New York, 1975, pp. 673-678.

FREE-FLOW ELECTROPHORESIS IN SPACE

K. Hannig and H. Wirth

Max-Planck-Institut für Biochemie,
Martinsried, Federal Republic of Germany

Abstract

The ability to minimize convection and sedimentation in a microgravity environment has encouraged the exploration of processing biological materials in space. The results of the electrophoresis experiments carried out aboard Apollo 14 and Apollo 16 provided the impetus to continue this work during Apollo-Soyuz-Test-Project mission in July 1975. For the first time, a free-flow electrophoresis experiment was flown aboard ASTP. The experiment was designed in order to conduct tests with biological cell material and to verify a free-flow electrophoresis experiment concept by operation in space. As a result of this experiment, the possibility of separating living cells under gentle conditions in space will be discussed. The aim of a first experiment using the free-flow electrophoresis in space also includes the experience of necessary and useful modifications for the design and handling in further applications of such an electrophoresis apparatus. This will be discussed in this paper.

Electrophoresis is an electrokinetic phenomenon based on the transport of charged particles

Presented as Paper D.2.7 at the COSPAR Symposium on Materials Sciences in Space, Philadelphia, Pa., June 9-10, 1976.

in an electric field. Predominantly in biology and medicine, but also in engineering and chemistry, electrophoresis is used to separate particles which possess a different charge, for example, proteins, viruses, and even cells. Electrophoresis can be carried out on Earth with high resolution. But its processing capacity is limited. Gravity effects such as heat convection and sedimentation limit its efficiency because, in order to fight these disturbing influences, the cross-sectional dimensions of electrophoresis chambers must be kept small. Under zero-gravity conditions, however, there should be no limits in this respect.

These theoretical assumptions were the background of NASA activity some years ago, namely, to utilize the lack of gravity in orbital spacecrafts for scientific and commercial applications of electrophoresis, for example, to isolate and purify sera or other biological substances of high activity. But remember that, even in the absence of gravity, other limiting factors emerge such as the heat transfer from the liquid medium in an electrophoresis chamber. A rough calculation shows that effectivity can be increased by a factor of 10 at equal or better resolution compared with similar ground equipment. Thus this reason alone would not justify the immense costs for design and adaption of electrophoresis apparatuses to space application. Only additional biological tasks of outstanding importance illustrate its necessity.

Electrophoresis may be capable of assisting in solving many phenomena such as growth, metabolism, genetics, and immune responses that occur in a different manner under low-gravity conditions. Thus electrophoresis may be a powerful aid in fractionation and purification of cell culture products or in preparation of vital and purified cell material for further investigation, a purpose that can be fulfilled in the future Spacelab. But it seems to be too early to predict any applicability to commercial production of biological material in space in the present state of development. At this moment, we just are learning how to utilize it, and one step this way was verified by both electrophoresis experiments MA-011 and MA-014 during the ASTP carried out in July 1975 (see Fig. 1).

The American experiment MA-011 and the German one MA-014 were very different systems for very different purposes. The MA-011 electrophoresis apparatus is a static system with one limited sample volume, developed for high resolution and various electrophoretical methods as, for example, isofocusing or isotachophoresis techniques. The apparatus MA-014 was designed for free-flow electrophoresis with special regard for high sample throughputs at high resolution. In the free-flow method (see Fig. 2 for principal), the sample to be separated is introduced continuously in a fine stream into a flowing buffer curtain. Perpendicular to its direction of flow, an electric field of high tension is applied. Particles with different surface charge density are deflected from the flow direction of the buffer by an angle determined by the flow rate and the electrophoretic mobility of the particles. At the end of the buffer curtain, the separated zones can either be collected continuously or, as in the MA-014, analyzed by monitoring the optical absorption pattern across the buffer curtain.

Since this electrophoresis system is a continuous one, theoretically no limits exist in re-

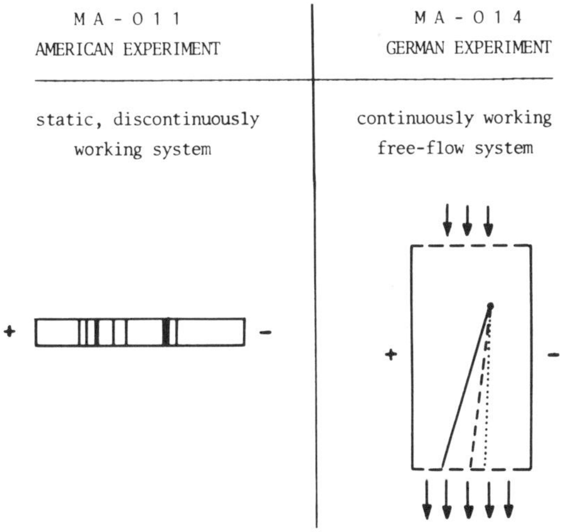

Fig. 1 Electrophoresis experiments on the A S T P.

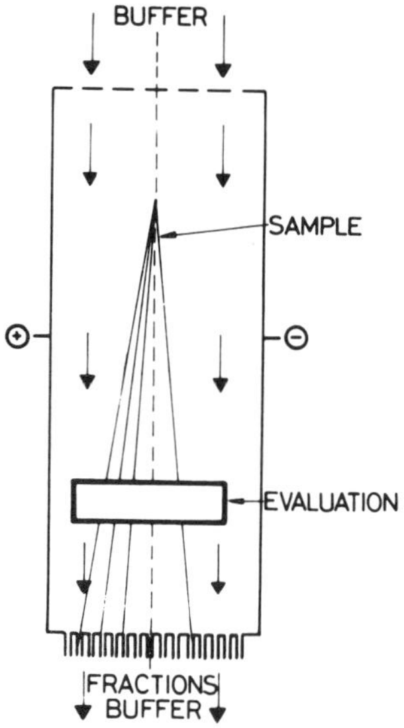

Fig. 2 Principle of free-flow electrophoresis.

spect to the amount of cells to be separated, in contrary to each static system. In practice, the limit is given by the time necessary to process a certain amount. This time may be reduced by high sample dosage rates, possible only in wide separation chamber gaps. A second advantage is the possibility of changing samples with a relatively high frequency without interrupting the experimental functions, which means without disturbing established equilibrium.

With regard to the use of electrophoresis in weightless areas, it is necessary for us to distinguish between effects that are caused by gravitation, i.e., sedimentation and thermal convection, and those effects that are independent of this. Of course, under lack of gravitation, only the gravitation-dependent effects (sedimentation and convection) can be eliminated, and thus a higher throughput with larger separation chamber gap dimensions can be obtained.

The resolution of electrophoretic separation is, however, determined independent of gravitational effects, above all by means of a methodologically caused band-broadening, which exists as well under lack of gravitation. The band-broadening effects result mainly from three phenomena (see

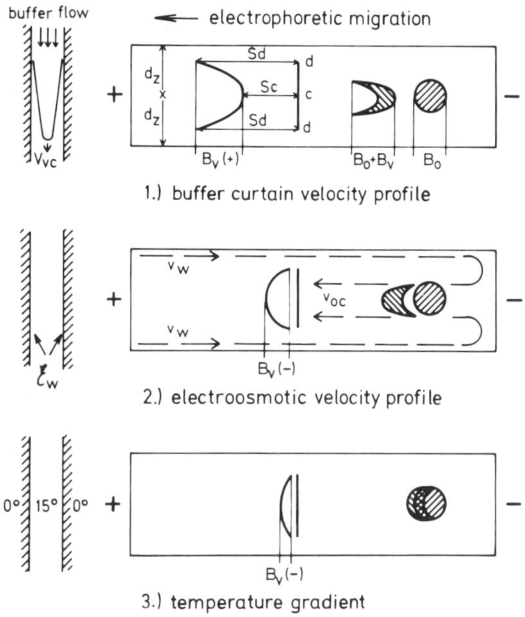

Fig. 3 Band broadening causes.

Fig. 3): 1) Poisseuille velocity profile of the liquid curtain; 2) the electroosmotic velocity profile; and 3) the temperature gradient throughout the liquid curtain thickness, increasing with liquid curtain thickness and electric power. The thermal diffusion, because of the extremely short separation times in free-flow electrophoresis, can be neglected.

It could be shown that the opposing tailing effects of electroosmosis and the temperature gradient to the effect of the velocity profiles can be compensated for by appropriate adjustment of the chamber wall zeta potential. The practical relevance of this observation is that band-broadening is reduced if samples are centered in the middle of the liquid curtain. Furthermore, sample band width should be adjusted to values with a starting bandwidth of less than half the liquid curtain thickness.

The objective of MA-014 was essentially to clarify these advantages and to test the performance of this principle for possible application in further orbital laboratories. Subsequently the main purposes and problem areas were as follows: 1) test of applicability to zero-gravity conditions; 2) performance of separation experiments at high sample throughput; 3) investigation of thermal and convection properties of chambers with high gap width; 4) investigation of the possibility of separating preserved living cells at high viability percentage for preparative purposes; and revealing weak points in this complex system in order to meet them with suitable modifications in a further system. The complete design and production were carried out by Messerschmidt-Bölkow-Blohm in contract with the German Federal Administration for Research and Technology. The project management was guided by the Gesellschaft für Weltraumforschung.

The design goal was to meet the various and sometimes difficult-to-solve problems arising not only from electrophoresis but also from the given spacecraft interfaces. The result was a compact machine working almost automatically and consuming as little manpower as possible. Sample collection was avoided because of volume limits for the instruments. Evaluation was done by scanning the absorption pattern across the separation gap, digitizing the data, and storing scientific and housekeeping data as well on a tape recorder.

Some figures may help to understand the most important functional blocks. The heart of the apparatus is the separation chamber to be seen on the front port (Fig. 4). It consists of two cooling plates adjusted in such a way that the gap between them is exactly parallel and 4.0 mm in width. The left and right sides of the gap, with a distance of 28 mm, are closed by ion exchange membranes separating the chamber buffer from the electrode channels. Within these, the electrodes of 180-mm effective length are placed to provide the electric field. The electrode buffer flow is achieved by means of a tooth-gear pump; meanwhile, buffer curtain and sample flow are performed by peristaltic pumps.

The samples are stored in a special cooling compartment, an integral part of the apparatus. Be-

Fig. 4 MA-014 apparatus.

fore operating the experiment, the sample containers are removed from the freezer compartment and inserted into the sample inlet. During separation, development of the zones is monitored optically through windows at the downstream end of the cooling plates or gap walls respectively. The light passing the chamber gap is attenuated by the separated zones, and the resulting absorption pattern is measured by a diode array. The scanned data are digitized and recorded on tape.

At the side, the tape recorder and a second-redundant-one are located. Not only the absorption pattern but all housekeeping data such as voltage, fluid flow rates, temperature, and so on are stored on the tapes.

On the top of the experiment, the operating panel is to be seen with sample containers, switches, and indicator lamps. The whole box was mounted to a so-called coolplate in the spacecraft, linked to the spacecraft cooling system. The following samples were separated: 1) rat bone-marrow cells; 2) rat spleen cells; 3) mixture of human and rabbit erythrocytes; and 4) rat lymph node cells, in addition to human erythrocytes. Samples 1-3 were freshly prepared and stored in the experiment chilled at $4^{\circ}C$ for approximately 45 hr during launch preparation, launch, and several mission activities until experiment run. Sample 4 (rat lymph node cells) was prepared simultaneously, chilled down to $-20^{\circ}C$, and then stored at $-85^{\circ}C$ in the same liquid nitrogen that was used and developed for the American experiment MA-011. Each sample contained 1.5 cm^3 cell suspension with about 120×10^6 cells. 11×10^6 cells/min were separated.

Some days after splashdown, we started the evaluation of the tape-stored data in our Institute. The simultaneously recorded housekeeping data confirmed proper run of all functional blocks. The scientific data, however, revealed that the light source of the absorption-measuring optics had an exceeding brightness, and therefore the measuring range was overranged by far. The reason was a very simple one: the halogen lamp suffered from lack of internal convection as a consequence of zero gravity. This fact made it very difficult to understand the recorded data.

However, during the stationary phase of the separation, irregularly occuring pulses (we call them "events") were recorded whose pattern reflected the expected course of the separation curves. These seemed to be caused by cell aggregation in the region of the separated bands. This assumption could be confirmed in two ways:

1) An aliquot of the sample used in the ASTP flight was separated under the same conditions on mission day in Space Center in an identical apparatus under Earth conditions. Analysis of this undisturbed tape showed, besides the expected cell distribution curves, stray pulses caused by cell aggregation and with a greater absorption. The

accumulation at the same location (frequency distribution of the "events") during a separation time of approximately 2 min yielded distribution curves that were similar to normal separation curves.

2) In order to check this finding and secure a reliable assertion, such separations were repeated a number of times with the engineering unit apparatus. Here each experiment was performed and evaluated with normal and increased lighting. It could be established clearly that the analysis of the periodically occuring cell aggregations at the measuring location was alone representative of the actual cell distribution. The difficult evaluation and coordination of indirect information were performed with the aid of a data-processing computer (Siemens 4004) in our Institute. Thus the following conclusions were possible:

1) Bone marrow cells (Fig. 5) in electrophoretic experiment MA-014 demonstrated only slight readiness in forming aggregates. This is because of the low gradient of these cells. Yet the distribution curve indicates a good separation. Comparing the "orbit" separation and the result of KSC experiment, it is striking that there is no correlation between electrophoretic mobility and quantitative distribution. The mobility distribution in KSC experiment is beyond the empirical data of

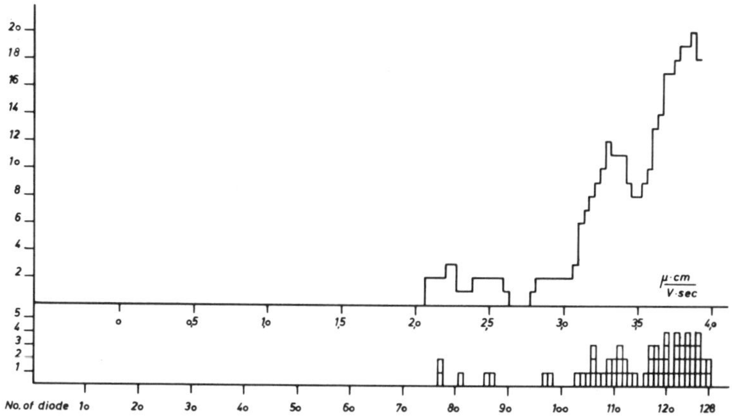

Fig. 5 Rat bone marrow.

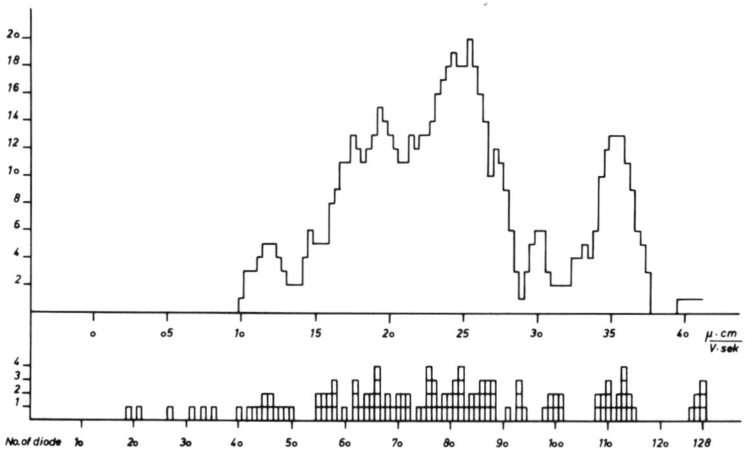

Fig. 6 Human and rabbit red blood cells.

former separation experiments. This fact, which is found only in the previous separation, remains unclear. The mobility data received in the "orbit" experiment coincide well with those obtained in similar separations being realized in MPI laboratory.

2) The "peak" representing human erythrocytes (Fig. 6) seems to be greatly homogeneous. The width of half-height is significantly lower than in KSC separation. Mobility data and empirical data also coincide to a high degree. The distribution of rabbit erythrocytes, however, seems to be exceptionally wide-ranged. This is possibly because of the distinct behavior in forming aggregates. We might assume that rabbit erythrocytes in the field of slow mobility have appeared in exceptional frequency and thus have reached a predominance in the "events" distribution curve. High selectivity obtained in "orbit" is indicated strongly by a sharp small peak between two erythrocyte main peaks. As shown in other experiments, these are genuine aggregates of human and rabbit erythrocytes. They always develop to a small extent if both cell sorts are in suspension.

3) The clearest result was received in spleen-cell separation experiments (Fig. 7). The quantity of information ("event") was adequate to perceive even finer details of separation. The cell distri-

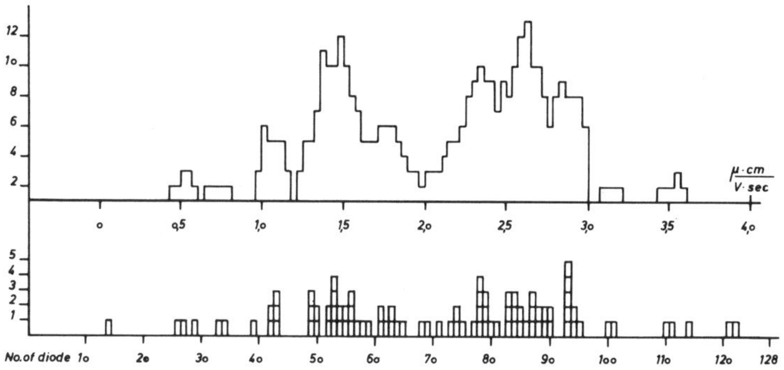

Fig. 7 Rat spleen cells

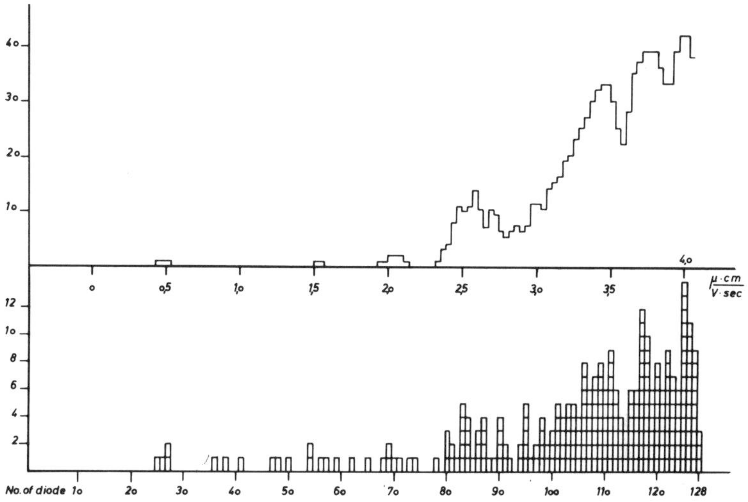

Fig. 8 Rat lymph-node with human red blood cells.

bution curve achieved in "orbit", according to registrated "events", demonstrates quantitative and qualitative similarity to those achieved in the comparative ground experiment. The frequency distribution of the "events" is analogous to the "absorption" pattern.

4) As described, lymph node cells and human erythrocytes (Fig. 8) had been frozen and were thawed just a little while before starting the experiment. Empirically, we must take into account a higher loss of vital cell material. Moreover, this is revealed in an increasing readiness to form aggregates. In fact, the number of registrated "events" proved to be the highest of all. Com-

paring the separation curves achieved in the "orbit" and in KSC, the favoring effect of space conditions was striking.

In summary, it must be confirmed that in the present interpretation of separation results some uncertainties are to remain. They are due to the disturbance in the optic detection, but the accumulation of "events" in quite definite areas of the data "channels" is too striking to be considered accidental.

The partly rare informations certainly do not admit exact quantitative statements concerning mobility, width of the half-height, and concentration ratios. Despite these restrictions, the present experiment must be regarded to have been successful. As a pilot experiment with its numerous risks according to its nature, the scientific result essentially corresponded to the expectations.

SPACE PROCESSING PROGRAM OF THE NATIONAL BUREAU OF STANDARDS

R. L. Parker*

National Bureau of Standards, Washington, D.C.

Abstract

The work of the National Bureau of Standards (NBS) for NASA's space processing program is described. The general emphasis of the NBS work has been on ground-based studies of those aspects of space which possibly could provide a unique environment for making materials more perfect or more pure. Individual projects on crystal perfection in melt growth, evaporative purification, composites, melt shape, vapor transport, and surface traction are described.

History

Although our earliest contacts with NASA's space processing or manufacturing effort date back to 1968 or 1969, direct assistance to NASA by NBS in this area began in 1971 at a relatively modest level and has developed since then into a fairly substantial program. Initially the work involved two areas: Czochralski growth and chemical vapor transport reactions. In 1972, the NBS program was expanded to include work on evaporative purification, surface tractions, and composite materials. In 1973, an additional task on melt shape in weightless crystal growth was added. All were continued up to the end of 1975, at which time the work on composites and on surface tractions was completed; the other work continues. References 1-3 describe our space processing work in detail.

General Aim of NBS Space Processing

The objective of the NBS program is to perform ground-based studies of those aspects of space which possibly could

---

Presented as Paper D.1.5 at the COSPAR Symposium on Materials Sciences in Space, Philadelphia, Pa. June 9-10, 1976.

*Senior Scientist, Metallurgy Division.

provide a unique environment for making materials more perfect or more pure. The approach taken deals primarily with experimental and theoretical studies of the absence of gravitational forces on those materials preparation processes where the presence of gravity may be important in reducing perfection or purity. Of course, the specified tasks undertaken to further the objective were chosen so as to bear a substantial relation to specific NBS skills in the field of materials processing.

Specific Task Aims and Selected Results

Task 1: Crystal Perfection in Czochralski Growth (M. Kuriyama, W. J. Boettinger, and H. Burdette)

In this project, one of the two earliest ones that we have undertaken for NASA, a detailed study has been conducted on the factors affecting crystal perfection in the growth of metal single crystals by the Czochralski technique. One reason for doing this is the belief that space processing in zero g may employ crystal pulling equipment bearing a fairly close resemblance to ground-based equipment, perhaps using a pedestal melt in space compared to a crucible-contained melt on the ground. Another reason is the major use of the Czochralski technique to grow crystals in industry. For the assessment of crystal perfection in metal crystals, the known existing nondestructive evaluation techniques, such as Lang diffraction topography, are not sensitive enough. One of the important objectives is to establish a sensitive diffraction topography and an accurate routine method for the assessment of metal crystals.

Both copper and nickel single crystals have been grown under various conditions to produce specimens, some of which are of extremely high crystal perfection. The crystals are sliced and polished carefully using acid saw techniques and then are studied by x-ray topographic techniques, particularly by the newly developed asymmetric diffraction topography (ACT). Among the variables investigated has been the effect of fluid flow parameters (crystal rotation speed in the melt, crucible rotation speed) and crystallographic parameters on the crystal perfection. Fluid flow variables, especially thermal convection, are expected to be different in the microgravity of space, and therefore their careful study on Earth should be undertaken. Another effect on Earth is the weight of the crystal and the resulting stress on the grown crystal portion during the pulling operation. A third is the orientation of the axis of the crystal.

Figure 1 shows a $(2\bar{2}0)$ surface reflection of a copper single-crystal disk using the asymmetric double-crystal topo-

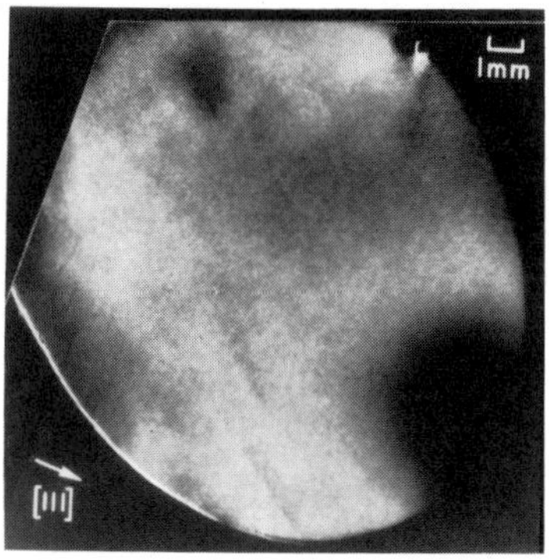

Fig. 1 $2\bar{2}0$ surface reflection x-ray topograph of as-grown Czochralski-grown copper single-crystal slice using asymmetric double-crystal camera (ACT).

graphic camera. This crystal shows rather good perfection, as evidenced by freedom of defects: the flat white area is aligned within 4 sec. of arc. It was found that the crystal and crucible rotation speeds should be similar to produce such good crystals. Bottlenecking of the seed also was important. It also was found that <100> crystals were best, and arguments relating to dislocation locking on the eight slip systems ({111} planes) were made.

Work on nickel has shown that sizable nickel single crystals of good perfection can be grown, sliced and assessed by x-ray topographic techniques (Fig. 2). Effects of growth

Fig. 2 Czochralski-grown Ni single crystal.

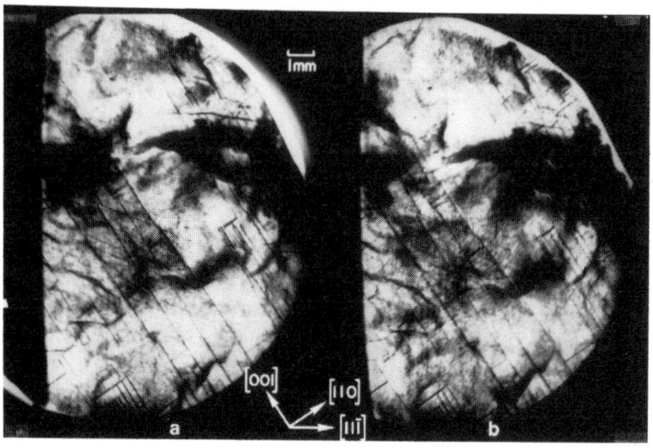

Fig. 3 $11\bar{1}$ transmission topographs of good-quality as-grown Ni crystal slice using asymmetric crystal x-ray topography (ACT). a) $\underset{\sim}{O}$-diffracted beam; b) $\underset{\sim}{H}$-diffracted beam.

parameters have been studied. Of great interest is the observation of magnetic domains by transmission x-ray topography (Fig. 3). No one has succeeded previously in observing, in bulk crystals, such domains in the entire volume, and this technique may prove to be of importance in characterizing and improving magnetic materials.

Task 2: Evaporation Purification of Ultrahigh-Purity Materials (R. C. Paule, W. J. Boettinger, and F. S. Biancaniello)

The prospect of containerless processing for a wide range of materials in zero g led us to consider the process of evaporative purification, particularly of such refractory materials as Al_2O_3 or Mo, which can be contaminated easily when heated in the presence of a contacting crucible. Evaporative purification, which may be carried out by heating a levitated drop at high temperatures either in vacuum or in oxidizing or reducing ambients at low pressure, relies on the selective distillation out of impurities. Computer calculations have been made of the degree of purification expected in quite general cases. For example, they show that, for the specific case of a well-mixed melt of Al_2O_3 heated in a low pressure of oxygen at 2400°K with initially 10 ppm of CaO present, the impurities would be reduced substantially in several minutes, with only very little loss of Al_2O_3 (Fig. 4).

Experimental studies on Earth of levitated Al_2O_3 await development of a suitable means for suspending and heating droplets of this substance. We have carried out mass spectrometric studies of the relative abundances of the various vapor species from molten Al_2O_3 at the end of an Al_2O_3 rod and also

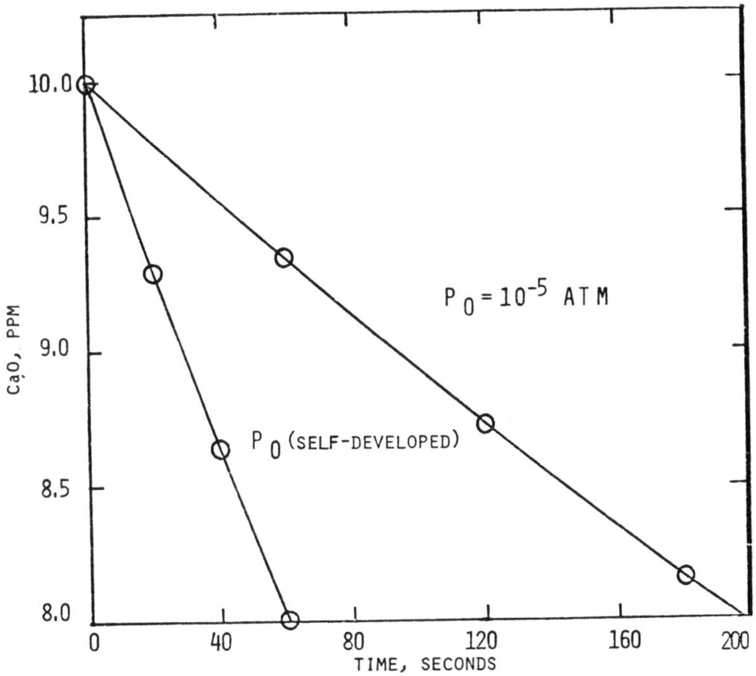

Fig. 4 Calculated CaO vaporization from Al_2O_3 at 2400°K.

have studied the effects of nonequilibrium radiative heating of the specimen. We have gone forward, however, to study experimentally the evaporative purification of levitated liquid molybdenum droplets of about 4 g each. The Fe impurity was reduced rapidly from 50 ppm to 50 ppb. Figure 5 shows our rf levitation setup, and Table 1 shows the results. That the cleanup of Fe takes place so rapidly and completely is a good indication of the efficacy of the stirring of the molten droplet by the rf field. Of course, in zero g and/or with other heating mechanisms, the stirring may well be different.

Task 3: Composite Materials (H. Yakowitz)

This task has been concerned with composites and with methods for characterizing them, especially by scanning electron microscopy and by energy dispersive x-ray microanalysis. Methods for determing the x-ray distribution in depth within the material have been obtained. The use of electron channeling patterns to determine strain in the bond area has been developed. Composites consisting of reinforcements of silicon carbide, tungsten, pyrolytic graphite, and sapphire

Fig. 5 Radio-frequency levitation apparatus showing coil.

Table 1 Summary of Evaporative Purification Experiments on Molybdenum

Initial material	
Sample number	Fe content, ppm (by mass)
A	54.0
	54.2
B	46.9
	47.5
C	43.8
	43.9

Purified material

Sample number	Maximum temp. (a) °K	Time completely molten, sec.	Fe fraction, ppb (by mass)
2-3	2950	57	22.9[b]
2-7	2959	88	26.3[b]
2-13	2936	6	45.0[b]
3-21	2896	0	1340.2
3-24	3035	198	350.3
4-2	2989	8	31.8[b]
4-9	3016	44	32.9[b]
4-14	2896	0	483.4
4-16	3013	41	78.0
5-2	2944	195	20.1[b]
5-12	2983	306	175.2
5-15	2950	309	314.5
7-1	3016	470	33.7[b]

[a]Based on melting point of Mo of 2896°K.
[b]The sensitivity of this chemical analysis (as determined by the blank Fe level) is 50 ppb. Hence, these values should be considered as <50 ppb.

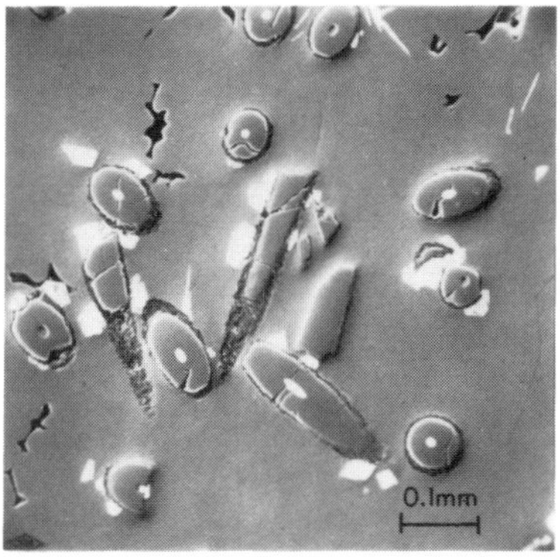

Fig. 6 SEM photograph of SiC-Al composite showing details of reaction zones between SiC fibers and aluminum matrix.

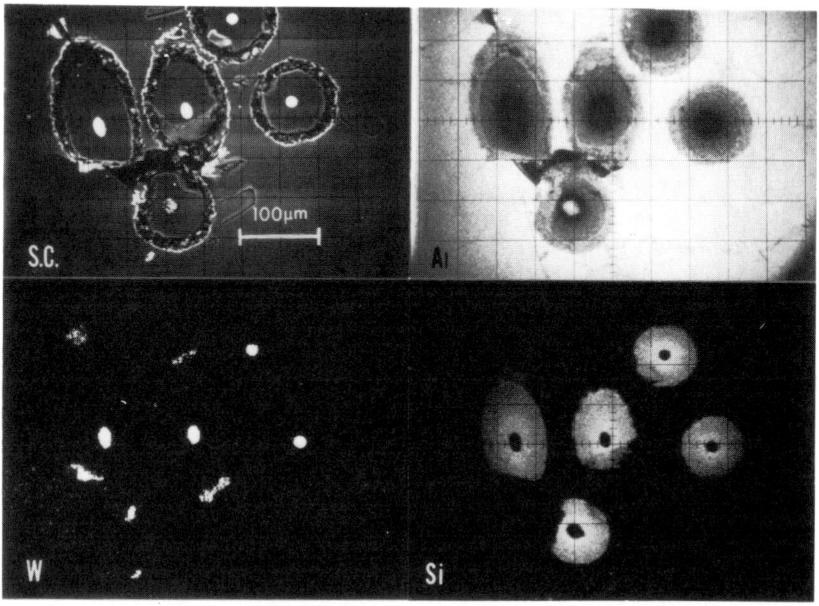

Fig. 7 Phase locations in SiC-Al composite by x-ray scanning microanalysis.

have been studied. Figure 6 shows a SiC-Al composite, and in Fig. 7 some of the phases present in the composite are identified, including tungsten present as a core of the SiC.

Task 4: Melt Shape in Weightless Crystal Growth (S. R. Coriell and S. C. Hardy)

Molten zones play a key role in crystal growth, zone melting, and zone refining on Earth, where more than 100 tons/

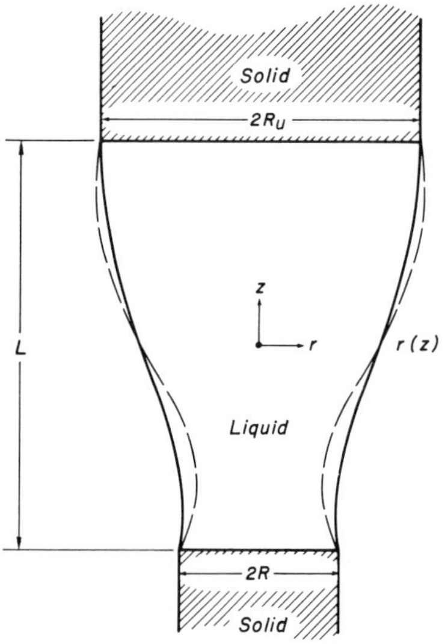

Fig. 8 Calculated stable liquid zones between solids of radii Ru and R. For these zones, (L/R)=5, Ru=2R, and volume $V=(7/3)\Pi R^2L$, in zero gravity. The solid curve corresponds to zero rotation, whereas the dashed curve corresponds to a finite rotation.

yr. of silicon, for example, are prepared by this process; it is expected that they also will play a key role in zero g space processing. Experimental and theoretical investigations of the floating zone process of crystal growth and purification have been carried out, with particular emphasis on microgravity conditions. Figure 8 shows the geometry of a liquid of length L between two solid cylinders that are coaxial. Coriell, Hardy, and Cordes have calculated the shape and stability of such zones for various Bond numbers ε, where $\varepsilon=\rho gR^2/\gamma$ (ρ is liquid density, γ surface tension, and g gravitational acceleration). Figure 9 shows a comparison of numerical (solid line) and experimental (points) results for the maximum stable zone length (vertical zones) as a function of the Bond number. These measurements were made with water zones between steel rods, using air and dibutylpthalate as the containing fluid. The dash line is an earlier result by Carruthers and Grasso. Finally, Fig. 10 shows the agreement between photographed and calculated zone shapes in 1 g, where $V=0.02\ cm^3$, R=0.12 cm, L=0.49 cm and γ=72 ergs/cm , no rotation. Of course a knowledge of zone shape is important for growing crystals of constant diameter.

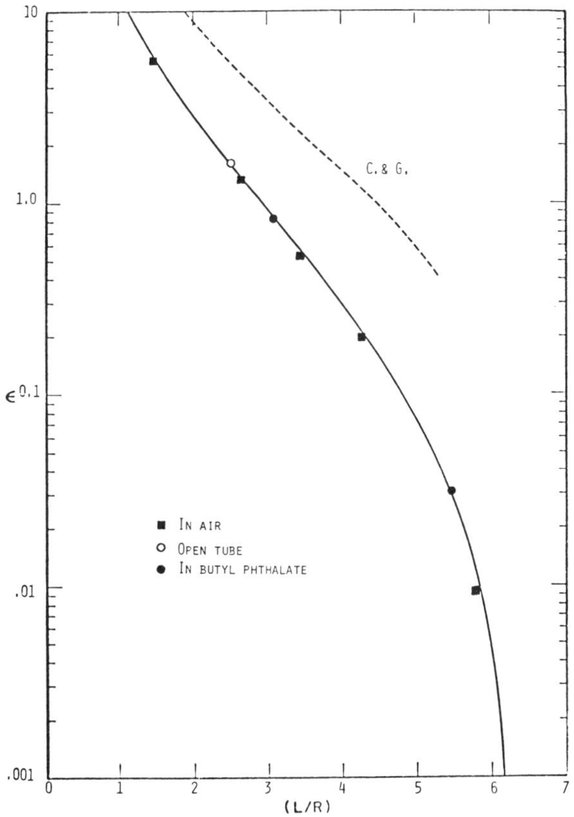

Fig. 9 Maximum stable zone length for vertical zones as a function of Bond number ε. Solid line, calculated; points, experimental; dashed line, earlier result of Carruthers and Grasso.

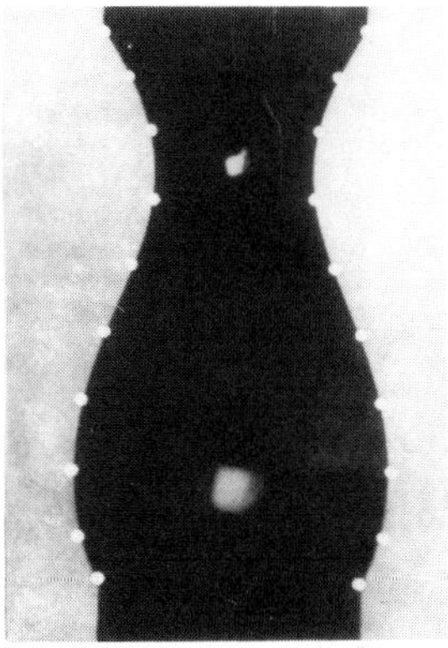

Fig. 10 Comparision of observed and calculated zone shape for water between two steel rods (volume=0.020 cm^3, R=0.12 cm, L=0.49 cm, γ=72 mJm^{-2}, no rotation).

Table 2 Summary of Hg_2Cl_2 transport experiments in vertical tubes

Temperature[a] °C Top	Temperature[a] °C Bottom	Pressure[b], atm	Time, hr	Amount transported, g	Path length, cm	Transport Rate, g/hr	Δρ, atm
				Maximum convection			
240	310	0.01	96	2.0	13	0.021	0.12
380	400	1.0	48	20.0[c]	13	>>0.4[c]	0.5[d]
410	470	3.8	69	22.2[c]	13	>>0.3[c]	8.8
				Minimum convection			
392	350	0.44	4.5	0.27	12	0.059	0.9
405	325	0.20	7.0	3.31	12	0.473	1.6[d]
410	350	0.44	7.0	2.83	10	0.404	1.5[d]
410	350	0.44	7.5	4.95	7	0.660	1.5[d]

[a] Temperature at source (hotter) and deposition (colder) end of transport tube.
[b] Equilibrium vapor pressure at lower temperature.
[c] Entire charge transported, actual rate not known.
[d] Assuming no dissociation of vapor.

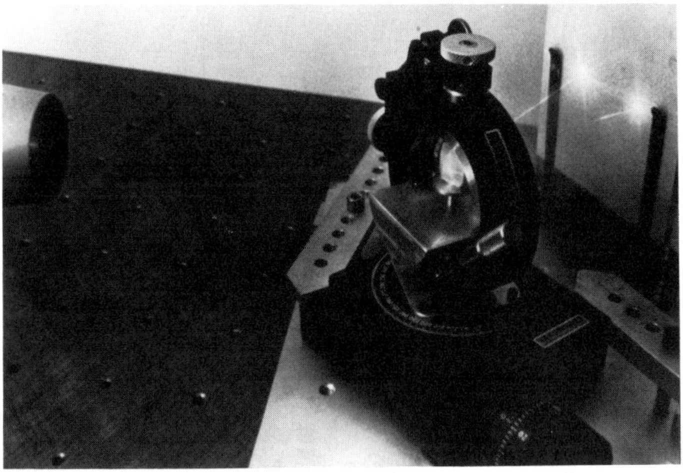

Fig. 11 Illustrating high degree of birefringence in Hg_2Cl_2 prism using beam of laser light.

Task 5: Vapor Transport Crystal Growth (H. S. Parker)

Although chemical vapor transport crystal growth has been carried out in zero g by Wiedemeier, it does have the complexity of two phenomena taking place concurrently: crystal growth and chemical reactions. We have been carrying out physical vapor transport crystal growth with the aim of investigating this technique and for definition of the limitations that may be imposed by convection effects in a temperature gradient. The growth of mercurous chloride by an evaporation-condensation mechanism was chosen not only because of its adaptability to this method but also for potential technological importance as an infrared polarizing material. Table 2 shows some of the pertinent transport data, in which the effects of convection have been varied by appropriate orientation of the tube (in gravity). Figure 11 shows the remarkable degree of birefringence obtainable with this material, grown from the vapor phase.

Task 6: Surface Traction and Related Phenomena (A. L. Dragoo)

The role of surface-traction-induced convection, in the absence of gravity-driven buoyancy convection, long has been recognized as of possibly major importance in space processing. We have investigated the pattern of thermocapillary convective cells in a liquid drop with an axially symmetric temperature field. Figure 12 shows streamlines and stagnation points for

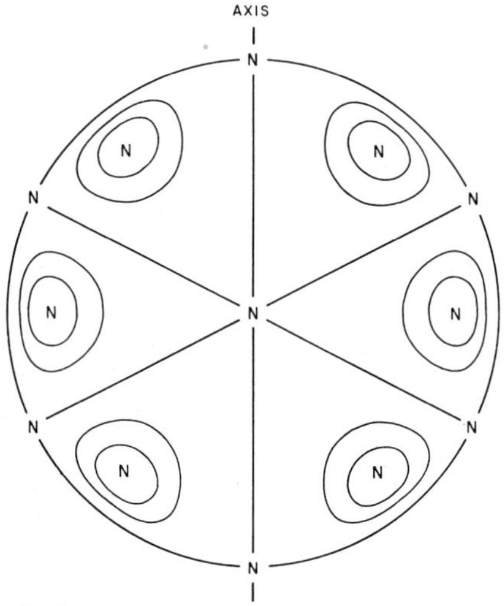

Fig. 12 Calculated cross-sectional pattern of thermocapillary convective cells in liquid drop with axially symmetric temperature gradient; showing streamlines and stagnation points.

Table 3: Calculated thermocapillary circulation for metal and oxide liquids [a]

	γ_T, mN/m/°K	Temp. T_o, °K	Viscosity, mPa-sec	$\lvert\tau\rvert$, sec
		Metals		
Aluminum	-0.356	930	4.5	0.14
		1070	2.5	0.08
Copper	-0.06	1370	4.5	0.9
		1470	3.9	0.7
Mercury	-0.2049	290	1.554	0.0869
		470	1.052	0.0588
		Oxides		
Al_2O_3	(0.1)[b]	2400	0.11	13
		2600	0.062	7
B_2O_3	0.0354 (18)	1410	5.02	1620
	at 720°K	1670	2.01	651
SiO_2	0.031	2280	717	8×10^5
	at 2000°K	2680	102	1×10^5
		2820	46.4	5×10^4

[a]Temperature gradient at the poles has a magnitude of 1 deg/cm.
[b]Estimated.

a particular mode of convection. Circulation times for both metal and oxide droplets, for a 1 deg/cm temperature gradient, are shown in Table 3 and depend strongly, of course, on the viscosity. Yet it does appear that good stirring could be obtained even in this small a gradient. This work has been applied to a study of the enhancement of evaporative purification rates.

References

[1] Passaglia, E. and Parker, R. L., "NBS Space Processing Research," NBSIR 76-980, Feb. 1976, National Technical Information Service, Springfield, Va.

[2] Passaglia, E. and Parker, R. L., "NBS Space Processing Research," NBSIR 74-611, Nov. 1974, National Technical Information Service, Springfield, Va.

[3] Passaglia, E. and Parker, R. L., "NBS Materials Science and Manufacturing in Space Research," NBSIR 73-402, Nov. 1973, National Technical Information Service. Springfield, Va.

CZOCHRALSKI GROWTH OF CRYSTALS IN 0 G AND 1 G

H. Wenzl*

Institut für Festkörperforschung, Kernforschungsanlage
Jülich, Jülich, West-Germany

Abstract

Modified Czochralski growth arrangements are presented which can be used in 0 g. They are intermediate growth systems between Bridgman and zone melting processes. Differences between Czochralski growth in 1 and 0 g are discussed. In 0 g, the melt at the growth interface is thermodynamically stable, whereas in 1 g it is only metastable. Meniscus shapes have been calculated for selected boundary conditions in 1 and 0 g. In 1 g, the hydrostatic pressure at the growth interface normally is determined by the position of the growth interface, whereas in 0 g the hydrostatic pressure in the melt and the position of the interface usually can be varied independently from one another.

1. Czochralski Crystal Growth arrangements in 1 g and 0 g

Growth of single crystals from the melt in 1 g can be achieved in a controlled way by the Bridgman, Czochralski, or zone melting method. In Skylab, the first crystal growth experiments in 0 g were performed with the comparatively simple Bridgman method. For future crystal growth processes in Spacelab, zone melting seems to be favored, because it has several adavantages over the other methods: 1) the melt is not in contact with hot crucible walls and cannot be contaminated easily; and 2) in 0 g the diameter of the crystal no longer is restricted by the limited value of the surface

---

Presented as Paper D.2.3 at the COSPAR Symposium on Materials Sciences in Space, Philadelphia, Pa., June 9-10, 1976.
* Director.

tension, as is the case in 1 g. On the other hand, the zone melting process requires skillful operators or sophisticated control systems.

Therefore, we propose to consider also modifications of the Czochralski method for crystal growth in Spacelab, because the Czochralski method is intermediate between the Bridgman and zone melting methods: it uses hot crucibles to contain the melt as in the Bridgman method, but the growth interface is free, not in contact with crucible walls, as in the zone melting method. The further discussion of Czochralski growth in 1 and 0 g is based on Ref. 1.

Figure 1 shows schematically the growth of a single crystal with the Czochralski method in 1 g. A few characteristic features will be pointed out:

1) The temperature gradient near the growth interface points downward; therefore, convection sets in easily and controls heat and mass transfer.

2) The hydrostatic pressure in the liquid decreases linearly with increasing height z according to $p = p_o - dgz$, where p_o is the pressure at the horizontal melt surface in the crucible, d the density, g the gravitational acceleration,

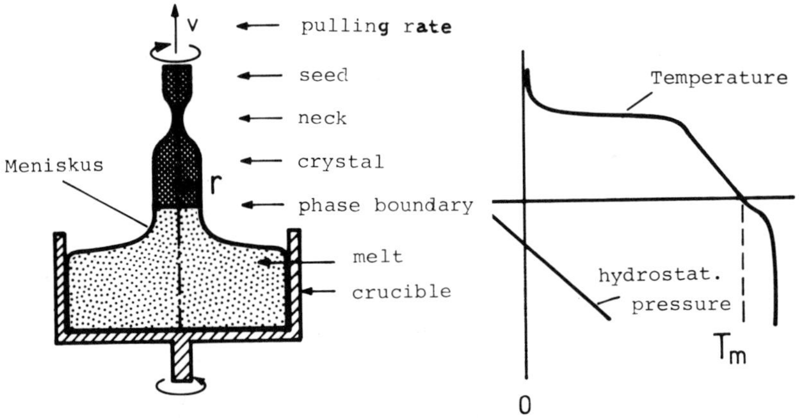

Fig. 1 Left: schematic cross section of crystal growth process with Czochralski method in 1 g. The crystal is withdrawn with the speed v from the melt during the growth process. Heaters and other technical details are not shown. Right: hydrostatic pressure in melt and temperature along axis as a function of vertical position (schematic). T_m is the melting point isotherm that essentially coincides with the growth interface.

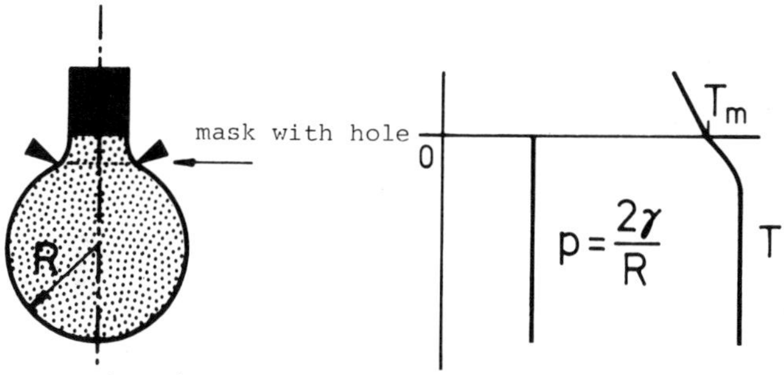

Fig. 2 Schematic picture of Czochralski growth process in 0 g without crucible. p is the hydrostatic pressure, γ the surface tension of the melt, and R the radius of the spherical surface of the melt. A nonwetting mask helps to shape the meniscus at the growth interface.

and z the vertical coordinate (z = 0 at horizontal melt level in crucible). Usually, p is negative at the growth interface: the liquid tends to boil.

3) The crystal is subject to elastic stress because of its own weight and because of surface tension and hydrostatic pressure at the interface. If the crystal is about 10 cm long, has a diameter of 1 cm and a density of 10 g/cm^3, the stress due to its own weight exceeds 10^7 dyn/cm^2 at the neck, with a diameter of about 1 mm. This stress already can be larger than the critical stress at which plastic deformation and, therefore, deterioration of the crystal quality starts.

Figure 2 shows an arrangement at 0 g with the corresponding temperature and hydrostatic pressure as a function of vertical position. The melts tends to form a sphere; the crucible is no longer necessary to contain it. Near the growth interface, external forces must be used to shape the meniscus and balance the forces with which the crystal pulls on the melt at the interface (surface tension and melt-solid interaction). These forces can be applied on the surface by means of a nonwetting mask, as shown in the figure, or in the bulk near the surface by means of electromagnetic induction.

A more advantageous arrangement is shown in Fig. 3: the melt is contained in a cylinder with a piston. In this way, the hydrostatic pressure in the melt can be controlled easily. Here and in the further discussion, it is assumed that wetting of the containers by the melt is negligible.

The thermodynamic stability of solid and liquid in the various growth arrangements can be characterized qualitative-

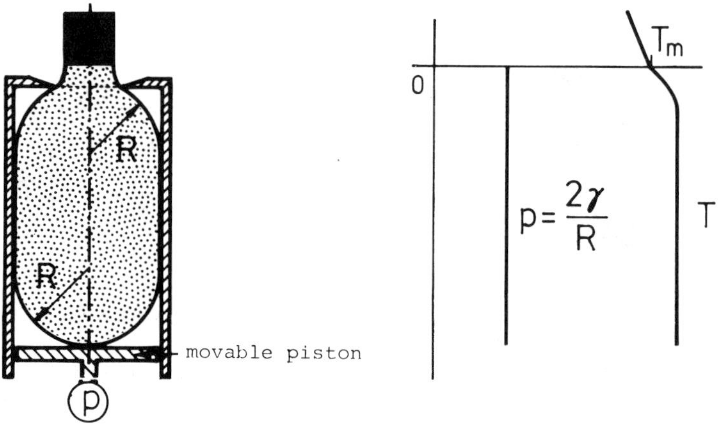

Fig. 3 Schematic picture of Czochralski growth process in 0 g in a cylindrical crucible with piston and mask.

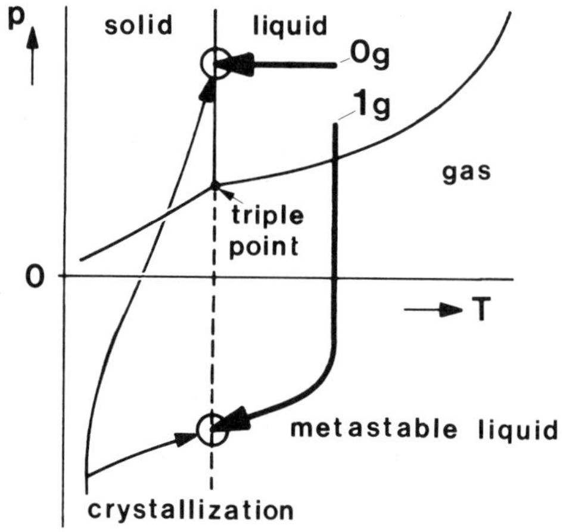

Fig. 4 Schematic phase diagram of monocomponent material. Heavy lines indicate temperature (T)-pressure (p) relations for Czochralski growth melts in 1 and 0 g.

ly by using the phase diagram in Fig. 4 and applying thermodynamics locally. In 0 g growth, the liquid and solid are inherently stable against gas bubble formation (boiling), whereas in 1 g one must rely on the long relaxation time necessary for formation of bubbles in the unstable region of both phases near the phase boundary. But pure liquids boil catastrophically only at hydrostatic pressure below about -1000 bar and are, therefore, metastable in normal 1 g crystal growth processes, in which hydrostatic pressure of the order of 10 mbar occur in the melt near the growth interface.

2. Static Meniscus Shapes

Uelhoff and Mika have calculated axisymmetric meniscus shapes for Czochralski growth in 1 g[2,3]. The calculations are based on the Gauß-Laplace equation $\gamma(1/R_1 + 1/R_2) = p_o - dgz$, with γ as surface tension, R_1 and R_2 the two principal radii of curvature, p_o the hydrostatic pressure at z = 0 (see fig. 6), d the density, and g the acceleration of gravity. In 0 g, the term dgz vanishes. The right side describes the hydrostatic pressure in the liquid as a function of position z, the left side the force per unit area normal to the surface due to the surface tension. Both pressures must be equal for static[1-3] meniscus shapes. The results of the numerical solutions are plotted in cylinder coordinates (z, r), transformed into dimensionless quantities by $\rho \equiv r/K$, $\zeta \equiv z/K$, with pressure p

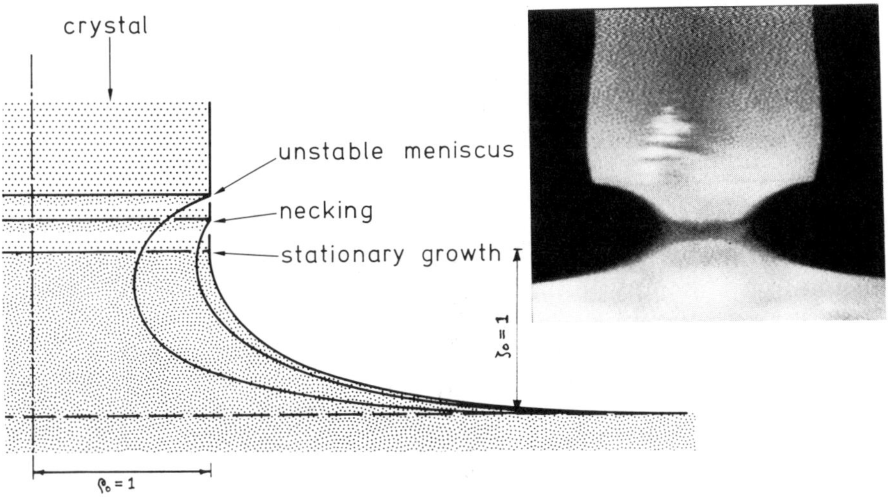

Fig. 5 Static meniscus shape for Czochralski growth in 1 g in cross section through axis of axisymmetrical arrangement according to calculations of Uelhoff and Mika[2,3]. 1) Stationary growth with constant crystal diameter (assuming φ = 0 for this case; see fig. 6). 2) Decrease of crystal diameter during further growth by pulling the crystal upward. 3) Unstable meniscus. Meniscus tends to separate from crystal by small disturbance. Insert: television picture of Czochralski growth of copper at the moment of separation of unstable meniscus from crystal (exposure time about 10 msec, crystal diameter 10 mm).

as additional parameter, used in dimensionless form as $\pi \equiv p/K_p$, with $K \equiv (\gamma/gd)^{1/2}$ and $K_p \equiv (\gamma gd)^{1/2}$. For copper, one calculates the following numerical values: K = 3.7 mm; K_p = 2.2 Torr = 3 mbar = 3 10^3 dyn/cm^2 = 300 Pa. The pressure of 3 mbar exists in a free liquid sphere of radius r(sphere) = $2\gamma/K_p$ = 9 mm and a free liquid cylinder of radius r(cylinder) = γ/K_p = 4 mm in the case of copper. The Bond number is related to K by Bo = $(\ell/K)^2$, where the length ℓ describes the linear extension of the meniscus. Figure 5 shows an example of the results in 1 g. These shapes have been verified in growth experiments on copper.

The calculations have been extended to 0 g growth assuming an arrangement as in Fig. 3, with definitions described in Fig. 6. In Figs. 7-8 calculated meniscus shapes are shown for a few values of the parameters ρ_o, ρ_1, and π. The height of the interface ζ_o is determined essentially by the melting temperature isotherm. This isotherm has to be adjusted by varying the heat flow into the interface from the melt (by changing the temperature of the bulk of the melt). The same value of the meniscus angle α (Fig. 6) can be reached for different values of the interface height ζ_o if the pressure π is adjusted, whereas in the normal 1 g arrangement a certain value of α is correlated uniquely with a definite value of ζ_o. But similar arrangements as proposed for 0 g also could be used in 1 g, adding an additional degree of

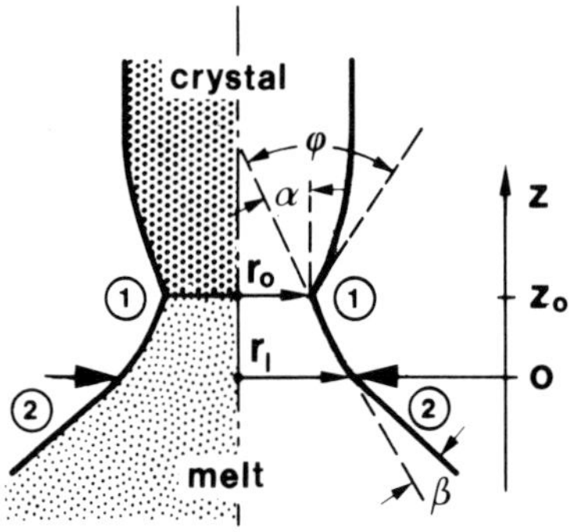

Fig. 6 Definition of meniscus angle α, to be distinguished from contact angle φ. 1 - 1 defines radius r_o; angle α is not restricted. Arrows 2 - 2 indicate position of mask, defining radius r_1 of hole; angle β is not restricted. (For 1·g $z \equiv \zeta \cdot K$; $r \equiv \zeta \cdot K$; $p \equiv \pi \cdot K_p$, for 0·g $z \equiv \zeta \cdot r_c$; $r \equiv \rho \cdot r_c$; $p = \pi \cdot \gamma / r_c$, where r_c = radius of cylindrical crucible).

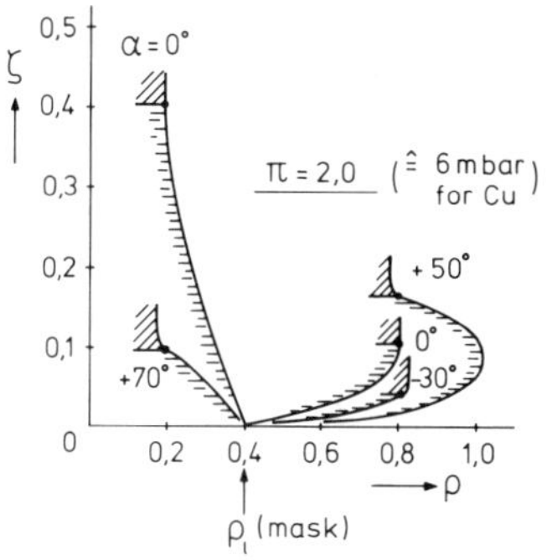

Fig. 7 The lines mark various static meniscus shapes in a cross section through the axis of the axisymmetric arrangement in cylinder coordinates with height ζ and radius ρ (normalized coordinates; see Fig.6). The (ζ,ρ) position of the edge of the crystal at the growth interface is indicated by the shaded corner. Similar menisci exist also for other pressures π. Stationary growth (constant crystal radius) is possible for $\alpha = 0^{\circ}$ (if the contact angle $\varphi = 0^{\circ}$ also[4]). The crystal radius decreases for $\alpha<0^{\circ}$ and increases for $\alpha>0^{\circ}$ during further growth by pulling.

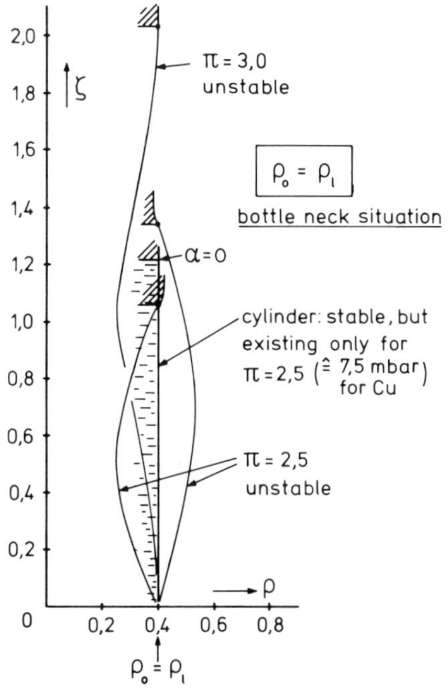

Fig. 8 Meniscus shapes for $\rho_0 = \rho_1$.

freedom for adjusting α. A variation of the contact angle α is necessary during growth, to be able to vary the crystal diameter, e.g., during necking. In principle, a crystal growth experiment in 0 g could follow the sequence in time shown schematically in Fig. 9.

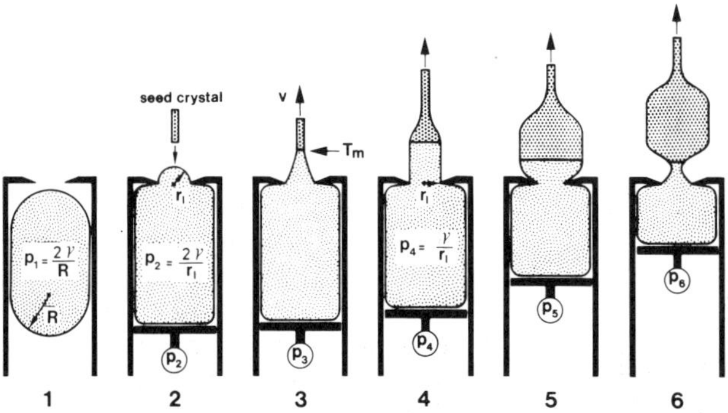

Fig. 9 Crystal growth in 0 g by Czochralski method. Sequence of typical moments: 1) Cylindrical container with nonwetting melt. 2) Piston induces increased hydrostatic pressure until maximum pressure is reached when melt is protruding as hemisphere out of circular hole in mask with radius r_1. 3) Contact with seed crystals is established at isotherm T_m of the melting temperature (increasing temperature in downward direction). The crystal diameter increases during further growth with pulling speed v. The meniscus shape can be changed by varying either p_3 or position of isotherm T_m. 4) Cylindrical meniscus shape is possible only for a specific pressure $p_4 = \gamma/r_1$ ("bottleneck" in growth sequence as far as freedom of choice of pressure is concerned). 5) Decrease of crystal diameter. 6) Further decrease of crystal diameter (beginning of necking or end of growth process).

3. Conclusions

Modified Czochralski arrangements can be useful growth methods in 0 g. In comparing 1 and 0 g Czochralski arrangements, the essential features can be summarized as follows:

1) The melt is thermodynamically stable in 0 g arrangements, whereas it normally is only metastable in 1 g because of small negative hydrostatic pressures existing in the melt at the growth interface (tendency of boiling). In principle, 0 g is advantageous over 1 g from this point of view, although in practice the difference is probably negligible.

2) In normal 1 g Czochralski arrangements, the hydrostatic pressure at the interface is determined by the interface position ζ_o; it is not a free parameter as in 0 g. The meniscus shape wanted must be generated by varying ζ_o, which in turn is determined by the melt temperature and heat flow conditions.

3) In 0 g the interface position ζ_o and the hydrostatic pressure p are independent parameters. For generating the meniscus shape wanted, one can vary either ζ_o or p. Here seems to exist an advantage over the situation in 1 g.

4) In 0 g the hydrostatic pressure is the same everywhere in the melt. Therefore, buoyancy driven convection processes are negligible, in contrast to the situation in 1 g, where they usually dominate heat and mass transfer. Whether pure diffusional heat and mass transfer is advantageous for the quality of the crystal or not cannot be decided generally.

References

[1] Wenzl, H., Mika, K., Müller-Krumbhaar, H., und Uelhoff, W., "Kristallzucht im Weltraum", Jül-1182, April 1975, Bericht der Kernforschungsanlage Jülich, Jülich, West-Germany.

[2] Uelhoff, W., and Mika, K., "Calculations of Shape and Shape Stability of Menisci in Czochralski Growth with Tables to Determine Meniscus Heights, Maximum Heights and Capillary Constants," Jül-1195, May 1975, Bericht der Kernforschungsanlage Jülich, Jülich, West-Germany.

[3] Mika, K., and Uelhoff, W., "Shape Stability of Menisci in Czochralski Growth and Comparison with Analytical Approximations", Journal of Crystal Growth, Vol. 30, month 1975, p. 9.

[4] Wenzl, H., Fattah, A., and Uelhoff, W., "Measurements of Contact Angles for Copper, Gold and Germanium during Czochralski Growth", to be published in Journal of Crystal Growth.

INTEREST AND DIFFICULTIES OF 0-G STUDIES OF THE MECHANISMS OF EUTECTIC GROWTH

Clément Lemaignan* and Yves Malmejac †

French Atomic Energy Commission Grenoble, France.

Abstract

As the theoretical knowledge in the field of eutectic growth gave only a very incomplete explanation of the possible mechanism of defect creation, it seemed reasonable a few years ago to look forward to an improvement in the microstructures when operating in conditions of absence of gravity-induced thermal convection. In fact, this suppression of convection is only one among many modified by the spatial environment conditions, as it was confirmed by the results of the first 0-g experiments, which were difficult to correlate. The present paper will describe the possible modifications of the very diverse mechanisms involved in an eutectic solidification owing to the effect of spatial environment, the influence of those particular conditions not being necessarily propitious with respect to each of them.

Nomenclature

G_L = thermal gradient in the liquid °C/cm
R = Solidification Rate cm/sec.
D_L = Liquid interdiffusion coefficient cm^2/sec
λ = Interlamellar or interfiber spacing cm.

Presented as Paper D.2.4 at the COSPAR Symposium on Materials Sciences in Space, Philadelphia, Pa., June 9-10, 1976.

* Research Metallurgist.

† Director of the Laboratory of Solidification.

Introduction

In the wide field of materials space processing, some of the advantages and disadvantages that may be expected from the space conditions are easier to define now than a few years ago, before any preliminary experiment. The importance of the results of the Skylab and Appollo Souyouz Test Project programs is demonstrated especially in the field of eutectic growth. Since a high level of mechanical strength and of physical efficiency of those in situ composites will depend on the absence of specific growth faults, the prevention of faulting and the improvement in the microstructures when operating in conditions of absence of gravity-induced thermal convection were the first areas for space experiments. In fact, the results of the first 0-g experiments, which were difficult to interpret, confirmed that this suppression of convection was only one among other conditions and parameters that were modified by the space environment. Our aim is to describe some of the possible modifications of the very diverse mechanisms involved in a typical eutectic solidification owing to the effect of 0-g conditions, their influence not being necessarily propitious with respect to each of them.

Analysis of the convection effects

Eutectic solidification is the mechanism leading from a single liquid phase to two distinct solid phases. As a function of their potential applications as structural, mechanical, electronic, optical, or magnetic materials, they are studied widely at present. It was verified that these unidirectionally solidified eutectic materials, of whichever morphology (lamellar or fibrous), included in classical ground conditions a great number of defects that were attributed first to convection currents in the liquid phase. So the first space investigators expected, simply from the absence of convection, important improvements in the quality and regularity of the structures. In fact, the first results obtained have been very irregular, the relative disappointment concerning mainly lamellar metallic eutectics[1], whereas results concerning fibrous alkali halides were far more encouraging[2].

That means only that the space conditions are not a wonderful medicine to every problem encountered on Earth, and also that the complexity of an oriented eutectic growth process is as high in space as on the ground, the numerous involved mechanisms being always homogeneous and heterogeneous nucleations, heat and mass transport, coupled growth of the phases; influence of boundaries or external surfaces of the systems, equilibria of surface tensions, necessary relations between phase spacing and growth rate or interface undercooling, agitation of the bath and its consequent solute redistribution, and mechanical effects. The combination of these various mechanisms, among which some will be modified in various ways by the space environment, results in usually very defective oriented structures.

Consequently, although the hydromechanical effect of the convection initially was considered as the main origin of the defects, it is no longer possible to attribute to it the unique responsibility: the effects will vary from one system to another as a function of the development of the isolated phases in the liquid ahead of the principal interface and also of their morphology and size. Such an influence will thus be greater for small-size eutectic fibers than for more voluminous lamellae, and for more brittle alkali halide phases than for more mechanically resistant metallic phases. In fact, the real influence of the lack of convection due to weightlessness can be studied only across the modifications occuring for an optimized system that may be obtained at will with fibrous or lamellar morphology as a function of the experimental parameters[3]. It will be necessary to pick out an eutectic system with a very brittle dispersed phase whose mechanical properties are as well known as possible, and to compare the results observed on Earth and in space for different dimensions of this dispersed phase: the diameter of such fibers is approximately a linear function of the experimental quantity $R^{-1/2}$. It also will be highly interesting to compare similar modifications observed on strictly identical materials obtained without convection in space and on the ground: in space, in addition to the suppression of convection, many other mechanisms will be modified, whereas on Earth the creation of a magnetic viscosity (by a magnetic field) opposes only the convection currents without modifying surface tension and nucleation or segregation properties. So, to be efficient, the hydrodynamic properties of the liquid phases have to be studied closely in the exact vicinity of the eutectic point.

It is necessary to keep in mind that the liquid phase that is able to modify the solid structures mechanically is precisely the one that lies immediately over the eutectic point. So they are the hydrodynamic properties of this particular liquid which have to be considered, and not the ones of a liquid phase of similar composition but observed and known in a very different temperature range. It also is necessary to study every secondary source of residual convection to try to separate the mechanical consequences of the convection from the other possible mechanisms. It is much more important to use the advantages of 0-g conditions to gain a more precise knowledge of the global influence of convection on Earth than to attempt immediately to improve the morphological quality of some eutectic crystals that are difficult to grow in 1-g conditions.

In space, the wetting properties of the substrates and heat-transport phenomena are modified. A result of these two changes can be a very marked modification of interface curvature which can affect the mechanisms of defect creation and elimination, and also some mechanisms of parasitic nucleation. It would be useful to introduce in the field of eutectic growth the techniques of interface marking as developed by Witt[4] to analyze the resulting possible modifications of curvature of the moving solid-liquid interface.

Stability of Eutectic Solidification

Crystalline growth specialists are accustomed to defining stable growth conditions as a function of an impurity concentration of the order of 1 ppm. However, eutectic composition is never known with an accuracy of better than 5.000 ppm, and mechanisms of growth destabilization resulting from the existence of the constitutional supercooling phenomena appear for monophases as well as for eutectics, giving cells and primary phase dendrites. Experimental work performed on some eutectic systems has confirmed this analysis. Figure 1 gives a schematic representation of experimentally determined dendrite-eutectic boundaries (curves 1 and 2), and two main remarks concerning their positions have to be made:

1) There exists a finite domain of stable eutectic growth[5], instead of this single predicted eutectic point at $G_L/R = 0$.

2) The stability curves are not symmetric around the eutectic composition but are shifted toward lower or upper concentrations; also, they do not have equal slopes.

The first point was explained by Jackson[6]: at low values of the G_L/R ratio, the possible maximum dendrite growth rate is lower than the imposed solidification rate, thus leading to the disappearance of the dendrites and resulting in a maintained classical eutectic structure. The second observation can be explained only by the modifications introduced by the thermodiffusion on the solidification

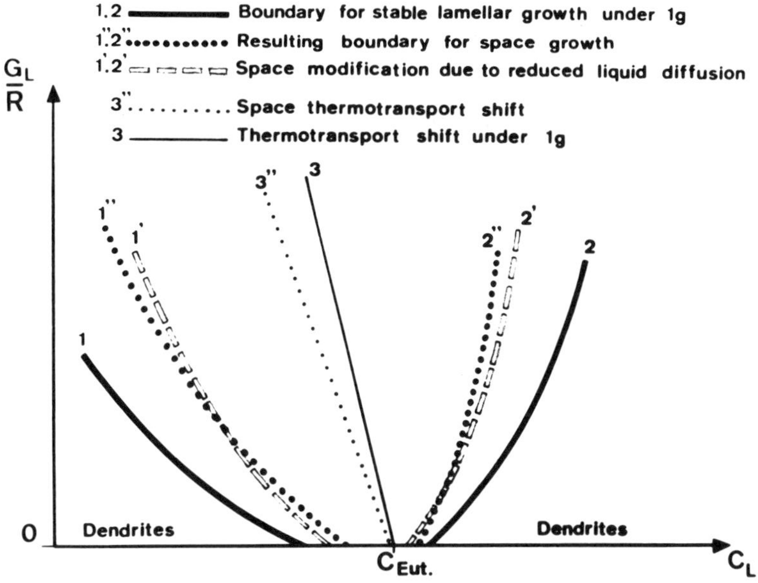

Fig.1 Schematic plot of the dendrite-eutectic transition under 1- and 0-g conditions.

conditions. The imposed thermal gradient induces a flux of solute atoms which modifies the composition near the solid-liquid interface[7]. In all of the situations reviewed, such a composition shift does explain the dissymmetry of the experimental curves of Fig.1. Curve 3 describing the composition shift is approximately the axis of symmetry of the two boundary curves 1 and 2. These reminders of classical ground results are necessary to discuss now some possible modifications in a space environment. Several parameters are not supposed to change in space: eutectic composition and liquidus slope. R is an experimental parameter that can be equalized in space and on the ground. On the other hand, G_L is also an experimental parameter, but as a result of the suppression of thermal convection it will be higher in space than on Earth for the same furnace parameters. This modification would act to improve the stability.

The value of the liquid interdiffusion coefficient D_L is known to be reduced greatly in the space environment[8], and this reduction will influence the constitutional supercooling condition, which will be more difficult to realize, and so the solidification interface will be less stable. This results in the two new boundary curves 1' and 2' of Fig.1.

The thermotransport will be more important, since it will be less compensated by diffusion. This effect leads to higher values of the deviation from eutectic composition near the solid-liquid interface. The mean displacement of composition in the space conditions can be compared in Fig.1 (curve 3") to the one obtained on the ground (curve 3). The overall balance of the different involved modifications should give a drastic modification of the constitutional supercooling criterion in a space environment and of the resulting boundary curves 1" and 2". This will limit the possibility of conserving the regular eutectic structure for reasonable values of the G_L/R ratio. Consequently there will be a tendency to initiate more quickly destabilization mechanisms leading to dendrites. So, it is far more important to know the exact eutectic composition and the values of the interdiffusion and thermodiffusion coefficients in the space conditions than on Earth.

Some Problems of Nucleation

This study can be done by comparing maximum supercoolings and the resulting morphologies in experiments at 1 and 0 g in various containers, and at 0 g, with and without a container to suppress any influence of a substrate. It is reasonable to consider that the sizes of the clusters and critical nuclei, and their circulation in the liquid, may be modified in these various experimental conditions, and this will affect the distribution, the morphology, and the dimensions of the phases in the resulting solid materials. Those studies of the nucleation behavior will be conducted for a wide enough range of compositions around the eutectic point to be able to introduce the composition modifications of the liquids resulting from possible wetting phenomena or from thermodiffusion effects. The space environment gives us a unique opportunity to separate nucleation and growth mechanisms and to correlate the existing information about the structure of liquid eutectic alloys, by means of various physical and structural methods[9], to the pure nucleating behavior of identical alloys.

Relations between Interlamellar Spacing and Growth Rate

It has been observed[3] in terrestrial[10] conditions that the classical law $\lambda^2R = C$ was not observed exactly in the range of the lowest values of R. This abnormal evolution can be a consequence of the composition modifications because of the effect of thermodiffusion. In space conditions, the efficiency of the thermodiffusion would have to be greater, and so the validity of this hypothesis would be tested when comparing $\lambda(R)$ values obtained in 0- and 1-g conditions. In parallel, it would be possible to get information on possible modifications of the surface energy equilibria[11] and on the growth kinetics[12] in the space environment and to verify if they are different from the ones that we can observe on Earth.

Analysis of the Structures

It must be kept in mind that analysis of the different types of defects, their space distribution, their density, and their evolution as a function of the various crystallization parameters is a very difficult and inaccurate task, even in the very rare cases where it is possible to use global, or analytic, complementary methods. The most recent quantitative studies give results with an accuracy of only 50%[13]. Thus, if we want to evaluate with an acceptable precision (e.g., 10%) the influence of space conditions on defect creation mechanisms, it is first indispensable to improve the accuracy of those quantitative analyses. This imposes the task of defining the best system, that is, the most convenient from the point of view of the nature of the phases present for complementary methods. This accuracy of analysis is the only guarantee of the usefulness of the results obtained.

Conclusion

We prefer not to consider that the main interest of the space conditions is to improve the quality of the eutectic morphologies. There is actually some evidence that a very precise control of the growth parameters[3] is much more efficient than the absence of convection, at least in the case of lamellar eutectics, the situation appearing to be different with fibrous eutectics[2].

But there are a lot of theories about the various mechanisms involved in an eutectic solidification process which need to be performed in conditions of absence of any segregation, parasitic nucleation, or mixing of the liquid in order to be verified or adjusted. These conditions can be realized fully in the space environment. For this reason, we believe that the space environment must be used to improve our knowledge of the basic mechanisms rather than to obtain more or less spectacular but isolated results. The importance of such results will be dependent on the quality of the realization of the experiment[14] which means always a very good knowledge of the liquid alloys fluid physics behavior, but the present state of knowledge gives us the opportunity to prepare the next experiments with a precision never before attained.

References

[1]Hasemeyer,E.A., Lovoy,C.V., and Lacy, L.L., "Skylab Experiment M 566 Copper-Aluminium Eutectic", Skylab Results M-74-5, 1974, p. 457.

[2]Yue, A.S., and Yu, A.J., "Halide Eutectic Growth", Skylab Results M-74-5, 1974, p.469.

[3]Malmejac, Y., "Controlled Growth of Al-Al_2Cu Eutectic Crystals", 2nd Conference on In situ Composites, Sept.1975, Lake George, N.Y.

[4]Gatos, H.C. and Witt, A.F., "Interface Marking in Crystals", ASTP Program Exp. Ma-060, 1976, p. 25-1.

[5]Mollard, F.R., and Flemings, M.C., "Growth of Composites from Melt", Transactions of the Metallurgical Society of American Institute of Metallurgical Engineers. Vol 239, Oct. 1967, p.1526-1534.

[6]Jackson, K.A.,"The Dendrite Eutectic Transition in Sn-Pb Alloys" , Transactions of the Metallurgical Society of American Institute of Metallurgical Engineers.Vol 243, July 1968, p.1275-1279

[7]Verhoeven, J.D., Warner, J.C., and Gibson, E.D., "Effect of Thermotransport upon of Eutectic Composite Growth in Sn-Pb Alloys", Metallurgical Transactions, Vol.3, June 1972, p.1437-1441.

[8]Ukanwa, A.O., "M 558 Radioactive Tracer Diffusion", Skylab Results M-74-5, 1974, p. 425.

[9]Malmejac, Y., and Desré, P., "Rapport d'A.T.P.: Etude des Liquides Eutectiques Ag-Ge", Rapport CNRS, 1976, Paris.

[10]Favier, J.J., "Etude Morphologique de Structures Eutectiques Lamellaires", Thesis Ph.D., 1976, Grenoble, France.

[11]Tiller, W.A., "Liquid Metals and Solidification", American Society of Metallurgy, 1968, Cleveland, Ohio.

[12]Racek, R., "Modes de Croissance et Structures d'Eutectiques", Thesis Ph.D., 1973, Nancy, France.

[13]Riquet, J.P., "Etude des Défauts de Solidification dans l'Eutectique Al-Al_2Cu", Thesis Ph.D., 1975, Grenoble, France.

[14]Malmejac, Y., "Review of Possible Eutectic Alloy Solidification Experiments", ASE Symposium, April, 1976, Frascati, Italy.

INFLUENCE OF THE FORCE FIELD ON EUTECTIC STRUCTURE OF ALLOYS

A. S. Okhotin, L. K. Livanov, M. Ya. Tzviling, and Yu. V. Cheshlya

Space Research Institute, Academy of Sciences, Moscow, USSR

Abstract

Alloy crystallization in space occurs under the condition of the absence of the gravitational field. This paper deals with studying the force field influence on the structure of eutectic alloys. Crystallization of Pb-Sb and Bi-Cd alloys was carried out in centrifuges with accelerations from 1 to 120 g at the rate of cooling 2 and 20 deg/min. It is disclosed that, in the case of slow cooling of alloys (2 deg/min), the force field influence consists of grinding the eutectic and changing its morphology. In the case of faster cooling (20 deg/min), the force field does not have sufficient influence on the electric structure; therefore, in the alloys that have been crystallized at 120 g, the structure is grinded more after slow cooling than after fast cooling.

The absence of the gravitational field inside the spacecraft somewhat effects the behavior of liquid metallic melt and the processes of its solidification as already shown in some earlier tests.[1,2] In particular, it was found that the eutectic structure obtained under conditions of weightlessness is finer than that obtained under the usual conditions on Earth.[2]

This paper deals with the results of studying the influence of the force field caused by acceleration (a) that significantly exceeds acceleration of gravity (g). These investigations have been initiated in order to find out how the gravi-

---

Presented as Paper D.2.5 at the COSPAR Symposium on Materials Sciences in Space, Philadelphia, Pa., June 9-10, 1976.

tational field (or its absence) influences the structure of metallic alloys, as well as for the purpose of optimizing the space experiment conditions.

For their study, the alloys have been selected consisting of two components with unlimited mutual solubility in the liquid state, insignificantly soluble in each other when they are solid, and crystallizing with the eutectic formation. In our opinion, just when two phases crystallize from the liquid melt of the eutectic composition (being essentially different in their composition and in their properties), the influence of the force field caused by accelerations on the obtained structure should manifest itself more completely.

The alloys of the Sb-Pb system and the Cd-Bi system of the eutectic composition were under investigation. The specimens and weights from 20 to 25 g and diameter of 6 mm were melted and crystallized in a special crystallizer freely suspended by means of centrifuge levels. In so doing, the following parameters were controlled: the maximum temperature of melt heating (t), the time of its exposure at this temperature (τ), the mean rate of alloy cooling up to its complete solidification (ν), and the acceleration (a) that the centrifuge achieves during heating, exposure, and cooling. The experiment was designed according to a planning matrix for the total factor experiment 2^2. The cooling rate and the actual acceleration were taken as the variable factors. Table 1 presents the compositions of the tested alloys and the experimental conditions.

The metallographic samples were made on the obtained specimens along the central longitudinal sections of ingots, and their structure was analyzed over the section as a whole. The dispersion of the eutectic structure of specimens was estimated comparatively for that particular zone of the section. The specific surface of phase-to-phase interface (D), defined in units of $cm^2 \times cm^{-3}$ using Saltikov's method,[3] was considered as a dispersion criterion. The alloy microstructure was viewed at the light and electron scanning microscopes, with enlargement from 50 to 1200x. The value of D was determined based on 90

Table 1 Composition of tested alloys and experimental conditions

System	Composition	t°,C	τ,min	ν,°C/min	a/g
Sb-Pb	11 - 89	500	15	2; 20	1; 120
Cd-Bi	40 - 60	400	15	2; 20	1; 120

measurements; the results were processed statistically. The fiducial probability of the results is 95%.

The metallographic analysis of the ingot structure, totally confirmed by the chemical analysis, showed that the ingots along their longitudinal section turned out to be heterogeneous as regards their composition. The upper part of the ingot, as should be expected, was enriched by an element with lighter specific weight, and its lower part by a heavier element. The eutectic structure without any redundant crystals was observed only at the middle part of ingots. Hence the eutectic structure was analyzed for the metallographic sample zones at 10 to 15 mm from the lower edge of the ingot. Figure 1 gives examples of the eutectic structure of the alloys. Sb-Pb alloy has the eutectic structure (Figs. 1a and 1b), where the phase is enriched by plumbum (dark background) and there are crystals of antimonious phase with indefinite shape (light granules). As the cooling rate increases from 2 to 20°C/min and the applied acceleration varies from 1 to 120 g, the eutectic structure does not change.

Cd-Bi alloy has the normal rot eutectic structure (Figs. 1c and 1d) that consists of rots of Cd phase located in Bi

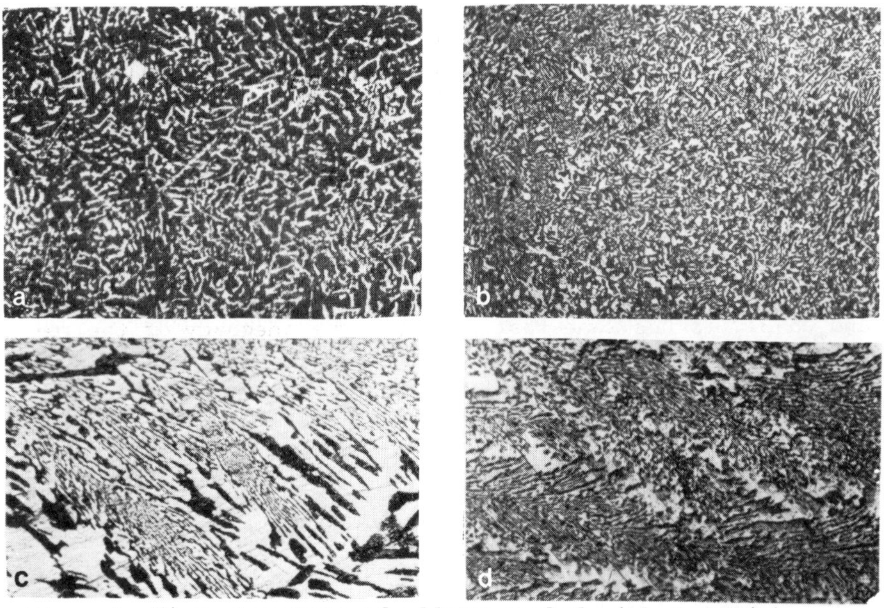

Fig. 1 Microstructure of alloys cooled with 2 deg/min rate. a) Alloy Sb-Pb x 200; acceleration 1 g. b) Alloy Sb-Pb x 200; acceleration 120 g. c) Alloy Cd-Bi x 100; acceleration 1 g. d) Alloy Cd-Bi x 100; acceleration 120 g.

matrix (light background). The changing of the cooling rate and the applied acceleration during crystallization (within the limits taken in this work) does not also result in changing the eutectic structure, although in some cases the structure grinding is seen visually if, e.g., Figs. 1c and 1d are compared.

Hence the preliminary metallographic analysis showed that the variations of v and a within the selected limits do not change the eutectic structure of alloys under study. For the quantitative characteristic of the structure, this allows its dispersion to be limited by the estimation based on the value of D which has been taken as an optimization parameter (y) while planning.

Table 2 presents the planning matrix and the results of the structure dispersion estimates. The bottom part of the table gives the variances in the estimation of the optimization parameters, and the regression equations with the significant coefficients. Here the experimental and handbook values of Fisher's criterion, Fi_{exp} and Fi_{hand}, also are given (in order to check the adequacy of the equations to the analyzed surface of response), as well as the number of degrees of freedom f and the significance level α.

It is seen from the analysis of the results obtained that the form of the regression equations characterizing the changing of the Sb-Pb and Cd-Bi structure dispersion is the same: the term bx_1 is absent in both equations. It means that, with $x_2 = 0$, i.e., during crystallization under the conditions of the 60.5 g acceleration action, the cooling rate of melt does not influence the structure dispersion. To check this, the experiments on crystallization of the alloys with acceleration equal to 60 g (v = 2 and 20 deg/min) were carried out. The results of these experiments (see Table 2) showed that the structure dispersion for two rates of cooling, both for Sb-Pb and Cd-Bi, is the same that confirms the adequacy of the regression equations obtained.

It was found, based on the experiment performed and the analysis of its results, that the acceleration applied during crystallization results in grinding the eutectic structure of alloys Sb-Pb and Cd-Bi if the melt cooling rate corresponds to the lower level (2 deg/min). In this case, the acceleration effect manifests itself in the fact that, with the acceleration equal to 120 g, the structure of alloys after slow cooling turns out to be less dispersive than after faster cooling.

It is necessary to define the value of x_2 for the relative acceleration equal to zero in order to forecast the

Table 2 Planning matrix and experimental results[a]

	Variables: Cooling rate v, deg/min	Variables: Relative acceleration a/g	Test No.	Optimization parameter; specific surface of interphase boundaries $D \times 10^{-3}/cm^2/cm^3$ Sb-Pb (y_1)	Cd-Bi (y_2)
Zero level	11	60.5			
Variation range	9	59.5			
Upper level	20	120			
Lower level	2	1			
Code for variables	X_1	X_2			
Planning	-	-	2; 5	7.0	0.68
matrix	-	+	3; 7	14.3	1.34
2^2	+	-	1; 6	11.8	0.83
	+	+	4; 8	11.1	1.05
Check experiments	+	0	1; 3	9.7	0.83
	-	0	2; 4	10.3	0.80

[a]Sb-Pb alloy: $S_1^2 = 4.0$, $y_1 = 10.9 + 1.6\ X_2 - 1.9\ X_1X_2$;
Cd-Bi alloy: $S_2^2 = 0.036$, $y_2 = 0.95 + 0.20\ X_2 - 0.13\ X_1X_2$;
$F_{1\ exp} = 7.1 < F_{1\ hand}\ (f_1 = 4;\ f_2 = 3;\ \alpha = 0.05) = 9.1$;
$F_{2\ exp} < F_{2\ hand}\ (f_1 = 4;\ f_2 = 3;\ \alpha = 0.05) = 9.1$.

structural variations that should have occurred during crystallization of alloys under weightlessness. In this case, $x_2 = -1.017$. According to Table 2, the eutectic structure dispersion in this case should not differ essentially from that obtained during crystallization on the Earth without overloading, provided that the eutectic morphology is not changed.

References

[1]Belyakov, I. T. and Borisov, U. D., "Technology in the Cosmos," Maschinostroenie, Moscow, USSR, 1974, p. 290.

[2] Proceedings, Symposium on Processing and Manufacturing in Space, March 25-27, 1974.

[3] Saltikov, S. A., "Stereometric Metallography," Metallurgia, Moscow, USSR, 1970.

INFLUENCE OF GRAVITY ON CHEMICAL VAPOR DEPOSITION PROCESSES

G. Wahl*

Brown Boveri Cie; Central Research Laboratory, Heidelberg, Germany

Abstract

Chemical vapor deposition processes (CVD) are influenced by many parameters (pressure, gas composition, gas flow, etc.). One of these parameters is gravity, which affects (provided that there are density differences in the gas) primarily the convection and consequently the total CVD process. The numbers that characterize the influence of gravity on the convection are given. The influence of gravity is described as twofold: it affects the convection in the stationary case, and it creates instabilities. In order to be able to investigate the impact of gas convection on deposition processes, the hydrodynamic theory of a CVD process is described, where the component B is deposited from a gas mixture A,B (mole fraction of B << mole fraction of A). The theoretical results are compared with deposition experiments of Si_3N_4 and SiO_2 according to the reactions $3SiH_4 + 4NH_3 \rightarrow Si_3N_4$ and $SiH_4 + O_2 \rightarrow SiO_2$ (N_2 dilution).

Presented as Paper D.2.6 at the COSPAR Symposium on Materials Sciences in Space, Philadelphia, Pa., June 9-10, 1976. Parts of this paper were presented at the International Conference on Metallurgical Coatings, San Francisco, April 5-9, 1976 and will be published in Thin Solid Films, 1976. This study was supported by the Federal Ministry for Research and Technology (Bundesministerium für Forschung und Technologie), Germany. The author is indebted to P. R. Sahm for helpful discussions and to E. Lischer, A. Neidig, and P. Zenz for assistance with the experimental work.

* senior scientist.

1. Introduction

The properties of layers or crystals deposited by chemical vapor deposition (CVD) are dependent strongly on deposition parameters. One of these parameters is gravity g, whose amount normally cannot be changed on the Earth. Spacelab experiments, however, make it possible to decrease the amount of g and to achieve values as low as [1,2]

$$g = 10^{-3} g_{Earth}$$

The first part of this paper describes the gravitational effects on convection in CVD processes, and the second part gives a hydrodynamic theory for a simplified CVD process. The theoretical results will be compared with visualization experiments, and with Si_3N_4 and SiO_2 deposition experiments. The hydrodynamic theory enables us to calculate the convection and to study its influence on the properties of the deposited material.

2. Influence of Gravity on Convection in CVD Processes

In chemical vapor deposition processes (CVD), a chemical reaction on or near a substrate surface yields deposits from the gas phase. A CVD apparatus consists of two components: a source for the reactive gas mixture, and a reaction chamber with the substrate. Two types of CVD processes can be distinguished: [3-5]

1) In the closed-tube system (Fig.1), the reaction tube is filled with the source material on one side. The substrate,

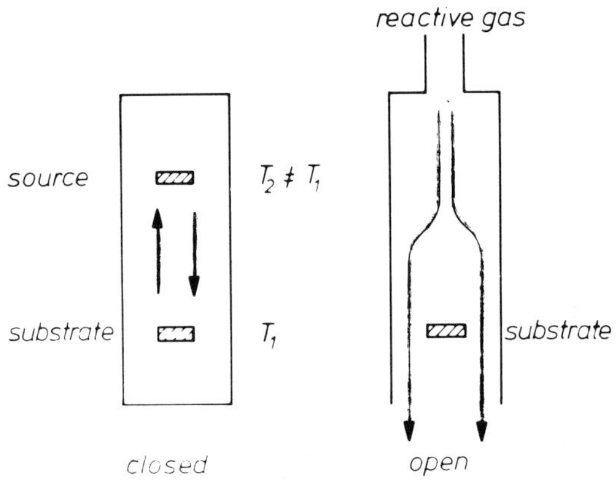

Fig. 1 Schematics of a closed- and open-tube CVD process.

on which the deposition takes place, is fixed on the other side. The tube is filled with a reactive gas. The source material and the substrate material are heated up to different temperatures $T_1 \neq T_2$ (experiments with $T_1 = T_2$ are discussed in Ref. 6), so that the thermodynamic equilibria at the source and at the substrate are different, which causes a chemical transport from the source to the substrate.

2) In the open-tube system (Fig.1), a reactive gas is led through the reaction chamber, where the reactive gas is, in most cases, mixed outside the reactor.

The chemical deposition process occurs in both cases in a series of steps: 1) convection caused by a) forces from outside (forced convection), b) pressure differences inside of the reactor, and c) the interaction between the gravitational force and density differences; 2) diffusion processes; 3) chemical reactions in the gas phase; 4) adsorption on the surface; 5) diffusion processes on the surface; 6) chemical reaction and nucleation on the surface; and 7) desorption of the reaction products from the surface.

All of these processes are interdependent and additionally depend on the temperature field that is formed in the gas phase. They cause the structure of the deposited material and can be changed by varying the deposition parameters, including the parameter g. Gravity exercises a direct influence only on convection (point 1c), and this takes place only if there are density differences in the gas. The density differences can be cuased by thermal expansion effects and by chemical reactions.

The effect of gravity on the convection can be studied in a gas- or liquid-filled enclosure (as an example, for a closed-tube reactor), which consists of two parallel infinite horizontal plates at a distance d (Fig. 2, Benard problem[7-9]). The lower plate is heated up to the temperature T_b and the upper plate to the temperature $T_u \neq T_b$. Chemical reactions are not supposed to take place. At g=0 there is no convection in the enclosure regardless of the temperature difference $\Delta T = (T_b - T_u)$. This applies also to $g \neq 0$, provided that $T_u > T_b$. If, however, $T_u < T_b$, thermal convection can be caused by gravity. The generated flow patterns can be characterized by the Prandtl number Pr ($= \eta c_p/\lambda, \eta$ = viscosity, c_p=specific heat, λ=heat conductivity) and the Rayleigh number Ra=PrGr, where the Grashof number Gr is defined by

$$Gr = g l^3 \Delta T \rho^2 \beta / \eta^2 \qquad (1)$$

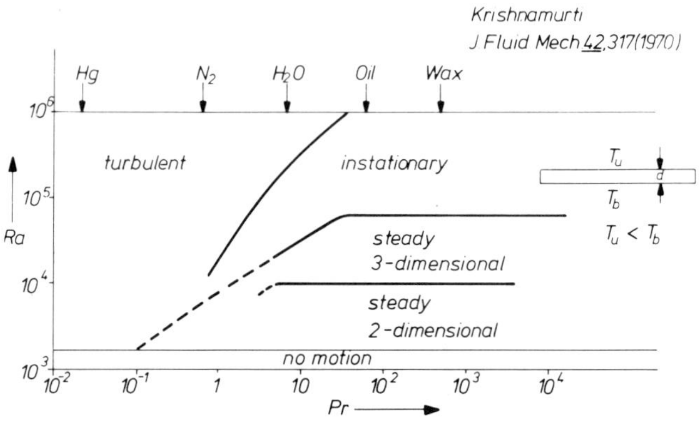

Fig. 2 Flow patterns formed at $g=g_{Earth}$ in an enclosure consisting of two parallel infinite horizontal plates filled with a gas or a liquid with different Pr numbers.[8,9]

where l is the geometric parameter (in this case $l \equiv d$), ρ is mean density, β is thermal expansion coefficient ($\beta = 1/T$ for an ideal gas), and $\Delta T=T_b-T_u$.

The following interrelationship between the Rayleigh number and the flow pattern was found (Fig. 2). There is no convection at small Ra<1700. A steady flow pattern occurs at higher Ra. With further increasing Rayleigh numbers, instationary flow conditions are generated, which finally degenerate to a turbulent gas flow.

Gravity-induced convection occurs in other geometries as well. The convection in a cylindrical vertical enclosure was investigated in Ref. 10, where the aspect ratio $\gamma=r/d$ (r=radius, d=distance between the lower plate with the temperature T_b and the upper plate with the temperature T_u) was varied in the range $0.5 < \gamma < 8$. The convection in a horizontal rectangular and cylindrical enclosure with a temperature difference between both side walls was investigated in Ref. 11.

The convection that is produced by the interaction of gravity and chemically induced density differences is more complicated if the gravity-driven convection is superimposed by the Stefan convection,[3] which is generated if molar density differences in the gas are produced by chemical reactions. In order to characterize the influence of gravity on the gas flow, the following more general definition of the Grashof number Gr must be used

$$Gr = g\rho\Delta\rho l^3/\eta^2 \tag{2}$$

where $\Delta\rho$ is a typical density difference in the gas. Equation (1) can be derived from this definition if $\Delta\rho$ is caused by thermal expansion only, because $\Delta\rho$ then can be expressed by $\Delta\rho = \rho\,\beta\,\Delta T$. As the gravity-driven convection does not exist at $g = 0$, the Stefan convection alone determines the flow pattern.

In open-tube CVD systems, a superposition of forced convection and gravity-driven convection is the rule. The effect of gravity on the flow patterns can be described by the number.[12,13]

$$C = Gr/Re^2 \tag{3}$$

where Gr stands for the gravity-driven convection, and the Reynolds number is Re ($=\rho v l/\eta$, v characteristic velocity) for the forced convection. The influence of gravity on the gas flow can be neglected if $Gr/Re^2 < C_1$. At $Gr/Re^2 > C_2$ ($>C_1$), the flow is determined only by gravity. In the range

$$C_1 < C < C_2 \tag{4}$$

the gas flow is influenced by gravity and forced convection. The values C_1 and C_2 are geometry-dependent.

To sum up, the primary effect of gravity on CVD processes may be described to be twofold: gravity 1) changes the stationary flow pattern, and 2) creates instabilities, which were investigated in Refs. 14 and 15. At $g = 0$, these instabilities do not exist, and stationary flow conditions are generated which cannot be reproduced at $g = g_{Earth}$. Chemical transport experiments of GeSe and GeTe[16] have shown that the flow pattern at $g \to 0$ produces more perfect properties in comparison with experiments at $g = g_{Earth}$.

3. Hydrodynamic Description of a CVD Process

3.1 Theory

The following calculations were made for the deposition geometry shown in Fig. 3 (as an example of an open-tube system). The gas flows perpendicularly onto the deposition surface F-E. More details about the deposition geometry are

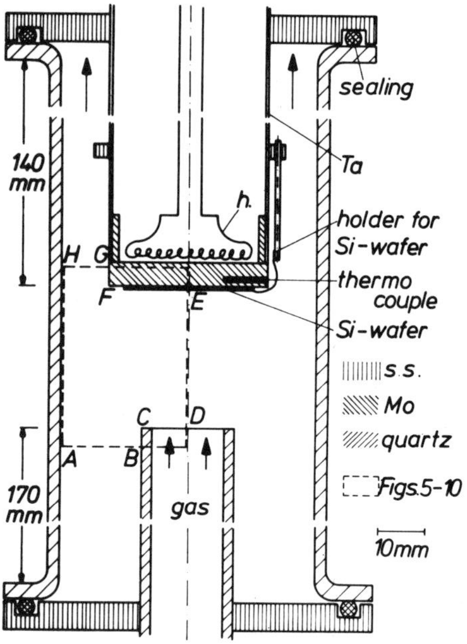

Fig. 3 Reactor used for the calculations and CVD experiments for the deposition of SiO_2 and Si_3N_4 (s.s.: stainless steel; h.: heating).

given in Ref. 17 and in Sec. 3.3. The gas consists only of two components A and B, with the mole fractions $x_B << x_A$ (or mass fractions $y_B << y_A$), where B is deposited on the deposition surface F-E (Fig. 3), which is heated to the deposition temperature T_d. The thermodynamics and the kinetics of the process may be described by the mole fraction x_{Bd} as a boundary condition on the deposition surface. The calculations and the experiments are restricted to the laminar and incompressible flow. Thermodiffusion effects and chemical reactions in the gas phase are neglected. The calculations were made in the range A,B,C,D,E,F,G,H (Fig. 3).

For the calculation, it is necessary to solve the following equations:[12,18-20]

1) Continuity equation for the total density

$$\mathrm{div}\ \rho^+ \vec{v}^+ = 0 \tag{5}$$

2) Continuity equation for the component B

$$\vec{v}^+ \rho^+ \mathrm{grad}\ Y_B^+ = (1/ReSc)\mathrm{div}\ \rho^+ D^+ \mathrm{grad}\ Y_B^+ \tag{6}$$

3) Continuity equation for the energy

$$\rho^+ c_p^+ \vec{v}^+ \text{grad}\, \Theta^+ = (1/RePr)\text{div}\, \lambda^+ \text{grad}\, \Theta^+ \tag{7}$$

4) Continuity equations for the momentum (the equation for only one component is given)

$$\rho^+ v_x^+ \frac{\partial v_x^+}{\partial y^+} + \rho^+ v_z^+ \frac{\partial v_x}{\partial z^+} =$$

$$-\frac{\partial p^+}{\partial x^+} + \frac{1}{Fr}\rho^+ \vec{n}^+ + \frac{\partial}{\partial x^+}\left[\frac{\eta^+}{Re}\left(2\frac{\partial v_x^+}{\partial x^+} - \frac{2}{3}\,\text{div}\,\vec{v}^+\right)\right]$$

$$+\frac{\partial}{\partial y^+}\left[\frac{\eta^+}{Re}\left(\frac{\partial v_x^+}{\partial y^+} + \frac{\partial v_y}{\partial x^+}\right)\right] + \frac{\partial}{\partial z^+}\left[\frac{\eta^+}{Re}\left(\frac{\partial v_z^+}{\partial x^+} + \frac{\partial v_x^+}{\partial z^+}\right)\right] \tag{8}$$

In these equations, only dimensionless parameters were used. The Cartesian coordinates x,y,z, velocity components v_x, v_y, v_z, temperature T, density ρ, pressure p, mass fraction y_B, heat conductivity λ, viscosity η, specific heat c_p, and binary diffusion coefficient D of B in A are replaced by

$$x^+, y^+, z^+ = \frac{x}{R_o}, \frac{y}{R_o}, \frac{z}{R_o}, v_x^+, v_y^+, v_z^+ = \frac{v_x}{v_o}, \frac{v_y}{v_o}, \frac{v_z}{v_o},\quad \Theta^+ = \frac{T-T_o}{T_d-T_o}, p^+ = \frac{p}{\rho_o v_o^2}$$

$$\rho^+ = \rho/\rho_o, Y_B^+ = (Y_B - Y_{Bd})/(Y_{Bo} - Y_{Bd}), \lambda^+ = \lambda/\lambda_o, \eta^+ = \eta/\eta_o$$

$$c_p^+ = c_p/c_{po}, D^+ = D/D_o$$

where R_o is the nozzle radius, v_o the mean gas velocity in the nozzle, T_d the deposition temperature, and $T_o, \rho_o, Y_{Bo}, \lambda_o, \eta_o, c_{po}, D_o$ the gas properties in the plane C-D in Fig. 3. The vector $\vec{n}$ is the unit vector in the direction of gravity.

Besides Eqs. (5-8), the ideal gas law must be fulfilled, which in the incompressible case (Ma << 1, neglecting pressure-induced density differences) has the form $\rho/\rho_o = T_o/T$ or the dimensionless form

$$\rho^+ = [\Theta^+(Q-1)+1]^{-1} \qquad (Q \equiv T_d/T_o) \tag{9}$$

According to Eqs. (5-9), the gas flow is determined by the Reynolds number Re $(=\rho_o v_o R_o/\eta_o)$, the Prandtl number Pr $(=\eta_o c_{po}/\lambda_o)$, the Schmidt number Sc $(=\eta_o/\rho_o D_o)$, the Froude number Fr $(=v^2_o/gR_o)$, the temperature quotient Q_+ $(=T_d/T_o)$, and the temperature-dependent functions $\eta^+, \lambda^+, c_p{}^+, D^+$.

In addition, the following boundary conditions must be fulfilled:

1) In the gas inlet (C-D in Fig. 3): the gas density ρ_o, the mass fraction y_{Bo} of the component B, the gas temperature T_o $(=300^oK)$, the velocity profile $v_z=f(r)$ (v_z is the velocity component in the direction of the axis, and r is the radial distance from the axis). In our case, the velocity profile can be assumed to be a Hagen-Poiseuille profile $v_z=2v_{o}[1-(r/R_o)^2]$. The thickness of the nozzle wall was neglected.

2) In the gas outlet (H-G): no axial change of all gas properties.

3) On the surface heated to the deposition temperature T_d (E-F, F-G): deposition of the component B $(Y_B=Y_{Bd})$, deposition temperature T_d, no gas flow. The thickness of the silicon wafer (350μm, see Sec. 3.3) was neglected.

4) At the cold walls (B-C, A-H, and A-B): no deposition, temperature T_o $(=300^oK)$, no gas flow at the walls. For all calculations, the deposition chamber was assumed to be closed along A-B in order to save computation time. The influence of that change on the flow and the deposition is small.

The mass deposition rate is defined by the equation

$$\dot{m}_B = \rho D \text{grad } Y_B \tag{10}$$

or by

$$Sh = (\rho^+ D^+/ReSc) \text{ grad } Y^+_B, \tag{11}$$

where the Sherwood number Sh $[=\dot{m}_B R_o/D_o\rho_o(Y_{Bo}-Y_{Bd})]$ describes the mass deposition. The gradient in Eqs. (10) and (11) must be formed perpendicularly on the deposition surface.

The influence of gravity is characteristized by the Froude number. The following relation can be derived from the definitions of Fr, Re, and Gr [Eq. (2)]

$$Gr = (Re^2/Fr)(\Delta\rho_o/\rho_o) \tag{12}$$

The Sherwood number is a function of all parameters mentioned

$$Sh = f(r_s^+, Re, Sc, Pr, Q, \eta^+, \lambda^+, D^+, c_p^+) \quad (13)$$

In the isothermal case, the function can be simplified to

$$Sh = g(r_s^+, Re, Sc) \quad (14)$$

At $Gr/Re^2 < C_1$, the mass deposition rate is independent of Fr

$$Sh = h(r_s^+, Re, Sc, Pr, Q, \eta^+, \lambda^+, D^+, c_p^+) \quad (15)$$

At constant Re, the Sherwood number is pressure-independent because all other numbers in Eq. (15) are pressure-independent. This means that the deposition rate

$$\dot{m}_B = D(\rho_o/R_o)(Y_{Bo}-Y_{Bd})\cdot h(r_s^+, Re, Sc, Pr, Q, \eta^+, \lambda^+ D^+, c_p^+) \quad (16)$$

is pressure-independent, too.

For the numerical solution, the boundary-value problem was transformed into cylindrical coordinates. The problem then depends only on the coordinate z in the direction of the axis and on the radius r. Instead of the velocity components v_r^+, v_z^+, the stream function $\psi^+[\rho^+ v_z^+ = (1/r^+)(\partial\psi^+/\partial r^+);\ \rho^+ v_r^+ = -(1/r^+)(\partial\psi^+/\partial z^+)]$ and the vorticity $w^+[=(\partial v_r^+/\partial z^+) - (\partial v_z^+/\partial r^+)]$ were introduced. The resulting elliptical boundary-value problem was simplified according to Ref. 20 [neglecting the term S in Eq. (2.22-46) in Ref. 20] and solved by the finite-difference method described in Refs. 20 and 21 in the range ABCDEFGH in Fig. 3. The values of $\psi^+, w^+, \rho^+, Y_B^+, \Theta^+$ were calculated in the nodes of a grid (Fig. 4), which was formed by 20 equidistant lines in the r direction, including the lines along H-G, F-E, C-D, A-B, and 15 equidistant lines in the z direction, including the lines along A-H, B-C, F-G, D-E. In addition, five further equidistant grid lines in the r direction were outlined between the deposition surface and the first parallel grid line in order to calculate the boundary layer near the deposition surface F-E in Fig. 3. The computer program was written in Fortran IV. Normally, 100-200 iterations were necessary to reach convergence (criterion of convergence: fractional change of two successive iteration steps $< 5\cdot 10^{-4}$).

3.2 Results and Comparisons with Visualization Experiments

The calculations were carried out mostly for a N_2-SiH_4 mixture ($x_{SiH_4} \ll x_{N_2}$). The heat conductivity and the

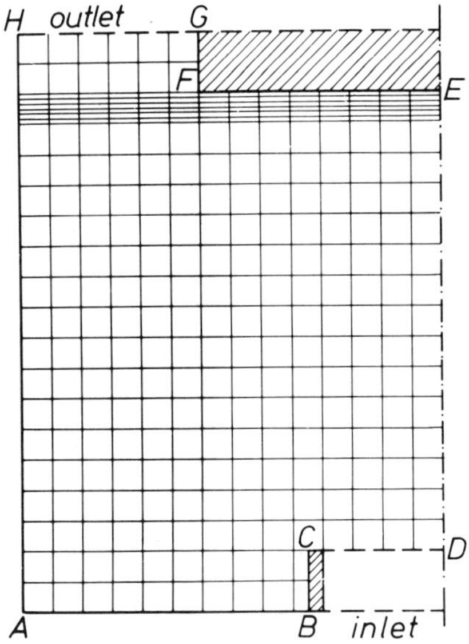

Fig. 4 Grid of the computer calculation. (ABCDEFGH: see Fig. 3)

viscosity of N_2 were taken from Ref. 22, whereby the temperature dependence of these values was extrapolated by a straight line in a log-log plot, resulting in

$$\lambda/\text{cal-sec}^{-1}\text{-cm}^{-1}\text{-}^{o}\text{K}^{-1} = 62\text{x}10^{-6}\ (T/300^{o}K)^{0.84} \quad (17)$$

$$\eta/P = 1.8\text{x}10^{-4}\ (T/300^{o}K)^{0.62} \quad (18)$$

The temperature dependence of the heat capacity c_p=7cal-$^oK^{-1}$-mol^{-1} was neglected.[23] The diffusion coefficient of SiH_4 in N_2

$$D/cm^2s^{-1} = 0.16\ (T/300^{o}K)^{1.7}\ (p/atm)^{-1} \quad (19)$$

was derived from the critical temperature and volume of N_2 and SiH_4 by Eqs. (11-10 to 11-17) in Ref. 24. The resulting Prandtl number Pr and Schmidt number Sc were Pr = 0.73, Sc = 0.9.

Figures 5-7 show flow patterns computed at different flow conditions. The parameters at the streamlines are values of the stream function ψ^+. The differences between the flow patterns in Figs. 5-7 are caused mainly by the effect of gravity. As there are no temperature differences in Fig. 5 and therefore no density difference in the gas, the flow pattern is not dependent on gravity, and the number C has the value C=0. Figure 6, however, where C=22, shows an influence of gravity. The flow pattern in Fig. 7 is

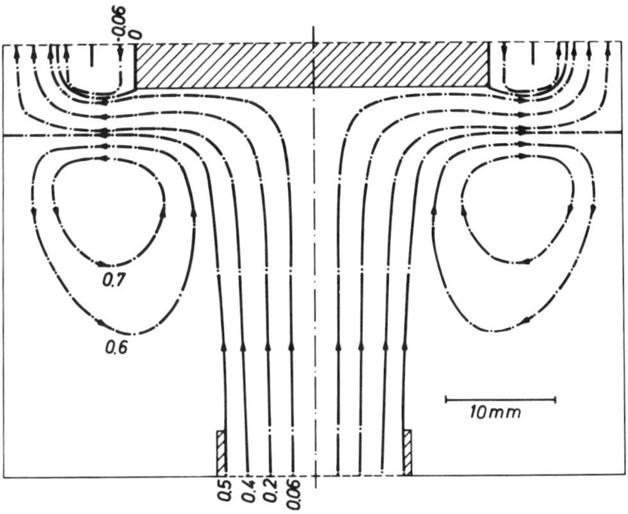

Fig. 5 Calculated streamlines in N_2 (Re = 50, T_d = 300°K, Fr = 0.09, Gr/Re = 0), Parameter: dimensionless stream function $\psi^+=\psi/\rho_o v_o R_o^2$.

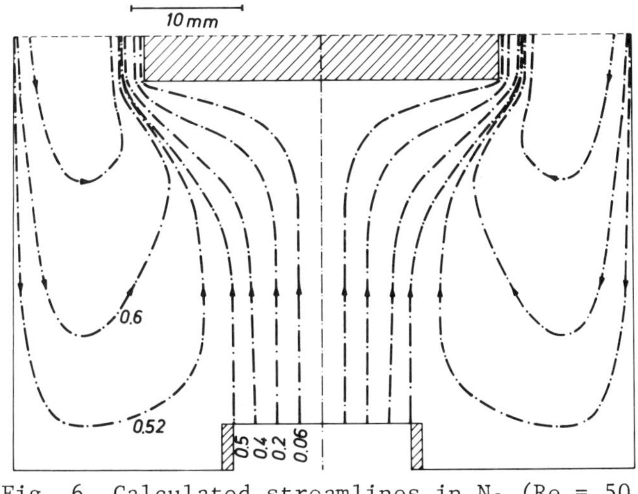

Fig. 6 Calculated streamlines in N_2 (Re = 50, T_d = 900°K, Fr = 0.09, Gr/Re^2 = 22), Parameter: dimensionless stream function $\psi^+=\psi/\rho_o v_o R_o^2$.

computed with the same characteristic numbers as in Fig. 6, the only difference being the reversed position of the reaction chamber.

Flow patterns were calculated at different Re (50<Re<250), as well as different deposition temperatures (300°K<T_d<1300°K). The number C_1 was found to be $C_1 \simeq 1$. At C<1, the flow pattern

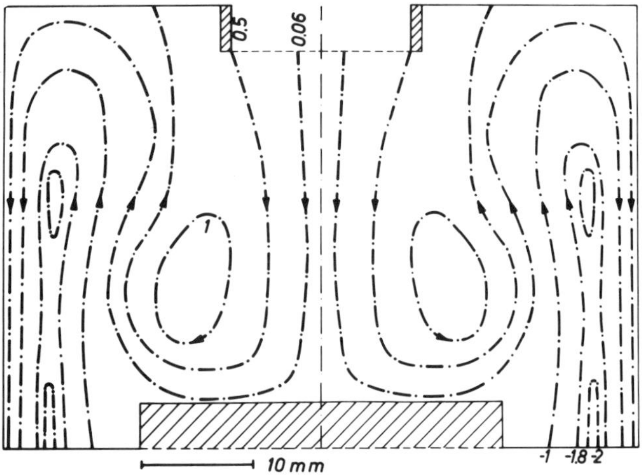

Fig. 7 Calculated streamlines in N_2 (Re = 50, T_d = 900°K, Fr = 0.09, Gr/Re^2 = 22), Parameter: dimensionless stream function $\psi^+=\psi/\rho_o v_o R_o^2$.

is similar to the one in Fig. 5. The calculated patterns are in good agreement with the experimental flow patterns displayed in Figs. 8-10, which were obtained by the $TiCl_4$-H_2O method described in Ref. 13.

The deposition rates, which means the Sherwood numbers Sh on the deposition surface (E-F in Fig. 3), were calculated

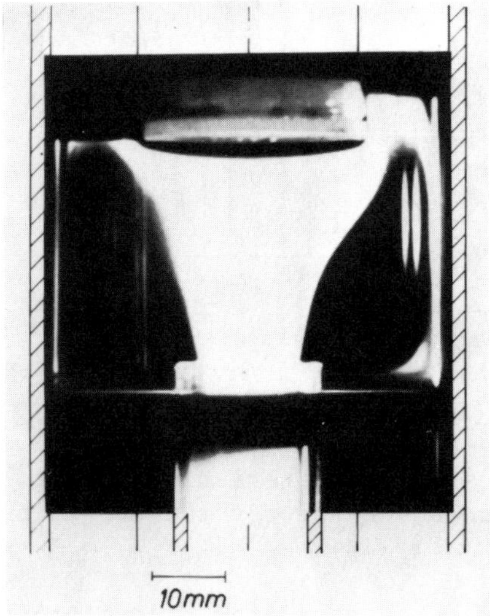

Fig. 8 Experimental flow pattern. Flow conditions as in Fig. 5.

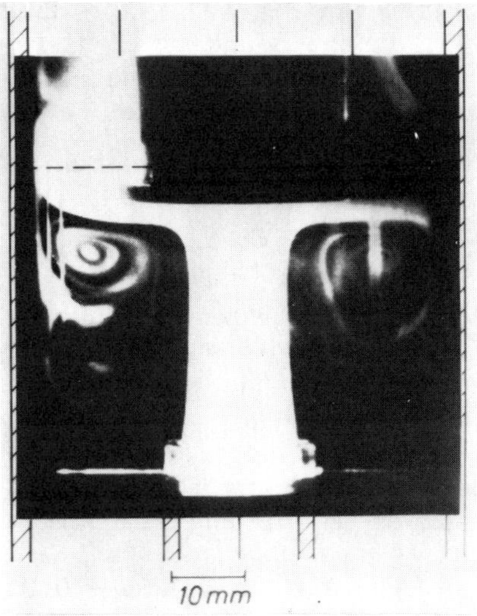

Fig. 9 Experimental flow pattern. Flow conditions as in Fig. 6.

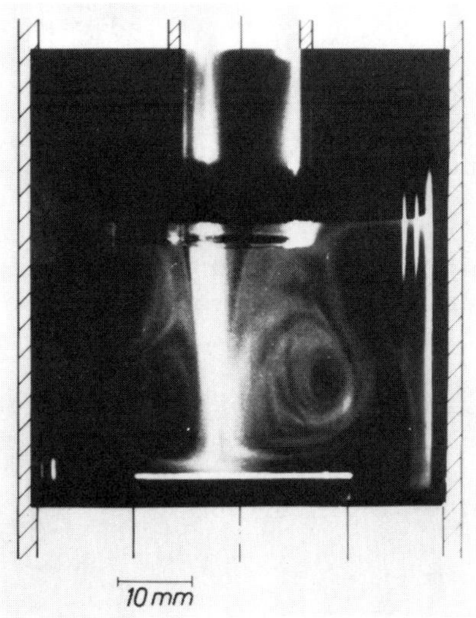

Fig. 10 Experimental flow pattern. Flow conditions as in Fig. 7.

for different Reynolds numbers and deposition temperatures for a N_2-SiH_4 gas mixture. Under isothermal conditions, the Schmidt number also was varied.

All calculated Sherwood number profiles on the deposition surface (E-F in Fig. 3) had a maximum Sherwood number Sh_s in the stagnation point (E in Fig. 3). The Sherwood number decreased to 0.5 Sh_s at the boundary of the deposition surface (point F in Fig. 3). We found that the profiles can be described approximately by the relation

$$Sh = Sh_s f(r_s) \tag{20}$$

in the following ranges: 1) 50<Re<250, $T_{do}=T_o$, 0.8<Sc<8; and 2) 50<Re<250, 300°K<T_d<1300°K, N_2-SiH_4 mixture $Gr/Re^2<1$, whereby the deposition surface was arranged above the nozzle (Fig. 3). [The function $f(r_s)$ is shown in Figs. 12 and 14 (r_s is the distance on the deposition surface from the stagnation point).]

In the isothermal case, the following relation was found for the Sherwood number Sh_s in the stagnation point

$$Sh_s = \alpha\, Sc^{1/3} Re_{max}^{1/2}, \quad \alpha = 0.65 \pm 0.02 \tag{21}$$

where the Reynolds number Re_{max} is calculated with the maximum velocity v_{max} in the nozzle. Since in the case of a Hagen-Poiseuille profile the relation $v_{max} = 2v_o$ is fulfilled, the Reynolds number Re_{max} is connected with Re by $Re_{max} = 2Re$. Equation (21) is in good accordance with boundary-layer approximations for a gas flowing perpendicularly toward an infinite circular plate with the velocity v_{max}. For this flow, the same dependence on Sc and Re and the factor $\alpha = 0.55$ was found.[12,25,26] Refs. 12 and 26 made these boundary-layer approximations for the heat transfer. The found relations can be transformed into mass-transfer relations by replacing the Nusselt number Nu and the Prandtl number Pr by Sh and Sc (heat-mass-transfer analogy).

For the nonisothermal case, the temperature dependence of the Sherwood number Sh_s can be described by

$$Sh_s = 14.1\ (T_d/300^oK)^{0.47} \tag{22}$$

for a N_2-SiH_4 gas mixture.

3.3 Comparison with CVD Experiments

The SiO_2 and Si_3N_4 deposition experiments according to the reactions

$$3\ SiH_4 + 4NH_3 \rightarrow Si_3N_4$$
$$SiH_4 + O_2 \rightarrow SiO_2$$

were carried out in the reactor shown in Fig. 3. The silicon wafer was fixed to the hot plate, which was heated by electron bombardment or resistance heating. For the calculation of the CVD process, it is assumed that during the deposition process a constant SiH_4 mole fraction $x_d(SiH_4)$ on the deposition surface is maintained. Since NH_3 or O_2 is in excess in the reactive gas mixture, the deposition is determined by the SiH_4 diffusion to the surface. An estimation according to the Wilke method[24,27] shows that the SiH_4 diffusion can be described by the binary diffusion coefficient D of SiH_4 in N_2. In our case, the N_2 data for λ, η, and c_p can be taken. Therefore, the considerations of Sec. 3.2 can be applied, resulting in the Sherwood numbers Sh for the mass transport of SiH_4 to the surface. All SiH_4 transferred to the surface is assumed to react to Si_3N_4 or SiO_2. Thus it is possible to calculate the deposition rate Si_3N_4 or SiO_2 from the transfer of SiH_4 to the surface.

The CVD experiments were carried out in the geometry shown in Fig. 3, with the deposition surface above the nozzle. Figure 11 shows the measured Si_3N_4 deposition rates $\dot{s}_s$ at the stagnation point at different pressures and temperatures for the following deposition conditions

$$x_o(SiH_4) = 0.0018,\ x_o(NH_3) = 0.033,\ x_o(Ar) = 0.018$$
$$950^oK < T_d < 1100^oK,\ 200\ \text{Torr} < p < 760\ \text{Torr}$$
$$\text{total flow } i_{tot} = 5.12\ l\ \text{min}^{-1}\ (Re = 250,\ Gr/Re^2 < 1)$$

where Ar is the dilution gas of the commercial SiH_4.

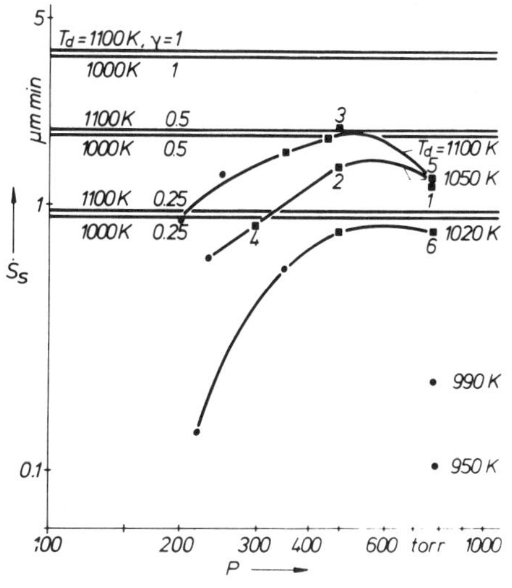

Fig. 11 Theoretical and experimental thickness growth rates $\dot{s}_s$ of Si_3N_4 in the stagnation point vs pressure p. (▮: the measured profile is in accordance with the calculated profile).

The $\dot{s}_S$ were determined by the interference maxima of a monochromatic light source (λ = 4050 Å), which were measured automatically by a photocell during the deposition process. All measurements showed that the thickness is proportional to the deposition time t.

In addition, the theoretical lines of the deposition according to Eq. (22) are displaced in Fig. 11 with the deposition temperature T_d and the quotient

$$\gamma = [x_o(SiH_4) - x_d(SiH_4)]/x_o(SiH_4)$$

as parameter, where γ has the maximum value γ=1 if $x_d(SiH_4)$=0.

Figure 12 shows experimental deposition profiles in comparison with the predicted curve. The experimental profiles were measured by observation of the interference colors. A good accordance with the predicted profile (as in Fig. 12) was found for those points of measurement in Fig. 11 marked by squares. Further profiles were measured on layers produced under the deposition conditions of points 1 and 5 in Fig. 11 but with different $x_o(NH_3)$: $0.016 < x_o(NH_3) < 0.13$. These profiles shows a good accordance with the predicted curve, too.

At low temperatures, the profiles became irregular but always showed a maximum at the stagnation point. These irregularities probably are caused by the very strong temperature dependence of the deposition rate in this deposition range. Obviously, small changes of the surface temperature can produce a changing of the deposition rate.

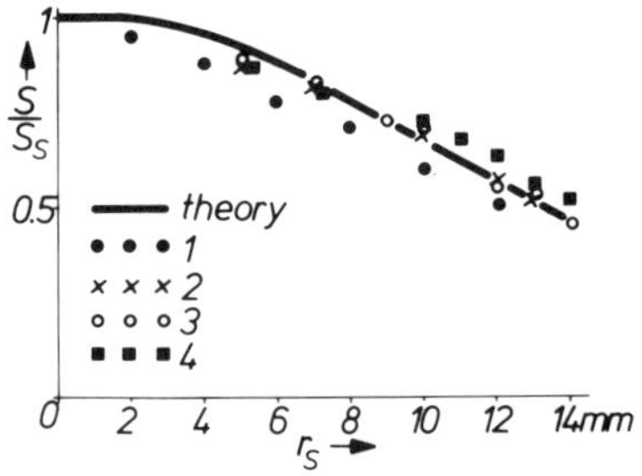

Fig. 12 Theoretical and experimental profiles on the silicon wafer. The numbers relate to the numbers on the measuring points in Fig. 11 (s: local thickness; s_S: thickness in the stagnation point).

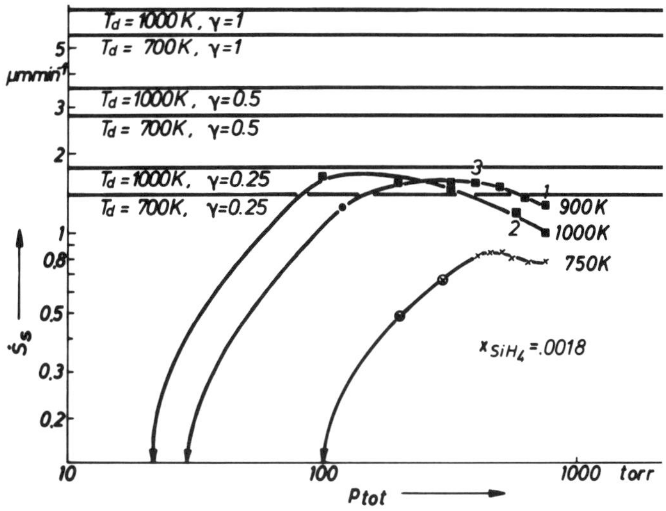

Fig. 13 Theoretical and experimental growth rates $\dot{s}_s$ of SiO_2 in the stagnation point vs pressure p (▮: measured profile; ⊗: crater profile; ↓: no deposition measured).

Figure 13 shows results of the SiO_2 deposition which were made for the deposition conditions

$$x_o(SiH_4) = 0.0018,\ x_o(O_2) = 0.065,\ x_o(Ar) = 0.036$$
$$750^oK < T_d < 1000^oK,\ 20\ Torr<p<760\ Torr$$
$$\text{total flow } i_{tot} = 5.12\ l\ min^{-1}\ (Re = 250,\ Gr/Re^2<1).$$

The theoretical lines for different T_d and γ also are outlined. At the points 1,2,3, the deposition profiles were measured and compared with the theoretical curve, as shown in Fig. 14. A

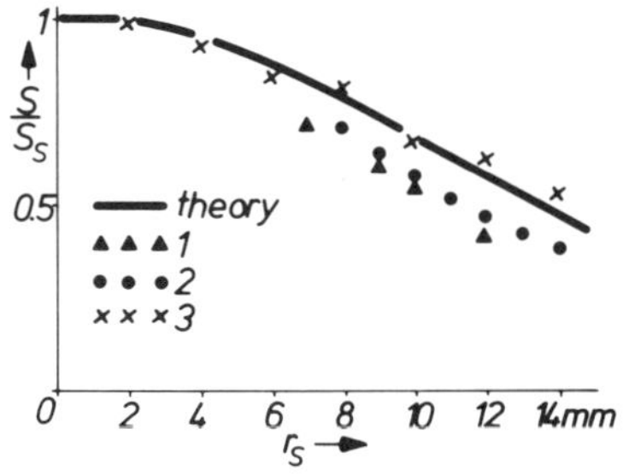

Fig. 14 Theoretical and experimental profiles on the silicon wafer. The numbers relate to the numbers at the measuring points in Fig. 13.

similarly good agreement with the theory was found for all samples produced at the deposition conditions 100 Torr$<p<$760 Torr, $900^{o}K<T_d<1000^{o}K$. With decreasing temperature or decreasing pressure, the profiles become flatter and finally degenerate to a crater profile with a minimum deposition rate in the stagnation point.[17]

All of these measurements show that the studied CVD processes have deposition ranges in which the deposition profiles coincide with the calculations. As to absolute values of the deposition rates, only one fitting parameter (γ) is necessary for each profile. This parameter must be deduced from Figs. 11 and 13. There are, however, ranges where our model is not applicable. In these ranges, more complicated boundary conditions are necessary for calculating the deposition profiles.

3.4 Discussion

In Sec. 3, a simple CVD process was calculated with only one diffusing component. But it is possible to expand this method to CVD processes with more than one diffusing component, provided that they are in small fractions in a dilution gas. In this case, the diffusion of each component is governed by an equation such as Eq. (6). If the mole fractions of the reactive components are not small, then the Stefan-Maxwell equations[28] must be taken instead of the Ficks law (diffusion current proportional to the concentration gradient). Chemical reactions in the gas phase can be taken into account by adding reaction terms.

In the CVD experiments described, the deposition calculations fit the experimental data. For other deposition parameters or other CVD reactions, more complicated boundary conditions are necessary. In most cases, the chemical reactions on the surface and their kinetics are not predictable. Therefore, the boundary conditions can be determined only by comparison of calculations with experiments.

The calculation just presented enables us to predict the local deposition rate. If we want to investigate the crystal structure of the deposited material (defect structure, morphology, stoichiometry), experiments are necessary. The calculations are, however, useful in defining the deposition conditions on the surface.

4. Conclusions

Gravity influences CVD processes mainly by gravity-induced convection and by generation of gravity-induced instabilities provided that there are density differences in the gas. (This is always the case in CVD experiments.) At g=0, it is possible to create flow conditions that do not exist at $g=g_{Earth}$.

More perfect crystal properties were obtained by Wiedemeier et al.[16] (chemical transport of GeSe and GeTe) under g=0 conditions. A g=0 experiment in Spacelab is justified if one is certain that flow patterns at g=0 yield deposition parameters that produce better properties (for example, crystal structure, deposition rate, etc.) than at $g=g_{Earth}$.

In order to decide in which regimes g=0 experiments are useful, the influence of the convection on a CVD process was investigated. By hydrodynamic considerations, flow conditions and the parameters by which flow patterns are to be controlled have been formulated.

References

[1] "Requirements and Concepts for Material Science and Manufacturing in Space," Payload Experiment Study, Contract NAS 8-29938, June 1973, TRW System Group, Redondo Beach, Calif.

[2] "Erste Richtlinien zur Benutzung eines Weltraumlabors für Materialforschungs (MS)-Experimente," 1973, ERNO Raumfahrttechnik GmbH, Bremen, Germany.

[3] Faktor, M. M. and Garrett, I., Growth of Crystals from the Vapor, Chapman and Hall, London, 1974.

[4] Schäfer, H., Chemische Transportreaktionen, Verl. Chemie, Weinheim, 1962; English ed., Chemical Transport Reactions, Academic Press, New York, 1964.

[5]Amick, J. A. and Kern, W., "Chemical Vapor Deposition Techniques for the Fabrication of Semiconductor Devices," Proceedings of the 2nd International Conference on Chemical Vapor Deposition, edited by J. M. Blocher, Jr. and J. C. Withers, The Electrochemical Society, Princeton, N.J., 1970, p. 551.

[6]Nickl, J. J., Koukoussas, J. D., and Mühlratzer, A., "Untersuchungen über den isothermen chemischen Transport," Journal of Less Common Metals, Vol. 32, August 1973, p. 243.

[7]Chandrasekhar, S., Hydrodynamic and Hydromagnetic Stability, Clarendon Press, Oxford, 1970.

[8]Krishnamurti, R., "On the Transition to Turbulent Convection. Part 2. The Transition to Time-Dependent Flow," Journal of Fluid Mechanics, Vol. 42, Part 2, June 1970, p. 309.

[9]Dismukes, J. P. and Curtis, B. J., "A Survey of Convective Instabilities in Silicon CVD Systems," Proceedings of the 2nd International Symposium on Silicon Science and Technology, edited by H. R. Huff and R. R. Burgess, The Electromechanical Society, Princeton, N.J., 1973, p. 258.

[10]Charlson, G. S. and Sani, R. L., "Thermo-convective Instability in a Bounded Cylindrical Fluid Layer," International Journal of Heat and Mass Transfer, Vol. 13, September 1970, p. 1479.

[11]Klosse, K. and Ullersma, P., "Convection in a Chemical Vapor Transport Process," Journal of Crystal Growth, Vol. 18, Feb. 1973, p. 167.

[12]Schlichting, H., Grenzschichttheorie, Verlag Braun, Karlsruhe, Germany, 1965.

[13]Takahashi, R., Sugawara, K., Nakazawa, Y., and Koga, Y., "Convective Mass Transfer Analysis of Silicon Epitaxial Deposition, Part 1. Observation of Gas Flow Patterns in Reactors," Proceedings of the 2nd International Conference on Chemical Vapor Deposition, edited by J. M. Blocher, Jr. and J. C. Withers, The Electrochemical Society, Princeton, N.J., 1970, p. 695.

[14]Curtis, B. J. and Dismukes, J. P., "Effects of Natural and Forced Convection in Vapor Phase Growth Systems," Journal of Crystal Growth, Vol. 17, December 1972, p. 128.

[15]Rosenberger, F., De Long., M.C., and Olson, J. M., "Heat Transfer and Temperature Oscillations in Chemical Vapor Transport Growth I," Journal of Crystal Growth, Vol. 19, July 1973, p. 317.

[16]Wiedemeier, H., Klaessig, C., Irene, E.A., and Wey, S. J., "Crystal Growth and Transport Rates of GeSe and GeTe in Micro-Gravity Environment," Journal of Crystal Growth, Vol. 31, December 1975, p. 36.

[17]Wahl, G., "Chemical Vapor Deposition of SiO_2 and Boro- and Phospor-Silicate Glasses by the Reaction of SiH_4,B_2H_6 or PH_3 with Oxygen," Proceedings of the 5th International Conference on Chemical Vapor Deposition, edited by J. M. Blocher, Jr., H. E. Hintermann and L. H. Hall, The Electrochemical Society, Princeton, N.J., 1975, p. 391.

[18]Oswatitsch, K., "Physikalische Grundlagen der Strömungslehre," Handbuch der Physik, Vol. VIII, edited by S. Flugge, Springer-Verlag, Berlin 1959, p. 1.

[19]Brauer, H., Stoffaustausch, Verlag Sauerländer, Frankfurt, 1971.

[20]Gosman, A. D., Pun, W. M., Runchal, A. K., Spalding, D. B., and Wolfshtein, M., Heat and Mass Transfer in Recirculating Flows, Academic Press, London, 1973.

[21]Mazille, J. E., "Etude et Résolution Numérique d'un Problème d'Aerothermochimie," Thesis, 1973, Grenoble.

[22]Weast, R. C., Selby, S. M., and Hodgman, C. D. (eds.), Handbook of Chemistry and Physics, 46th ed., Chemical Rubber Co., Cleveland, Ohio, 1965-1966.

[23]Stull, D. R. and Prophet, H. (eds.) JANAF Thermochemical Tables, 2nd ed. NSRRDS-NBS-37, 1971, National Bureau of Standards.

[24]Reid, R. C. and Sherwood, K., The Properties of Gases and Liquids, McGraw-Hill, New York, 1966.

[25]Wahl, G., "The Chemical Vapor Deposition of Fluoride Tungsten-Measurements and Thermodynamic Calculations," Proceedings of the 4th Conference on Chemical Vapor Deposition, edited by G. F. Wakefield and J. M. Blocher, Jr., The Electrochemical Society, Princeton, N.J., 1973, p. 425.

[26]Kezios, S. P., "Heat Transfer in the Flow of a Cylindrical Air Jet Normal to an Infinite Plane," Ph.D. Thesis, 1956, Illinois Institute of Technology.

[27]Wilke, R. C., "Diffusional Properties of Multicomponent Gases," Chemical Engineering Progress, Vol. 46, February 1950, p. 95.

[28]Byrd, R. B., Stewart, W. E., and Lightfoot, E. N., Transport Phenomena, Wiley, New York, 1960.

OBSERVATIONS OF THE LIQUID/SOLID INTERFACE IN LOW GRAVITY MELTING

Guenther H. Otto*

The University of Alabama in Huntsville, Huntsville, Ala.

and

Lewis L. Lacy+

NASA George C. Marshall Space Flight Center, Huntsville, Ala.

Abstract

Time-lapsed photography of the liquid/solid interface of a melting ice cylinder was taken on Skylab 3 over a period of 3 hours. The same experiment was simulated on Earth such that morphological and thermodynamic differences could be noted. A study of the returned color film clearly shows the dominance of surface tension effects in low-gravity melting. In the Skylab experiment, the ends of the ice cylinder melted first with the water being driven by surface tension onto the cylindrical surfaces. At any time, the principle of minimum surface area governs the overall appearance of the water-ice globule which changed from a cylindrical to a spherical shape. The latent heat of melting in low gravity is supplied only by radiation (81%) and conduction (19%), whereas in 1-g, the radiative (38%) and convective (55%) mode of heat transfer dominate over the conductive portion (7%). Information also is provided on containerless melting and heat transfer in space in the absence of convective air currents.

Presented as Paper 74-1243 at the AIAA/AGU Conference on Scientific Experiments of Skylab, Huntsville, Ala., October-November 1974. Mr. D. Hardin and Mr. D. Homesley of The University of Alabama in Huntsville helped with the data reduction. Work performed under NASA Contract NAS8-27809.

*Physics Department.

+Space Sciences Laboratory.

Introduction

The low-gravity environment associated with Skylab has provided extensive experimental results in the area of material sciences.[1] These investigations consisted mainly of studying the returned materials that were melted and then resolidified in low gravity. The purpose of this science demonstration (TV-111) was to study visibly the melting process in space with the absence of convective heat transfer and compare it with the same process on Earth. The experiment was made possible by the request of the Skylab 3 crew during their mission for additional scientific investigations.[2] This science demonstration was designed to simulate the essential aspects of the melting process in low gravity as a representation for the technique of containerless melting. The water-ice system was selected because of the availability of the necessary materials onboard, the negligible impact on the mission, the ready availability of all significant data, and the good visibility of the liquid/solid interface which represented a "transparent furnace."

In this paper, we will discuss the heat flow into a solid material which is melted by an isotropic heat source. The integrated heat input into such a system is experimentally available through the image of the time-dependent liquid/solid interface of the melting ice. This melting process, both on ground and in low-gravity environment, will be analyzed in regard to the classical modes of heat transfer by radiation, conduction, and convection. It can be expected in low gravity that the heat input is strongly affected by the reduced mode of convective heat transfer.

Experiment Description

An ice cylinder was frozen by the crew onboard Skylab 3 by supplied instructions from the ground. A specified amount of water from the drinking water dispenser was injected in an empty plastic pill container (30-mm diam and 75 mm long) which had a wooden cotton swab inserted to provide support for the ice. Astronaut Jack Lousma reported[3] that he "shook the water to the point where it did not have any bubbles to speak of in the solid mass." After freezing overnight in the onboard food freezer,[4] the ice and container were weighed in space, and, from five mass measurements, an average value of 49.4 ± 0.2 g was given. After making the necessary corrections for container and cotton swab, the mass of the ice to be melted was found to be 39.7 ± 0.2 g (1.40 oz). With the heat of fusion

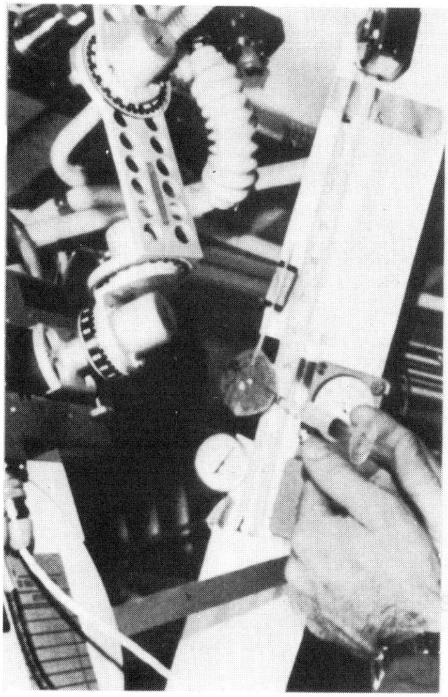

Fig. 1 Experimental setup for the Skylab ice melting.

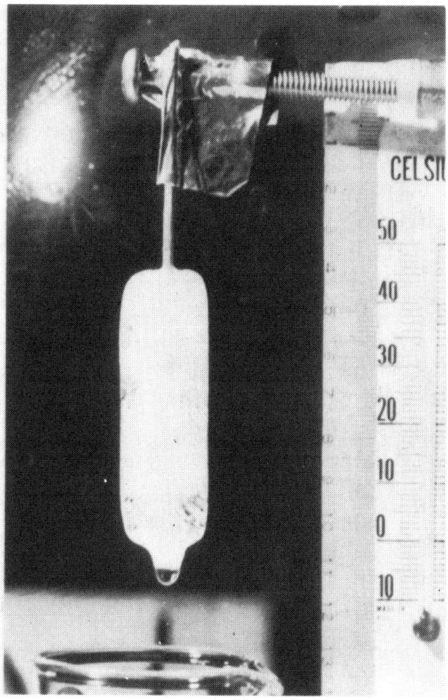

Fig. 2 Experimental setup for the ground-control ice melting.

for ice being 79.8 cal/g, a total of 3170 cal or an equivalent of 13,250 J is needed for the complete melting process.

The ice cylinder, contained on a cotton swab, was mounted in the field of view of a data-acquisition camera so that the cylinder could melt freely into a sphere of water, as shown in Fig. 1. Also visible were a portable clock and a thermometer. The air velocity at the location of the experiment was measured by the astronaut and was found to be negligible. The air temperature at this location was read as 78 °F (25.5 °C). These background data are summarized in Table 1.

The Skylab experiment was duplicated carefully in the laboratory with regard to air temperature, atmospheric pressure (5 psia), and gas composition (75% O_2, 25% N_2). A partial view of the ground-control setup in a belljar is shown in Fig. 2. For the ground-control experiment, the melt water was collected in a measuring beaker. Volume readings ($\pm$ 0.1 cm^3) were made every 5 min, and thus an accurate value of the accumulative heat input into the ground-control ice cylinder was obtained. The first derivative of this curve with respect to

Table 1 Summary of data from the low-gravity ice melting

Primary Skylab data	
Mass of ice with container and sawb, g	49.4 ± 0.2
Inner diameter of plastic container, cm	3.0
Air temperature, °C	25.5 ± 0.3
Air velocity, cm/s	0 ± 0.5
Total melting time, min	190 ± 5
Derived data	
Ice cylinder	
Mass of ice, g	39.7 ± 0.2
Volume, cm^3	43.2
Diameter, cm	3.0
Length, cm	6.1
Surface area, cm^2	71.6
Density, g/cm^3	0.918
Water sphere	
Volume, cm^3	39.7
Surface area, cm^2	56.3
Radius, cm	2.12

time gives the instantaneous heat flow rate ($\dot{Q}$ total). Average values for the length and diameter of the melting cylinder were obtained from the photographic record. Similar curves were generated from the Skylab data.

Experiment Results

General Observations

The melting ice cylinder was intermittently photographed by the astronauts 22 times with an approximate time interval of 10 min. Some selected views are given in Fig. 3. Although the pictures were slightly out of focus, the objectives of this investigation were completely fulfilled. The following details can be taken from the photographs: general appearance of the ice, time-dependent shape of the water-ice globule, time-dependent location of the water-ice interface, and total melting time.

A study of the returned film results in some of the following observations:

1) The total melting time in zero gravity for the specified ice cylinder was 190 ± 5 min. This duration is an accor-

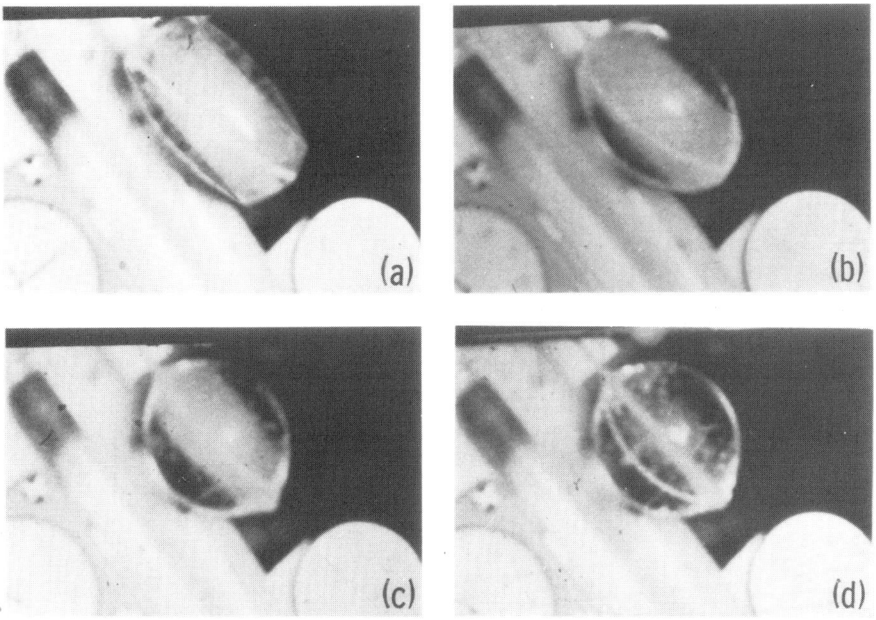

Fig. 3 The melting ice cylinder onboard Skylab after 45, 80, 115, and 180 min.

dance with voice transcripts from the astronauts[3] which can be correlated with the photographs. The total melting time for an identical ice cylinder on Earth is 130 $\pm$ 2 min.

2) The cylindrical ends melt first, whereas the diameter of the ice decreases slowly.

3) The water from the melting ends is driven by surface tension onto the cylindrical surfaces.

4) The overall shape goes from cylindrical to spherical with an intermediate approximate ellipsoidal shape. A spherical shape of the water-ice globule is first evident at half of the total melt time, when the water completely surrounds the melting ice. A schematic of the relative geometrical shapes for both the low-g and 1-g melting can be seen in Fig. 4. At any time, the principle of minimum surface area seems to govern the overall geometry of the water-ice globule.

Geometric Analysis and Data Reduction

To obtain the temperature-dependent amount of melt water in the low-gravity melting, needed for heat flow considera-

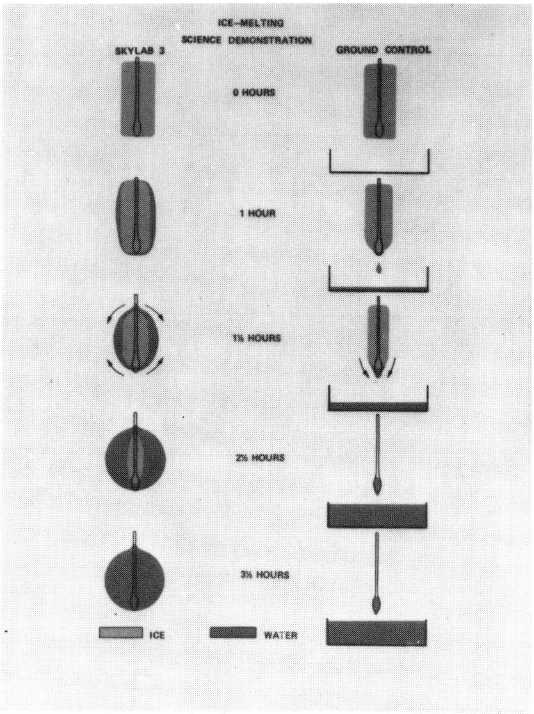

Fig. 4 Comparison of the time-dependent water-ice geometry for low-g and 1-g melting.

tions, the volume of the remaining ice was calculated from the photographic dimensions. A cylindrical shape of the ice could be reasonably taken during the entire melting process. The photographic dimensions were tied to the real dimensions by our knowledge that the total amount of water in spherical form was 39.7 cm^3. Corrections have been applied to the diameter of the ice cylinder because of a distortion due to the lens effect of the water globule and for the differences in specific volume between water and ice. The accuracy of the experimental data obtained is better than 5%. The length and diameter of the ice cylinder in 0-g, as a function of melting time, are given in Fig. 5. Whereas the total melting may be defined as the condition existing for $d = 0$, the length approaches a finite value as the diameter approaches zero. The same considerations apply for melting in 1-g. For the ground-control case, the dimensions of the cylinder also are plotted in Fig. 5. In comparing the dimensions for the low-g and 1-g melting, a large difference in length and diameter is noted. The length, in the low-gravity melting, decreases faster with time when compared

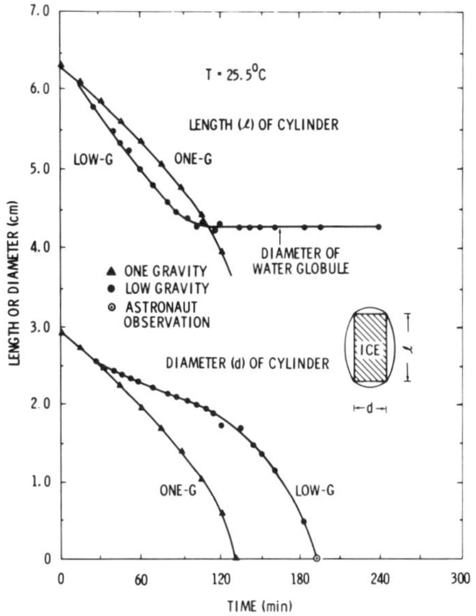

Fig. 5 Time-dependent dimensions of the melting ice cylinder on Earth and on Skylab.

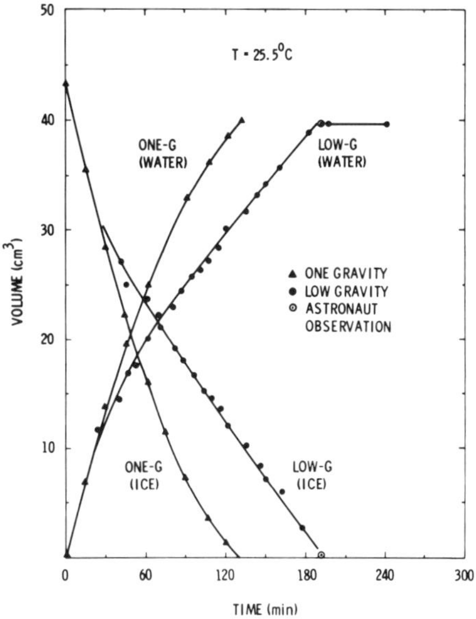

Fig. 6 Time-dependent volume of ice and water on Earth and on Skylab.

with 1-g conditions; however, after 100 min, it reaches a finite value determined by the diameter of the water globule.

By using the data from Fig. 5, the time-dependent volume of water and ice can be calculated. These volumes are given in Fig. 6. The volume for the ground-control case, which was measured directly, is also given in Fig. 6. Again, the end of the melting process is determined by the condition $d_{ice} \to 0$. The astronauts' observation for total melting agrees well with the extrapolation of the experimental data. It should be mentioned that the change in volume for ice or water with time is a nonlinear curve for the ground experiment, whereas it is a linear function for the Skylab experiment ($t > 70$ min). On the basis of these curves, the total heat flow into the ice will be derived and will be compared with theoretical values of heat flow for both the low-g and 1-g melting.

Heat Flow Analysis

The transfer of energy (latent heat) arising from the temperature difference between the melting ice and its surroundings can be determined by the following mechanisms: radiation, conduction, and convection. An experimental measure for the total heat flow is the amount of melt water being generated. We will now calculate the individual contributions into the ice cylinder and then compare the sum of the individual contributions with the experimentally observed value. However, we will not consider minute convective contributions caused by g-jitter[5] or surface tension-driven convection,[6] because the experimental technique is not sensitive to these effects. A detailed analysis has been given earlier.[7]

Heat Transfer by Radiation

The ice is surrounded by air at 25.5 °C which emits isotropic thermal radiation with a wavelength of 10 μm. Using the absorptivity of ice[8] for this wavelength, the Stefan-Boltzmann law can be applied to calculate the radiative heat flow into the ice. Since the surface area of the melting ice is not constant but changes as a function of time, this heat flow also is a function of time. There is a significant difference in the heat flow on Skylab for t > 90 min, where a spherical shape is observed. From then on, the radiative heat flow in low gravity is nearly constant. Two distinct heat flow rates, corresponding to the initial cylindrical geometry and the final spherical geometry, have been calculated

$$\dot{Q}_r(t = 0) = 0.219 \text{ cal/sec} \; ; \quad \dot{Q}_r(t = 90 \text{ min}) = 0.172 \text{ cal/sec}$$

This calculation assumes a surface temperature of 0 °C for the melt water. During the terminal stages of melting on Skylab, the surface temperature of the melt water may rise slightly. For example, a 2 °C rise of surface temperature would affect the amount of radiative heat input by only 7%.

Heat Transfer by Conduction

Since gases are generally poor heat conductors, it is expected that this contribution will be small. For an exact calculation of this heat flow rate, a partial differential equation must be solved for both cylindrical and spherical geometry. In our calculation, only the spherical case will be considered, since it more closely resembles the 0-g melting geometry. Using the conductivity for dry air, which is the same as for oxygen,[9] the following conductive heat flow is calculated

$$\dot{Q}_d(t = 0) = 0.042 \text{ cal/sec} \; ; \quad \dot{Q}_d(t = 90 \text{ min}) = 0.041 \text{ cal/sec}$$

We see that the conductive contribution is only 20% of the heat flow by radiation.

Heat Transfer by Convection

The air surrounding the ice is not in a forced movement and, therefore, the conditions for natural convection apply. The gravitational field is the activator in this type of heat transfer. It has been verified in the laboratory that laminar flow is observed[11] during the 1-g melting process, as shown in the laser interferogram of Fig. 7. The Newton rate equation can be applied to this problem, and the heat transfer coefficient for small cylinders is taken from McAdams.[10] The convective contribution depends on the temperature difference, the surface area, and the length of the cylinder. With the above considerations, the following heat flow is calculated for the 1-g case

$$\dot{Q}_V(t = 0) = 0.321 \text{ cal/sec}$$

The contribution due to natural (1-g) convection is about 50% larger than the radiative contribution.

As shown later, the experimental results for the melting on Skylab can be explained by disregarding any convective heat flow. The ice melting on Skylab was performed below water tank #2 in an area selected by the astronauts for minimum air flow.

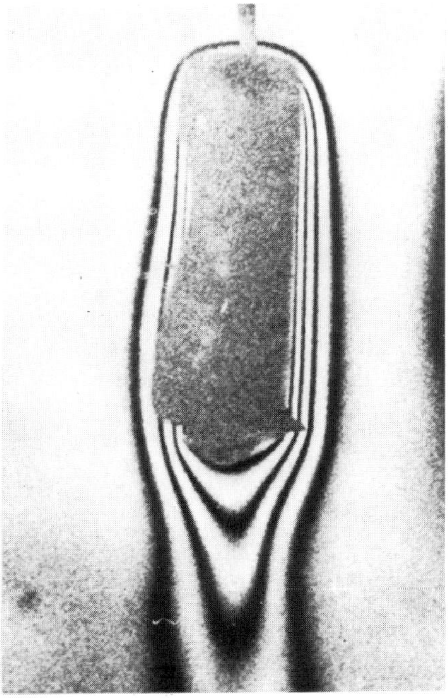

Fig. 7 Verification of laminar air flow around melting ice in the ground-control experiment. Temperature isotherms are made visible by laser interferometry.

The air velocity at the experiment location was measured to be less than 0.5 cm/s which is the lowest meaningful reading on the air flow meter. A forced-convective air flow of 0.5 cm/s would contribute no more than 0.021 cal/sec for the Skylab experiment which would correspond to 7% of the total low-g heat flow.

Total Heat Transfer

Figure 8, calculated from Fig. 6, contains the accumulative heat inputs for both the ground control and Skylab melting. Both curves end when a total of 3.17 kcal has flowed into the ice. For the ground-based melting, the total theoretical heat input at the beginning (t = 0) would be: 0.582 cal/sec which compares favorably with the experimental value of 0.610 cal/sec obtained from Fig. 8. Although it will not be shown here, it has been found that the theoretical and experimental values of the heat flow agree to within the experimental accuracy of 6% over the entire melting duration.[11] It can be concluded from these calculations that, for the ground-based melting, the total heat flow is composed of 55% convection, 38% radiation, and 7% conduction.

According to Fig. 8, a constant heat flow of 0.203 cal/sec is observed for the Skylab melting for t > 60 min, correspond-

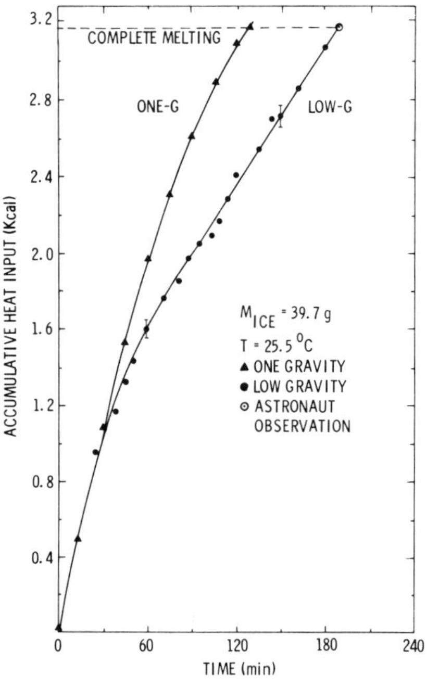

Fig. 8 Accumulative heat input into melting ice on Earth and on Skylab.

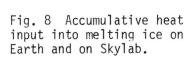

Table 2 Comparison of heat flow (cal/sec) into ice on Earth with that on Skylab for t = 60 min

	1-g	low-g
Theory		
Radiation	0.16	0.17
Conduction	0.04	0.04
Convection	0.24	....
Total	0.44	0.21
Experiment		
Total	0.46	0.20

ing to the stage when spherical symmetry is achieved. From the previous calculation, the radiative heat flow at t = 90 min is 0.172 cal/sec. Adding to this value the expected conductive contribution on Skylab of 0.041 cal/sec, a subtotal theoretical value of 0.213 cal/sec is obtained. This amount is comparable to the experimentally observed value, leaving no room for a convective heat flow contribution. The Skylab data rules out the existence of any forced or natural convective heat transfer. A comparison of the heat flow into the ice on Earth with that on Skylab at t = 60 min is given in Table 2. From the above considerations, it may be concluded that the latent heat of melting in low-g is supplied by 81% radiation and 19% conduction.

During both the 1-g and low-g experiments, the water-ice system may have given up heat by evaporation losses. Additional ground-based experiments indicated that a maximum of 1.4 volume percent of the water could have evaporated.[11] Evaporation losses, therefore, would provide for a maximum negative heat flow of 0.025 cal/sec which corresponds to about 10% of the total heat flow. Considering in addition the reduced heat flow due to raised surface temperature and the increased heat flow due to forced convection, as discussed above, it is found that some contributions tend to cancel out. In the worst case, these secondary heat sources will not exceed 10% of the total heat input. Thus, according to the results given in Table 2, the theory and experiment agree to within the experimental accuracy.

Conclusions and Recommendations

The returned photographic data from Skylab illustrates the importance of surface tension for low-gravity containerless melting. In the Skylab experiment, the ends of the ice cylinder melted first with the water being driven by surface tension onto the cylindrical surfaces. At any given time, the principle of minimum surface area seems to govern the overall appearance of the water-ice globule. Using the image of the liquid/solid interface of the melting ice cylinder, the total heat transfer under 1-g and low-g conditions was determined and compared with theoretical estimates. It was concluded that the latent heat of melting on Skylab occurred entirely by radiation (81%) and conduction (19%). Whereas in 1-g, natural convection supplies most (55%) of the latent heat with radiation (38%) and conduction (7%) being of less importance. Since direct observations of the liquid/solid interface allows for an accurate determination of the morphological and thermodynamic states in low-gravity melting, it is recommended that additional investigations be performed using direct observations to study both low-gravity melting and solidification.

References

[1] Proceedings of the Third Space Processing Symposium — Skylab Results, NASA Rept. No. M-75-5, June 1974.

[2] Bannister, T. C., "Skylab 3 and 4 Science Demonstrations," NASA TM X-64835, March 1974.

[3] NASA Johnson Space Center, Houston, Texas, Voice Transcripts of Skylab 3, September 20-21, 1973.

[4] Belew, L. F. and Stuhlinger, E., Skylab — A Guide Book, NASA Rept. No. EP-107, 1973.

[5] Grodzka, P. G. and Bannister, T. C., "Heat Flow and Convection Demonstration Experiments Aboard Apollo 14," Science, Vol. 176, 1972, pp. 506-508.

[6] Bourgeois, S. V. and Brashears, M. R., "Fluid Dynamics and Kinematics of Molten Metals in the Low Gravity Environment of Skylab," AIAA Paper No. 74-205, January 1974, New York.

[7] Otto, G. H. and Lacy, L. L., "Observations of the Solid/Liquid Interface in Low Gravity Melting," AIAA Paper No. 74-1243, October 1974, New York.

[8] Zemansky, M. W., Heat and Thermodynamics, 5th edition, McGraw-Hill, New York, 1967, p. 100.

[9] American Institute of Physics Handbook, 3rd edition, McGraw-Hill, New York, 1972.

[10] McAdams, W. H., Heat Transmission, 3rd edition, McGraw-Hill, New York, 1954, p. 167.

[11] Otto, G. H., "Studies on Immiscible Alloys," Final Report, Contract NAS8-27809, January 1976.

THE STABILITY OF LIQUID DISPERSIONS IN LOW GRAVITY

Lewis L. Lacy*
NASA George C. Marshall Space Flight Center,
Huntsville, Ala.

and

Guenther H. Otto+
The University of Alabama in Huntsville,
Huntsville, Ala.

Abstract

The stability of three different dispersions of oil and water prepared on Skylab 4 is compared with the same dispersions made on Earth. The stability of the emulsions has been studied by two independent optical techniques. An analysis of the data indicates that all the investigated emulsions were stable over a period of 10 hr, whereas the fluids separated completely on Earth in 10 sec. This experiment indicates that the rate of coalescence in low gravity is less than 3 X 10^{-6} times that on Earth. A Stokes' model calculation of the sedimentation rates indicates that the Skylab dispersions were more stable than expected, because the residual spacecraft accelerations, in the range of 10^{-3} to 10^{-4} g, tend to cancel or average out. The parameters obtained for this experiment are compared with those of liquid metals to determine whether the same stability could be achieved with immiscible alloys.

The results published here are extracted from Paper No. 74-1242 presented at the AIAA/AGU Conference on Scientific Experiments of Skylab, Huntsville, Alabama, October 1974 and Paper No. 74-668 presented at the AIAA/ASME 1974 Thermophysics and Heat Transfer Conference, Boston, Massachusetts, July 1974. Work performed under NASA Contract NAS8-27809.

*Space Sciences Laboratory.
+Physics Department.

Introduction

Two liquids may be defined as immiscible if they show limited mutual solubility in a given temperature and pressure range. Thermodynamically, the two liquids within the immiscible region do not obey the regular solution laws and exhibit large positive deviations from Raoult's linear relationship between activity and concentration. On an atomic scale, immiscibility is evident when the attractive dipole-dipole forces between like atoms (or ions) are stronger than the equivalent interaction between unlike atoms. By mechanically or ultrasonically dispersing immiscible liquids, emulsions can be formed. In doing so, one of the liquids breaks up into small droplets which are dispersed in the matrix or continuous phase. Numerous investigations[1] have been performed in studying the formation, stability, and various physical and rheological properties of emulsions. It is generally understood that the stability of emulsions is controlled by such gravity-dependent influences[2,3] as sedimentation (i.e., creaming), flocculation and coalescence and such physically intrinsic influences[4,5] as electrostatic repulsion, van der Waals' attraction and interfacial forces. These effects have been the subject of extensive studies for oil-in-water and water-in-oil emulsions.[1,2]

To help overcome the gravitational effects and to stabilize the emulsions against coalescence, various surfactants or emulsifying agents are used. Such surface active agents construct an energy barrier between the individual droplets so that they are capable of withstanding a certain amount of force before coalescing.[2] Likewise, surface active agents assist in reducing the size of the dispersed phase into the range of a few microns or less such that the influence of gravitational forces is diminished. The advantage of a low-g environment is that the basic properties and stability of emulsions can be studied without the influence of surface active agents. By greatly reducing the rate of sedimentation and coalescence, metastable dispersions can be prepared and processed in low gravity when such dispersions would be impossible or impractical to maintain on Earth. A demonstration experiment[6] (TV-102) was performed on Skylab 4 to study visibly the stability of three oil-water emulsions in low gravity as compared to Earth. The purpose of the experiment was to investigate the relative influence of gravity on the rate of sedimentation and coalescence of two well-characterized liquids, Krytox oil and water, after the liquids were finely dispersed on Skylab. Related experiments dealing with the solidification of metallic dispersions have been performed on Apollo 14,[7] Skylab,[8] Apollo-Soyuz,[9] and drop towers.[10-12]

Table 1 Characteristics of the Krytox-water emulsions

Parameter	Vial #1	Vial #2
Volume fraction oil	0.25	0.75
Matrix fluid	Water	Krytox
Surface tension of matrix, dyn/cm	16	72
ρ_m, g/cm^3	1.00	1.86
η_m, cp	1.00	63
V_t, cm/s	2.4	0.53
r, mm	0.11	0.42
n, 10^3/cm^3	45	0.80

Experimental Description

To study the behavior of immiscible liquids in a low-g environment, the classic example[1] of oil and water was chosen because the fluids are transparent and are well characterized by the data given in Table 1. Since the two components of the system are considerably different in density, the dispersions obtained on Earth are highly unstable and will separate completely in 10 sec.

The experimental package designed for the Skylab 4 mission, as shown in Fig. 1, consisted of three transparent plastic vials (Oak Ridge Type Centrifuge Tubes, manufactured from unbreakable polycarbonate), each containing a different fraction of oil and red-colored water and mounted in a stainless steel frame. Three vials, each having a total volume of 10 ml, were filled, respectively, with 25, 50, and 75% volume of degassed Krytox 143 AZ oil, and the remaining volume was filled with colored degassed water. To prevent air from being trapped, the vials were sealed while submerged under water, using a screw cap containing an O-ring seal. Vacuum tests were performed on ground to insure that the vials would not leak while in orbit. A small brass nut was included in each vial to disperse the liquids when the vials were shaken in zero gravity. To separate the two fluids while in orbit, a 50-cm long string was attached to the top of the stainless steel frame containing the vials. The string allowed the astronaut to swing the vials in a circular arc and thereby generate a centrifugal force of about 2 g. To enhance visibility and aid in evaluating the results, a card with black parallel lines was installed behind the frame so that the lines would be visible

Fig. 1 Experimental package designed for Skylab Science Demonstration TV102. The clear areas at the bottom of the vials are Krytox oil, and the dark areas are red-colored water.

through the liquids. The experiment was designed such that the parallel lines were invisible for a good emulsion and clearly visible when the liquids were separated.

The 0-g part of the experiment consisted of shaking the three vials and sequentially photographing the appearance of the three emulsions over a period of 10 hr. The first 5 min of the experiment were also recorded on video tape. The elapsed time after dispersing the liquids was determined by an astronaut timer placed beside the vials and in the field of view of a 35-mm camera. The ground-based experiment was performed in an identical fashion except that high-speed motion pictures (120 frames/sec) were taken instead of still pictures, since the emulsions completely separate in 1 to 10 sec on Earth.

Photographs of the emulsions prepared on Earth are shown in Fig. 2. It can be seen that the dispersions obtained are highly unstable. The concentrations of oil and water in the three vials were chosen such that in vial #1 (from left to right) water is the matrix; in vial #2 oil is the matrix, and in vial #3, with a volume ratio of 50%, water is again the matrix. At 0.7 sec after the end of the mixing action, it can seen from Fig. 2a that the dispersed oil has cleared completely from the water matrix in vials #1 and #3 because of the low viscosity of the water. Gravity-induced coalescence of the

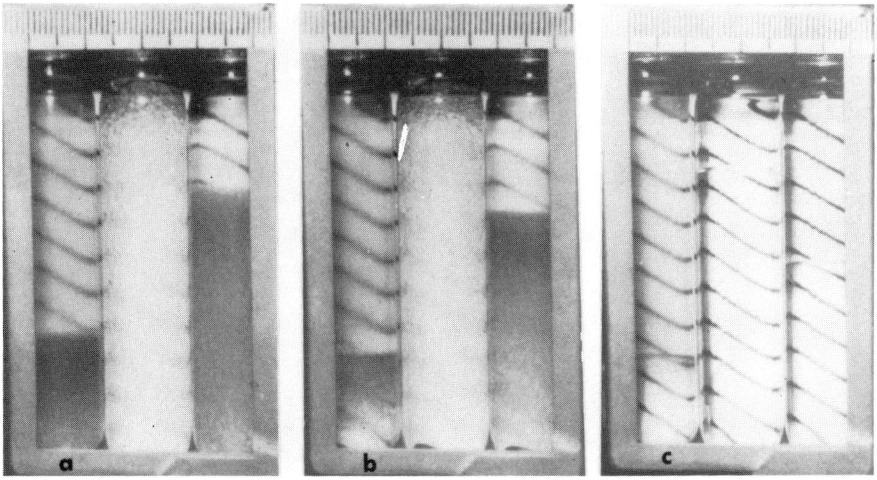

Fig. 2 Demonstration of the instability of the emulsions on Earth. (a) ≈ 0.7 sec after mixing, (b) ≈ 3 sec after mixing, and (c) ≈ 10 sec after mixing. The parallel background lines are 6 mm apart.

dispersed oil droplets already has occurred. In contrast, vial #2 does not yet show an appreciable amount of sedimentation because of the relatively high viscosity of the oil matrix. After 3 sec, as seen in Fig. 2b, the degree of separation by coalescence has progressed whereas, after 10 sec (Fig. 2c), a complete separation of the two liquids is observed.

Experimental Results

Stability of Dispersions

Figure 3 is a reproduction of a color photograph, taken from the Skylab video tape, where the appearance of the emulsions can be seen after 4 min. It should be noted that the quality of the original color transparencies and video data is much better than can be reproduced here.

The relative stability of the low-gravity and 1-g emulsions was determined by two techniques. The first consisted of determining the volume fraction of separation of the emulsions, using the parallel background lines. As gravity-induced sedimentation separates the emulsions into clear oil and water, the background lines become visible in the photographs and can be counted. The results of such an analysis

(a)

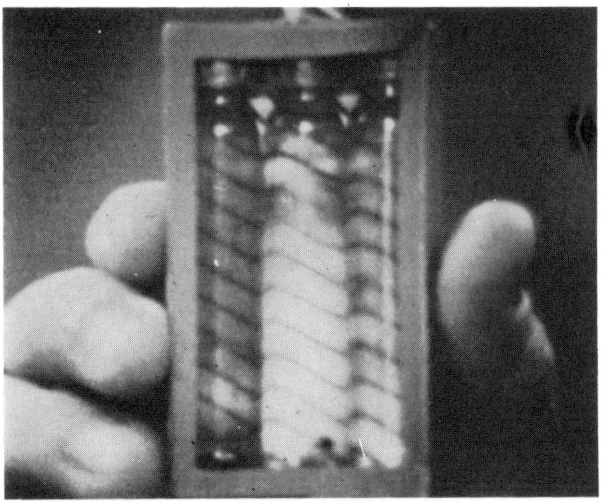

(b)

Fig. 3 (a) Demonstration of the increased stability of the emulsions in low gravity. This picture was taken 4 min after mixing and is representative of all the Skylab data up to 10 hr. (b) Separated emulsions by centrifuging on Skylab.

are shown in Fig. 4 where the percentage of separation is shown for vials #1 (water matrix) and #2 (oil matrix) as a function of time after mixing. As seen in Fig. 4, the emulsions are highly unstable on Earth with the 25% oil mixture showing significant separation in only 0.1 sec and the 75% oil

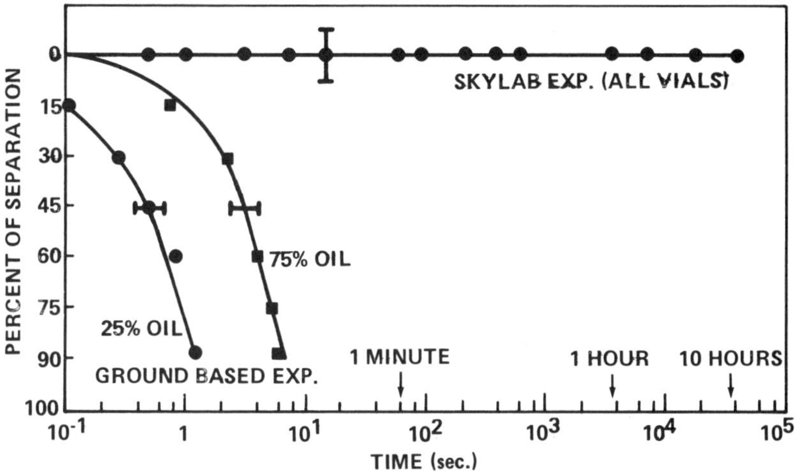

Fig. 4 The volume fraction of separation of two oil-water emulsions in low gravity and 1-g compared as a function of time. The 25% oil mixture is more separated after 0.1 sec on Earth than the same mixture is after 10 hr on Skylab.

emulsions a comparable amount of separation in only 0.8 sec. Both vials show complete separation in 2 and 10 sec, respectively. The results for vial #3 (50% oil) are intermediate between vials #1 and #2 and have been omitted for clarity. The horizontal error bars for the ground-based experiment represent the uncertainty of establishing the time for a given visibility of the background lines. The vertical error bar for the Skylab experiment represents the probable sensitivity for the technique.

As shown in Fig. 4, dispersed liquid immiscibles are many orders of magnitude more stable in low gravity than on Earth. An estimate of the increased stability in low gravity can be made by realizing that the Skylab emulsions are less separated after 10 hr (3.6×10^4 sec) than the 25% oil mixture is after 0.1 sec on Earth. Thus, these results indicate that such dispersed immiscibles are at least a factor of 3.6×10^5 more stable on Skylab than on Earth. Likewise, it can be concluded that the coalescence rate has been reduced on Skylab to 3×10^{-6} times that on Earth. The same number is obtained when the data are analyzed directly in terms of a coalescence rate. For example, we have found that the coalescence rate for vial #1 is approximately 2×10^5 coalescing particles/cm^3s on Earth and less than 0.6 $cm^{-3}s^{-1}$ on Skylab. As shown by a Stokes' model calculation in the next section, the Skylab emulsions are between one and two orders of magnitude more stable than was expected.

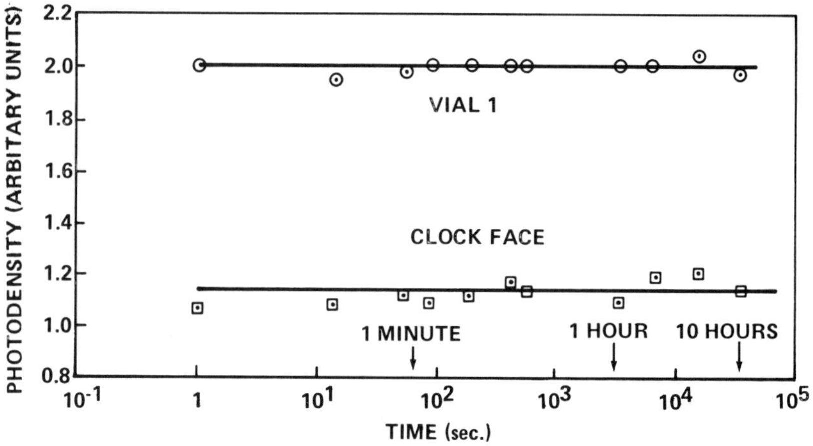

Fig. 5 Red (magenta) color density of the returned Skylab film as a function of time after mixing. The white clock face served as a standard.

The stability of the low-g dispersions also has been studied by a photodensitometry technique. This technique consisted of measuring the red color density (magenta film dye) of the returned 35-mm color transparencies as a function of time. The results are shown in Fig. 5 together with the results of similar measurements made on the white clock face which acted as a standard. The relatively small scattering of the data is probably associated with the film exposure and processing conditions. The results of the photodensity studies indicate, as with the previous technique, that the low-g dispersions were stable during the 10 hr of observation time.

Determination of Particle Size

The dispersed particles in an emulsion will move under the influence of any convective or inertial force at a terminal velocity, V_t, given by Stokes' law[13]

$$\vec{V}_t = 2r^2\vec{a}(\rho_d - \rho_m)/9\eta_m \tag{1}$$

where $\vec{a}$ is the acceleration level acting on particles of radius r and density ρ_d dispersed in a matrix fluid of viscosity η_m and density ρ_m. Equation (1) is a model that assumes independent motion of spherical particles. Second-order collective effects can be included in Eq. (1) by considering interparticle forces such as van der Waals' attraction, and by considering η_m to be the viscosity of the total dispersed system. For the ground-based experiment, all the variables of Eq. (1)

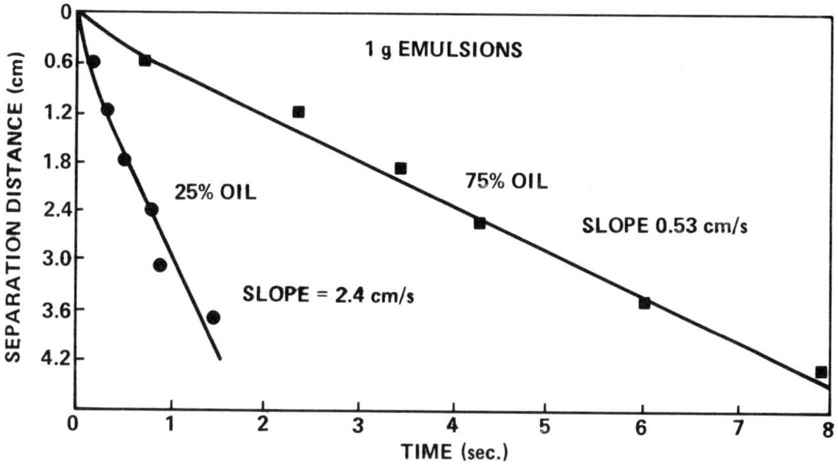

Fig. 6 The separation distance of the oil-water emulsions as a function of time after mixing on Earth. The slopes can be used to determine V_t and the average particle radius.

are known except r if it is assumed that the main accelerating force is due to action of gravity.

The high-speed film, from the ground-based experiment, was used to determine the separation distance, defined as the length of fluid cleared of dispersed particles, as a function of time. The results are given in Fig. 6. As predicted by Eq. (1), the separation distance is a linear function of time. The slope of the two straight lines is V_t for the appropriate oil mixture. The measured values of V_t and the calculated values of r are given in Table 1. Since the low-g emulsions were mixed in an identical fashion, it is expected that similar particle radii will be produced for the Skylab experiment. An estimate of n, the number of dispersed particles per unit of volume, also is included in Table 1.

Theoretical Considerations and Comparison with Metallic Systems

On Skylab, the gravitational forces are reduced to the range[14] of 10^{-3} to 10^{-4} g which in turn diminishes the rate of sedimentation in the dispersions. This effect will be discussed later. However, even in a 0-g environment, dispersed immiscible liquid systems may still separate by coalescence of droplets. The low-g dispersions can be considered as a metastable state because of the large interfacial energy involved. Any intrinsic force or motion (i.e., like Brownian motion, van der Waals' attraction, or interfacial forces) which leads to collision may also cause coalescence of the droplets. Coalescence effects will be most pronounced when the volume ratio of the two liquids is about 50:50 and an already close contact can be anticipated. In a dispersed system, the total interfacial energy will, therefore, decrease as adjacent particles coalesce where the excess energy is dissipated as convective motion in the system. These convective currents, in turn, can enhance the probability for collision and lead to additional coalescence.

The system will only then be stable in zero gravity when the collisional forces are smaller than the stabilizing forces such as electrostatic repulsion. It has been shown in a separate calculation,[11] not included here, that the destabilizing influences such as Brownian motion and diffusion-assisted Ostwald ripening are of secondary importance for the Krytox-water system.

Whereas the intrinsic effects of coalescence have been considered only qualitatively, the separation of the dispersions caused by sedimentation can be assessed quantitatively. According to Eq. (1), significant particle velocities could occur in the Skylab experiment due to the residual inertial accelerations of the spacecraft (i.e., 10^{-3} to 10^{-4} g). Such residual accelerations can cause sedimentation or creaming and lead to higher localized concentration of particles and subsequently to an increase in the coalescence rate. An estimate of the time required for such sedimentation to occur is given in Table 2 where it is assumed that the characteristic distance is the diameter of a vial (1.2 cm) and that the particle radii are the same as those found in the ground-based experiment.

According to Table 2, significant sedimentation or creaming should be expected in each of the Skylab vials. Since no sedimentation (or coalescence) was observed in the Skylab experiment, the low-g dispersions appear to be one or two orders of magnitude more stable than expected. The apparent increase in stability of the low-g emulsions could be understood if it is assumed that the vectorial components of the residual-spacecraft accelerations change with time and tend to cancel out when averaged over a period of time.

Are the previously described results also applicable to immiscible-liquid-metal systems? To answer this question, we may use Eq. (1) to specify the propagation velocity of the instability front as shown in Fig. 6. Thus, the degree of instability of immiscible metals on Earth is controlled by such parameters as viscosity, particle radii, and differences in density. We also know that before the dispersed particles can

Table 2 Estimated sedimentation times, τ_c, required to separate the Skylab Krytox-water emulsions for various average acceleration levels

Average Acceleration, g	τ_c(25% Krytox)	τ_c(75% Krytox)
10^{-3}	8.8 min	38 min
10^{-4}	1.5 hr	6.3 hr
10^{-5}	15 hr	63 hr
Particle Radius, mm	0.11	0.42

coalesce in space, they must have sufficient kinetic energy to overcome and force out the matrix fluid surrounding each dispersed particle. Thus, coalescence in low gravity is expected to be dependent upon the viscosity of the matrix phase and the interfacial energy of the dispersed phase.

If one compares[6] the viscosity of liquid metals to Krytox oil and water, it is found that the oil-water system brackets the viscosity values of common liquid metals. The difference in density between metals can vary from 0.4 to 7 g/cm^3 as compared to a density difference of 0.86 g/cm^3 for our system. Thus, the degree of instability of the monotectic alloys, as specified by Eq. (1), should be comparable to the results found for the Skylab system.

The major difference between the Krytox-water system and metallic systems is the much larger surface tension found for liquid metals.[6] Exact values of interfacial tension for metallic liquids would depend upon the temperature and solubility, but approximate values[15] of interfacial tension can be found by taking the differences between the surface tension of the component liquids. Thus, the Krytox-water system should have an interfacial tension of about 60 dyn/cm as compared to 300 to 500 dyn/cm for the metallic systems. An increase in the interfacial tension will require an increase in the kinetic energy of the colliding particles before coalescence can take place. Therefore, it is expected that dispersions involving the metallic immiscible liquids in low gravity should have a comparable stability.

Conclusions

The stability of Krytox-water emulsions prepared on Earth and on Skylab has been studied by two optical techniques. It has been demonstrated that a completely stable dispersion of two immiscible liquids, which are very unstable on Earth, can be obtained in space. The stability of the low-g prepared emulsions is at least 3.6 X 10^5 times more stable in space than on Earth. The low-g levels associated with space flight (10^{-3} to 10^{-4} g) offer an ideal environment for studying the intrinsic physical and chemical processes of such dispersed systems which are impractical to study on Earth. The Skylab emulsions were one or two orders of magnitude more stable than expected by considering sedimentation caused by the residual-spacecraft accelerations. The apparent increase in the stability of the Skylab dispersions is believed to be associated with a time averaging or canceling out effect of the small residual accelerations. Since the important parameters of the discussed experiment, such as viscosity and density differences, are similar to those found for common liquid-metal immiscible systems, the metallic systems, likewise, should be very stable in low gravity.

References

[1]Emulsion Science, edited by P. Sherman, Academic Press, New York, 1968.

[2]Kitchener, J. A. and Mussellwhite, P. R., "The Theory of Stability of Emulsions," ibid., pp. 77-130.

[3]Albers, W. and Overbeek, J.Th.G., "Stability of Emulsions of Water in Oil," Journal of Colloid Science, Vol. 15, December 1960, pp. 489-502.

[4]Albers, W. and Overbeek, J.Th.G., "The Correlation Between Electrokinetic Potential and Stability," Journal of Colloid Science, Vol. 14, October 1959, pp. 501-518.

[5]Boyd, J., Parkinson, C., and Sherman, P., "Factors Affecting Emulsion Stability and the HLB Concept," Journal of Colloid and Interface Science, Vol. 41, November 1972, pp. 359-370.

[6]Lacy, L. L. and Otto, G. H., "The Stability of Liquid Dispersions in Low Gravity," AIAA Paper No. 74-1242, October 1974, New York.

[7]Yates, I. C., "Apollo 14 Composite Casting Demonstration," NASA Final Report TM X-64641, March 1972.

[8]Reger, J. L., "Immiscible Alloys Compositions," Proceedings of the Third Space Processing Symposium - Skylab Results, Vol. 1, NASA Report No. M-74-5, 1974, pp. 133-158.

[9]Ang, C. Y. and Lacy, L. L., "Monotectic and Syntectic Alloys: Experiment MA044," Apollo-Soyuz Test Project Preliminary Science Report, edited by R. Giuli, NASA TM X-58173, February 1976, pp. 24-1 to 24-25.

[10]Lacy, L. L. and Otto, G. H., "Electrical Resistivity of Gallium-Bismuth Solidified in Free Fall," AIAA Journal, Vol. 13, February 1975, p. 219.

[11]Markworth, A. J., Oldfield, W., Duga, J., and Gelles, S. H., "Investigations of Immiscible Systems and Potential Applications," Final Report on NASA Contract NAS8-29748, April 1975.

[12]Otto, G. H., "Studies on Immiscible Alloys," Final Report on NASA Contract NAS8-27809, January 1976.

[13]Glasstone, S. and Lewis, D., Elements of Physical Chemistry, Van Nastrand, New York, 1962, p. 147.

[14]Holland, R. L., NASA, Marshall Space Flight Center, Private Communication, 1976.

[15]Partington, J. R., An Advanced Treatise on Physical Chemistry, Vol. 2, Wiley, New York, 1962.

SOLIDIFICATION OF NaCl-NaF EUTECTIC IN SPACE

A.S. Yue* and J.G. Yu†
University of California, Los Angeles, Calif.

Abstract

Continuous and discontinuous NaF fibers, embedded in a NaCl matrix, have been produced in space and on Earth, respectively. The production of continuous fibers in a eutectic mixture was attributed to the absence of convection current in the liquid during solidification in space. Image transmission and optical transmittance measurements of transverse sections of the space-grown and Earth-grown ingots were made with a light microscope and a spectrometer. It was found that better optical properties were obtained from samples grown in space. This was attributed to a better alignment of NaF fibers along the ingot axis.

I. Introduction

When a tube of a binary eutectic liquid solidifies unidirectionally, one of the two phases can form fibers or platelets in a matrix of the second phase. For example, when a eutectic liquid of NaCl and NaF solidifies, fibers of NaF form in a matrix of NaCl.[1]

Fiberlike and platelike eutectics produced on Earth are limited in perfection by the presence of a banded structure,[2,3] discontinuity,[4] and faults[5,6] due to vibration and convection currents in the melt during solidification. The presence of these defects renders the solid-state eutectic devices inefficient and useless.[7]

Presented as Paper No. 74-646 at the AIAA/ASME Thermophysics and Heat Transfer Conference, Boston, Mass., July 15-17, 1974. This work was supported by NASA under Contract NAS 8-28310. The authors would like to thank B.K. Yue and D. Silkey for their work on the preparation of the ampoules and metallography of the samples.

*Professor of Engineering and Applied Science.
†Graduate Student.

If the solidification process is performed in a space environment, where there is no vibration and convection current in the melt, there is reason to believe that continuous fiber can be produced in a eutectic mixture. Thus, the solid-state properties of such eutectics will be strongly anisotropic, and this will make possible various exciting device applications.

The purposes of this paper are 1) to produce continuous NaF fibers embedded in a NaCl matrix in a space environment, and 2) to measure the relevant optical properties of the space-grown and Earth-grown NaCl-NaF eutectics. Explanations of differences in properties are given in terms of the scattering and absorption characteristics of the materials.

II. Experimental Procedure

The NaCl-21 wt % NaF eutectic mixtures were made from 99.96 wt % NaCl and 99.70 wt % NaF and solidified in an induction unit under a protective atmosphere. Figure 1 is a schematic drawing of an ampoule, which consists of a stainless-steel tube (i.d. = 0.375 in.), a high-purity graphite disk separating the sample and the resistance-welded stainless-steel plug. An OFHC copper tubing 1/4 in. in diameter and 1-1/2 in. long was brazed together with the plug. The assembly was placed in a cartridge.

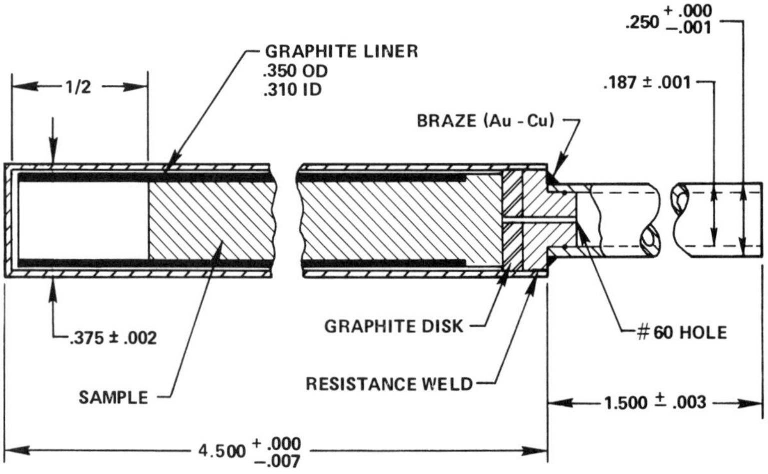

Fig. 1 Sketch of an ampoule.

The resolidification experiment was carried out in a multipurpose electric furnace.[8] One-half inch of the eutectic sample adjacent to the graphite disk was unmelted and the remaining portion of the sample was melted and resolidified unidirectionally toward the empty space of the ampoule as indicated in Fig. 1. The solidification rate was 0.6°C/min and the temperature gradient was 50°C/cm.

III. Results and Discussion

The experimental results are divided into three parts. The first part concerns the macro- and microstructures of the samples that were grown in Skylab 3 and on Earth. The second part concerns the extraction of continuous NaF fibers embedded in a NaCl matrix. The third part concerns the optical property of the NaCl-NaF eutectic. Comparison of the experimental results between the Earth-grown and space-grown samples will be discussed in terms of scattering and absorption characteristics of the eutectic.

Macro- and Microstructures

Figure 2 is a representative macrograph of the three samples grown in Skylab 3. Careful inspection on the surface of the sample revealed no reaction between the NaCl-NaF eutectic sample and graphite container. The original shape and length of the sample remained unaffected after resolidification in space.

Figure 3 is a macrograph showing the solid-liquid interface, striations revealed in the resolidified portion of the sample (on the right of the interface), and the unsolidified

Fig. 2 Macrograph of NaCl-NaF eutectic, grown in Skylab 3 (1.4X).

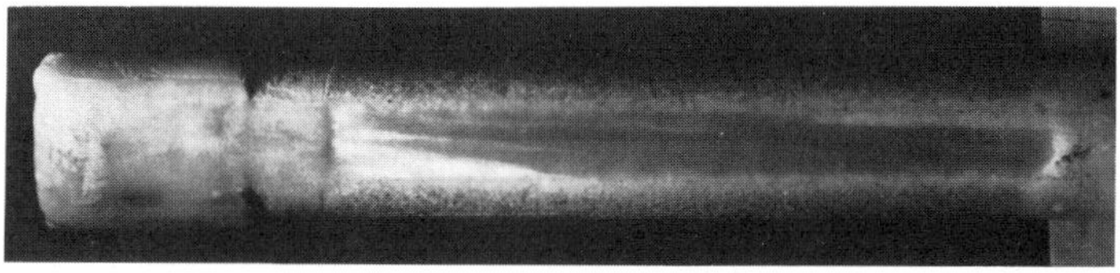

Fig. 3 Macrograph showing the solid-liquid interface of the Skylab-grown NaCl-NaF eutectic (2X).

Fig. 4 Enlarged portion of the solid-liquid interface (411X).

portion of the sample (on the left of the interface). An enlarged portion of the solid-liquid interface is given in Fig. 4, which shows that, at the beginning of the solidification process, the NaF fibers were grown in the direction not parallel to the growth direction, as evidenced by the presence of elliptical cross sections of NaF fibers near the solid-liquid interface. The shapes of these fibers are similar to those of the unmelted portion, with the exception that their sizes are larger because of a slower freezing rate. This indicates that the direction of heat extraction during the onset of resolidification is normal to the growth direction. This was tentatively attributed to improper insulation design. However, at a distance not far away from the initial solid-liquid interface (about 0.12 cm), the NaF fibers began to align toward the growth direction, indicating that the direction of heat extraction was normal to the advancing solid-liquid interface.

A representative micrograph of continuous fibers aligned in the growth direction is given in Fig. 5, which shows that

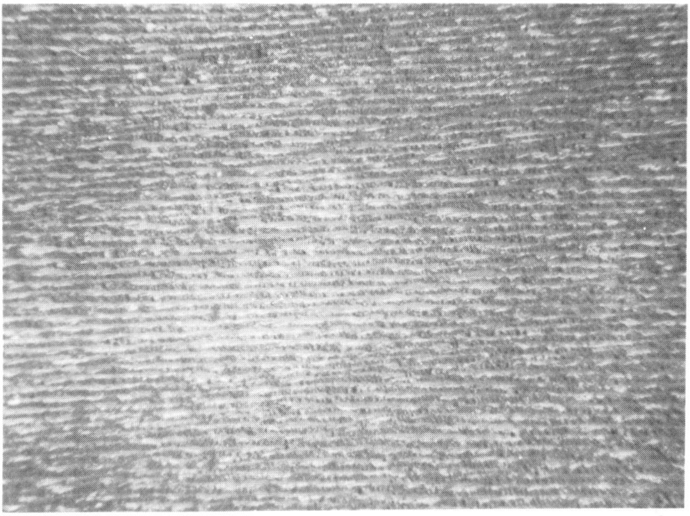

Fig. 5 Micrograph of the longitudinal section of the Skylab-grown NaCl-NaF eutectic showing continuous and regularly spaced NaF fibers (135X).

the NaF fibers are regularly spaced and parallel. When the same NaCl-NaF eutectic was grown on Earth with convection currents, the resulting eutectic microstructure is represented by Fig. 6, which shows that the solidified NaF fibers are embedded randomly in the NaCl matrix along the longitudinal section of

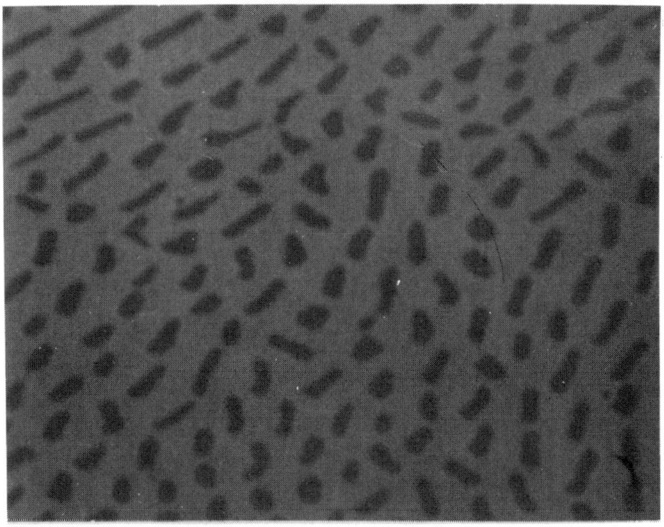

Fig. 6 Micrograph of the longitudinal section of the Earth-grown NaCl-NaF eutectic showing discontinuous NaF fibers (1500X).

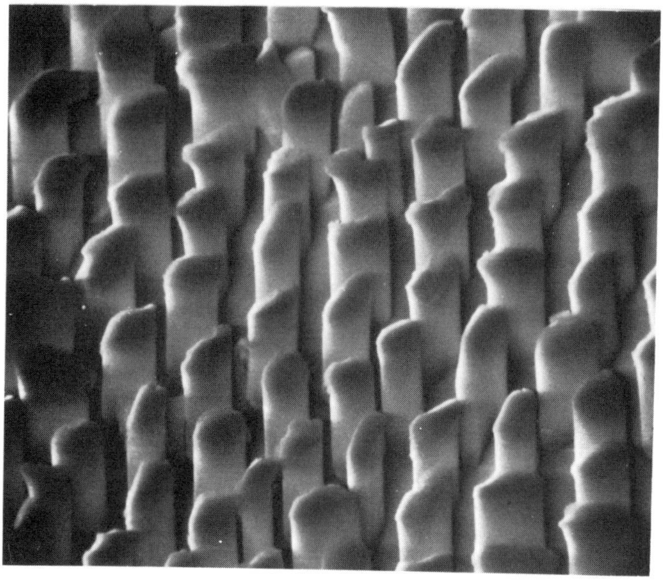

Fig. 7 Scanning electron micrograph of the Skylab-grown NaF fibers, (3200X).

the ingot. A scanning electron micrograph showing the shapes of the fibers is given in Fig. 7, which is the perspective view of the rectangular NaF fibers, sticking out of the continuous NaCl matrix. Notice that all of the fibers are aligned in one direction, indicating that the direction of heat flow was perpendicular to the advancing solid-liquid interface during the solidification process in the Skylab.

Although single-grain eutectic has not been produced in the presence of microgravity in space, the NaF fibers are aligned very evenly and parallel to the growth direction. Evidence in support of this statement is given in Fig. 8a, which is a picture taken from a sample grown in space. A filtered light was shone at the tail end of the sample. Because of good alignment and regular distribution of NaF fibers along the sample axis, light was transmitted from the tail end through the resolidified portion of the sample to the melted solid-liquid interface, which is about 1.4 cm away from the top of the sample. Light was not transmitted through the unmelted portion of the sample because that portion of the ingot was grown on Earth, and the fibers did not line up with the sample axis. Note the homogeneity of the sample as revealed in Fig. 8a. Figure 8b is a picture taken from a sample grown on Earth in an induction furnace. An attempt was made to shine a light at one end of the sample, but it did not travel very far

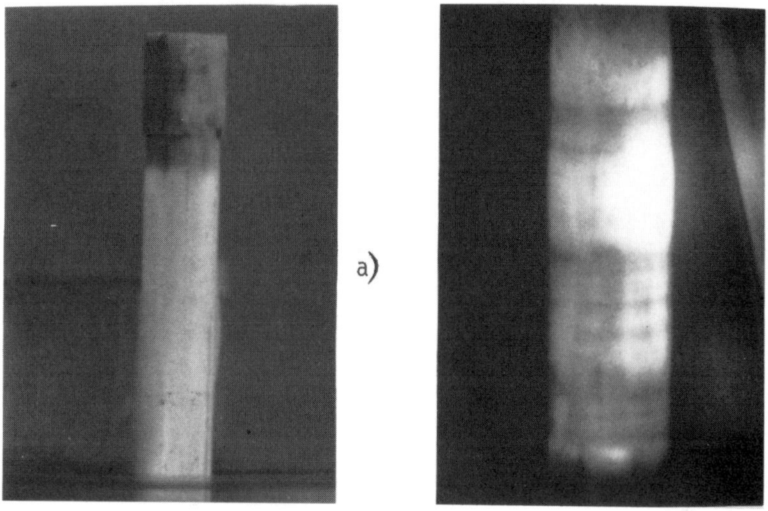

Fig. 8 Macrographs of a) Skylab-grown (1.2X) and b) Earth-grown (2X) NaCl-NaF eutectics.

because the NaF fibers were not aligned in the direction of the light. However, when light was shone on the side of the sample as indicated by the white spot in Fig. 8b, transmittance of light occurred in the direction perpendicular to the sample axis, indicating that some of the fibers also are perpendicular to the sample axis. Banded microstructure was evidenced in Fig. 8b, in agreement with our original prediction. In the absence of gravity, a nonhomogeneous crystal can be transformed to a homogeneous one if it is grown in a space environment.

Sodium Fluoride Fibers

In a 0-g environment, there is no difficulty in mixing two liquid phases of different densities. Furthermore, vibration levels in space will be far lower than those on Earth. Consequently, a continuous fiber eutectic mixture can be produced in a space environment, and microstructure sensitive to convection currents and vibration can develop undisturbed.

Figure 9a is a macrograph of a space-grown ingot that has been immersed in methyl alcohol for five weeks. The surface of the undissolved portion of the ingot is encased with a skeleton of NaF fibers. An enlarged portion of the ingot containing the unsolidified portion is given in Fig. 9b.

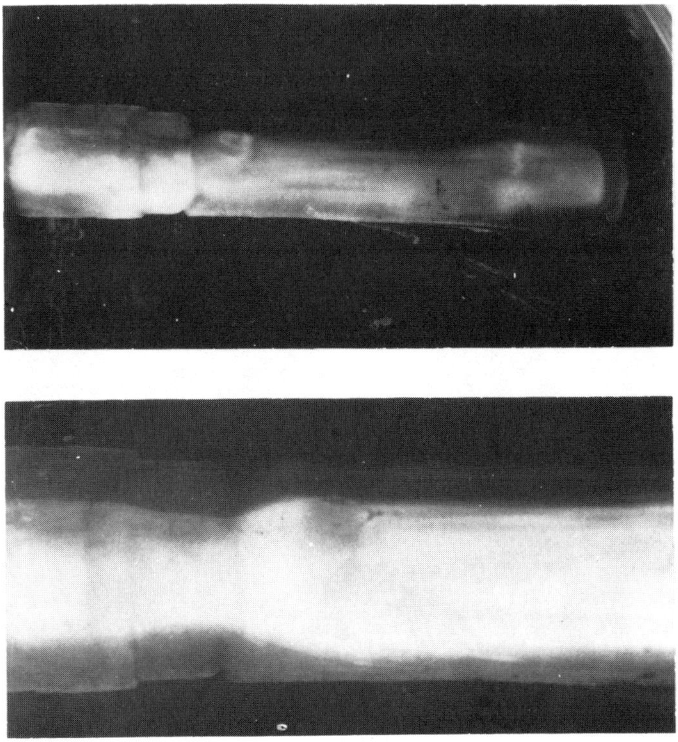

a)

b)

Fig. 9 Skylab-grown ingots encased with continuous NaF fibers: a) 2X, and b) 4.3X.

Notice that, on the right-hand side of the interface, the undissolved portion of the eutectic ingot reveals the presence of striations along the ingot axis. However, the striation directionality was not evident in the unsolidified portion of the ingot, indicating that the fibers are short and randomly distributed. Figure 10a proves that the growth of fibers was originated at the solid-liquid interface. Figure 10b is a picture of the end cross section of the unsolidified portion of the ingot, showing that the short NaF fibers produced on Earth are perpendicular to the cylindrical surface of the ingot.

Image Transmission

Image transmission properties similar to those of fiber optic materials were obtained with an NaCl-NaF eutectic.[9] Since it had discontinuous NaF fibers, far better results will

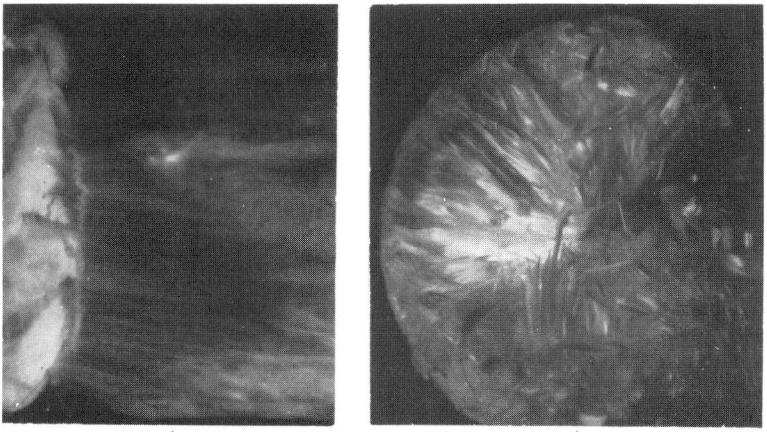

a) b)

Fig. 10 a) Continuous NaF fibers grown initially from the solid-liquid interface, and b) Discontinuous and randomly oriented fibers of the Earth-grown ingot end (8.6X).

be obtained if the same eutectic can be produced in space with continuous fibers. Two cylindrical samples with 2.5 cm thickness were cut from Skylab-grown and Earth-grown samples. Image transmission experiments were made on these two samples. Their results are given in Fig. 11. Figure 11a shows that an image was transmitted from a source (a sheet of paper containing Skylab) through the length of the sample to its surface. The transmitted image has the same dimension as the source, indicating that the NaF fibers are perpendicular to the plane of the paper. However, the transmitted image is not as clear as the original image of the source, indicating that there is a loss through transmission. This phenomenon is common to all fiber optics materials.[10] A transmitted image was not observed from a sample grown on Earth, as evidenced in Fig. 11b. This is attributed to the presence of discontinuous and randomly distributed NaF fibers in the NaCl-NaF eutectic produced on Earth.

Optical Transmittance

Figure 12 is a plot of transmittance vs wave number k (40×10^2 to 4×10^2 cm^{-1}) for NaCl-NaF eutectics, prepared on Earth and grown in the Skylab. The eutectic sample thicknesses taken from the transverse sections of the ingots were 0.107 in. For the NaCl-NaF eutectic grown on Earth, where there were convection currents present in the liquid during growth, the transmittance was about 10% over a narrow range of

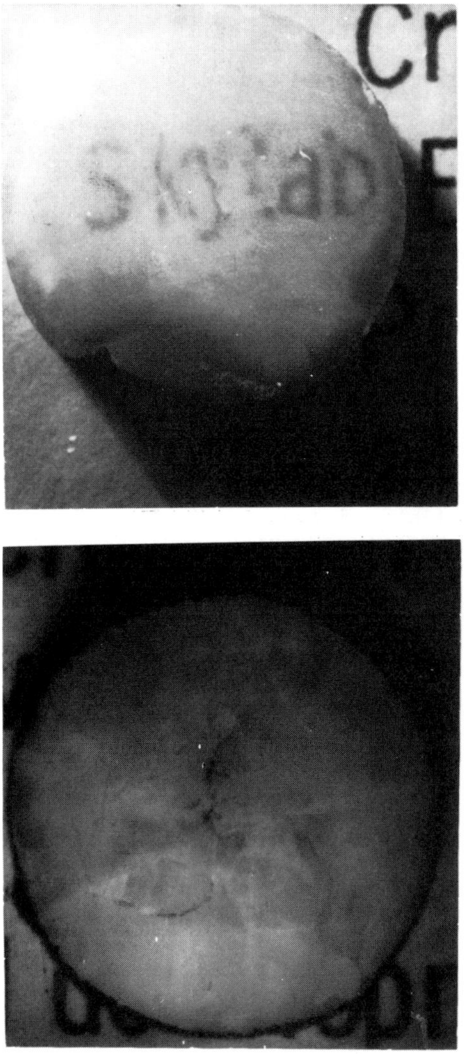

a)

b)

Fig. 11 Image transmission macrograph of a) Skylab-grown and b) Earth-grown NaCl-NaF eutectics (sample thickness = 2.5 cm, 8.5X).

wave numbers, as indicated in Fig. 12. When the same eutectic was grown in space, where there were no convection currents in the liquid during growth, the transmittance was increased to 65% over a much larger range of wave numbers. This was attributed to the achievement of producing continuous NaF fibers embedded in a continuous NaCl matrix so that the losses due to reflection and refraction of light within the eutectic

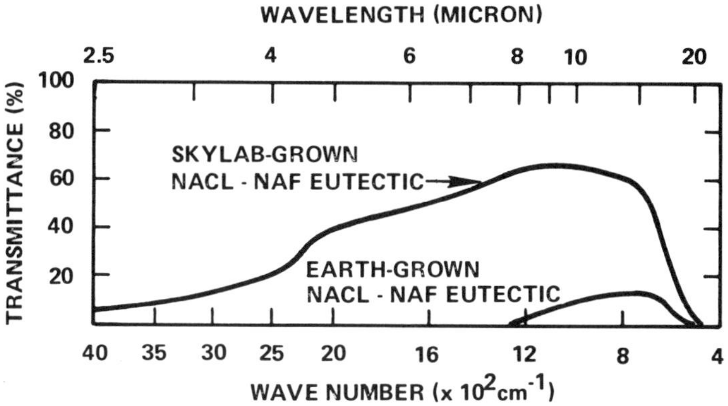

Fig. 12 Far-field infrared transmittance curves for NaCl-NaF eutectics grown on Earth and in space (sample thickness = 0.107 in.).

specimen have been reduced greatly. The shape of the transmission curve for the Skylab-grown NaCl-NaF eutectic is of great interest. At $k > 40 \times 10^2$ cm^{-1}, the transmittance of this eutectic approaches zero. The explanation is that the interfacial atoms at the fiber-matrix interface are mismatched. When incident light is directed at the surface of a eutectic sample, a fraction of the incident light transmitted through the eutectic sample will decrease due to scattering. This observation is in agreement with the fact that the higher the wave number (or the shorter the wavelength), the higher the loss through scattering.

The effect of thickness on the transmission curve is given in Fig. 13, which indicates that the thinner the sample, the

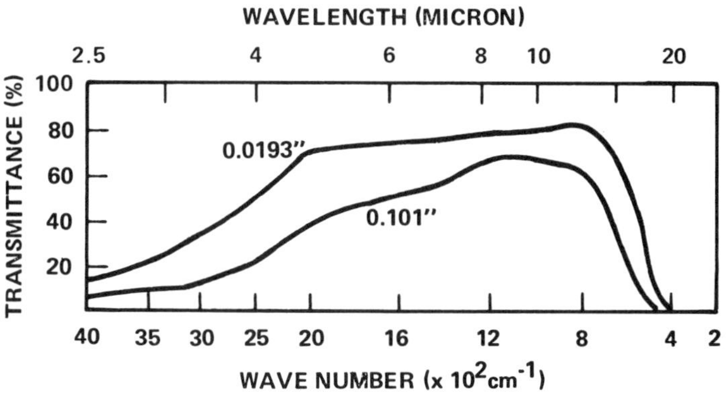

Fig. 13 Far-field infrared transmittance curves for Skylab-grown NaCl-NaF eutectic of varying thicknesses.

higher is the transmittance for a fixed wave number. This observation is in agreement with Lambert's law of absorption. The basic principle from which the law was derived is that the fraction of radiation absorbed in passing through a thin layer of matter is proportional to the thickness of the layer and the absorption coefficient, which depends upon the nature of the abosrbing matter and the wavelength of the radiation.

IV. Conclusions

The following conclusions can be drawn from this investigation:

1) Continuous NaF fibers, regularly arranged in a fault-free NaCl matrix, have been produced in the Skylab experiments. The success in producing continuous fibers is due to the absence of convection current in the liquid during solidification.

2) Larger transmittance over a wider wavelength and better image transmission were obtained from the Skylab-grown ingots. This is due to an excellent alignment of NaF fibers embedded in the NaCl matrix.

References

[1] Loxham, J.G. and Hellawell, A., "Constitution and Microstructure of Some Binary Alkali Halide Mixtures," Journal of the American Ceramic Society, Vol. 47, No. 4, April 1964, pp. 184-188.

[2] Yue, A.S. and Clark, J.B., "Determination of the Eutectic Composition by the Zone-Melting Method," Transactions of the Metallurgical Scoiety of AIME, Vol. 221, April 1961, pp. 383-389.

[3] Lemkey, F.D. and Thompson, E.R., "Nickel and Cobalt Eutectic Alloys Reinforced by Refractory Metal Carbides," Metallurgical Transactions, Vol. 2, June 1971, pp. 1537-1544.

[4] Crossman, F.W. and Yue, A.S., "Unidirectionally Solidified Ti-TiB and Ti-Ti_5Si_3 Eutectic Composites," Metallurgical Transactions, Vol. 2, June 1971, pp. 1545-1555.

[5] Yue, A.S., "Microstructure of Magnesium-Aluminum Eutectic," Transactions of the Metallurgical Society of AIME, Vol. 224, October 1962, pp. 1010-1015.

[6] Kraff, R.W. and Albright, D.L., "Microstructure of Unidirectionally Solidified Al-$CuAl_2$ Eutectic," Transactions of the Metallurgical Society of AIME, Vol. 221, June 1961, pp. 95-102.

[7] Weiss, H., "Electromagnetic Properties of Eutectic Composites (A Critical Review)," Metallurgical Transactions, Vol. 2, June 1971, pp. 1513-1521.

[8] Seidensticker, R., "System Design for Free Fall Materials Processing," Third Space Processing Symposium, April 30-May 1, 1974, NASA George C. Marshall Space Flight Center, Huntsville, Ala.

[9] Batt, J.A., Douglas, F.C., and Galasso, F.S., "Optical Properties of Unidirectionally Solidified NaF-NaCl Eutectic," Ceramic Bulletin, Vol. 48, August 1969, pp. 622-626.

[10] Laybourn, P.J.R., Gambling, W.A., and Jones, D.T., "Measurement of Attenuation in Low-Loss Optical Glass," Opto-Electronics, Vol. 3, August 1971, pp. 137-144.

LOW-GRAVITY HOMOGENIZATION AND SOLIDIFICATION OF ALUMINUM ANTIMONIDE

Choh-Yi Ang*
Universities Space Research Association,
Charlottesville, Va.

and

Lewis L. Lacy+
NASA Marshall Space Flight Center,
Huntsville, Ala.

Abstract

The III-V semiconducting compound AlSb shows promise as a highly efficient solar cell material, but it has not been commercially exploited because of difficulties in compound synthesis. Liquid state homogenization and solidification of AlSb were carried out in the Apollo-Soyuz Test Project Experiment MA-044 in the hope that compositional homogeneity would be improved by negating the large density difference between the two constituents. Post-flight analysis and comparative characterization of the space-processed and ground-processed samples indicate that there are major homogeneity improvements in the low-gravity solidified material.

Introduction

Certain potentially useful alloys or material systems are difficult to synthesize on Earth because of sizable differences in the specific gravity of the constituents, which result in undesirable buoyancy and convection influences during homogenization of the melts as well as in the initial stages of solidification and grain growth. The near zero-gravity con-

---

Presented as Paper D.2.1 at the COSPAR Symposium on Materials Sciences in Space, Philadelphia, Pa., June 9-10, 1976.
*Consultant, Marshall Space Flight Center.
+Solid State Physicist, Space Sciences Laboratory.

ditions attainable in spaceflights therefore have been utilized by investigators[1] not only to study low-g effects on various rate processes, but also to synthesize materials for demonstration and verification of the unique advantages of space processing. The recently completed Apollo-Soyuz Test Project (ASTP) mission had onboard several materials science experiments. One part of our ASTP Experiment MA-044[2] was concerned with the remelting of microstructurally inhomogeneous polycrystalline aluminum antimonide (AlSb) followed by homogenization and solidification under low-g conditions. The objective of the primary experiment was to determine whether homogeneity of this intermetallic compound could be improved by negating the gravity-induced convective influences. The secondary experiment[2] deals with a study of diffusion and the kinetics of dispersion in the monotectic binary Pb-Zn and will be reported elsewhere.

Among the III-V semiconducting compounds, AlSb (see phase diagram in Fig. 1) has been neglected for many years because of difficulties in synthesizing polycrystalline and single crystal materials,[3,4] with homogeneous composition and reproducible physical and semiconducting properties. Theoretically, AlSb with an energy gap of 1.62 eV is a highly efficient solar cell material,[5,6] but the difficulties in material synthesis and unstable properties of the laboratory samples have hampered efforts in commercial exploitation. By starting with zone-refined polycrystalline AlSb and keeping all experiment parameters identical for flight and ground sample, our investigation therefore was an attempt to study the one conspicuous factor of density differential (Al/Sb = 2.7/6.6) during liquid phase homogenization and liquid/solid transformation upon cooling.

The in-depth characterization of ASTP-tested samples and ground-based tested (GBT) counterparts is still in progress. Nevertheless, the microstructural and other analytical studies completed thus far already have indicated major differences between low-g and one-g samples.

Experimental Procedures

The details of sample preparation, pre-flight testing, and post-flight preliminary examination have been reported elsewhere.[7] Only the experiment parameters that are pertinent to the discussions are summarized here.

As previously mentioned, the starting material was zone-refined polycrystalline AlSb containing no more than

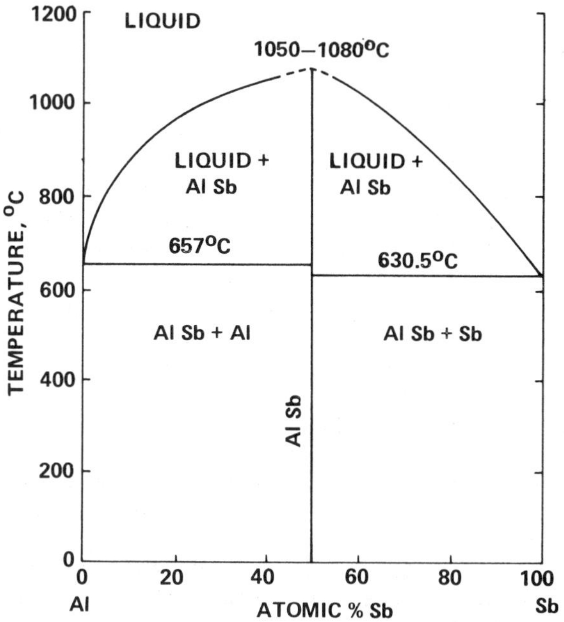

Fig. 1 Phase diagram of Al-Sb.

0.001 wt % oxygen and an overall correct stoichiometric content of Al and Sb. Microstructurally, this best commercially available material is not homogeneous. A typical grain of the starting material is shown in Fig. 2. In addition to the compound phase, the material consists of Al-rich and Sb-rich phases.

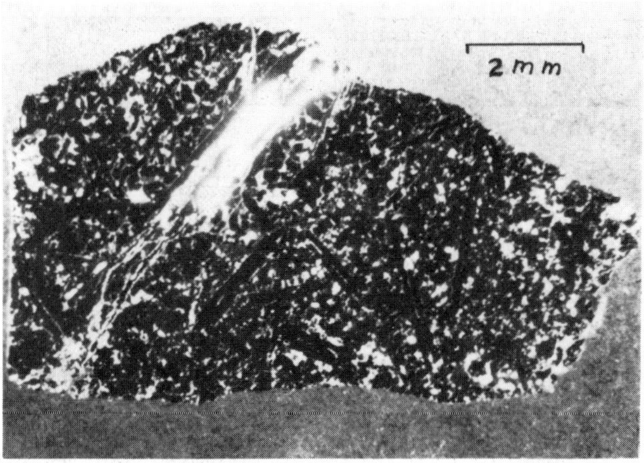

Fig. 2 Macrostructure of a typical AlSb starting material (8X).

The powder samples, each weighing 2 to 3 g, were loaded in purified dense graphite crucibles which were capped and in turn encapsulated in stainless steel ampoules. All steps in sample handling, including encapulation, were carried out in an ultra-pure argon atmosphere. The loaded ampoules were preheated for 10 min at 1125-1150°C before loading into especially constructed furnace cartridges. Schematics of the cartridge and ampoule assemblies are shown in Fig. 3, and an exposed view of a cartridge and ampoules can be seen in Fig. 4. In this experiment three samples were processed on ASTP and ten samples were processed on the ground, using triple-cavity furnaces of identical design and similar performance characteristics. Except for one GBT sample and the samples processed during the prototype furnace tests, the ASTP samples and their one-g counterparts had essentially the same thermal history. The homogenization temperature was 1128-1132°C, which is about 50°C above the highest reported melting point of the compound. The entire 15-hr thermal cycle from heating and programmed 1-hr soaking to helium-assisted cooling in the ASTP multipurpose furnace was accomplished at g-levels $\leq 1 \times 10^{-3}$ g during the spaceflight.

In addition to examination of the cartridges and ampoules,[7] the planned sample characterization tasks include

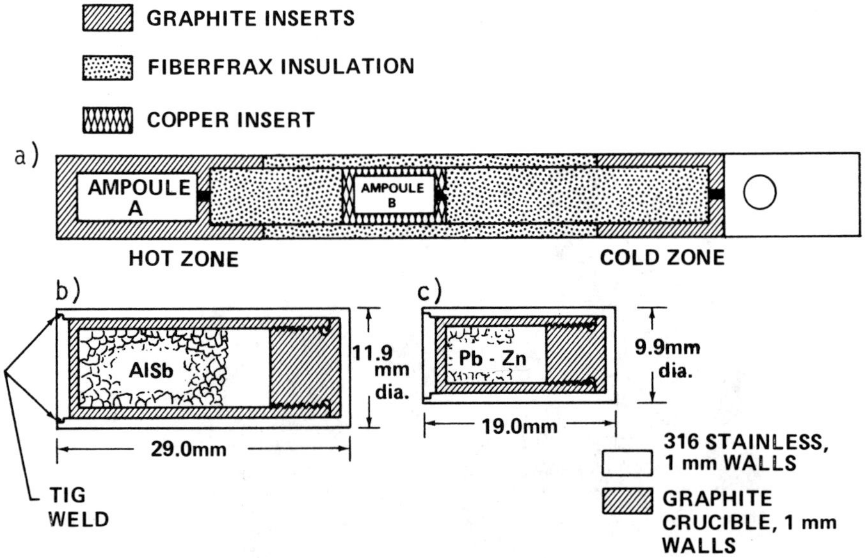

Fig. 3 Schematic of cartridge assembly and ampoules. a) Stainless steel cartridge assembly, b) Ampoule A, c) Ampoule B.

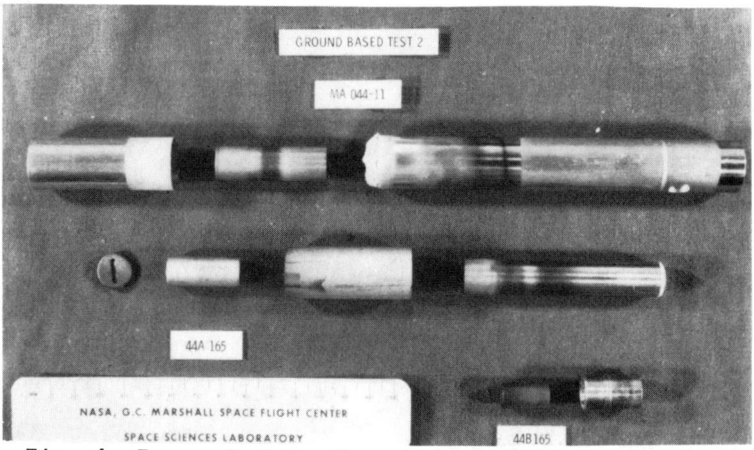

Fig. 4 Exposed view of cartridge and ampoules.

metallography, microhardness testing, scanning electron microscopy (SEM), energy-dispersive x-ray analysis (EDAX), chemical analysis, digital imaging analysis (DIA), x-ray diffraction, ion microprobe mass analysis (IMMA), and electrical resistivity testing. So far, only a number of samples have been characterized, and not all planned tests have been performed on any one sample. Therefore, this report summarizes significant observations on the ASTP and one-g samples examined to date and postulates mechanisms or reasons for the observed improvements in microstructural homogeneity.

Characterization Results

The metallographic examination of resolidified samples indicates that complete remelting and recrystallization had taken place during the prescribed thermal cycling. The typical microstructures of ASTP, GBT, and prototype-tested (PT) samples are shown in Fig. 5. All microstructures examined show the presence of dark primary grains and a light secondary phase. The secondary phases in the two one-g samples are not unlike those in the starting material (Fig. 2) and are present in much larger amounts than in the low-g samples. In fact, in the ASTP samples, the small amounts of the secondary phase appear to be inclusions along the boundaries of the primary grains. Microhardness readings taken on a PT sample section indicate that the primary phase has a Vickers number of ~ 400, whereas, the softer secondary phase has a hardness number of ~ 60.

To assess the differences in amount of the secondary phases in low-g and one-g samples, the computer-aided tech-

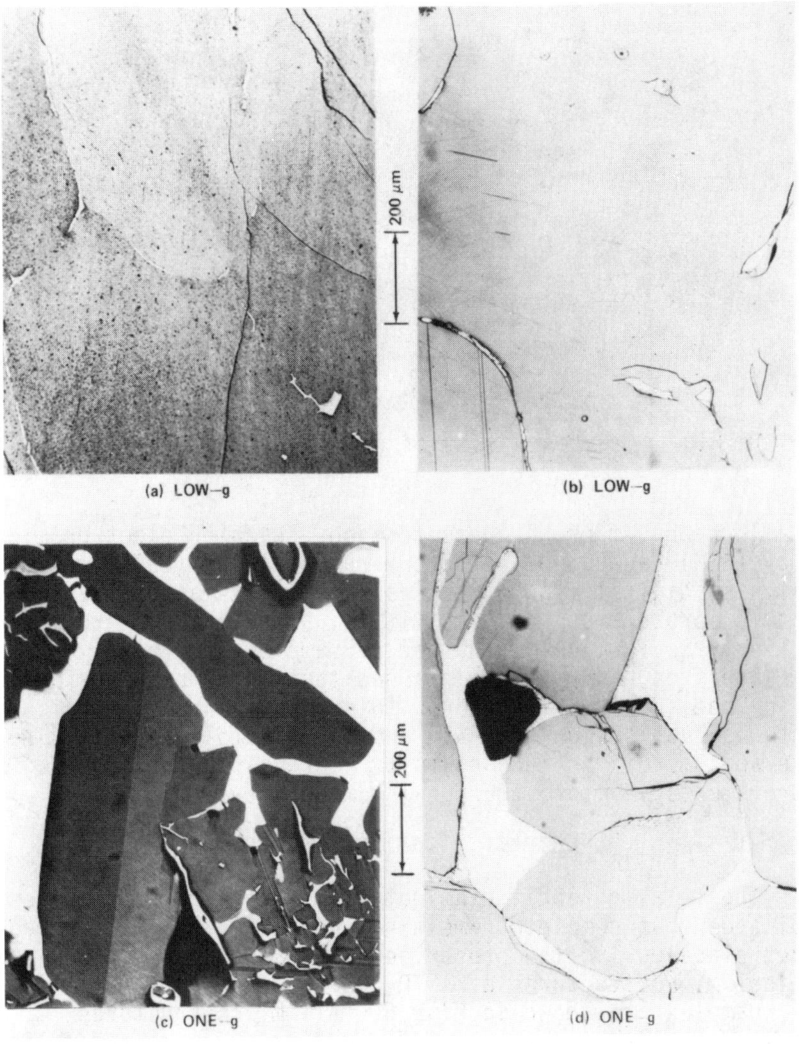

Fig. 5 Typical microstructures (50X) of low-g and one-g processed AlSb samples, showing differences in amounts of the primary grains and the secondary phases. a) ASTP A185, b) ASTP A164, c) PT A127, and d) GBT A141.

nique of digital imaging analysis was used as a tool for quantitative microstructural analysis. Figure 6 is a quantitative comparison of the AlSb microstructures shown in Fig. 5(a) and 5(c). It can be seen in Fig. 6 that the secondary phase has been reduced by low-g homogenization from

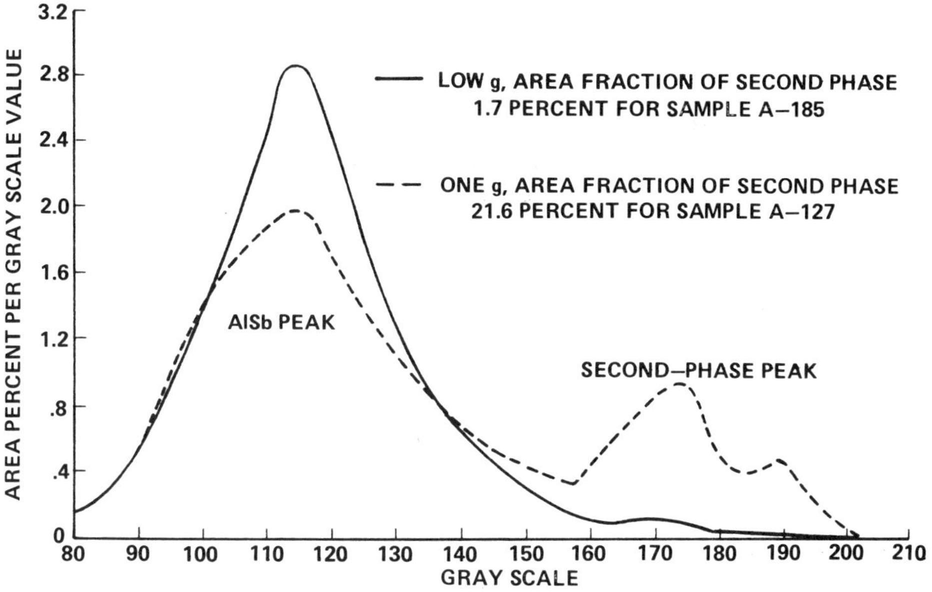

Fig. 6 Quantitative comparison of AlSb microstructures.

21.6% to 1.7%. A similar reduction of secondary phases has occurred throughout the ASTP sample as shown in Fig. 7. Across the 8-mm width of the sample sections, the plot in Fig. 7 shows that the one-g GBT sample has a very nonuniform distribution of its secondary phase. In comparison with the ASTP sample, the one-g sample has a maximum of 20 and an average of 5 times more of the secondary phase.

The results of x-ray diffraction and SEM/EDAX indicate that the primary grains in the samples are the AlSb intermetallic compound and the secondary phases are either Al-rich or Sb-rich in composition. A preliminary semiquantitative IMMA analysis on one GBT and one PT sample also confirms the EDAX results but further indicates that both the primary AlSb grains and the secondary phases vary in stoichiometric proportion of the two constituents. A plot of the ratios of Al to Sb ions detected from three locations on the PT sample A132 is shown in Fig. 8.

The electrical resistivities of one ASTP sample and two one-g samples were determined with the use of a 4-point probe at different locations on polished sectional surfaces. The typical or average value of resistivity is 12 Ω-cm for the ASTP sample, as compared to 6 x 10^{-3} Ω-cm for the one-g

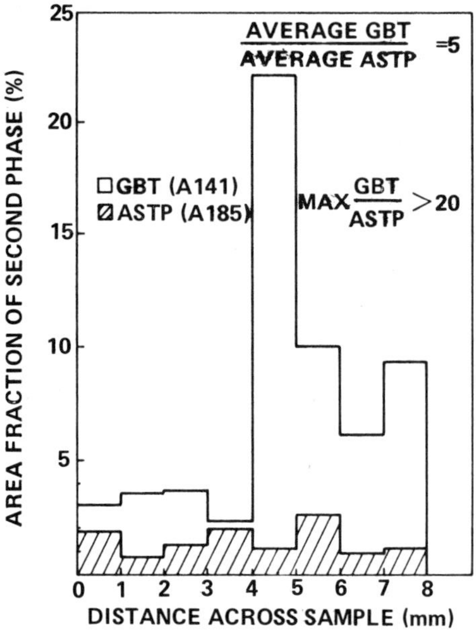

Fig. 7 Comparison of AlSb microstructural homogeneity across sample sections.

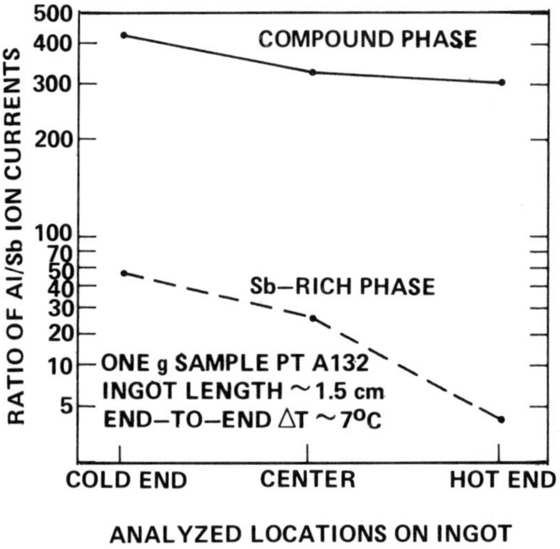

Fig. 8 Ratios of Al and Sb ions detected by IMMA from selected locations on the polished section of PT sample A132.

samples. The measured resistivity of the ASTP sample essentially agrees with the reported values for AlSb. On the other hand, a material containing large amounts of Al-rich or Sb-rich phases would exhibit much lower resistivity, as indicated by the one-g samples.

Because of the limited number and small size of the samples, extensive chemical analysis has been deferred to latter stages of the characterization program. Nevertheless, one GBT sample of AlSb was cut into wafers and analyzed by using the method of atomic absorption spectroscopy. The weighted average of Al contents from five wafers is 19.2 wt %, which is 1 wt % higher than the theoretical Al content in AlSb.

Discussion

Although not yet completed, the characterization tasks conducted thus far have yielded results which indicate that the liquid phase homogenization of AlSb was much more effective when it was carried out in space under low-g conditions. Since the starting material contained Al-rich and Sb-rich phases, homogenization in the melt would be influenced by the competing mechanisms of diffusion and gravity-driven convection. Based on what we have observed microstructurally, the liquid state diffusion appears to be the dominant mechanism for the improved homogeneity of the low-g samples. The inhomogeneity that persisted in the one-g melted samples probably was caused by the large differences in density that existed between the different phases in the starting material.

The homogenization of a binary system may be accomplished by interdiffusion between different regions with respectively high and low contents of one of the two constitutents. If we assume that the concentration, C, of this constituent varies sinusoidally with distance, x, about some average, then a solution of the second Fick's law is

$$C/C_m = \sin(\pi x/\ell)/\exp(\pi^2 Dt/\ell^2) \qquad (1)$$

where C_m is the initial maximum variation in concentration, ℓ is the effective diffusion distance between the two phases, D is the temperature-dependent diffusion coefficient, and t is the homogenization time. It should be understood that Eq. (1) describes a diffusion process and does not take the convection-induced effects into consideration. In the homogenization of AlSb in space, if we assume an average value for the liquid diffusion coefficient, D, of about 1×10^{-5} cm^2/sec and an average center-to-center distance (ℓ) of 1 mm between the two phases in the starting material, then Eq. (1) would indicate that a 1-hr soak time would homogenize the sample effectively even when the initial maximum fluctuation in concentration involved an elemental phase. As previously discussed, the analysis of the ASTP samples has confirmed the anticipated results experimentally.

To further understand the competitive mechanisms of diffusion and convection associated with any homogenization processes, we propose a liquid state homogenization number, H, and define it as

$$H = \frac{\text{convective distance}}{\text{diffusion distance}} \simeq \frac{d^2 g \Delta\rho}{5\eta} \ \frac{t}{D} \qquad (2)$$

where d is the average grain size or cluster size of the phase in question, g is the gravitational constant, $\Delta\rho$ is the density difference between the primary and the secondary phase, and η is the liquid viscosity. This expression is essentially a comparison between a Stoke's law-type model and a Fick's law-type model for specifying distances for particle movement. We believe that this expression should be useful for designing space processing experiments which involve rate processes of binaries in the liquid state. If $H \gg 1$, gravity-induced convection becomes the dominant mechanism, and a diffusion process as described by Eq. (1) would be relatively ineffective in achieving homogeneous melts. On the other hand, if $H \ll 1$, then Eq. (1) shows that liquid state diffusion would homogenize melts quickly in a low-g field.

Although we do not have precise values for this analysis, Eq. (2) would indicate, for the homogenization of AlSb, the ratio of H_{ASTP}/H_{GBT} would be $\leq 1 \times 10^{-3}$ (the g-level) if it is assumed that other parameters are the same for both the low-g and one-g case. If one chooses reasonable values for the parameters of Eq. (2), then it is seen that $H_{GBT} > 100$, which illustrates the observed experimental difficulties in achieving homogeneous AlSb melts on Earth.

The foregoing empirical diffusion and homogenization analyses also assume that the secondary phase has a uniform composition, and the Al-Sb binary system does have the feature of syntectic transformation of two liquids into a compound of constant composition upon solidification. Our preliminary IMMA analysis of one PT sample not only indicated that the secondary phase has a varying composition, but that the "compound" AlSb also may have a range of homogeneity not unlike many other intermetallic compounds,[8] such as Cu_3As, AgZr, BeCo, Be_2Cr, ZrB_2, Ti_5Si_3, AlLi, or $AlPd_2$.

Conclusions

Comparison of the microstructures of the ASTP and ground samples of AlSb reveals major microscopic and macroscopic homogeneity improvements in the material processed in space. The low-g homogenized samples contain 5 to 20 times less of the unwanted secondary phases than the one-g counterparts. This conclusion is supported by other characterization techniques which were described only briefly in this paper. A liquid-state-homogenization analysis indicates that gravity-induced convection, caused by a density difference between the primary and secondary phases, prevents homogenization on Earth. Furthermore, by greatly reducing the convective influence, liquid phase interdiffusion can effectively homogenize the melts in a low-g space environment.

The findings of this ASTP experiment indicate that other unique binary systems which are difficult to synthesize on Earth because of gravity-induced effects may be advantageously processed in space. The containerless zone melting and leveling of these types of materials in a future space laboratory will provide samples of sizes and configurations suitable for more extensive investigations.

References

[1] Snyder, R. S., "Summary of the Pre-ASTP Results," presented at the Second European Symposium of Material Sciences in Space, Frascati, Italy, 1976.

[2] "Apollo-Soyuz Test Project: Preliminary Science Report," NASA TMX-58173, Feb. 1976.

[3] Allred, W. P., Mefferd, W. L., and Willardson, R. K., "The Preparation and Properties of Aluminum Antimonide," Journal of the Electrochemical Society, Vol. 107, Feb. 1960, pp. 117-122.

[4] Willardson, R. K. and Beer, A. C., eds., Semiconductors and Semimetals. Physics of III-V Compounds, Vol. 4, Academic Press, New York, 1968, p. 59.

[5] Rittner, E. S., "Use of p-n Junctions for Solar Energy Conversion," Physical Review, Vol. 96, Dec. 1954, pp. 1708-1709.

[6] Loferski, J. J., "Theoretical Considerations Governing the Choice of the Optimum Semiconductor for Photovoltaic Solar

Energy Conversion," Journal of Applied Physics, Vol. 27, July 1956, pp. 777-784.

[7]Ang, C. Y. and Lacy, L. L., "Monotectic and Syntectic Alloys: ASTP Experiment MA-044 Postflight Preliminary Technical Report," NASA TMX-64956, Sept. 1975.

[8]Metals Handbook, American Society for Metals, Vol. 8, 1973, or Hansen, M., Constitution of Binary Alloy, McGraw-Hill, New York, 1958.

G-JITTER CONVECTION OF CONFINED FLUIDS IN LOW GRAVITY

L. W. Spradley*, S. V. Bourgeois+, and F. N. Lin+

Lockheed Missiles & Space Company, Inc., Huntsville, Ala.

Abstract

G-jitter convection, caused by time-varying accelerations imparted on a heated container of fluid in low gravity, is investigated analytically. The mathematical model used is constructed from the Navier-Stokes equations, which are solved with a finite-difference method on a digital computer. Results are presented for typical space processing configurations and anticipated g-jitter levels, with emphasis on sounding rocket applications. The calculations indicate that g-jitter can cause significant temperature oscillations, increase or decrease local heat transfer, and produce oscillatory convective flow patterns. These factors can have significant effects on important processes such as crystal growth (banding, for example) and separation techniques.

Nomenclature

A_g = peak-to-peak amplitude of gravity (jitter) variations, cm/sec^2

A_T = peak-to-peak amplitude of temperature oscillations, ^oC

Presented as Paper 75-695 at the AIAA Thermophysics Conference, Denver, Colo., May 27-29, 1975. We sincerely thank T.C. Bannister of NASA-MSFC and J.R. Carruthers of Bell Laboratories for their many helpful discussions. This work was supported by NASA Contracts NAS8-27015 and NAS8-29610; we gratefully acknowledge this support.

*Senior Mathematical Engineer, Space Processing Group.

+Scientist Associate-Research, Space Processing Group.

A_v = peak-to-peak amplitude of velocity fluctuations, cm/sec

C_p = heat capacity of liquids, cal/g

D = diameter of container, cm

g = dimensionless gravity level (gravity/Earth gravity)

g_E = Earth gravity, 980 cm/sec^2

$\bar{g}$ = minimum level of gravity during g-jitter oscillations normalized by Earth gravity (gravity/g_E)

Gr = Grashof number

k = thermal conductivity of liquid, cal/cm-sec-^{o}C

L = length or height of container, cm

Nu = Nusselt number

P = pressure

Pr = Prandtl number, $\mu C_p/k$

r = radial coordinate of container, cm

R = radius of container, cm

Ra = Rayleigh number, $\rho^2 C_p \beta g \Delta T L^3/\mu k$

T = temperature, ^{o}C

u = radial or lateral component of velocity in the fluid, cm/sec

v = axial or vertical component of velocity in the fluid, cm/sec

W = width of container, cm

x, y = Cartesian coordinates, cm

z = axial coordinate of container, cm

Greek

β = coefficient of thermal expansion, 1/^{o}C

γ = aspect ratio of container (height-to-diameter)

λ_g = period of g-jitter, sec

λ_T = period of temperature oscillations, sec

λ_v = period of velocity oscillations, sec

μ = viscosity, g/cm sec

η = aspect ratio of container (width-to-height)

ρ = density, g/cm^3
ω_g = frequency of g-jitter, Hz
ω_T = frequency of temperature oscillations, Hz
ω_v = frequency of velocity oscillations, Hz
ψ = stream function, cm^2/sec

Introduction

NASA has been studying space processing applications (SPA) since 1968.[1] One of the primary advantages foreseen for conducting manufacturing processes in the low-gravity environment of space is the absence of buoyant natural convection and sedimentation. Most of the processes proposed to date for space manufacturing have been designed to take advantage of this particular phenomenon. Gravity is not the only driving force for natural convection, however, and other naturally occurring and often-present forces such as vibrations, surface tension, electromagnetic forces, and thermal expansion also can give rise to considerable fluid motion and increased heat transfer. Thus, natural convection can exist and be a dominant factor in space manufacturing processes.

Random mechanical vibrations can arise from such factors as astronaut movement, machinery operations, and spacecraft maneuvers. Previous space processing experiments on Apollo[2,3] and Skylab[4] missions indicate that gravitational forces varied in magnitude with time. Thus, the SPA experiments to be conducted aboard the Apollo-Soyuz Technical Pro[illegible]m (ASTP) also will experience these vibrations. Upcoming sounding rocket experiments also are likely to be subject to these vibrations.

This study consists of an analytical investigation of convection in an enclosure that is heated in low gravity. The gravitational body force is taken as a time-varying function using anticipated sounding rocket accelerations, since accelerometer flight data are not available. A computer program was used to calculate the flow rates and heat transfer in fluids with geometries and boundary conditions typical of space processing configurations. Calculations were made for both a constant acceleration and for time-varying accelerations (termed "g-jitter"). The term "g-jitter" convection is coined to describe fluid flow and associated transport phenomena caused by any time-varying accelerations imparted on a container fluid. The study has revealed that g-jitter convection can cause significant changes in flow structure and temperature distributions in confined fluids that are heated in a low-g environment. Among the processes most likely to be affected drastically by convection are various crystal growth procedures and material separation techniques, such as electrophoresis and Soret methods. These phenomena must be understood and explained if any significant process of this type is to be designed for space manufacturing. In Sec. II, related previous studies are discussed. Problem formulation and solution techniques are described in Sec. III. Results are given in Sec. IV, whereas implications for space processing are contained in Sec. V.

II. Related Studies

An overview of the status of vibrations on convective heat transfer is given by Richardson.[5] The few analyses that exist on vibrational convection with application to space processing indicate that mechanical vibrations and g-jitter can do the following:

1) Increase or decrease local (at isolated points on a surface) heat transfer substantially.[5]

2) Increase total heat transfer significantly in a few configurations.[6-8]

3) Drastically affect convection by altering the transitions from quiescent-to-laminar flow[9, 10] and from laminar-to-turbulent flow.[5, 11-13]

Also of importance to SPA, vibrations can alter the boundary layer thickness, which adversely can affect dopant distributions in crystal growth.[14]

It recently has been found that g-jitter can have a profound affect on convective motion and heat transfer in the microgravity environment of space. These low-gravity results were obtained from Apollo 14 and 17 heat flow and convection experiments and compare with several earlier vibration analyses done on Earth[5] and theoretically.[7, 16] The Apollo convection data were the first ever obtained in sustained low-gravity conditions.

The theoretical analysis by Gebhart[7] deals directly with convection caused by random disturbances likely to prevail in spacecraft. Assuming that shear stresses account for most of the convection, Gebhart obtained a relation between Nusselt number (comparison of random convection and pure conduction) and elapsed time between impulses. The analysis treats only small-amplitude vibrations. It does not take into account substantial fluid flow that would result from large-amplitude disturbances. However, the analysis should give order-of-magnitude effects. An increase in heat transfer between 300 to 400% is predicted during frequent impulses of small amplitude in low gravity.[3]

Other studies of interest include those that analyze coupling of convection by gravity vibrations. The effect of steady mechanical vibrations for various frequencies and amplitudes on heat transfer in confined fluids was studied by Pak et al.[6] Based on experimental data, a correlation was developed relating increased heat transfer to heating rate, fluid properties, and amplitude and frequency of vibration. These results show that gravity and vibration forces couple in an anulling manner; i.e., more heat is transferred by vibrations in the uncoupled case than in the coupled case. This is in agreement with the analysis of Richardson.[5] In a low-g environment, therefore, vibrations will be much more of a problem than they are on Earth.

Also in the area of vibration-gravity coupling, the papers by Gershuni et al.,[9] and Gresho and Sani[10] are of primary interest. These analyses examine the stability (quiescent-to-laminar transition) of a heated fluid layer undergoing vertical oscillations in a constant-gravity field. The results can be applied equally as well to vibration in constant-g or a stationary layer undergoing g-jitter. The conclusions reached by these qualitative analyses are as follows:[9, 10]

1) Gravity modulation can affect significantly the stability limits of a heated fluid layer. Any positive Rayleigh number (heating from below) can be stabilized for some range of frequency and amplitude. Any negative Rayleigh number (heating from above) can be stabilized for some range of frequency and amplitude, with high frequency and large amplitude being the most destabilizing.

2) With heating from below, there may occur two distinct types of flow patterns: a) At low-to-moderate frequency, the response will be synchronous with the forcing frequency, and there will be net fluid motion along the streamlines, although there will be flow reversal during part of the cycle. The Nusselt number usually will be less than that with no vibration, since the vibration is a stabilizing influence.
b) at high frequency the response will be subharmonic; there

will be no net flow along the streamlines, and the Nusselt number will be significantly lower than that with no modulation.

3) With heating from above, the flow pattern will be predominantly subharmonic, with no net flow and rather low Nusselt number. There may exist a small range of intermediate frequency for which the flow response will be synchronous.

Zenkovskaya[17] theoretically analyzed the convective stability of a fluid layer heated from below that was subjected to high-frequency gravity oscillation. The layer was enclosed in an infinitely long square cavity. On the basis of averaged and linearized convection equations, the author discovered a stabilizing influence from high-frequency vibrations. The dependence of the critical Rayleigh number on a vibration parameter was derived, but interpretation of results must await translation of the article from Russian.

One other pertinent Russian study by Burde[18] has been translated. Burde considered the problem formulated by Zenskovskaya,[17] but used a numerical finite-difference technique to solve the nonlinear unsteady convection equations. Thus, both the critical Rayleigh number and the development of flow patterns were studied. The results were obtained for a Prandtl number of unity, for Grashof numbers (Gr) between 2×10^3 and 6×10^3, for dimensionless amplitudes (A) between 0 and 10, and for dimensionless frequencies (ω) between 6 and 200. A typical result is shown in Fig. 1, which is a graph of stability in the (A, $1/\omega$) plane for Gr = 3000. Regions of instability are shaded. In the absence of vibrations, the critical Grashof number, Gr_c, is 2700. The line A = 0 corresponds

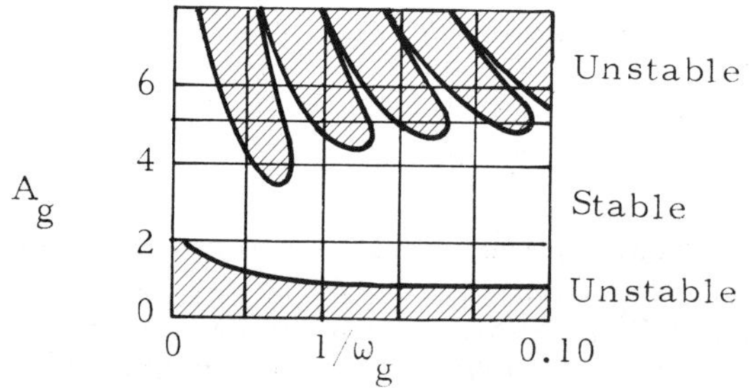

Fig. 1 Instability regions of a cavity subjected to various vibrations for a Grashof number of 3000.[18]

to instability when vibrations are absent and $Gr > Gr_c$. The lower region of instability borders this line. Above this region lies a strip of stability for certain A values even though $Gr > Gr_c$. For sufficiently larger amplitude (larger A), modulation again produces increasing fluid oscillations. In Fig. 1 this corresponds to the upper resonant regions of instability. These results are said to be in agreement with Zenskovskaya's.

Other results in the Burde study show that for $Gr < Gr_c$, the lower region of instability vanishes. This lower instability region first appears for $Gr = Gr_c$, and its width grows monotonically with increasing Gr, until eventually no stabilizing region is left in the (A, ω) plane. Information on flow patterns and temperature profiles in unstable regions also is given. Figure 2 illustrates stream functions within the cavity in three unstable regions for a fixed $Gr > Gr_c$ as follows: 1) Fig. 2a for flow in the lower instability region of Fig. 1, 2) Fig. 2b for the leftmost upper instability region in Fig. 1, and 3) Fig. 2c for the second-to-leftmost upper instability region in Fig. 1. In conclusion, Burde shows that, depending on frequency and amplitude of oscillation, g-jitter either can stabilize or destabilize convection in fluids heated from below. Also of primary significance to SPA are the flow pattern alterations shown in Fig. 2; i.e., g-jitter causes the unicellular flow to become multicells. Such multicellular flow will lead to increasingly nonuniform solutal boundary layers and uneven dopant distributions within solidified single crystals.[14]

Few of the preceding analyses can be applied directly to SPA with quantitative results. Thus, the analysis described in the following section was conducted to obtain answers to questions about g-jitter such as the following:

1) Will flow and temperature oscillations arise; and if so, what will be their amplitude and frequency?

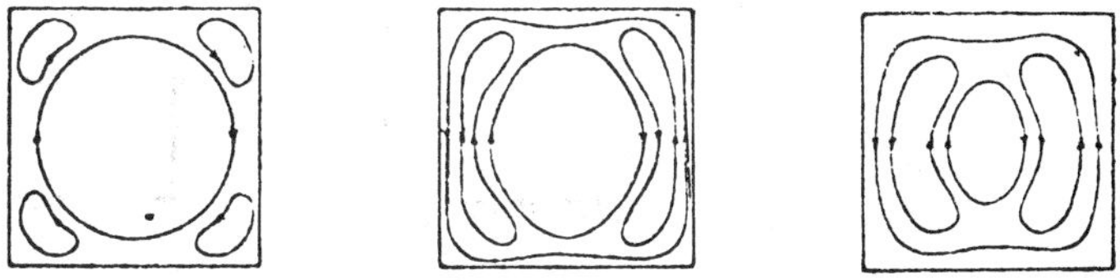

a. b. c.

Fig. 2 Streamlines for various instability regions in a vibrating cavity.[18]

2) How will flow patterns be affected; i.e., will multi-cells arise, disrupt uniform boundary layer widths, and adversely affect crystal growth?

III. Problem Formulation

The study of g-jitter convection was performed by utilizing the Lockheed convection analysis (LCA) computer program.[19] The LCA program is a general purpose digital computer code for natural convection analysis. Among the capabilities of the program are 1) rectangular or cylindrical geometries; 2) gases or liquids; 3) transient and steady-state analyses; 4) confined fluids and free-surface flows; 5) time-varying body force; 6) temperature-dependent material properties; 7) heating from the side or from below; 8) combinations of heat flux and temperature boundary conditions; and 9) two-dimensional or axisymmetric laminar flow. A complete formulation of the various models utilized by the program is given in Spradley and Churchill.[19]

A typical formulation now is given for the g-jitter problem using a rectangular geometry and Cartesian coordinates. Figure 3 shows the geometry, coordinate system, and configuration of the model. A rectangular box of width, W, and length, L, confines a fluid between rigid boundaries. The

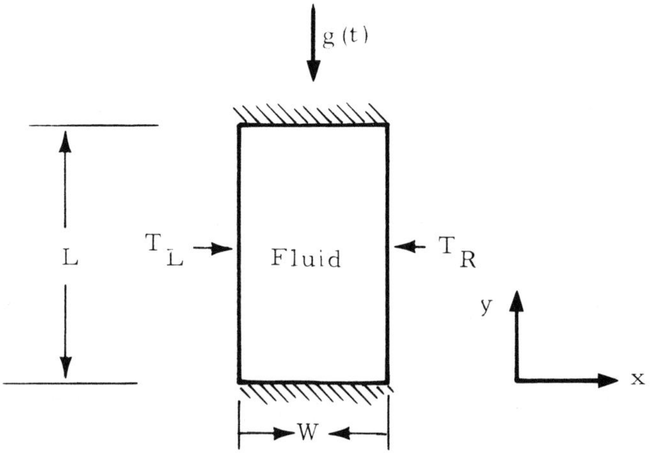

Fig. 3 Typical configuration, coordinate system, and boundary conditions.

fluid initially can be at rest and isothermal. The gravitational oscillation is time-dependent and in the direction of the -y axis. As the left wall is heated, flow is initiated by buoyancy due to density gradients. The problem now consists of determining the flow characteristics and heat transfer as a function of time, or until a steady-state is reached.

The mathematical formulation of the problem is in terms of the Navier-Stokes equations in primitive variable form. Assumptions made in this illustrative case are 1) material properties except density are constant; 2) laminal flow of a Newtonian fluid; 3) viscous effects in the momentum equation are for incompressible flow; and 4) viscous dissipation, radiation, and compressibility are neglected in the energy equation. The governing equations are given below in terms of dimensionless variables and in conservation law form.

X-Momentum

$$\frac{\partial}{\partial t}(\rho u) + \frac{\partial}{\partial x}(\rho u^2) + \eta \frac{\partial}{\partial y}(\rho u v) = -\frac{\partial P}{\partial x} + \left(\frac{\partial^2 u}{\partial x^2} + \eta^2 \frac{\partial^2 u}{\partial y^2}\right)$$

Y-Momentum

$$\frac{\partial}{\partial t}(\rho v) + \frac{\partial}{\partial x}(\rho u v) + \eta \frac{\partial}{\partial y}(\rho v^2) = \overline{G}(\rho - 1)\, g(t)$$

$$- \eta \frac{\partial P}{\partial y} + \left(\frac{\partial^2 v}{\partial x^2} + \eta^2 \frac{\partial^2 v}{\partial y^2}\right)$$

Continuity

$$\partial \rho/\partial t + \partial/\partial x\ (\rho u) + \eta\ \partial/\partial y\ (\rho v) = 0$$

Energy

$$\frac{\partial}{\partial t}(\rho T) + \frac{\partial}{\partial x}(\rho u T) + \eta \left(\frac{\partial}{\partial y}\right)(\rho v T) = \frac{1}{Pr}\left(\frac{\partial^2 T}{\partial x^2} + \eta^2 \frac{\partial^2 T}{\partial y^2}\right)$$

State Relation

$$\beta \Delta T + (\Delta \rho/\rho) - K \Delta P = 0$$

where the dimensionless groups are

$\eta = W/L$ Aspect ratio

$\bar{G} = -\bar{g}_E W^3/\nu^2$ Buoyancy parameter (similar to Grashoff number)

$Pr = \mu C_p/k$ Prandtl number

$\beta = -1/\rho_o (\partial\rho/\partial T)_P$ Coefficient of thermal expansion

$K = 1/\rho_o (\partial\rho/\partial P)_T$ Coefficient of isothermal compressibility

Details of the dimensional analysis and reference variables are given by Spradley and Chruchill.[19]

Boundary conditions for the equations can be various combinations of wall heat fluxes; temperatures; and no-slip, free-slip, and free-surface conditions. A simplified set are the following

Typical Initial Conditions

$u = v = 0 \quad \rho = 1$

$T = 1 \quad P = 1$

Typical Boundary Conditions

$u = v = 0$ at solid walls

$T(x = 0, y) = T_L \qquad \partial T/\partial y = 0$ at $y = 0$

$T(x = 1, y) = T_R \qquad \partial T/\partial y = 0$ at $y = 1$

The mathematical model is complete except for a form for the g(t) body-force parameter. The results presented here utilize three different forms for g(t) and are discussed in Sec. III.

A finite difference method is used for obtaining numerical solutions to the equations. The basic method is that of Spradley and Churchill.[19] It utilizes an explicit finite-difference,forward-marching method. Centered differences are used for all terms except the convection terms, where a conservative-donor method is applied. The grid consists of a sequence of cell-centered points with the spacings Δx, Δy constant, but not necessarily equal. The utility of the method is that it yields both transient and steady-state solutions, is conditionally stable, and numerically conservative. The solution process begins at some time when a flowfield is known. This can be t = 0, with the fluid isothermal and at rest, or at $t = t_f$, where the flowfield is supplied from the solutions for a previous case. The flow for "heating-from-below" cases is initiated by either a temperature perturbation from the conductive state or by using the flow from a previous case. The starting flow for the cases presented here consists of using a sinusoidal temperature perturbation to introduce a single two-dimensional roll cell in the container. From the initial data, the equations are solved to march the solution forward in time to yield the velocity components, density, and temperature profiles at all grid points in the container. The solutions are mapped as isotherm contours, streamlines, and/or velocity vector fields. The LCA program, the numerical technique, and solution algorithms have been verified for many sample problems by comparing them with previous theory and experimental data.[19, 20] The program is in production status for use on a Univac 1108 multiprocessor computer system.

IV. Results

Many cases of fluids undergoing thermal processing in containers and g-jitter, typical of space processing, have been simulated using the LCA computer program. Discussed in the following paragraphs is a comparison of the LCA solutions with previous investigators for verification of the model. A study of constant gravity vs surface-tension-driven convection then is given. This demonstrates that the presence of fluid-fluid interfaces can give rise to convection equal to or greater than buoyancy convection. Thus, even though the effects of g-jitter may be substantial, it must be kept in mind that surface-tension convection may be the controlling phenomenon in low gravity. Additionally, the sensitivity of fluids and geometries to g-jitter convection are discussed, as well as the results of g-jitter studies of liquid melts similar to those of the Skylab multipurpose furnace.

Model Verification

Results obtained from the LCA program have been compared with those obtained by previous investigators, in particular the results of Wilkes and Churchill.[21] Comparisons that show the details of streamlines and isotherms are given in Ref. 19. The comparison is for a completely filled box of water being heated on the left wall, which is parallel to the direction of the gravitational forces of 10^{-4} g. A schematic of the configuration is given in Fig. 4.

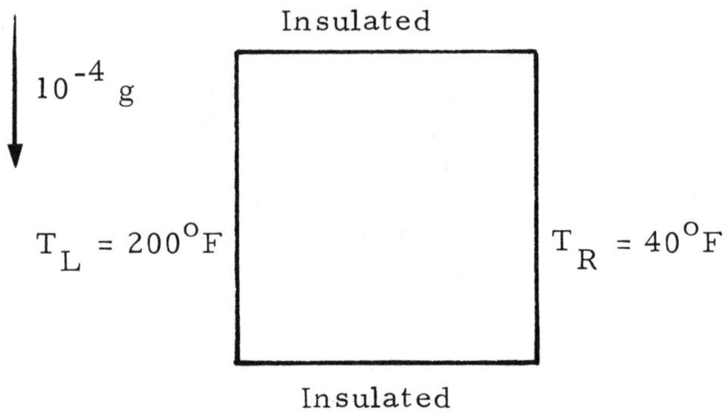

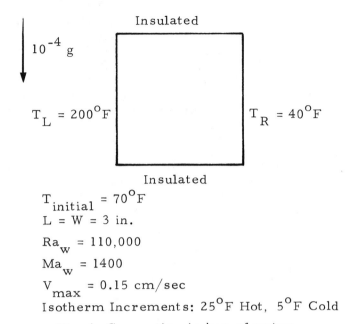

$T_{initial} = 70^oF$
$L = W = 3$ in.
$Ra_w = 110{,}000$
$Ma_w = 1400$
$V_{max} = 0.15$ cm/sec
Isotherm Increments: 25°F Hot, 5°F Cold

Fig.4 Convection in box of water.

For this particular configuration, the flowfield develops a bicellular-flow pattern during the transient phase. However, the steady-flow pattern is unicellular. As the steady solution is approached, the cells seen in the transient phase coalesce. As shown in Figs. 5 and 6, this is observed in both the results obtained by Wilkes and Churchill[21] and from the LCA program. Although these solutions are not necessarily at the same point in time, still they illustrate that the geometry of predicted transient and steady-state flowfields are very similar.

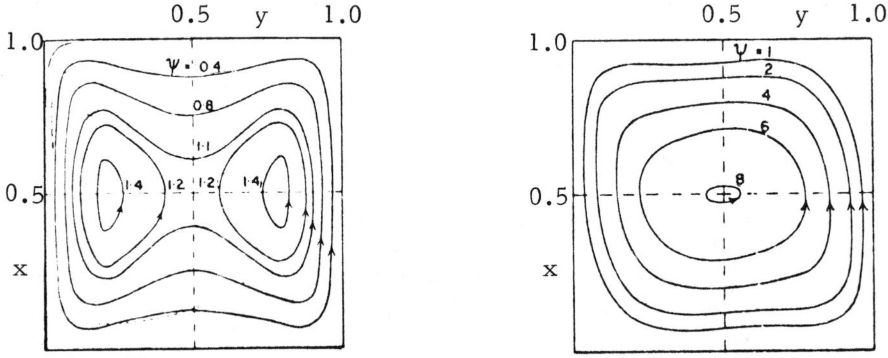

Transient Steady State

Fig. 5 Streamlines from Wilkes and Churchill.[21]

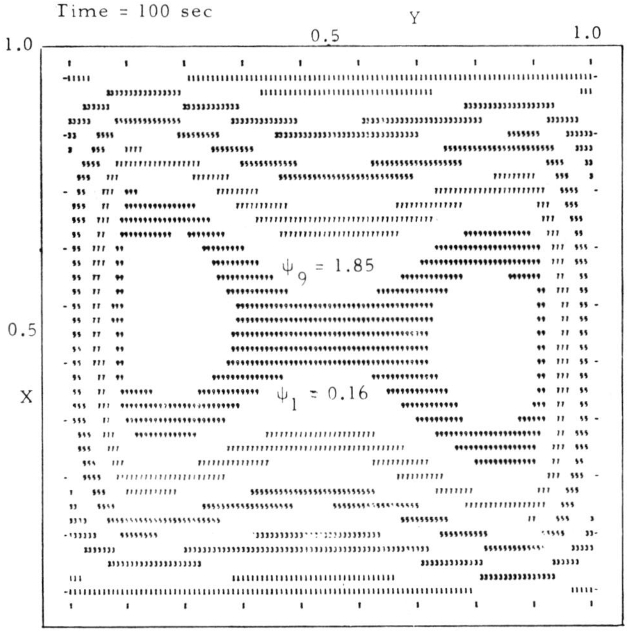

a. Transient

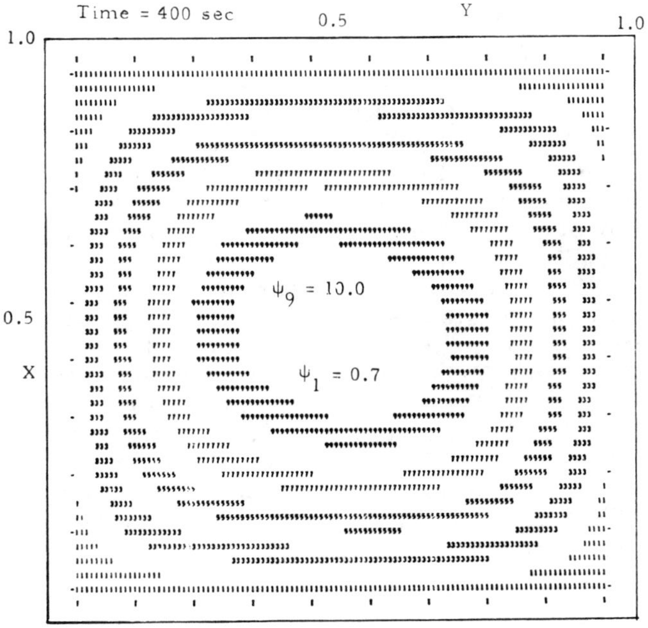

b. Steady State

Fig.6 Streamlines from Lockheed convection analysis for side heating water in a box (no free surface).

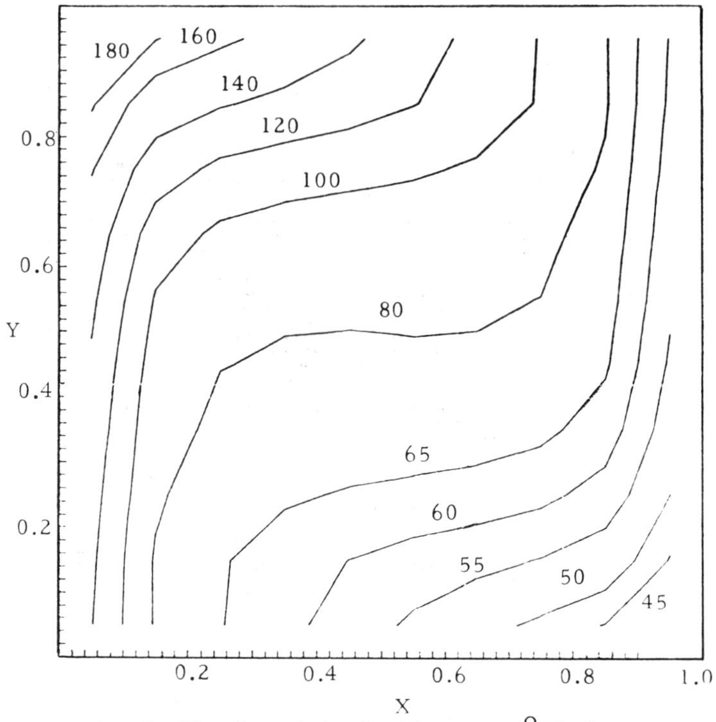

Fig. 7 Steady-state isotherms (°F) from Lockheed convection analysis for side heating water in a box (no free surface).

Figure 7 shows the steady-state isotherms for the situation just discussed. These are, of course, most important for space processing melt-growth applications, since temperature gradients are of utmost importance in melt crystal growth. Although these results are not rigorous for the growth of metal crystals such as silicon or germanium, they do indicate a problem that might be encountered in the growth of crystals in an aqueous solution or in a metal oxide, both of which have a Prandtl number near that of water. It is well known that a flat solid-liquid interface is desired for the growth of large high-quality crystals. The solid-liquid interface, of course, is determined by the shape of the isotherm corresponding to the melt or freezing temperature. One can see from the figure that the isotherms are far from being flat.

Free-Surface Effects

The configuration in Fig. 4 also has been analyzed for the case of a free boundary on the top side of the box. This provides an additional driving force to the convection known as the Marangoni effect.

The free-surface problem is of interest for space processing applications because the float zone processing of materials is of considerable interest. It is worthwhile to note that with this additional driving force, the flow pattern (see Fig. 8) is somewhat different from the case of a closed container. Also, the flow does not go through the bicellular pattern in the transient phase; i.e., it goes immediately to a unicellular configuration. Figure 8a shows the transient streamlines for the same point in time as Fig. 6a. Isotherms are shown in Fig. 9. Comparing Figs. 7 and 9, for the closed vs open container, respectively, indicates that although the streamlines are similar, the isotherms are significantly different along the cold wall. This difference can have important effects on a growing crystal, which may result in increased defect densities.

Configuration Sensitivity Analysis

The objective of this portion of the study is to identify those fluids and container geometries that are most sensitive to g-jitter convection. The approach used is to select geometric configurations and test fluids, and to perform a series of calculations with the LCA program. Figure 10 shows the three selected configurations for the analysis. They consist of a) a rectangular cell heated from the side; b) a rectangular cell heated from below; and c) a cylindrical cell heated from below. The flow in the heating-from-below cases was initiated by a temperature perturbation. The mode of flow was forced to be a single two-dimensional roll cell in order to avoid three-dimensional effects. The g-jitter cases were started using the established flow patterns from the constant-g solutions. The effects of g-jitter then can be determined by the degree of perturbation from the constant-g mode. The containers are assumed to be completely full. Thus, Marangoni convection is absent.

An important property of fluids for convective analysis is the Prandtl number, $Pr = \nu/\alpha$, which is the ratio of momentum diffusivity, ν, to thermal diffusivity, α. This dimensionless parameter was used to aid in selecting three fluids for further study. Mercury has a low Prandtl number (~ 0.01), which is typical of liquid metals used in space processing experiments. The Prandtl number for most gases is an order of 1.0 (helium ~ 0.68) and provides a mid-range Prandtl number fluid. Water, with a Prandtl number greater than 1.0,

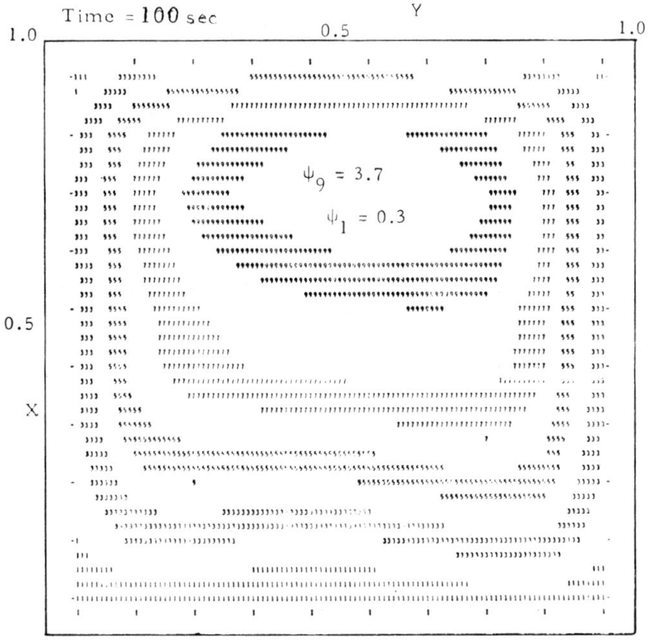

a. Transient

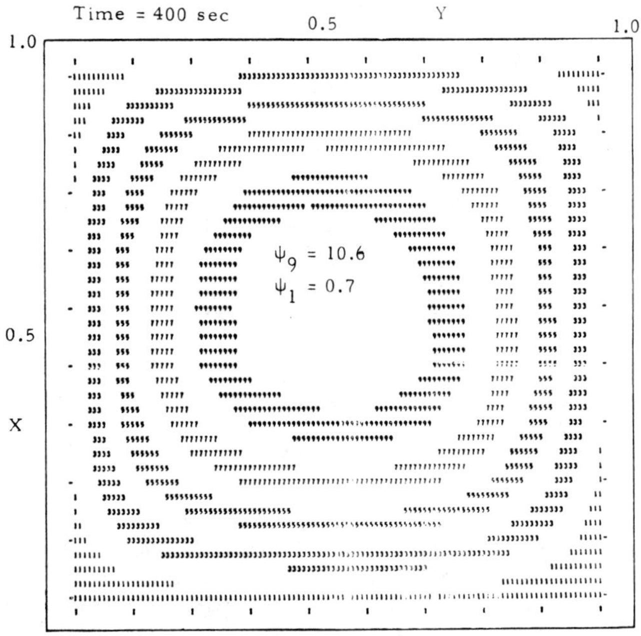

b. Steady State

Fig. 8 Streamlines with Marangoni effect (side heating box of water with free surface).

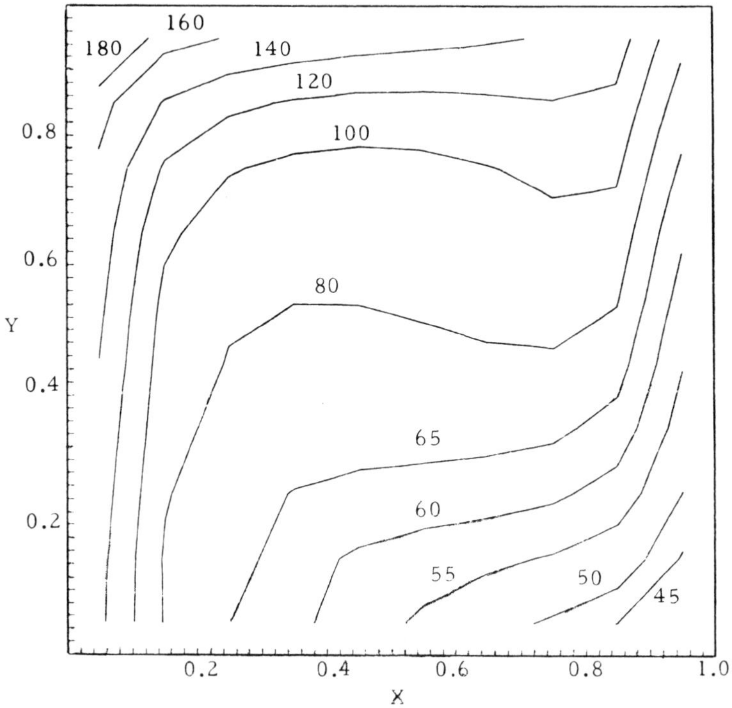

Fig. 9 Steady-state isotherms (°F) for the case with Marangoni effect (side heating box of water with free surface).

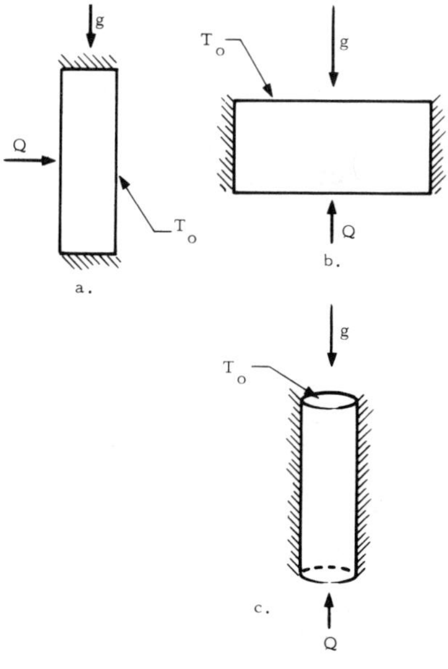

Fig. 10 Configurations used in computer models of g-jitter convection.

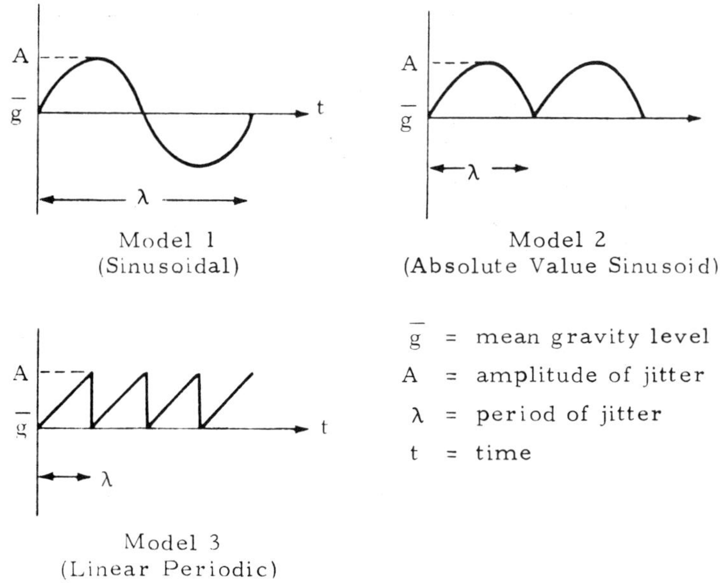

Fig. 11 G-jitter models used for parametric sensitivity study.

was selected for its simplicity of use and to provide a larger-Prandtl-number fluid. These three fluids were selected for further study based on similarity to fluids used in space processing and because they span the range of Prandtl numbers from ~0.01 to 10.0.

A parametric study was done using three models of the g-jitter shown in Fig. 11. The mean g, the amplitude, and the period were parameters in the solutions. Parametric values were selected to span the range of anticipated acceleration levels on sounding rockets. The computer models thus consist of combinations of the three configurations, the three test fluids, the three g-jitter models, and a range of amplitudes and periods. The computer runs were made generally from heat-up (t = 0) to approximately t = 360 sec.

Flow and Isotherm Pattern Effects. Figures 12 and 13 are typical of the results obtained with the computer models. These are shown for illustration of the effects of g-jitter on temperature profiles and flow patterns.

Figure 12 shows isotherm maps for three cases: a) rectangular box of water heated from the side; b) rectangular box of water heated from below; and c) cylindrical container of

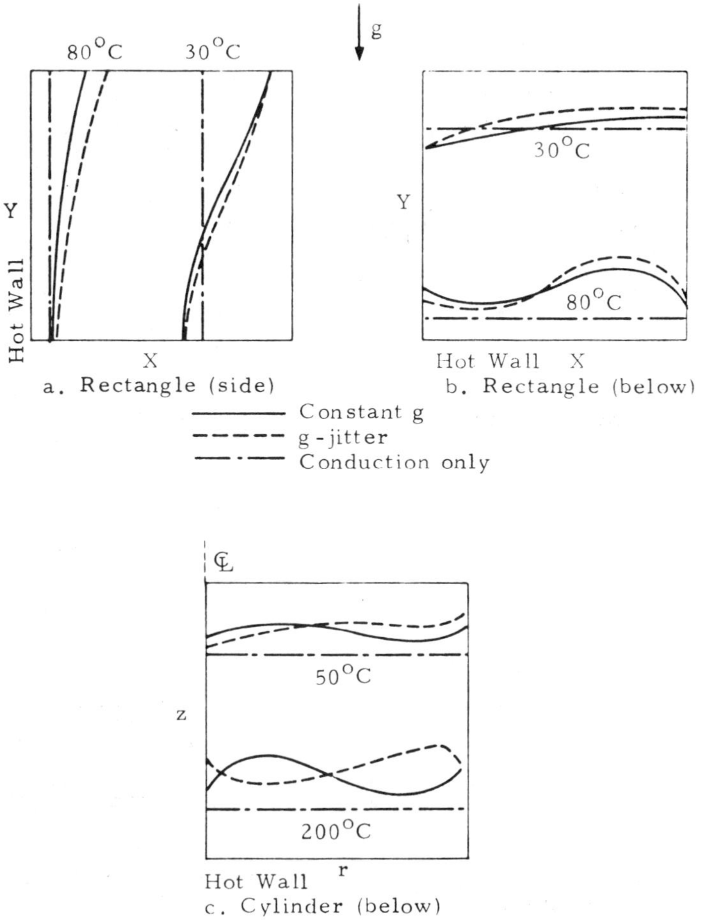

Fig. 12 Isotherms at t = 3 min for three configurations showing effect of g-jitter model.

mercury heated from below. The constant-g cases are for 10^{-3} g, and the g-jitter cases are for model 3 with g = 10^{-3}, $A_g = 10^{-3}$, and $\lambda_g = 1$ sec. Cases a and b use a constant hot-wall temperature T_h = 90°C, cold-wall T_c = 25°C, with the other walls adiabatic. Figure 12a shows that the 80°C isotherm is located farther into the water for the g-jitter case than for constant-g. The basic shape remains the same. Figure 12b shows the 80°C isotherm also has penetrated somewhat farther for the g-jitter case. These plots show that g-jitter can affect the temperature profiles and potentially influence space processing experiments that rely on flat isotherms.

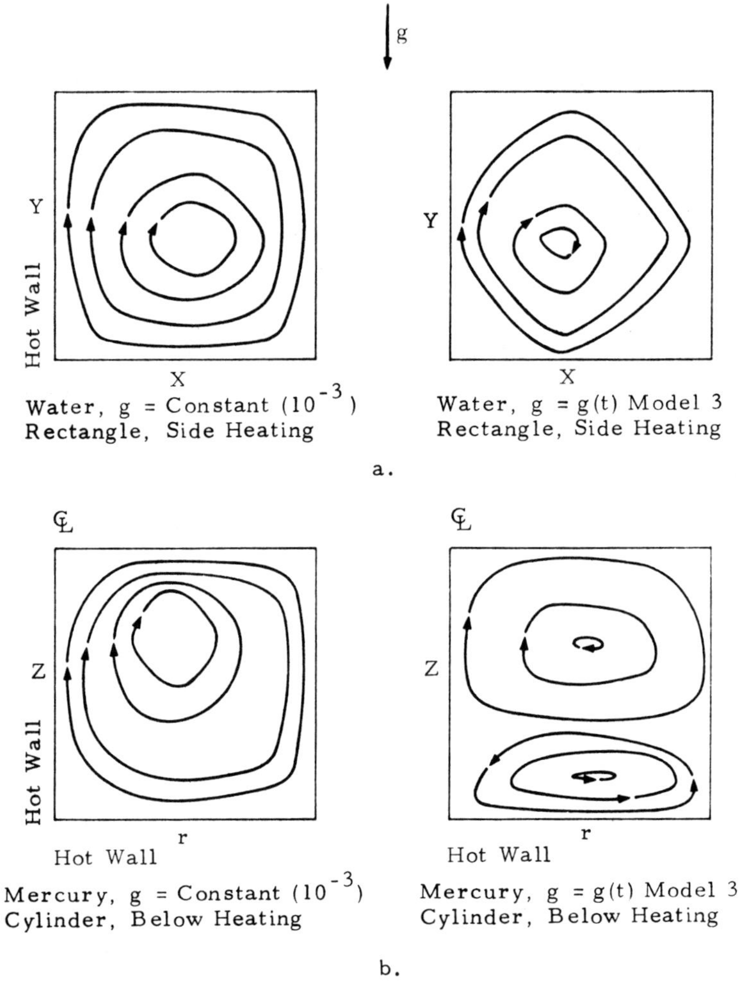

Fig. 13 Streamlines at t = 3 min showing effects of g-jitter on flow patterns.

Case 12c is for mercury in a cylinder heated from below. The hot-wall temperature is T_h = 200°C, cold-wall T_c = 25°C, with the adiabatic side wall condition. This figure shows a more drastic effect. The 200°C isotherm for the g-jitter case has changed shape, i.e., somewhat the inverse of the constant-g isotherm. This behavior results from a change in mode of the convection from a single cell to a double cell (as seen later in Fig. 13).

Figure 12 has shown typical results that were obtained. The numerous cases that were run show similar behavior, and are not shown. A measure of the sensitivity to g-jitter, given in terms of temperature-difference, is discussed in the next subsection.

Figure 13 provides another measure of the effects of g-jitter. These are streamlines plotted in the x-y (r-z) plane for two configurations. Figure 13a is the rectangular box of water heated from the side (same conditions on Fig. 12a). The constant-g streamlines are the usual single roll seen in most investigations. The corresponding streamlines for the g-jitter case shows a skewness toward the hot wall and also a change in shape. The general circular patterns for constant-g are more elliptic for the case of g-jitter. Figure 13b shows an even more pronounced effect. This case is the cylinder of mercury heated from below (same conditions as Fig. 12c). The single two-dimensional roll cell has broken off into a two-cell pattern. The flow pattern in this cell was found to oscillate between the single cell and the multiple cell. The period of oscillation could not be determined from the present form of data output. These flow patterns do show a significant influence on an oscillatory-g profile. The streamlines for other cases analyzed showed similar behavior, but with each case having its own pecularities.

Thermal Sensitivity. A sensitivity parameter was selected to provide a means of comparing the numerous computer models that were run. This parameter consists of the maximum temperature difference between the g-jitter case and the corresponding constant-g case. This temperature difference for the various cases was obtained regardless of the position in the container or the time-point in the oscillation cycle where it occurred. However, the comparisons were made at the same point in the flow. This approach was necessary because of the complex nature of the isotherms, the differing geometries and boundary conditions, and the different g-jitter models. This ΔT_{max} should provide an adequate measure of the sensitivity of the configuration to g-jitter convection.

Table 1 summarizes the results of the analysis. The left-most entries in the matrix show the configuration, fluid, and heated-wall maximum temperature. Note that different values were used for water (90°C) than for the other fluids. The gravity parameter entry in the matrix consists of the mean $\underline{g}$, the amplitude A_g, and period λ_g for g-jitter model 3, the linear periodic profile. This model is used to summarize the results, since it produced the maximum convective effect and is probably most typical of actual g-jitter.

Table 1 Summary of sensitivity analysis

Configuration	Fluid	Wall temp.,	Mean g	A_g	λ_g	ΔT_{max}, °C $T_g - T_{jitter}$	Sensitivity rating	Nu/Nu_o
Rectangular	H_2O	90	10^{-3}	10^{-3},	0.1 sec	20	Excellent	1.20
				10^{-3},	1 sec	20		1.18
	Hg	260	10^{-3}	10^{-3},	0.1 sec	16	Excellent	1.06
				10^{-3},	1 sec	16		1.04
Rectangular	H_2O	90	10^{-3}	10^{-3},	1 sec	8	Good	1.02
	Hg	260	10^{-3}	10^{-3},	1 sec	6	Good	1.02
Cylindrical								
	H_2O	90	10^{-3}	10^{-3},	1 sec	12	Good	1.06
	Hg	260	10^{-3}	10^{-3},	1 sec	10	Good	1.12
	He	260	10^{-2}	10^{-3},	1 sec	3	Fair	0.95

The calculated ΔT_{max} is shown for each case in the matrix. A sensitivity rating is assigned based on the magnitude of ΔT_{max}. The rectangular cell "heated from the side" has the largest ΔT_{max}, i.e., most sensitive. The cylinder "heated from below" rates second, and the box "heated below" is third. The analysis also shows that, for a fixed configuration, water is the fluid most sensitive to those tested, with mercury next, and helium gas the least sensitive.

The last entry in the table is a heat transfer parameter. This parameter is a ratio of the Nusselt number with g-jitter, Nu, to the Nusselt number with constant g, Nu_o. This provides a measure of the influence of g-jitter on heat transfer beyond the usual constant-g natural convection values. The Nusselt numbers are calculated as average values by integrating the temperature gradients along the appropriate walls. The largest increase is ~20%, and this occurs for the rectangular box of water heated from the side. The smallest decrease is ~5%, and this occurs for the cylinder of helium heated below.

Furnace Melts

A portion of the cases analyzed dealt exclusively with containers of liquid metals undergoing thermal gradients expected to be typical of melt crystal growth space processing (e.g., the Skylab multipurpose furnace). Unfortunately, a question has arisen recently in the authors' minds about the accuracy of these results. Although the temperature oscillations obtained compared well with those of other investigators, the flow patterns do not seem to be realistic. Rather, they are probably remnants of the perturbations utilized to initiate flow in the computer model. These results are useful, however, in that they represent internal-g waves. Such waves are often the cause of temperature oscillations in crystal growth melts.[22, 23]

The similarity of the computer results to internal-g wave oscillations observed in melts is indicated by comparison with theory. The time period of temperature oscillations is predicted theoretically to be[22]

$$\lambda_T = 2\sqrt{2}\, L[g\,\beta\,\Delta T\, D]^{-1/2} \tag{1}$$

For the 10^{-3} g constant-g computer result (see case 4 of Table 3), λ_T = 2.5 sec., whereas Eq. (1) predicts λ_T = 3.0 sec.

Specifically, the g-jitter convection of molten indium-antimonide (InSb) in a cylindrical tube has been examined. This system was chosen for study because it most closely represents a typical crystal growth experiment that could be carried out aboard a sounding rocket. InSb was chosen because its physical properties are representative of most other space processing melts, and it also showed vary promising results aboard Skylab (Skylab experiments M560 and M562). The thermal conditions are typical of the Skylab multipurpose furnace. The orientation of gravity was chosen to be parallel to the heating direction. Even though actual accelerations on the experiment package will be three-dimensional, there probably will be one dominant direction.

Consideration is given to the system described in Table 2. The tube, 7.6 cm long and 1.4 cm diam, is filled with liquid InSb initially at 537°C. The cylindrical wall is insulated perfectly. The top and bottom ends of the tube are kept at 537°C and 780°C, respectively. The g-jitter is in the direction of negative z, and with its magnitude oscillating according to absolute sinewave as shown in Fig. 11b. Other types of g-jitter that have been studied include normal sinusoidal and sawtooth waveforms. Sensitivity of fluids to each waveform varies from least sensitive for normal sinusoidal, intermediate for absolute sinewave, and most sensitive for the "sawtooth." In what follows, results for several cases of absolute sinewave g-jitter will be presented and discussed.

Table 2 System parameters[a]

Container geometry	Right circular cylinder
Heating direction	Below
Fluid	Molten InSb
Temperature of cold wall, T_c	537°C
Temperature of hot wall, T_H	780°C
Diameter of container	1.43 cm
Length or height of container	7.62 cm
Rayleigh number, Ra	$\frac{\rho^2 C_p \beta \bar{g} \Delta T L^3}{\mu k} = 7.5 \quad 10^4 \bar{g} L^3$
Prandtl number, Pr	0.01
G-jitter	Absolute sin wave

[a]See nomenclature for description of symbols.

A summary of all of the g-jitter cases investigated is given in Tables 2 and 3. Temperature profiles for case 1 are shown in Fig. 14. In all cases, transient effects have damped out after 90 sec.

Abstracting pertinent information from cases 1, 3, 4, and 7, the effect of g-jitter frequency on temperature oscillations is seen to be significant. The amplitude of the temperature oscillations increases as the period of the g-jitter increases (or as jitter frequency decreases). The temperature oscillation frequency, however, is independent of the jitter (Table 3).

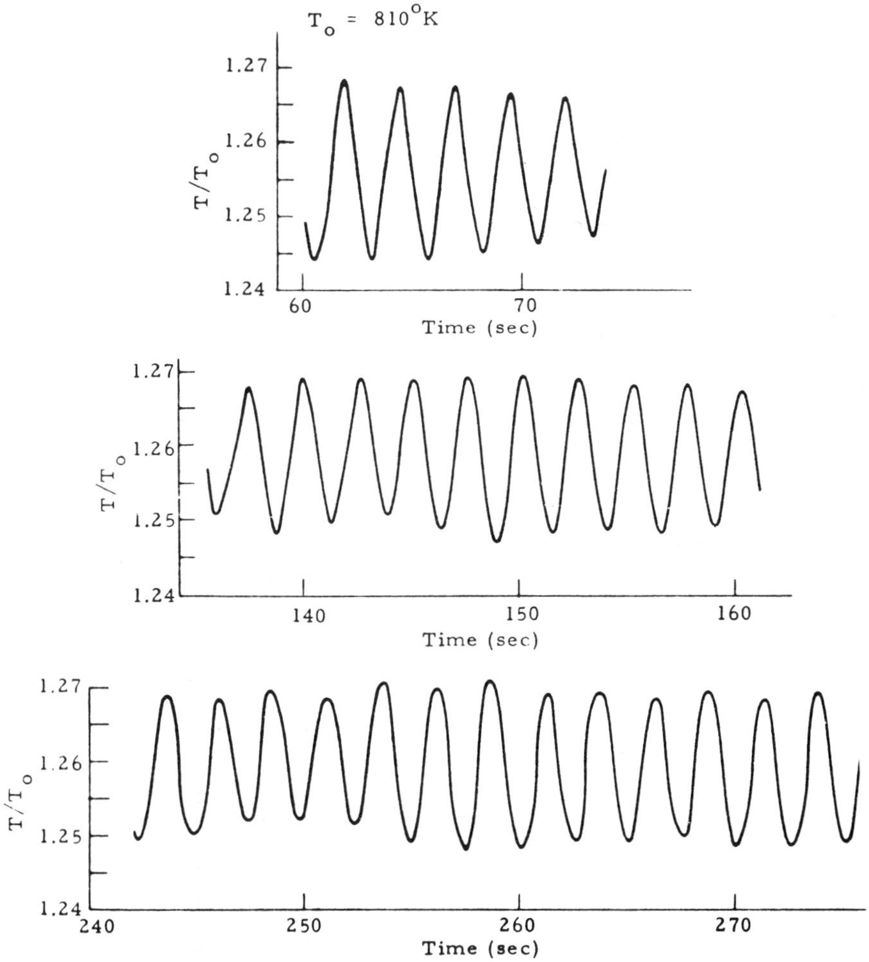

Fig. 14 Case 1 temperature oscillations at point (0.35R, 0.15L)

Table 3 Synopsis of g-jitter computer studies

		G-Jitter form			Run		Temperatures[a]		Velocities[a]	
Case	$\bar{g}$	$A/\bar{g}$	λ, sec	L, cm	time, sec	Ra	A_T, °C	λ_T, sec	A_V, cm/sec	λ_V, sec
1	10^{-3}	1.0	1.0	7.62	280	33,000	17.9	2.5	2.8	2.5
2	10^{-4}	3.0	1.0	7.62	90	3,000	---	2.5	---	2.5
3	10^{-3}	1.0	0.1	7.62	180	33,000	10.4	2.5	1.4	2.5
4[b]	10^{-3}	0.0	0.0	7.62	440	33,000	7.0	2.5	1.0	2.5
5[b]	10^{-3}	0.0	0.0	3.81	108	4,150	1.8	1.2	0.17	1.2
6	10^{-3}	1.0	1.0	3.81	145	4,150	4.8	1.2	0.5	1.2
7	10^{-3}	1.0	10.0	7.62	240	33,000	18.4	2.5	3.3	2.5
8	10^{-3}	0.5	1.0	7.62	170	33,000	12.5	2.5	1.5	2.5

[a] Temperature and velocity oscillations of InSb usually reported at position r = 0.35R, z = 0.55L inside the cylinder.

[b] Constant-g cases.

[c] All A_T values represent average values. A_{max} for case 1 = 20.4°C.

Cases 1 and 8 indicate that the amplitude of the temperature oscillation varies in proportion with the amplitude of the jitter, but the temperature frequency is again independent of jitter. This is a significant result and implies that the period of temperature oscillations is a function of the aspect ratio of the container and/or properties of the liquid, whereas the jitter and temperature gradient have no effect. The effect of aspect ratio on frequency is exhibited in cases 5 and 6.

An equally important result is seen in cases 4 and 5. At a constant-g of 10^{-3} g_E, temperature oscillations can arise in low-Prandtl-number fluids. This agrees with previous investigations at constant heating and no jitter, but these investigations were at the terrestrial gravity level.[23, 24, 25]

A comparison of these theoretical results with previous experimental studies[24] indicates good agreement. As shown in Table 4, the experimental temperature oscillations obtained by Kim, Witt, and Gatos[24] are very similar to those of the Lockheed convection computer program for similar values of Rayleigh number. Both studies were conducted for molten InSb heated from below in cylindrical containers under uniform gravity. Primary differences in the two studies are that the MIT experiment[24] utilized a moving boundary (crystallization front grows upward) and an aspect ratio of 8:1, whereas the Lockheed container's aspect ratio is 5:1 or 3:1.

Table 4 Comparison with experimental results for constant-g cases

Lockheed g-jitter model	MIT experiments[1]
Ra = 4100	Ra ≈ 3000
λ_T = 1.2 sec	λ_T = 3 sec
A_T = 1.8°C	A_T = 0.8°C
Ra = 33,000	Ra ≈ 40,000
λ_T = 2.5 sec[a]	λ_T = turbulent
A_T = 18°C	A_T = 10°C

[a]Model limited to nonturbulent flow.

The agreement is surprisingly good, considering the differences involved.

V. Summary and Implications for Space Processing

The primary conclusions of the preceding discussion are 1) g-jitter, along with surface tension, can enhance nonuniformities and transient oscillations in boundary-layer thickness of fluids during space processing; 2) g-jitter can affect convective instability points (e.g., when heating from below, no flow/laminar flow transition can be lowered or raised depending on frequency and amplitude of oscillation (see Fig. 1)); and 3) there are regions of g-jitter (mean-g level, amplitude, and frequency) where no convection arises for a given fluid, temperature gradient, and container. When natural convective flow exists in a space processing application, the preceding g-jitter effect on boundary layers usually will be detrimental to such processes as melt crystal growth.[14]

The g-jitter investigations of melt growth in the multipurpose furnace configuration indicate the following:

1) G-jitter can cause significant flow and temperature oscillations in liquid metals at 10^{-3} g, but little convection at 10^{-4} g, for the multipurpose furnace conditions.

2) Flow patterns can vary significantly through a single g-jitter cycle from unicellular to two or more cells.

3) Temperature oscillations of 20°C (peak-to-peak) over a period of 1 sec can occur due to g-jitter.

4) Temperature oscillations of 7°C (peak-to-peak) can occur in liquid metals, even in uniform gravity of 10^{-3} g_E.

5) Jitter frequency affects temperature oscillation amplitudes inversely (temperature amplitude increases with jitter period).

6) Temperature oscillation amplitude increases as jitter amplitude increases.

7) Temperature oscillation frequencies only depend on container dimensions and fluid properties (independent of jitter and temperature gradients).

8) Temperature and velocity response to g-jitter can be bimodal; i.e., a primary oscillation of a given frequency and amplitude can have, superimposed upon it, a distinct undulation of much longer frequency.

9) Significant banding and other deleterious effects could occur during space processing if g-jitter is not accounted for, and experiments are not designed to suppress it.

The g-jitter sensitivity studies of various fluids and configurations show many interesting facts and trends: 1) the effect of g-jitter on fluid flow and heat transfer is more pronounced at low-gravity levels ($\leq 10^{-3}$ g) than at 1-g conditions for comparable amplitude of oscillation; 2) the flow streamlines are altered from the circularized patterns produced by constant accelerations to elliptical, skewed patterns, and/or to multicellular flow; 3) the calculated temperature-time profiles tend to match the corresponding g-jitter model profile, but have a lower frequency and are out of phase due to thermal lag; 4) the calculated Nusselt numbers are strong functions of the amplitude of the jitter and much weaker functions of frequency; 5) the sinewave jitter produces the least effect on the flow profiles, and heat transfer and the linear periodic (sawtooth) jitter produces the largest effects; 6) fluids with Prandtl numbers near 0.01 and 10.0 show significant g-jitter effects whereas Prandtl numbers near 1.0 exhibit very little changes in heat transfer; 7) peak-to-peak temperature oscillations of 20°C/sec are calculated at periodic steady-state for the cases that exhibit maximum g-jitter influence; and 8) the maximum Nusselt number calculated for any of the cases is 1.2 for g-jitter convection, as compared to 1.0 for constant-g conditions. This maximum is attained for the rectangular box heated from the side at a mean g-level of 10^{-3} g using model 3 with Pr = 6.0.

The results of the present study have shown that, for the cases considered, g-jitter convection can have significant effects on fluid flow and heat transfer in confined fluids in low gravity. Each situation must be judged individually, however, as such changes as allowing a free surface to be present can change the results drastically.

The study also has shown that simple design considerations (such as adjusting aspect ratio or container geometry) can be utilized to minimize detrimental effects due to convection in micro-gravity. Thus, space manufacturing experiments can be designed to perform many processes in the absence of natural convection interference. Great care and skill must be utilized in these designs, as natural convection is a very complex phenomenon subject to many modes and driving forces.

VI. References

[1]"Manufacturing Technology Unique to Zero Gravity Environment," Third Space Processing Symposium Proceedings, NASA-Marshall Space Flight Center, Ala., Nov. 1, 1968.

[2]Grodzka, P.G. and Bannister, T.C., "Heat Flow and Convection Demonstration Experiments Aboard Apollo 14," Science, Vol. 176, May 1972, pp. 506-508.

[3]Bannister, T.C., Grodzka, P.G., Spradley, L.W., Bourgeois, S.V., Hedden, R.O., and Facemire, B.R., "Apollo 17 Heat Flow and Convection Experiments Final Data Analyses Results," NASA TM X-64772, July 16, 1973.

[4]Bourgeois, S.V., "Convection Effects on Skylab Experiment M566," LMSC-HREC TR D390330, Lockheed Missiles & Space Company, Huntsville, Ala., July 1974, p. 7.

[5]Richardson, P.D., "Effects of Sound and Vibrations on Heat Transfer," Applied Mechanics Review, Vol. 20, March 1967, pp. 201-217.

[6]Pak, H.Y., Winter, E.R.F., and Schoenals, R.J., "Convection Heat Transfer in a Contained Fluid Subjected to Vibration," Augmentation of Convective Heat and Mass Transfer, edited by A.E. Bergles and A.L. Webb, ASME, New York, 1970, p. 158.

[7]Gebhart, B., "Random Convection Under Conditions of Weightlessness," AIAA Journal, Vol. 1, 1963, pp. 380-383.

[8]Forbes, R.E., Carley, C.T., and Bell, C.J., "Vibration Effects on Convective Heat Transfer in Enclosures," Journal of Heat Transfer, Vol. 92, Ser. C, March 1970, pp. 429-438.

[9]Gershuni, G.Z., Zhushovitskii, E.M., and Iurkov, I.S., "On Convective Stability in the Presence of a Periodically Varying Parameter," PMM, Vol. 34, March 1970, pp. 470-480.

[10]Gresho, P.M. and Sani, R.L., "The Effect of Gravity Modulation on the Stability of Heated Fluid Layers," Journal of Fluid Mechanics, Vol. 40, June 1970, pp. 783-806.

[11]Donnelly, R. J., Reif, F., and Suhl, H., "Enhancement of Hydrodynamic Stability by Modulation," Physical Review Letters, Vol. 9, March 1962, pp. 363-364.

[12]Kezios, S. P. and Prasanna, K. V., "Effect of Vibration on Heat Transfer from a Cylinder in Normal Flow," ASME Paper 66-WA/HT-43, 1966.

[13]Bloor, M. S., "The Transition in the Wake of a Circular Cylinder," Journal of Fluid Mechanics, Vol. 19, February 1964, pp. 290-301.

[14]Carruthers, J. R., "Crystal Growth from the Melt," Treatise on Solid State Chemistry, Vol. 5, edited by N. B. Hannay, Plenum Press, New York, 1975, pp. 325-406.

[15]Smith, G. V., and Forbes, R. E., "The Effect of Random Vibration on Natural Convective Heat Transfer in Rectangular Enclosures," Augmentation of Convective Heat and Mass Transfer, edited by A. E. Bergles and A. L. Webb, ASME, New York, 1970, p. 158.

[16]Zenkovskaia, S.M., "Investigation of Convection in a Layer of Fluid in the Presence of Vibrational Forces," Isv. Akad. Nauk SSR, MZhG, Vol. 5, 1966.

[17]Zenkovskaya, S.M., "Study of Convection in a Fluid Layer in the Presence of Vibrating Forces," Isv. AKAD. Nauk SSSR, MZhG, Vol. 3, Jan. 1968.

[18]Burde, G. I., "Numerical Investigation of Convection Arising in a Modulated Field of External Forces," Izv. Akad. Nauk SSSR, MZhG, Feb. 1970, p. 196.

[19]Spradley, L. W. and Churchill, S. W., "Pressure and Buoyancy-Driven Thermal Convection in a Rectangular Enclosure," Journal of Fluid Mechanics, Vol. 70, August 1975, pp. 705-720.

[20]Spradley, L. W., "Thermoacoustic Convection of Confined Fluids in Low Gravity," AIAA Paper 74-76, Jan. 1974, Washington, D. C.

[21]Wilkes, J. O. and Churchill, S. W., "The Finite Difference Computation of Natural Convection in a Rectangular Enclosure," AIChE Journal, Vol. 12, Jan. 1966, pp. 161-166.

[22]Carruthers, J.R., "Origins of Convective Temperature Oscillations in Crystal Growth," Third American Conference on Crystal Growth, Stanford University, Palo Alto, Calif., 13 July 1975.

[23]Hurle, D.T.J., Jakeman, E., and Johnson, C.P., "Convective Temperature Oscillations in Molten Gallium," Journal of Fluid Mechanics, Vol. 64, April 1974, pp. 565-576.

[24]Kim, K.M., Witt, A.F., and Gatos, H.C., "Crystal Growth from the Melt Under Destabilizing Conditions," Journal of the Electrochemistry Society, Vol. 119, May 1972, pp. 1218-1224.

[25]Verhoeven, J.D., Physics of Fluids, Vol. 12, August 1969, pp. 1733-1737.

SUPERCONDUCTING PROPERTIES OF PB-SN-IN ALLOYS DIRECTIONALLY SOLIDIFIED ABOARD SKYLAB

W.T. Anderson, Jr.* and J.L. Reger*
TRW Systems Group, Redondo Beach, Calif.

Abstract

Superconducting alloys of Pb-Sn-In were solidified directionally in the absence of gravity-induced convection and segregation by processing in a near-weightless condition (0-g) aboard Skylab. Lead-rich and tin-rich lamellar structures were obtained with both high- and low-G/R (temperature gradient/solidification rate) samples processed at 0-g and at 1-g in a ground-based laboratory. Thinner, higher density lamellae were found with the 0-g specimens. Magnetization curves at 4.2 K showed hysteresis effects, with large areas under the curves indicating magnetic flux pinning by the normal-state tin-rich phase. More extensive flux pinning was found with the 0-g specimens with high G/R, which is attributed to only approximately 5% of the sample length that experienced the most beneficial directional solidification conditions. Upper critical field H_{c2} values were found to be in good agreement with the prediction of the Abrikosov theory of type II superconductors.

I. Introduction

Superconductivity is characterized by two related phenomena: the absence of electrical resistance to current flow and the exclusion of magnetic fields from the bulk of the material below a penetration depth λ from the surface. These phenomena arise from an attractive interaction between electron pairs, within a characteristic distance ξ (coherence length), which is produced by the interaction of the electrons with quantized lattice vibrations (phonons).[1,2] Superconducting materials

---

Presented as Paper 75-694 at the AIAA 10th Thermophysics Conference, Denver, Colo., May 27-29, 1975. Supported by NASA under Contract NAS 8-28309.
*Member of Professional Staff.

are classified as type I or type II, depending on their behavior to increasing external magnetic field strength H. Type I superconductors are pure elements that have long electron mean-free-paths and are characterized by $\xi > \lambda$. The external magnetic field is excluded from the bulk of the material (magnetic induction B = 0) up to a critical field H_c (thermodynamic critical field), at which the material reverts sharply to the normal state, and above which the field measured within the material is

$$\vec{B} = \mu\vec{H} \tag{1}$$

where μ is the permeability. (Gaussian cgs units are used, for which μ is nearly 1 for most materials.)

Other than the metals niobium and vanadium, type II superconductors are alloys with reduced electron mean-free-paths, and consequent increased normal-state resistivities from the scattering of electrons by foreign atoms, and are characterized by $\xi < \lambda$. In the presence of an external magnetic field H, a type II superconductor remains free of magnetic induction B up to a low critical field H_{c1}. Above H_{c1}, magnetic flux penetrates the material in the form of quantized filamentary fluxoids as predicted by Abrikosov.[3] The fluxoids consist of vortices of superconducting electrons surrounding a normal-state core of radius ξ containing the magnetic field. As H is increased further, magnetic flux penetration increases, by increase in the density of fluxoids, up to an upper critical field H_{c2}, above which the bulk of the material is in the normal state. A convenient method of observing the magnetic field penetration is by recording magnetization curves ($-4\pi M$ vs H), where $\vec{M}$ is the magnetization defined by

$$\vec{B} = \vec{H} + 4\pi\vec{M} \tag{2}$$

The effect of microstructure on the magnetic properties and electron current flow in type II superconductors has been discussed in a series of review articles.[4-9] Imperfections of many different kinds can act as trapping centers or barriers to flux movement, thus increasing the critical current density of the material. This effect of flux pinning results in hysteretic magnetization curves with large areas under the curves, which are proportional to the energy required to drive the sample normal. Ideal (defect-free) type II superconductors with reversible magnetization curves have low critical current densities.

The magnetic measurements discussed here were carried out to study these effects in directionally solidified Pb-Sn-In alloys processed in one- and low-gravity (1-g and 0-g) environments. Dispersion of the Sn-rich phase, which is nonsuperconducting at 4.2 K, may act as pinning sites to flux movement,[10] resulting in hysteresis effects with large areas under the magnetization curves.

Eutectic compositions may be formed easily into rod-like or lamellar structures by direction solidification under a very small temperature gradient. It has been shown by Mollard and Flemings, theoretically[11] and experimentally[12] with Sn-Pb alloys, that two phase alloys of compositions far from the eutectic can be solidified directionally in lamellar or rod-like morphologies if the G/R ratio (where G is the temperature gradient and R is the plane front solidification rate) is sufficiently large and there is an absence of convection. Hence, directional solidification of off-eutectic alloys is favored by a high-temperature gradient and a low-solidification rate. Other properties of the material also may be influenced by the solidification parameters. As R increases, the solute concentration in the solvent-rich phase should increase; and it was found experimentally with Sn-rich Sn-Pb alloys[12] that the lamellar spacing was proportional to $R^{-1/2}$. Also, the data of Mollard and Flemings[12] indicate that for alloys solidified at the same rate, the lamellar spacing decreased as the temperature gradient increased.

II. Sample Processing

Alloys with the composition 57 at.% Pb-21 at.% Sn-22 at.% In were solidified directionally in the M-518 furnace[13] as part of Skylab experiment M-557. The M-518 multipurpose electric furnace had the capability of thermally heating three cartridges simultaneously to a maximum temperature of 1000°C. The furnace contained two processing regions, an isothermal and a gradient region. Variable soak times at temperature and cooldown rates were available. The three capsules comprising experiment M-557 each contained three separate ampoules. All three ampoules contained different material systems; two (samples A and B) were processed in the isothermal region, and the Pb-Sn-In alloys (sample C) were processed in the gradient portion of the furnace. Thus, nine ampoules were processed simultaneously during each furnace run.

A schematic diagram of a cartridge in the M-518 furnace is shown in Fig. 1. The Pb-Sn-In C-samples were prepared from high-purity elements in the form of 1.8-mm-diam rods, 10 cm in length, by induction-melting in quartz containers under an argon atmosphere. The samples subsequently were cleaned in

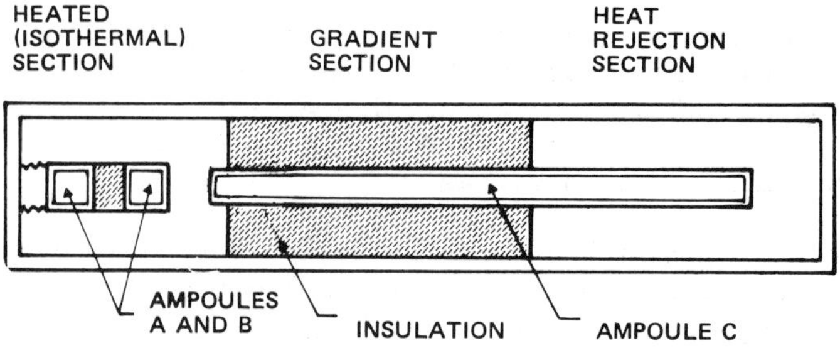

Fig. 1 Schematic diagram of Skylab cartridge in the M-518 furnace.

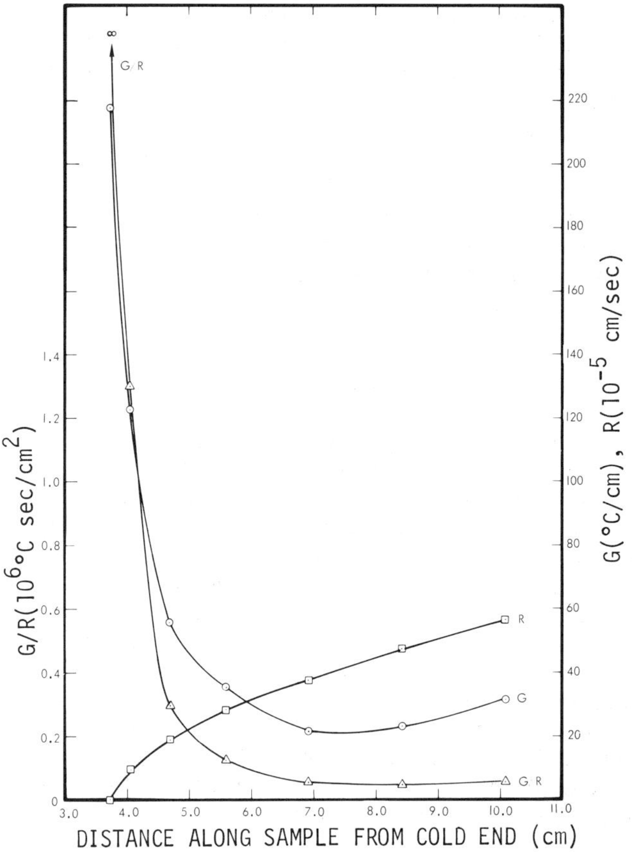

Fig. 2 Directional solidification parameters temperature gradient G, plane front solidification rate R, and G/R as a function of distance along sample from the cold end based on the data in Ref. 13 by J.W.H. Chi, Figs. 2 and 4.

Freon and placed in quartz containers under helium prior to directional solidification.

The values of the directional solidification parameters G, R, and G/R were determined by the samples processed in the isothermal region, because the primary goal of the M-557 experiment was to maintain an isothermal region for the A and B specimens. These parameters are shown in Fig. 2 as a function of the distance along the sample from the cold end. Approximately 3.7 cm of sample remained unmelted at the cold end. The conditions were less than ideal for directional solidification, particularly in that only approximately 1 mm of sample experienced a high-G/R ratio, but nevertheless, even the low-G/R portions of the samples were found to have lamellar morphologies after processing.

Micrographs of the regions directionally solidified at low G/R are shown in Figs. 3 and 4 for 0-g and 1-g processed samples, respectively. The Sn-rich lamellae are approximately 1.0 μm in the 0-g samples and 1.5 μm in the 1-g samples. High-magnification micrographs were not taken in the high-G/R region to prevent damage to the samples prior to magnetization measurements.

III. Magnetic Measurements

Both the 0-g and 1-g processed specimens were sectioned such that the maximum and minimum G/R-ratio regions were measured to determine the effect of lamellar morphology on the magnetic properties. The samples were cut in 2-cm lengths and placed to fit tightly in the center of coils wound with 10,000 turns of No. 36 copper magnet wire to a length of 3.4 cm. Permeability measurements were made as a function of the magnetic field by measuring the inductance at 1 kHz with the coils placed in the center of a superconducting solenoid with the axes approximately parallel to the field. Three coils could be arranged symmetrically about the axis of the solenoid, with the center of the samples separated by 2.5 cm. This allowed the samples to be within a sphere of less than 1% inhomogeneity in the magnetic field. The inductance measurements were made point-by-point in a constant magnetic field H, by increasing the field manually in increments of 237.5 Oe. Measurements were made on all three samples at each field point in approximately 1 min. A baseline was established by extending the measurements approximately 1000 Oe above H_{c2}. All measurements were made with the samples immersed in liquid helium at a temperature of 4.2°K.

Neglecting end effects, a measurement of the inductance as a function of the magnetic field is equivalent to measuring

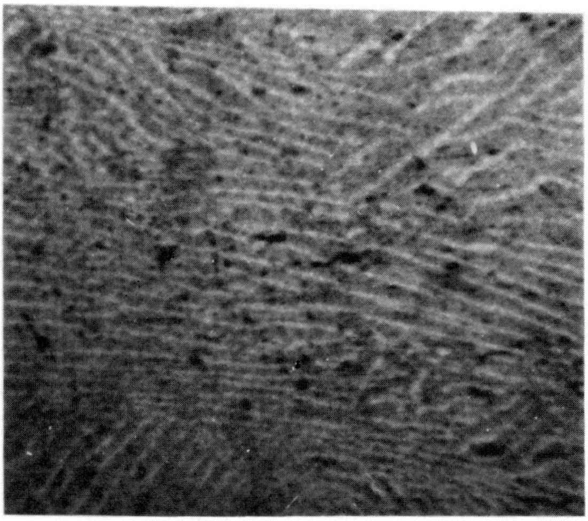

Longitudinal view, 1000X.

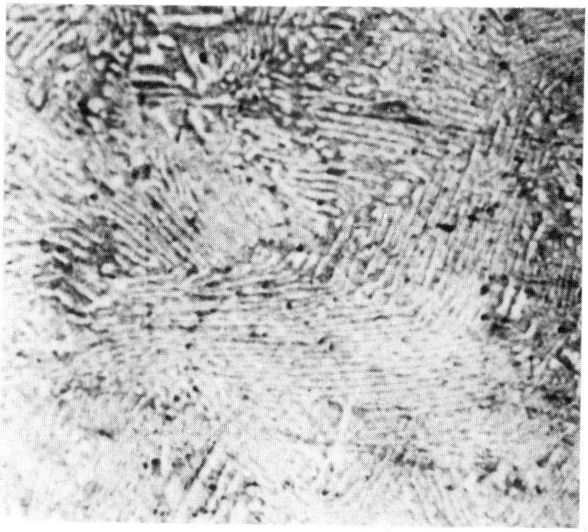

Cross-sectional view, 500X.

Fig. 3 Hot-zone (low G/R) photomicrographs of directionally solidified Pb-Sn-In alloys, Sample 10C (0-g).

the ac permeability of the sample as the transition is made from the superconducting to normal state. In order to obtain the upper critical field and to display hysteresis effects in the conventional manner, the data were converted to magnetization curves by using Eqs. (1) and (2) to obtain

$$-4\mu M = 1/a[(L_N - L)/L_N]H \qquad (3)$$

Longitudinal view, 1000X.

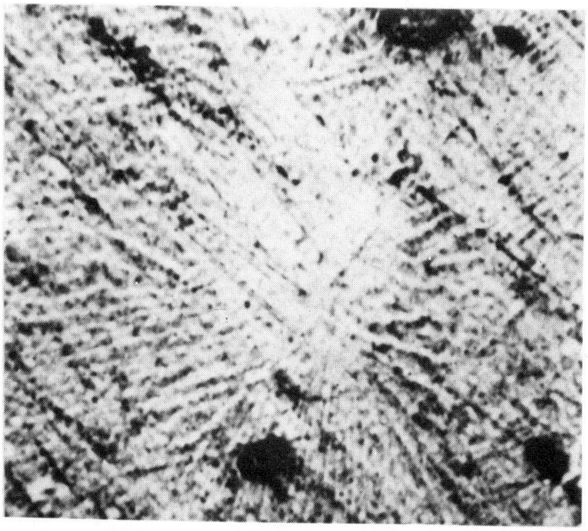

Cross-sectional view, 500X.

Fig. 4 Hot-zone (low G/R) photomicrographs of directionally solidified Pb-Sn-In alloys, Sample 1C (1-g).

where

$$L = (a\mu + 1 - a)L_N \quad (4)$$

In (4), L is the coil inductance, L_N is the coil inductance when the sample is in the normal state for $H > H_{c2}$

$$a = [L_N - L(0)]/L_N \quad (5)$$

is the fraction of the coil volume occupied by the superconducting phase of the sample, and L(0) is the inductance at H = 0.

Magnetization curves are shown in Fig. 5 for samples taken from the high-G/R end. Arrows indicate curves taken with increasing or decreasing magnetic field. Hysteresis effects are apparent, indicating the presence of trapped flux. Each curve, up and down in the field, required $\sim$ 1 hr to complete. Values of H_{c2} were taken at the point where the increasing field curve meets the abscissa when extrapolated to M = 0.

The 0-g, high-G/R samples show more pronounced hysteresis with larger areas under the curves, indicating more extensive flux pinning by the Sn-rich phase. These results correspond to more beneficial directional solidification conditions with low-gravity processing compared to the one-gravity processed samples. Curves taken for samples from the low-G/R end (both 0-g and 1-g), and for a sample taken from the region that remained unmelted during processing, showed behavior intermediate between the 0-g and 1-g, high-G/R samples. Flux pinning should increase as the lamellar thickness decreases and the alignment of the lamellae becomes more uniform in the direction of the magnetic field. Apparently, the reason that greater differences were not observed at different ends of the specimens is that at the high-G/R end, which is most favorable for directional solidification in terms of alignment, R was small, which tended to give large lamellar spacings. At the less favorable low-G/R end, R was largest, tending to give smaller lamellar spacings and increased pinning. Thus, the effects of high G/R tended to be offset by the low value of R under the conditions by which the alloys were processed. Also, as shown in Fig. 2, only approximately 5% of the high-G/R

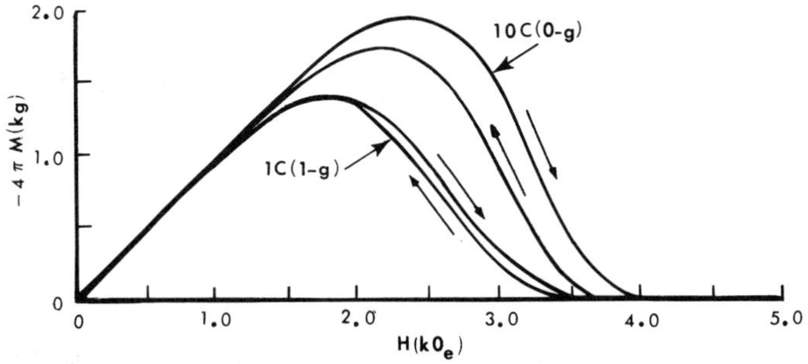

Fig. 5 Magnetization curves for one- and low-gravity processed Pb-Sn-In alloy samples from the high-G/R end.

samples actually experienced large-G/R values. The increased pinning with the 0-g high-G/R samples evidently resulted from a contribution from this small section, due to more uniform alignment of the lamellae. The absence of this contribution in the high-G/R 1-g samples indicates gravity-induced convection may have resulted in less uniform lamellae in these specimens. There also may be a tendency to form smaller lamellae than expected from the low values of R from the high gradient, as is evident in the data of Mollard and Flemings.[12]

These results differ from those obtained by Livingston[10] with alloys of the same nominal composition but with a different history of heat treatment. Livingston's alloys were quenched from the melt and the tin-rich phase allowed to precipitate by warming to room temperature for 1 hr. A discontinuous, mostly (unaligned) lamellar structure was obtained with the precipitate layers about 100-Å thick. Magnetization curves showed larger hysteresis than found with our directionally solidified alloys, which can be attributed to flux pinning by the much thinner tin-rich precipitate. The upper critical field was approximately H_{c2} = 2990 Oe at 4.2°K.

The thermal histories of the alloys investigated in the present study differed from that of Livingston in that lamellar structures were obtained by directional solidification. Apparently, under the conditions used for processing this alloy system the lamellar structure was much coarser ($\sim$ 1 μm), resulting in less flux pinning. Because of the low-solidification rates, the Pb-rich and Sn-rich phases probably represent compositions close to the phase diagram values. Thinner lamellae could be obtained by increasing the solidification rate, and perhaps also the gradient. Assuming the lamellar thickness varies as $R^{-1/2}$, the thickness could be reduced to 0.1 μm with $R \simeq 5 \times 10^{-2}$ cm/sec, which would require approximately 8 min of processing. The required temperature gradient would need to be increased by two orders of magnitude (to $\sim 2 \times 10^3$ °C/cm), but this would not be difficult to attain. Such large gradients would mean, however, that convection forces would be more important; hence, 0-g processing should yield more uniform structures.

The smaller flux pinning also may be related to the presence of the small ac magnetic field (20 Oe amplitude) in the measuring coil that superimposes a small hysteresis curve on the applied field. The consequent ac loss at the surface may result effectively in some degree of reduced pinning. A small contribution to the shape of the curves also may be present, possibly from surface superconductivity,[14] although the conditions for observing this effect were far from ideal.

The upper critical field values H_{c2} may be compared to the predictions of Abrikosov theory[3] of type II superconductors from the work on lead-based alloys by Livingston.[15] It was shown by Goodman[16] that the Abrikosov theory predicts H_{c2} increases with the normal-state residual resistivity ρ according to

$$H_{c2}/H_c = \sqrt{2}\,\kappa_o + 10.6 \times 10^{-6} \sqrt{\gamma}\,\rho \qquad (6)$$

in electromagnetic units, where κ_o is the Ginzburg-Landau parameter for the pure metal and γ is the coefficient of the electronic specific heat per unit volume in the normal metal. Assuming γ, and thus the density of states, remains unchanged on alloying, Livingston[15] measured ρ and H_c for annealed lead-base binary alloys with In, Hg, Bi, Sn, Tl, and Na and found good agreement with Eq. (6). Assuming the room temperature equilibrium concentration of Sn in Pb-Sn alloys (3.2 at.%)[17] remains in solution after directional solidification, the lead-rich phase should have an equilibrium composition of 69.9 at.% Pb, 3.2 at.% Sn, and 26.9 at.% In. Considering this to behave primarily as a Pb-In alloy with a contribution to the residual resistivity from both In and Sn, the upper critical field calculated from Livingston's data is H_{c2} = 4040 Oe, in good agreement with the experimental values in Table 1. The somewhat larger H_{c2} values for the high-G/R 0-g samples probably resulted from a slightly different composition in the lead-rich phase resulting from an absence of convection.

Table 1 Upper critical field H_{c2} values of Pb-Sn-In alloys (nominal composition, at.%: 57Pb - 21Sn - 22In)

Experimental	
0-g, high G/R	3.94 ± 0.10* kOe
0-g, low G/R	3.67 ± 0.11 kOe
1-g, high G/R	3.68 ± 0.07 kOe
1-g, low G/R	3.75 ± 0.13 kOe
Calculated	
	4.04 kOe

*Standard deviation of three samples.

IV. Conclusions

Pb-Sn-In alloys, directionally solidified aboard Skylab in the absence of gravity-induced convection and segregation, were found to have thinner lamellae (∿ 1 μm) than samples processed in a ground-based laboratory. Increased magnetic flux pinning by the Sn-rich phase was indicated from the small sections of the Skylab samples (∿ 5%) that experienced the most beneficial directional solidification conditions. Thinner lamellae, and hence, increased flux pinning, could be obtained by increasing the solidification rate. Lamellae down to 0.1 μm would not be difficult to obtain, but 0-g processing would be more important because of the large gradients required. Upper critical field H_{c2} values for the Pb-rich phase were found to be in good agreement with the prediction of the Abrikosov theory of type II superconductors.

References

[1] Bardeen, J., Cooper, L.N., and Schrieffer, J.R., "Microscopic Theory of Superconductivity," The Physical Review, Vol. 106, April 1, 1957, pp. 162-164.

[2] Bardeen, J., Cooper, L.N., and Schrieffer, J.R., "Theory of Superconductivity," The Physical Review, Vol. 108, December 1, 1957, pp. 1175-1204.

[3] Abrikosov, A.A., "On the Magnetic Properties of Superconductors of the Second Group," Soviet Physics-Journal of Experimental and Theoretical Physics, Vol. 5, December 15, 1957, pp. 1174-1182.

[4] Bean, C.P., "Magnetization of High-Field Superconductors," Reviews of Modern Physics, Vol. 36, January 1964, pp. 31-39.

[5] Anderson, P.W. and Kim, Y.B., "Hard Superconductivity: Theory of the Motion of Abrikosov Flux Lines," Reviews of Modern Physics, Vol. 36, January 1964, pp. 39-43.

[6] Livingston, J.D., "Defects and Magnetic Hysteresis in Type II Superconductors," Reviews of Modern Physics, Vol. 36, January 1964, pp. 54-58.

[7] Livingston, J.D. and Schadler, H.W., "The Effect of Metallurgical Variables on Superconducting Properties," Progress in Materials Science, Vol. 12, 1964, pp. 183-284.

[8]Kim, Y.B. and Stephen, M.J., "Flux Flow and Irreversible Effects," Superconductivity, Vol. 2, edited by R.D. Parks, Dekker, New York, 1969.

[9]Savitskii, E.M., Baron, V.V., Efimov, Y.V., Bychkova, M.I., and Myzenkova, L.F., Superconducting Materials, translated from Russian by G.D. Archard, Plenum, New York, 1973.

[10]Livingston, J.D., "Flux Pinning by Superconducting Precipitates," Applied Physics Letters, Vol. 8, June 1966, pp. 319-320.

[11]Mollard, F.R. and Flemings, M.C., "Growth of Composites from the Melt-Part I," Transactions of the American Institute of Metallurgical Engineers, Vol. 239, October 1967, pp. 1526-1533.

[12]Mollard, F.R. and Flemings, M.C., "Growth of Composites from the Melt-Part II," Transactions of the American Institute of Metallurgical Engineers, Vol. 239, October 1967, pp. 1534-1546.

[13]"Data Package for Cartridges for the Multipurpose Electric Furnace System M-518," Rept. WANL-TME-2831 for NASA Contract NAS8-28271, Vol. 1, November 1972, Westinghous Astronuclear Laboratory, Westinghouse Corp., Pittsburgh, Pa.

[14]Serin, B., "Type II Superconductors: Experiments," Superconductivity, Vol. 2, edited by R.D. Parks, Dekker, New York, 1969.

[15]Livingston, J.D., "Magnetic Properties of Superconducting Lead-Base Alloys," The Physical Review, Vol. 129, March 1, 1963, pp. 1943-1949.

[16]Goodman, B.B., "The Magnetic Behavior of Superconductors of Negative Surface Energy," IBM Journal of Research and Development, Vol. 6, January 1962, pp. 63-67.

[17]Hansen, M., Constitution of Binary Alloys, McGraw-Hill, New York, 1958.

Index to Contributors to Volume 52

Allen, R.E., *NASA Marshall Space Flight Center* **399**
Anderson, W.T.Jr., *TRW Systems Group* **567**
Ang, Choh-Yi, *Universities Space Research Association* **523**
Bannister, Tommy C., *NASA Marshall Space Flight Center* **173**
Berlad, A.L., *State University of New York* **89**
Bewersdorff, A., *DFVLR, Federal Republic of Germany* **347**
Bier, M., *Veterans Administration Hospital and University of Arizona* **41,125**
Bloom, H.L., *General Electric Company* **303**
Bourgeois, S.V., *Lockheed Missiles & Space Company* **189,535**
Brashears, M.R., *Lockheed Missiles & Space Company* **189**
Bredt, James H., *NASA Office of Applications* **333**
Bruckner, R., *Technische Universitat, Federal Republic of Germany* **111**
Carruthers, J.R., *Bell Laboratories* **33,207**
Cheshlya, Yu.V., *Academy of Sciences, USSR* **455**
Chi, J.W.H., *Westinghouse Electric Corporation* **285**
Duncan, C.S., *Westinghouse Electric Corporation* **285**
Elleman, D.D., *Jet Propulsion Laboratory* **151**
Facemire, B.R., *NASA George C. Marshall Space Flight Center* **207**
Ganiev, R.F., *Academy of Sciences, USSR* **67**
Gibson, E.G., *NASA Johnson Spacecraft Center* **207**
Grodzka, Philomena G., *Lockheed Missiles & Space Company* **173**
Haessner, F. *Technischen Universitat Braunschweig, West Germany* . . . **223**
Hannig, K., *Max-Planck-Institut, Federal Republic of Germany* **411**
Haynes, J.M., *University of Bristol, England* **57**
Heimbuch, A.H., *NASA Ames Research Center* **363**
Hemminger, W., *Technischen Universitat Braunschweig, West Germany* **223**
Kessler, J.O., *University of Arizona* **125**
Klett, M.G., *Lockheed Missiles & Space Company* **207**
Lacy, Lewis, L., *NASA George C. Marshall Space Flight Center* **483,495,523**
Laptchinsky, V.F. *Academy of Sciences, USSR* **67, 355**
Lemaignan, Clement, *French Atomic Energy Commission* **447**
Li, C.H., *Grumman Aerospace Corporation* **235**
Lin, F.N., *Lockheed Missiles & Space Company, Inc.* **535**
Livanov, L.K., *Academy of Sciences, USSR* **455**
Lukas, H.L., *Max-Planck-Institut, West Germany* **223**
Malmejac, Yves, *French Atomic Energy Commission* **447**
McKannan, Eugene, *NASA Marshall Space Flight Center* **383**
Okhotin, A.S., *Academy of Sciences, USSR* **67,355,455**
Olf, H.G., *Research Triangle Institute* **363**
Ostrach, Simon, *Case Western Reserve University* **3**
Otto, Guenther H., *The University of Alabama* **483,495**
Parker, J.A., *NASA Ames Research Center* **363**
Parker, R.L., *National Bureau of Standards* **423**
Reger, J.L., *TRW Systems Group* **567**
Saffren, M.M., *Jet Propulsion Laboratory* **151**
Sarma, G.S.R., *DFVLR, Federal Republic of Germany* **77**
Schindler, A., *Research Triangle Institute* **363**
Seidensticker, R.G., *Westinghouse Electric Corporation* **285**
Shonin, G.S., *Academy of Sciences, USSR* **355**
Siebel, Mathias P., *NASA Marshall Space Flight Center* **255**
Snyder, R.S., *NASA Marshall Space Flight Center* **399**
Spradley, L.W., *Lockheed Missiles & Space Company* **535**
Tzviling, M. Ya., *Academy of Sciences, USSR* **455**

Wahl, G., *Brown Boveri Cie, West Germany* **461**
Wang, T.G., *Jet Propulsion Laboratory* **151**
Wenzl, H., *Institut fur Festkorperforschung, Kernforschungsanlage Julich, West Germany* **437**
Wirth, H., *Max-Planck-Institut, West Germany* **411**
Wouch, G., *General Electric Company* **303**
Yu, J.G., *University of California* **509**
Yue, A.S., *University of California* **509**